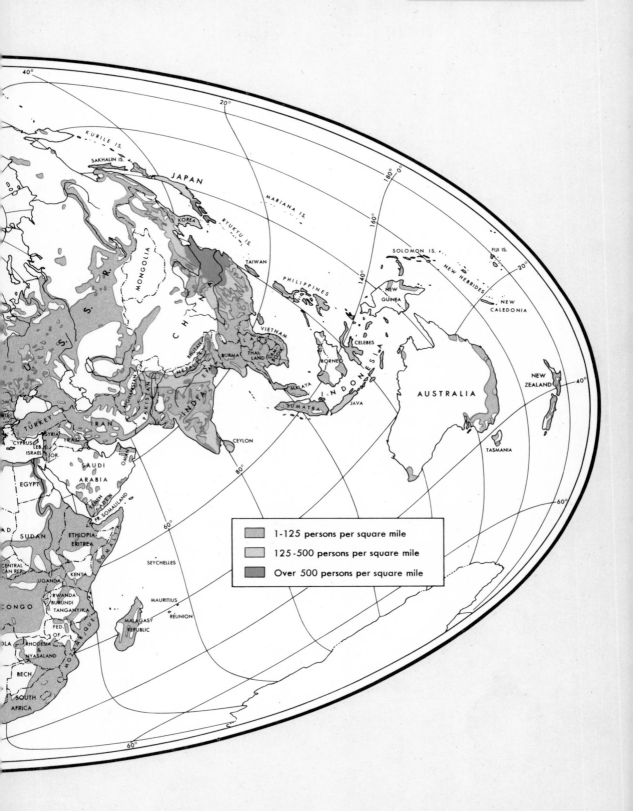

1-125 persons per square mile

125-500 persons per square mile

Over 500 persons per square mile

Map base by courtesy of American Geographical Society

INTRODUCTION TO
Human Geography

SAMUEL N. DICKEN   **FORREST R. PITTS**

University of Oregon

Blaisdell Publishing Company

A DIVISION OF GINN AND COMPANY
New York   Toronto   London

First Edition, 1963

Copyright © 1963, by Blaisdell Publishing Company,
a Division of Ginn and Company

Library of Congress Catalog Card Number: 63-7087

Printed in the United States of America

PREFACE

Most of the books in the titles of which "Human Geography" appears are organized on a regional basis; a few, such as Vidal's *Principles of Human Geography* and Brunhes' *Human Geography,* have a topical arrangement. After some experimenting with a regional organization and finding it somewhat cumbersome, the topical organization was adopted for this book. As an introduction to Human Geography, this volume is intended to introduce the reader to the broad concepts and methods of the subject rather than to establish principles or to present the greatest possible amount of factual material. Human Geography is looked upon as the study of man and his works or, more precisely, the study of the origin and distribution of man and the cultural features with which he is associated. It follows that the treatment must involve the perspective of time, since man and his works have evolved slowly through the centuries; it also follows that some attention must be given to man's physical environment, for man did not develop in a vacuum, but in specific places. Other than these basic principles, little attempt is made to define the limits of human geography; it is difficult to avoid excursions into neighboring fields, into other phases of geography, such as economic and political, or into anthropology, sociology, and economics. No attempt has been made to conform to a rigid definition.

It has been the intention of the authors to write this book with a sense for the problems involved, and to show the contribution that human geography makes toward their solution. Some of the problems of population— food supply, transportation, and conservation, among others—are introduced at several points. No final solutions are presented;

the suggestion is that a study of human geography is necessary to the understanding of these problems.

In the preparation of this volume, many persons have contributed directly or indirectly. To those familiar with the works of Vidal de la Blache, Jean Brunhes, and Carl Sauer, the magnitude of our debt to these stalwarts will be apparent. Professor Sauer has been a teacher, counselor, and an inspiration to the senior author for thirty-five years; but for his critical works in this field, this book would have been quite different and, we believe, inferior. His contributions to the volume, *Man's Role in Changing the Face of the Earth,* along with those of many others, represent a major "breakthrough" in Human Geography. To the junior author, Professor Robert B. Hall has been a guide and teacher for fifteen years, several of which were spent in joint field work in the Far East, where man's impact on the land is abundantly evident. He also wishes to record here the continuing inspiration derived from the writings and philosophy of O. H. K. Spate.

The late Professor Erhard Rostlund read the first draft of manuscript and offered many valuable suggestions. Elbert Burrill was helpful in the planning stage. Our colleagues in the Department of Geography, University of Oregon, Clyde Patton, Gene Martin, Fritz Kramer, and Carl Johannessen, gave many helpful suggestions for both the text and the illustrations. To the geographer (identity unknown) who read the final manuscript for the publisher we are deeply grateful for most helpful suggestions and constructive criticism. Emily Dicken criticized and typed the entire manuscript. To these and many more we are grateful; the shortcomings are our own.

SAMUEL N. DICKEN
FORREST R. PITTS

iii

ACKNOWLEDGEMENTS

The authors express their gratitude for permission to quote the following copyrighted textual matter:

Ashton, T. S. *The Industrial Revolution 1760-1830.* Oxford University Press, New York, 1958.

Bates, Henry Walter. *The Naturalist on the River Amazons.* Everyman's Library, E. P. Dutton and Company, New York, 1914.

Brown, Harrison. *The Challenge of Man's Future.* The Viking Press, New York, 1954.

Brunhes, Jean. *Human Geography,* abr. ed., trans. by Ernest F. Row. George C. Harrap and Company, Ltd., London, 1952.

Coon, Carleton S. *Caravan: The Story of the Middle East,* rev. ed. Henry Holt and Company, New York, 1958.

Coon, Carleton S. *The Story of Man.* Alfred A. Knopf, New York, 1955.

Dicken, Samuel N., and Hartshorne, Richard. *Economic Geography,* 2nd ed. D. C. Heath and Company, Boston, 1955.

Gosling, L. A. Peter. "The Relationship of Land Rental Systems to Land Use in Malaya," *Papers of the Michigan Academy of Sciences, Arts and Letters,* Vol. XLIV, The University of Michigan Press, Ann Arbor, 1959. (Copyright by The University of Michigan.)

Hutton, Graham. *Midwest at Noon.* The University of Chicago Press, Chicago, 1946. Copyright 1946 by the University of Chicago.

Koeppe, Clarence E., and DeLong, George C. *Weather and Climate.* McGraw-Hill Book Company, New York, 1958.

Kollmorgen, Walter M., and Jenks, George F. "Suitcase Farming in Sully County, South Dakota," *Annals of the Association of American Geographers,* Vol. 48, 1958.

————. "Sidewalk Farming in Toole County, North Dakota," *Annals of the Association of American Geographers,* Vol. 48, 1958.

Mason, Philip. *An Essay on Racial Tension.* Oxford University Press under the auspices of the Royal Institute of International Affairs, New York, 1954.

Pedler, F. J. *Economic Geography of West Africa.* Longmanns, London, 1955.

Polo, Marco. *The Travels of Marco Polo the Venetian.* Everyman's Library, E. P. Dutton and Company, New York, 1927.

Sauer, Carl O. "The Morphology of Landscape," *University of California Publications in Geography,* Vol. 2, No. 2, Berkeley, 1925.

Semple, Ellen Churchill. *Influences of Geographic Environment on the Basis of Ratzel's System of Anthropo-Geography.* Henry Holt and Company, New York, 1911.

Shapley, Harlow, ed. *Climatic Change.* Harvard University Press, Cambridge, 1953. Copyright by the President and Fellows of Harvard College.

Singer, Charles, and others, eds. *A History of Technology,* Vols. I, II, IV, and V. Oxford University Press, New York, 1954-1958. (By permission of The Clarendon Press, Oxford.)

Thomas, Elizabeth. *The Harmless People.* Alfred A. Knopf, New York, 1959.

Acknowledgement is made below to the original copyright holders and to publishers for material used in the illustrations and tables that appear in this book.

Fig. 3.1. Adapted with permission. Copyright © 1960 by Scientific American, Inc. All rights reserved.

Table 4.1. Based in part on information compiled in *Jews in Palestine,* by Abraham Revusky. Copyright 1935, 1936, by Vanguard Press, Inc. Based also on *Statistical Abstract of Israel.* International Publications Service, New York, 1961.

Fig. 6.2. Adapted from "Population—The Long View," by Frank W. Notestein, in *Food for the World,* edited by Theodore W. Schultz, by permission of The University of Chicago Press. Copyright © 1945.

Fig. 6.3. Pritchett, H. S. *A Formula for Predicting the Population of the United States* (from *Transactions* of the Academy of Science of St. Louis), December, 1890.

Fig. 6.4. Burgdörfer, Friedrich. *Volk ohne Jugend.* Kurt Vowinckel Verlag, Berlin Grunewald, 1939.

Table 6.2. Woytinsky, W. S. and Woytinsky, E. S. *World Population and Production.* The Twentieth Century Fund, New York, 1953, page 931.

Fig. 6.6. Adapted from the Food and Agriculture Organization of the United Nations.

Fig. 9.3. Adapted from *Water,* Yearbook of Agriculture. U.S. Department of Agriculture, 1955.

Fig. 9.4. Adapted from *Man's Role in Changing the Face of the Earth,* edited by William L. Thomas, by permission of The University of Chicago Press. Copyright © 1956.

Fig. 9.6. Adapted from *Water,* Yearbook of Agriculture.

Fig. 9.8. Adapted from *The Geographical Review,* January, 1958.

Fig. 9.9. Adapted from the Honolulu Water Board.

Fig. 10.1. Joseph Bixby Hoyt, *Man and the Earth,* © 1962 by Prentice-Hall, Inc., Englewood Cliffs, N.J. Adapted with permission.

Fig. 10.3. Adapted from *Soils and Men,* Yearbook of Agriculture. U.S. Department of Agriculture, 1938.

Fig. 12.5. Adapted from *Plants, Man, and Life,* by Edgar Anderson. Little, Brown and Company, 1952. By permission of Mr. Anderson.

Fig. 16.1. Van Royen, William, and Bowles, Oliver. *The Mineral Resources of the World,* Volume II. © 1954, Prentice-Hall, Inc.

Fig. 17.1. Reprinted from Volume I of *A History of Technology,* edited by Charles

Singer, E. J. Holmyard, A. R. Hall, and Trevor I. Williams. The Clarendon Press, Oxford, 1954-1958.

Fig. 17.6. Adapted from *A History of Technology,* Volume IV.

Fig. 18.6. Adapted from *Economic Geography,* by Samuel N. Dicken. Copyright © 1955, by D. C. Heath and Company. By permission of D. C. Heath and Company.

Table 20.1. From Interstate Commerce Commission and Civil Aeronautics Board publications.

Fig. 20.2. Adapted from *A History of Technology,* Volume II. Originally appeared in *Notes on the History of Ancient Roads and Their Construction,* by R. J. Forbes, Amsterdam, 1934. By permission of Mr. Forbes.

Fig. 26.5. Original by Zvi Griliches. Redrawn from *Science* with permission.

Fig. 27.6 and Fig. 27.8. Redrawn from *Comparative Population and Urban Research via Multiple Regression and Covariance Analysis,* by Donald J. Bogue and Dorothy L. Harris. Scripps Foundation for Research in Population Problems, Miami University, 1954.

Information used in Figures 4.2, 6.2, 6.3, 6.4, 6.6 and in Tables 4.1, 4.2, 4.3, 5.1, 6.1, 6.3, 6.4, 6.6 was found in the following sources.

United Nations. *Demographic Yearbook,* 1951.

———. *Monthly Bulletin of Statistics,* October, 1951.

———. *Population and Vital Statistics Reports,* July, 1951.

———. *Statistical Yearbook,* 1961.

Woytinsky, W. S. and Woytinsky, E. S. *World Population and Production.*

CONTENTS

PREFACE iii

PART I SOME BASIC FACTS

1 The People, the Place, and the Time 3
2 The Evolution of Human Geography 15

PART II THE PEOPLE

3 The Homeland and Early Migrations of Man 29
4 Migration and Growth of Population in Modern Times 41
5 The Present Distribution of Population 52
6 Future Population 70

PART III THE PLACE

7 Environment: The Importance of Place 89
8 Man's Adaptations to Climate 105
9 Water 124
10 Growth of the Soil 144

PART IV MAN'S USE OF THE EARTH AND THE MARK HE MAKES ON IT

11 Living Off the Land: Fishing, Hunting, and Gathering 163
12 From Weeds to Crops to Livestock 176
13 The Alteration of Grasslands and Forests 190
14 Houses and Settlements 199
15 Ownership of the Land 210

16   The Search for Useful Minerals   238
17   Man and Technology: The Role of Invention   250
18   Cities   266
19   Manufacturing   277
20   Roads, Rails, and Runways   288
21   Land Use and Conservation   301

PART V   TOWARD ONE WORLD

22   Men and the Sea   321
23   World Trade   331
24   Trade Routes and Centers   344
25   Men and Nations   355
26   The Spread of Ideas   379
27   Techniques in Human Geography   393

APPENDICES

A   Maps and Projections   409
B   The Use of Aerial Photographs in Human
     Geography   415
C   Climates   417
D   Soils   429
E   Population and Area   435

SELECTED REFERENCES   441

INDEX   447

LIST OF DIAGRAMS, CHARTS, AND TABLES

Diagrams and Charts

	PAGE
Glacial and Interglacial Stages	30
Intercontinental Migration	43
Projected World Population to 2000 A.D.	72
Projected population of the United States to 2900 A.D.	73
Three Basic Age Population Structures	73
Food patterns of selected countries	77
Arc of the earth's circumference	89
The Hydrologic Cycle	126
Human use water cycle	127
Hydrograph of Stream Flow	130
Qanat well	132
Maui well	133
Hypothetical Soil Profile	144
Comparison of Soil Profiles	149
Family tree of the wheats	182
Steam Power	257
Ideal city	272
Cross-sections of two Roman roads	290
Adoption of an innovation	389
Analysis of Variance from Linear Regression	403
Analysis of Covariance	406
Nomograph for visual determination of Köppen A, B, and C climates	420

	PAGE
Birth Rates in Selected Countries, Around 1950	49
Death Rates in Selected Countries, Around 1950	50
Area and population of the earth	53
Consumption of Selected Foodstuffs for Selected Countries	78
The World's Supply of Energy	80
Energy Produced	84
Cultivated Crops	179
Homeland of Plants	180
A Typology of Old World Agricultural Types	212
Mineral Resources of the World	240
Diffusion of the Potter's Wheel	251
Appearance of Wheeled Vehicles	251
Greek Inventions Prior to Our Era	252
Horsepower Generated by Various Prime Movers	256
Cost Per Ton Mile of Various Carriers	289
Percentage of trade with neighbors	336
Political and population changes	359
Areas Absorbed into Already Existing Political Units	359
Nations Formed Since 1944	360
Transmission of Chinese Techniques to Europe	382
Climatic Data for Selected Stations	424
Soil Classification in the Higher Categories	431

Tables

	PAGE
Jewish Immigration into Palestine, 1923-1960	45

LIST OF MAPS

	PAGE
Eugene, Oregon	5
Carcassonne, France	7
The world at the time of Herodotus	15
The world according to Ptolemy	17
The world according to Cosmas Indicopleustes	17
The Portolano Charts	18

	PAGE
The travels of Marco Polo, John Carpini, and Rubruck	20
The voyages of da Gama, and later trade routes	21
Prehistoric migrations in the Americas	33
The distribution of races before 1492	38
Land use in the Old World	39

ix

Land use in the New World   40
Currents of migration in modern times   42
United States dot and density population
  maps   54
Population map of Chile   62
Population map of Nigeria   63
Population map of Italy   65
Population map of the Ukraine   66
Sparsely populated areas of Japan   68
Average annual temperatures of the west-
  ern hemisphere   106
Distribution of the Eskimo   165
Aboriginal reserves in Australia   170
Plant origins in the Old World   178
Plant origins in the New World   179
Origin of seed plants and domesticated
  animals   181
Natural vegetation of the United States   192
United States forests in 1620 and 1962   197
Land holdings in an Arab village of
  Palestine   215
Irish landownership before and after con-
  solidation   224
Three kinds of farmers in the Great
  Plains   228
World uranium deposits   247
Hinterlands of Joplin, Missouri   269
Classification of cities   271
Chicago and vicinity   274
Persons engaged in manufacturing in the
  United States   278
North American manufacturing region   282
Manufacturing regions of western Europe   283
Manufacturing regions of the Soviet
  Union   284
Railways of the United States   295
World railways   296
World air routes   299
Agricultural regions of the United States   302
Roman map of the universal ocean   320
World ocean currents   324
Caribbean trade map   336
African trade map   338
Asian trade map   339
European trade map   340
World trade map   342
Rival trade groups in Europe   343
Port-outport trade centers   345
Hanseatic League towns   346
Inland waterways of northern Europe and
  the U.S.S.R.   349

Inland waterways of the United States   350
Great Lakes-overseas traffic   351
Ocean transport routes   352
German minority enclaves   357
India before independence   358
European claims to Africa, 1884   358
States of present-day India   361
International frontier   362
The shatter belt of eastern Europe   363
Indian reservations in the United States   364
Ethnic enclaves in China   365
Ethnic groups in the U.S.S.R.   365
National claims to Antarctica   367
Iceland's twelve-mile limit   369
Indus waters settlement plan   371
Heartland and Rimland   374
The "Chinese Melon"   375
Main treaty blocs of the world   376
Roman walls in Great Britain   377
North American radar warning systems   377
Spread of metal technology   381
Spread of railroads in Europe   384
Spread of hybrid corn in the United
  States   388
Isochronic map of the settlement of
  Georgia   395
Isochronic map of logging in western
  Oregon   396
Distribution of Baptists in the United
  States   401
Isopleth map of population density,
  northwestern Ohio   401
Map showing correlation and regression
  analysis   404
Spread of subsidized improvement of pas-
  ture, and simulation of spread of sub-
  sidized improvement of pasture   407
Principles of map projections   408
Cylindrical projections   410
Conic projections   411
Azimuthal projections, centered on the
  North Pole   411
Lambert Equal-Area projection   412
Gnomonic projection   412
Aitoff Equal-Area projection   412
Cahill's projection   412
The continuity of the world oceans   413
Maps of the Köppen climates   418
Major soil areas of the world   430
World population density   Front endpapers
World economies   Back endpapers

INTRODUCTION TO
Human Geography

Part I

SOME BASIC FACTS

*The things with which we (geographers) are concerned
are changing continuously and without end,
and they take place, for good reason, not anywhere
but somewhere, that is in actual situations
or places.*   Carl Sauer

CHAPTER 1

The People, the Place, and the Time

From a hilltop or from an airplane over the small city of Eugene, Oregon (a part of which is shown in the airphoto on the opposite page), an observer can study a sample of human geography. The mark of man is all over the land. Here it is the mark of a particular group of men who have their own ways of making a living and of living together, in a specific place at a definite time. Although the key object in this scene is man himself, he is by no means conspicuous. Very few of the 75,000 people who live within a radius of two miles from the center of this city are to be seen at any one time: some are sheltered in the houses, stores, factories, and other buildings; some are partially concealed in the automobiles in which they are riding. Only in the business district are many people to be seen and then only during shopping hours. To one who knows this city or similar cities it is evident that the population of the business district is dense by day and relatively sparse by night, that the density in the residential areas is moderate, decreasing in the suburban and rural margins. The varying patterns of population density have long been recognized as an important element in human geography.

The people are in motion. Some are moving along the streets, roads, and railroads. The chief highway runs east-west through the city (Fig. 1.1), accommodating per day about 25,000 vehicles which carry about 50,000 people in addition to freight. Lesser roads, radiating in several directions, carry heavy traffic only during rush hours. The railroad, paralleling the river, carries much freight, but comparatively few passengers; more people travel by air than by rail. The river, once a carrier of passengers and freight, is now used only as a source of sand and gravel, and as a ditch to carry off excess water and the discharge from the sewage disposal plant.

The movements of the people, taken as a whole, are both complicated and varied. Some move from the suburbs to the business district in the morning and back again at night; others visit the nearby towns regularly in connection with the distribution of goods and services. Still others, their eyes fixed on distant horizons, pass through the city without stopping. Some people are moving into the city from distant places, including some from foreign lands. Every state in the United States is represented, as well as dozens of foreign countries. This free movement of peoples has had and continues to have a profound effect on the way of life.

In little more than a century this locality has been profoundly changed by man; by comparison the previous occupation by Indians for several thousands of years made only minor changes. The most conspicuous

3

features are man-made: houses of all kinds, roads, bridges, reservoirs, radio and television antennae, and power lines. Every cultivated field, every cut-over slope, every row of planted hedge or trees is a witness of the changes man has made. The magnitude of the changes can be visualized only by a study of early records and an imaginative "restoration" of the landscape a century ago.

The structures have many shapes and styles, reflecting the diverse origin of the people, the available building materials, and the changing techniques of construction. Residences of many kinds, office buildings, churches, stores, warehouses, gasoline stations, and machine shops suggest the variety of use. Most of the structures are of wood, built solidly on concrete foundations; some buildings are almost entirely of concrete or masonry block construction; and the larger buildings in the business district are of steel and masonry. Good building stone is not available in the immediate vicinity and is little used. An English geographer, observing this city and noting the prevalence of frame wood construction, remarked more in wonder than disparagement, "In England we build only temporary houses of wood." To which a resident replied, "I expect to build a larger and better house in the near future. Why should I build this one of stone or brick?"

Eugene is expanding rapidly and has growing pains. The rapid growth is apparent from even a brief observation. New houses are under construction, especially on the outer margin of the city where houses are appearing in former orchards and fields; new streets are being laid out. There is an open spacing of the houses, reflecting the abundance of land and the desire of the pioneer spirit to have a "place of my own." This is in conflict with the needs of a growing industrial city with its requirements of water supply, electricity, sewage disposal, street paving, and school services, all of which may be supplied more readily to a compact urban settlement.

The site, the land on which the city is built, has played a passive role, perhaps, but its effect can be seen. The flood hazard of the river has limited the area of house construction; moreover, the problems of bridging the river have affected the pattern of the streets and the boundary of the city. Parts of the plain, including the best agricultural land, have been used for houses and other nonproductive purposes; such a use, based on an abundance of good land, is frowned upon or forbidden in many countries where good cropland is scarce. The hill near the center of the city is used as a reservoir site and as a park; in another land or at an earlier time it might have been used for defense and, consequently, might have become the core of the city.

The site includes the basic resources which support the people: forests, soils, water, and the mild, humid climate. Beyond the city limits one can see many signs of production: logging equipment on a slope a few miles away; fields of wheat, hops, and vegetables; orchards with fruits and nuts; dairy and beef cattle grazing on the pastures; a power shovel loading sand and gravel from the river bank. These, in addition to other signs of production, suggest that the people of this community supply a part of their own necessities, as well as a surplus for export. The most important productive activity in the vicinity is the processing of wood—from logs to lumber, plywood, and paper. This is obvious from the number of mills which receive the logs flowing into the community by truck and rail.

The time factor is of the greatest significance in the evolution of a city. Eugene was founded before the advent of the railroad but attained its greatest rate of growth and particular character with the introduction of the rails, the automobile, and the airplane. Since time and circumstance continue to influence the development of Eugene, it may be still too early to determine just what the ultimate character of the city will be.

On the other side of the world from Eugene, in the same latitude and on a similar

Fig. 1.1 A portion of Eugene, Oregon, and environs.

Fig. 1.2. Airview of Carcassonne, France, looking to the northwest. In the foreground is the walled, old city, occupying a low, isolated hill. The River Aude flows from left to right through the middle of the view.

site, lies a city of approximately the same size, Carcassonne, France (Fig. 1.2). The human geography of Carcassonne, however, is quite different from that of Eugene. Carcassonne is located on the River Aude where it emerges from the Pyrenees Mountains and turns toward the Mediterranean. Various Romans, Visigoths, and modern French peoples have occupied this site for nearly 2000 years; thus the city is a composite of the work of many builders and planners.

One of the most noticeable characteristics of the city is its compactness, with the houses huddled close together on the narrow streets. The Old City (*La Cité*) is built on a low hill, has a double wall, and was obviously planned for defense. Construction was begun in Roman times; continued by the Visigoths (6th century), it was essentially completed in the 13th century. Later the Old City deteriorated, but it was finally restored in modern times.

To the northwest, between the River Aude and the Canal du Midi, is the Low City, where most of the people live today (Fig. 1.3). The canal was constructed in the 17th century to provide water transportation from the Garonne River to the Rhone. Although less compact than *La Cité,* the roughly hexagonal pattern of the central section, to which the canal conforms in part, indicates that this newer city was also laid out with defense in mind. To the north of the Low City is the railroad, which is obviously an afterthought, and on other fringes are cemeteries, a normal school, a military barracks, and a slaughterhouse.

Changes have been many, but today the

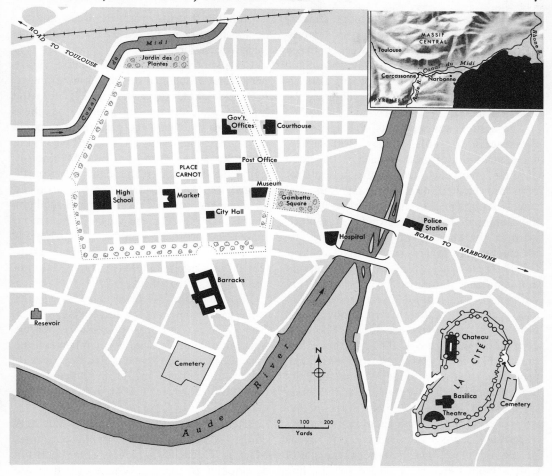

Fig. 1.3. A portion of Carcassonne, France. The old city is at the lower right, the canal and railroad at the upper left.

tempo of change is slow. The railroad took some of the traffic from the canal, and trucks on paved roads took nearly all the rest. The increased use of the automobile has brought with it many problems: the narrow cobblestone streets, suitable for pedestrians and a few carts, are totally inadequate for modern traffic; parking space is almost nonexistent. The streets are dark because of the continuous multistory buildings that constitute even the residential districts.

On the outer margin of the city where more land is available, there are a few modern houses in an open spacing. Although limited by the small number of automobiles, there is a definite tendency toward increased suburban settlement. After all, it is less than a mile from the center of the city to fairly open country.

Carcassonne lives mainly by agriculture, trade, and tourists. The agriculture is varied. In the lowland, vineyards and orchards predominate, but there are some fields of grains and vegetables, as well as some pastures. In the bordering mountains, the Pyrenees to the south and the Central Massif to the north, pasturage and forestry are important. There sheep are raised for wool, meat, and milk;

cattle provide meat, milk, and hides. Carcassonne is a "pass city" (the Gap of Carcassonne lies a few miles to the west) between Bordeaux and Marseilles, a point on a "land bridge" from one sea to another. Tourists come by the thousands for the climate, the vintages, the cuisine, and a view of *La Cité*.

The natural environments of Eugene and Carcassonne are quite similar. Both are located on rivers of medium size at the point of their emergence from lofty mountains; both are located also on main routes of travel. Although Eugene has more rain in the summer and Carcassonne is a little warmer, the climates of the two places are as nearly alike as any so far apart can be. On the other hand, it is easy enough to point out significant differences in the natural environment. The natural forest cover of Eugene is coniferous, that of Carcassonne (what little is left) is mostly deciduous. The Cascade Mountains, east of Eugene, are not exactly like the Pyrenees; furthermore, Eugene is on the west slope, Carcassonne on the north slope. However, a detailed study of the two cities and their surroundings would reveal that human geography depends in varying degrees on the character of the people, the place, and the time. If the site of Carcassonne were being settled for the first time today, it would be more like Eugene; if Eugene had been settled 2000 years ago by Europeans, it would be more like Carcassonne.

Five thousand miles southeast of Carcassonne, on the semihumid uplands not far from Pretoria, Union of South Africa, an entirely different aspect of human geography is to be seen. The land is different, as are the people and the mark they make on the land. The high plain is hummocky rather than flat, but it offers no particular focus for settlement—one place is as good as another. The original focus was probably a spring or an easy access to a nearby stream. It is a grassy plain with a few trees, either in clumps or as isolated individuals. People have been living in the plain for centuries: it is probable that the grass, the trees, and the people have been altered by their long, intimate association.

On a gently sloping hill is a native village with about 50 conical thatched huts arranged in a crude circle. From the air (Fig. 1.4) the huts resemble the tents of nomads, but these people are sedentary and pastoral. The circle of huts encloses a large kraal into which the cattle are driven at night. The chief's house, by far the largest, is at the highest part of the village; the houses downslope are arranged by the social order of the wives and retainers of the chief. Outside the village there are no fences and no roads—only narrow trails for the feet of men and beasts. There is occasional but scattered evidence of cultivation in the vicinity of the village.

By and large the men tend the cattle, while the women care for the farming duties. The Zulu do not regard cattle as merely household animals, but as members of the village. Each has a name which describes its color combinations and horn shapes; everyone in the village is familiar with each of the cattle.

The mainstay of the Zulu diet is sour milk curds, sometimes mixed with cornmeal. Meat is a delicacy which is eaten only on ceremonial occasions. Whenever cattle are slaughtered, each person by custom has a certain cut of the animal. No one else may have his part, and everyone gets some of each animal.

The daily routine of the Zulu illustrates his subsistence way of life. As day dawns, the herdboys take the cattle out to pasture beyond the few fields. The girls and some of the women fetch water from the stream in pots and calabash gourds. If it is summer, the rest of the women will go to the fields for hoeing and planting. The fields, which are relocated from time to time, are often near the kraal; some may be near the stream, others on the slope opposite the kraal.

Before noon the herdboys return with the cattle and milk them inside the kraal. Then, after the first meal of the day has been eaten,

Fig. 1.4. Airview of a Zulu village in South Africa. The huts are arranged in a crude circle enclosed by a fence. The large enclosure at lower left is a kraal for animals.

the cattle are driven back to pasture, guarded by the teen-age herdboys. At this time the women make mats and pottery or grind cornmeal. Later, after the midday heat is over, the women either go again to the fields or gather firewood. The men may work skins into shields and other objects, or they may sit around drinking the nutritious kaffir beer. Young men go courting at neighboring kraals, while the smaller boys sit in watch huts in the fields, protecting the crops from birds.

Just before sunset the cattle are brought home and locked into the inner kraal. The women return from the fields to cook the evening meal, and the young men return from courting. If the evening has moonlight, there is dancing; should it be dark, there are riddles, storytelling, and games around the fire.

All the village people are related to each other, for the village organization is the kin group. When the kraal head, or chieftain, dies the Zulu kraal generally breaks up; then, as a result, a move is made to new grazing and farming grounds not many miles away.

The Content of Human Geography

It is evident in the descriptions given above that the human scene is made up of varied phenomena: man himself, his houses, roads, cultivated fields, logged-over forests, factories, and mine dumps, for example. It is also indicated in those descriptions that every human settlement has a unique quality—the result of a certain group of people living on a specific site for a given time. The people, the place, and the time may be thought of as elements or facts out of which human settlements are fashioned; and since all the facts of human geography exist (or always occur) in definite localities, it is obvious that the areal distribution of those facts is of prime concern. The geographer first asks, "Where?", then "What is the meaning of the location?" The answers aid in answering the inevitable question, "Why?"

The most conspicuous facts of human geography are man's structures, such as houses, roads (Fig. 1.5), railroads, power lines, airports, and television antennae. These facts are the result of the nonproductive use of the earth, although they may be closely connected with production. Another set of facts involves the changes man has made in the animal, vegetable, and mineral kingdoms: for example, the cultivation of crops, the domestication and breeding of livestock, and the construction of an irrigation reservoir. A third group includes the destructive use of the land, as in the burning of forests and grasslands, the extermination of animal species, and the removal of a coal seam or a gravel bed.

In the process of making a living, man has left his mark on the land in many inconspicuous ways. He has exploited the mineral resources of the earth's crust both on the surface and beneath it. He has utilized the surface and ground waters by drilling wells, diverting streams, and constructing dams and aqueducts. He has cultivated plants and domesticated animals, adapting both to suit his needs. He has utilized the natural grasslands and forests and, sometimes uninten-

Fig. 1.5. Airview of the four-level Los Angeles City Interchange, looking to the northeast, approximately one half mile northwest of Civic Center. This is a transportation center for an urban complex with some five million people, most of whom use private automobiles for transportation. This picture was taken in mid-morning when the traffic was very light.

tionally, has made profound changes in them. He has hunted, grubbed, gathered, climbed, and fished throughout his habitat in order to use every possible item for food, clothing, shelter, or implement. As a result, man today eats many things which no other self-respecting animal would be willing to touch (if he had a choice) or be able to tolerate (if he were forced to eat).

In his wanderings and experiments man has acquired a number of "camp followers" which he might well have left behind. These include weeds which flourish on the land man has cleared, parasites which thrive on or in the human organism, and animals (such as rats, mice, and crows) which feed in man's fields and food bins. In the battle with these pests man wins many encounters, but he also loses some on specific fronts; in many cases the battle is a draw. A century or so ago termites, sometimes known as white ants, were limited to the tropical and subtropical lands. Today, because of the widespread shipment of wood, termites carry on their cleverly concealed destruction in the colder climates as well.

In making a living, man is sometimes conservative, often destructive. Farm lands in much of China have been cultivated for 40 centuries without substantial reduction of yield through careful tillage, including the generous use of human sewage. In other lands, as well as in other parts of China, a few years of improper farming have ruined the land for any future cultivation.

The Place

Man's mark on the land is not drawn on a uniform canvas—the "place" is as varied as human activity. A discussion of the "place" necessarily introduces the facts of physical geography, with which the essential facts of human geography are often correlated. The physical facts may be grouped under the heading of *environment,* which includes the following:

Climate: the average seasonal changes in the weather.

Landform: plains, plateaus, mountains, and many lesser forms.

Soil: the upper weathered part of the earth's crust.

Water: streams, lakes, swamps, springs, wells, and oceans.

Natural vegetation: forests, grasslands, and desert flora.

Minerals: those useful to man.

It will readily be seen that innumerable combinations of the above occur in various parts of the earth (Fig. 1.6). In the sample studies above, attention was called to the significance of the hills and rivers in Eugene and Carcassonne and of the plain in South Africa. In every human settlement some physical feature plays a role, a passive one perhaps and very likely a changing one. For many settlements, however, certain physical elements may have little meaning: to a mining community in the high Andes, climate and soil may be relatively unimportant; to a fishing town on the coast of Newfoundland, climate is more significant than soil and vegetation. It is not necessary for the student of human geography to be an expert in physical geography, but he must be aware of its possibilities. As Maximilian Sorre, the French geographer, has said, "The first task of human geography is the study of man, considered as a living organism, subject to determinate conditions of existence, and reacting to stimuli received from the physical environment."

Human geography impinges on a great variety of subjects and problems, such as conservation, overpopulation, and land-use planning. The relocation of a boundary line, the reapportionment of representatives, the construction of a new highway, the development of irrigation, the reclamation of a swamp, and the planning of a new subdivision are all of geographic interest. Professional geographers often make important studies bearing on these problems.

Fig. 1.6. A mining settlement in the Bolivian Andes, east of La Paz, producing tin and tungsten. Footpaths, stairs, and flat recreation fields (center and lower left) have been built into the mountainside for the use of the inhabitants.

The range of human geography is illustrated in the titles of research papers appearing in the professional geographic periodicals. For example, in the last few years the following titles have appeared:

"Irrigation Begins in the Columbia Basin."

"Remarks on the Geography of Language."

"Western Berlin: The Geography of an Exclave."

"Fishery Geography of the North Pacific Ocean."

"The Northern Region of Nigeria: The Geography of its Political Duality."

"Migrant Labor in Southern Rhodesia."

"The Functions of New Zealand Towns."

"The Mapping of Human Starvation: Diets and Diseases."

The Time

Geographical phenomena, both physical and human, are in a state of constant change, and any complete study must take this fact into consideration. Though the physical changes are slow, the changes in climate in certain regions in historic time have had some effect on human occupation. The changes in human phenomena have often been quite rapid: the introduction of new tools and new techniques has transformed some parts of the earth in the course of a few years. It is evident, then, that human geography must use the historical approach, in order to explain present-day phenomena. Some of the factual data of today may be less important than the historical explanation. It matters little that the population of a city is 50,000 or 55,000 today. Is it growing? How rapidly? What are the factors affecting its growth? A study of the records of the city in the past will not only aid in explaining its growth and character but may help solve some of its problems.

So, in human geography as in other human phenomena, there is constant change, progress, and recession. Settlements are born, grow, decline, and sometimes die; and the various operating forces are sometimes combined in patterns which can be understood only after an historical approach.

Some Methods and Tools of Human Geography

A few centuries ago geographers were largely limited in their studies to firsthand observations and interviews with travelers. There is still no substitute for "on the ground" studies, but today the geographer has a wealth of material to supplement firsthand observation. One of his most important tools is the map. Not only are there detailed maps for most parts of the earth—showing places, cities, towns, roads, rivers, and mountains; there are also special maps showing density of population, movements of people, races of men, language, crop systems, volume of trade, climate, natural vegetation, and many other phenomena. Thousands of atlases and millions of maps are to be found in the world's libraries.

In recent years a new technique has been developed which is revolutionizing the study of geography, as well as other subjects. This technique involves aerial photographs, or airphotos, many examples of which are reproduced in this book. Two types of photos are possible: the oblique—taken at low altitudes at an angle to show perspective (see Frontispiece); and the vertical—taken in an overlapping series from a plane usually flying at a constant altitude and in a straight line. These overlapping photos enable the viewer, with the aid of a simple stereoscope, to see features on the earth's surface in three dimensions. Most detailed maps are now made from these vertical photos with a minimum of ground surveying.

For centuries man has been studying the human scene with constantly improving methods and ever-widening understanding. The study of geography has involved not only painful exploration and painstaking observations but also the arrangement and interpretation of the information into meaningful patterns. As the techniques improve, the explanations continue to grow more complicated. Therefore, before beginning the study of specific topics in human geography, it will be well to consider briefly, in the next chapter, how some of the ideas and concepts of the subject developed.

Human Geography is a recent sprout from the venerable trunk of geographical science.
Paul Vidal de la Blache

CHAPTER 2

The Evolution of Human Geography*

Modern studies in human geography, like those in other subjects, are possible only because of the slow accumulation of knowledge through the ages. Geography began, perhaps, when a primitive man drew a map in the sand and described a new hunting ground to a companion. Centuries later geography was defined as the description of lands and peoples, a definition which is still acceptable today.

Many people made contributions to geography. The chief interests of such men as Homer, Herodotus, Plato, Aristotle, Darwin, and Agassiz were in other fields, but each played an important role in geography. Moreover, for at least 23 centuries, specialized geographers (recognized as such) have devoted their energies to the subject. Eratosthenes, Strabo, Ptolemy, Varenius, Ibn Haukal, Prince Henry the Navigator, Mercator, Humboldt, Ritter, Ratzel, Reclus, Vidal de la Blache, Mackinder, and Hettner are but a few of the many who have made great contributions to the subject through the centuries.

An Ancient Field of Study

The ancient Greeks were the first geographers of whom we have extensive records. Homer was considered an authority on

* For a more complete history of geography see R. E. Dickinson and O. J. R. Howarth, *The Making of Geography* (Oxford University Press, London, 1933).

geography in his time (9th century B.C.). Herodotus (484?-425 B.C.) was primarily an historian; however, traveling widely in Asia Minor, Greece, Persia, and Egypt, he made detailed studies based on observation, measurements, and interviews with the people (Fig. 2.1). Herodotus was a master not only of narrative but also of regional description, which is, in essence, the heart of geography. His description of Egypt, for example, is the result of careful inquiry and observation:

Egypt . . . is the gift of the river [Nile]. . . . From the coast inland . . . the breadth of Egypt is considerable, the country is flat, without springs, and full of swamps. . . . Up the country, Egypt becomes narrow, the Arabian hills . . . shutting it in upon the one side, and the Libyan Range upon the other. . . .

And of the agriculture he says:

. . . the husbandman waits till the river has of its own accord spread itself over the fields and withdrawn again to its bed, and then sows his plot of ground, and after sowing turns his swine into it—the swine tread in the corn—after which he has only to await the harvest.

Herodotus examined carefully the current explanations for the regular stages of the Nile, rejected all of them, and formulated a rather fanciful theory: "during winter the sun is driven out of his course by strong winds. . . . The country nearest the sun

14

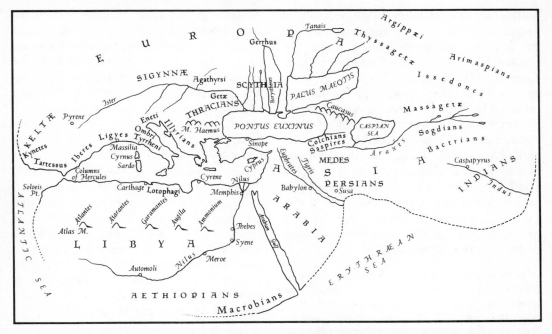

Fig. 2.1. Map of the world in the time of Herodotus, extending from Gibraltar to the Indus River. Note the direction of the Nile River and the position of the Black Sea (Pontus Euxinus). (Dickinson & Howarth, *The Making of Geography*. Oxford University Press.)

should be most short of water." Obviously, Herodotus did not understand the effects of the seasonal rainfall in the headwaters of the Nile. In addition to his geographical speculations, Herodotus wrote descriptions of the customs of the Egyptians, commenting in great detail on their clothing, food, and religion.

Plato (427-347 B.C.), the Athenian philosopher, showed his interest in human geography when he wrote of the "evil influence of the sea on men, making them unfriends and faithless toward their fellow citizens and neighbouring states." Plato's description of the mythical lost continent of Atlantis is a remarkable geographical fable. Aristotle (384-322 B.C.), a pupil of Plato, was a great compiler of geographic facts; his insistence on observation and experiment had a profound effect on geographic thinking at that time and later. Also, in his theoretical

considerations of the perfect state, he made some remarkable generalizations concerning political geography and the function of cities.

Eratosthenes, a Greek born about 276 B.C., was the librarian at Alexandria, then capital of Egypt. Probably the first person to use the term "geography" in written works, he made several noteworthy contributions to geography, including a critical history of the subject from the time of Homer. Eratosthenes also made a map of the world as he knew it, extending from the British Isles to the Ganges River and from the Equator to the Northern (Arctic) Ocean, with meridians and parallels at right angles to each other, unequally spaced.

Strabo, who lived from 64 B.C. to A.D. 20, was the most famous geographer of antiquity. Like Herodotus he was interested in observational knowledge of different parts of the earth, which he accumulated by extensive travels. Coming as he did from a family of means, he was able to devote his entire life to investigation, travel, and writing. He studied at Rome, traveled widely in Italy, Greece, Asia Minor, and Egypt as far south as Aswan, and spent more than five years in Alexandria. Strabo's great contribution to geography was 17 books describing the inhabited world. These included extensive descriptions of Spain, Gaul, Italy, northern and eastern Europe, Greece, Asia in general, the Far East, Persia, India, the Euphrates-Tigris region, Syria, and Arabia. That Strabo was interested also in the relationships between geography and the other sciences of the time is illustrated by his statement:

Now as for the matters which he regards as fundamental principles of his science, the geographer must rely on the geometricians who have measured the earth as a whole; and in their turn the geometricians must rely upon the astronomers; and again the astronomers upon the physicists.

Claudius Ptolemy lived in Alexandria in the 2d century A.D. and, like Strabo, prepared a geographic treatise of the world as it was known in his time. Ptolemy's descriptions were very much more exact than those of Strabo; and, perhaps because he developed the best maps of the time, his writings had much more influence, continuing to be the best descriptions of the world until well into the modern period when the great age of exploration began.

Ptolemy's first concern was the location of places and the collection of data for making maps. In this regard he surpassed any work done by previous writers. Ptolemy believed that the earth was a fixed sphere, neither revolving nor rotating, which had a circumference of about 18,000 miles. This measurement of the earth, given considerable publicity by Ptolemy, was to have a profound effect upon the explorations in the centuries to come; it indirectly influenced Columbus to make a voyage to the west, leading him to think that the eastern coast

of Asia was very close. Ptolemy divided the circumference into 360 parts (which later became our degrees); but, since his measurement of the earth was in error, his degree of latitude and longitude at the Equator was only 50 miles instead of 69 miles. Ptolemy made many maps, but the best known is the map of the world (Fig. 2.2) which was completed about A.D. 150. This was the first map to be developed on a grid of meridians and parallels, both of which were curved. The map extended from 20 degrees south latitude to 70 degrees north; and from the zero meridian, located in the Fortunate Isles (probably the Canary Islands) off the western coast of Africa, to eastern Asia. Ptolemy's map came into wide use in his day and continued in use for centuries to follow. During the Renaissance it was considered one of the important contributions to geography.

Geography in the Dark Ages

After Ptolemy the long intellectual night known as the Dark Ages descended upon geography and the world. The good works of the classical period and the contributions of Eratosthenes, Strabo, and Ptolemy were forgotten, ignored, or deliberately refuted by thinkers in the strait jacket of narrow theology. The sphericity of the earth was denied and imaginative theories of the shape of the earth were proclaimed. One of the common theories described a flat earth surrounded by the heavens with Jerusalem as a center. Another theory likened the earth to the Tabernacle of Moses, only larger. The known world shrank: a map of the world by Cosmas Indicopleustes about A.D. 540 (Fig. 2.3) extended only a little beyond the Euphrates River on the east and only to the Caspian Sea on the north, while Britain was entirely omitted. Compared to Ptolemy's map this was merely a schoolboy's sketch. Cosmas's book, *Christian Topography,* has been described as "systematic nonsense," because his narrow theological views colored everything he wrote. Travels during the Dark

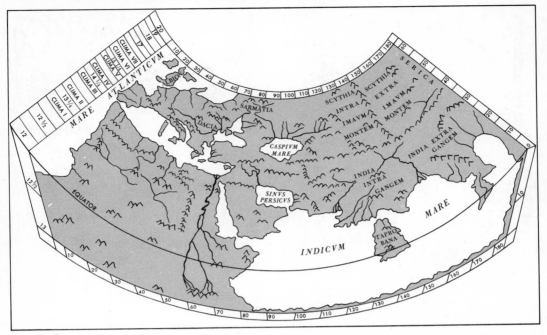

Fig. 2.2. The world according to Ptolemy. This map represents the summary of geography up to this time. It was on a definite conic projection with parallels and the indications of meridians on the margins. The continent of Africa extended to the eastward and connected with southeastern Asia. Taprobana (Ceylon) was much too large and the peninsula of India scarcely showed at all. Ptolemy's length of a degree of longitude was incorrect so his map scale was not accurate, but many of the details were excellent for the time.

Ages did make some contributions, however; and some scholars still read the classics (secretly perhaps) and continued to believe in the sphericity of the earth and in the value of observation and experimentation. One result of the extensive travels of the day was the preparation of crude guidebooks which aided pilgrims and crusaders in their journeys to the Holy Land.

Meanwhile, exploration continued on the margins of the known world, especially on the northwestern and eastern fringes. The Norsemen were gradually crossing the North Atlantic. Irish monks reached Iceland in about A.D. 795; the Norsemen arrived about a century later and began to settle the island. Greenland was reached by Eric the Red in A.D. 982; the mainland of America was seen by Bjarni about A.D. 986; and

Fig. 2.3. The world according to Cosmas Indicopleustes about A.D. 540. This map was little more than a diagram showing the great oceans surrounding all the land, the Roman Sea or the Mediterranean, and the Nile—with a fictional course coming from the southeastern part of the map. The map had very little detail. (Dickinson & Howarth, *The Making of Geography.* Oxford University Press.)

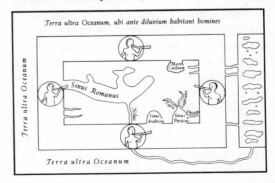

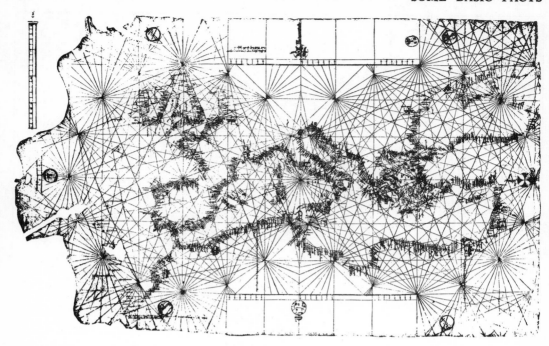

Fig. 2.4. The Portolano Charts. These charts were made by drawing a great many bearings in different directions from some point on the coast such as a cape and then drawing in the coastline between. For use by sailors, the various rhumb lines or bearings somewhat obscured any details of the coastline or of the land. But they represent great progress in the development of maps as compared to the Middle Ages. These charts did not have meridians or parallels.

Leif, son of Eric the Red, visited America in A.D. 1002. According to the sagas, several visits were made to America by the Norsemen, but the sagas were rather vague in their descriptions of the areas visited. Whatever the reason, little information concerning these discoveries reached the intellectual centers of the world at that time.

Shortly after the discovery of America by the Norsemen, attention was turned to the east and the Crusades. The Crusades gave a sharp impetus to travel and trade on both land and sea. The increased use of the Mediterranean resulted in the preparation of the Portolano charts (Fig. 2.4) which were the predecessors of the modern navigational charts. During this period the Canary Islands were rediscovered and some progress was made in the exploration of the western coast of Africa. The most important effect of the land journeys, including the Crusades, was the contact with the Moslem world, where geographic progress had been rapid and, therefore, much in contrast to that in the rest of the world.

Moslem Geography

Moslem geography developed along two main lines, mathematical and descriptive. In the first field one of the important contributions was the more accurate determination of longitude, with the result that the Mediterranean, which was exaggerated in length on Ptolemy's map, appeared in approximately its true proportion. Great strides were made also in descriptive geography, for which conditions were favorable. During this period of history, the Moslem world extended from Portugal and Morocco to Turkestan and the Indus River. Arab geographers were free to travel throughout this vast empire, a privilege which was largely denied to Europeans. Many Arab travelers were concerned primarily with lands and people, as the titles of some of their books suggest: *On Routes and Kingdoms, The Book of Countries,* and *Meadows of Gold and Mines of Precious Stones.*

Ibn Haukal traveled east to the Indus River in A.D. 953 and his book, *Book of Ways and Kingdoms,* was completed in A.D. 988. A comprehensive description of the Moslem Empire at its height, the book claims to make "geography a science which interests princes and peoples of all classes." Idrisi was one of the great Arab geographers who lived at the court of Roger II, King of Sicily. Idrisi's book, commissioned by King Roger, departed from the usual custom of the Arab geographers who described the world in terms of its political divisions. Instead, Idrisi divided the known world into seven latitudinal "zones," or "climates," after the manner of the early Greeks. Each "zone" was then divided into 11 parts by "meridians" drawn at right angles to the "parallels."

The Arab geographers also made great contributions to navigation and did some exploring on the margins of the known world, especially in the headwaters of the Nile, on the eastern coast of Africa, and in the Atlantic (where they probably reached Madeira).

The Reports of Marco Polo

Marco Polo was not the first of the great explorers of Inner Asia, but he is the best known because he traveled farther and wrote more complete reports than his predecessors. One predecessor, John de Plano Carpini, began a journey in A.D. 1245 which took him to the camp of the Mongols near Karakorum (Fig. 2.5); William of Rubruck made much the same journey a few years later.

Both wrote accounts of their travels which aroused little interest at the time. However, the influence of Marco Polo was profound and far-reaching. This man, the greatest traveler and keenest observer of the Middle Ages, wrote accounts of his travels which at first seemed unbelievable. Leaving Venice in A.D. 1271, Marco, with his father, Nicolo, and his uncle, Maffeo, took the caravan route across Asia to Peking: they traveled via Acre, Baghdad, Basra, and Ormuz; across Persia to Balkash; and thence through Kashgar and Yarkand. The Polos remained in China for 17 years, finally returning to Venice through the Straits of Malacca and along the coast of India to Ormuz, Persia. They had been away from Venice for 24 years.

It is impossible in this brief space to do more than suggest the broad scope of the observations of this great traveler of the Middle Ages. Marco Polo had a wide variety of interests. He observed the people and commented upon their habits and characteristics. He was very much interested in roads, methods of travel, and accommodations along the way. He was fascinated by the great cities of China, which were dominated at that time by the Grand Khan, and he described the large trade centers and the goods handled by them.

Of Kashgar, in the western end of the Tarim Basin, he said:

The province is extensive, and contains many towns and castles, of which Kaschcar [Kashgar] is the largest and most important. . . . [The people] subsist by commerce and manufacture, particularly works of cotton. They have handsome gardens, orchards, and vineyards. Abundance of cotton is produced there, as well as flax and hemp. Merchants from this country travel to all parts of the world; but in truth they are a covetous, sordid race, eating badly and drinking worse.[1]

Arriving at the magnificent court of the

[1] *The Travels of Marco Polo, the Venetian* (Everyman's Library), p. 92-93.

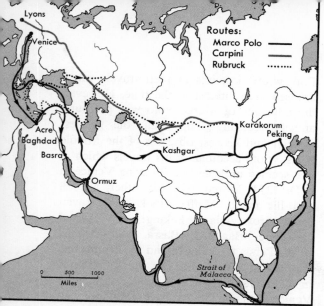

Routes:
Marco Polo ——
Carpini ——
Rubruck ········

Fig. 2.5. The travels of Marco Polo from Venice to China and back, and the routes of John Carpini and Rubruck.

Grand Khan at Peking, Marco Polo was particularly impressed by the city's system of roads and its messenger service:

From this city of Cambaluc [Peking] proceed many roads and highways leading to a variety of provinces . . . , and each road receives the name of the province to which it leads. . . . And the messengers of the Emperor in travelling from Cambaluc find at every twenty-five miles . . . a station which they call *Yamb*, . . . the "Horse-Post-House." And at each of those stations used by the messengers, there is a large and handsome building for them to put up at . . . At some of these stations, moreover, there shall be posted some four hundred horses, standing ready for the use of the messengers; . . .

Polo described the city of Sinju (Ichang):

It stands on the greatest river in the world [the Yangtze] . . . It is in some places ten miles wide, in others eight, in others six, and it is more than 100 days' journey in length from one end to the other. This is it that brings so much trade to the city; for on the waters of that river merchandize is perpetually coming and going, from and to the various parts of the world, enriching the city, and bringing a great

revenue to the Great Kaan. And I assure you this river flows so far and traverses so many countries and cities that in good sooth there pass and repass on its waters a great number of vessels, and more wealth and merchandize than on all the rivers and all the seas of Christendom put together.

Marco Polo also described the great port of Chungchow on the Yangtze River, which was

frequented by all the ships of India, which bring thither spicery and all other kinds of costly wares. It is the port also that is frequented by all the merchants of Manzi [the Yangtze area], for hither is imported the most astonishing quantity of goods and of precious stones and pearls, and from this city they are distributed all over Manzi [southern China]. And I assure you that for one shipload of pepper that goes to Alexandria or elsewhere, destined for Christendom, there come a hundred such, aye and more too, to this haven . . . ; for it is one of the two greatest havens in the world for commerce.

Polo gathered information about many countries that he did not visit, including Japan, the East Indies, and Madagascar, but his information about these countries was decidedly less reliable than that which came from his direct observation. For example, he described the roc, the great bird which was supposed to exist south of Madagascar. According to Polo, this bird was like an eagle in appearance, but many, many times larger —of sufficient size to carry an elephant! Little wonder that many doubted most of Polo's accounts. Nevertheless, the travels of Marco Polo were the most important of the period, and perhaps the most significant and remarkable travels of all times.

Shortly after Polo's return to Italy travel to China became even more difficult than before because of the increased hostility of the people along the way; as a result, centuries passed before more complete accounts of China were brought to the attention of the Europeans. The accounts of Polo's travels influenced the maps of his time and stimulated the European desire for trade with Asia. It is, perhaps, not too much to say that his travels encouraged the determined efforts of the Portuguese, a short time later, to reach the East by sailing around Africa.

The Period of Exploration and Discovery of the Oceans

More than a century after Marco Polo and his contemporaries had brought back news of the conditions in Inner Asia and China, the great period of exploring the oceans began. Exploration was stimulated more, perhaps, by desire for trade than by scientific curiosity. It may be useful to review the condition of geographical knowledge in the world at this time. The European world was thought to include little more than the Mediterranean countries, the North Sea countries, and the bordering lands. However, the various contacts with the Far East had furnished information about countries beyond the European world. Rumors concerning the unique products of the Far East percolated into western Europe. Interest in silk, jade, and spices was especially keen; this interest, more than anything else, stimulated the desire to find easy routes to Asia.

The Route Around Africa. In the first half of the 15th century Portuguese navigators concentrated on finding a route around the southern tip of Africa to Asia (Fig. 2.6). At first the difficulties seemed insurmountable. Many of the Portuguese still believed, with the early Greeks, that the ocean boiled at the Equator. Various accounts told of such navigational difficulties as very strong currents and winds along the African coast. Gradually, however, that coast was explored in a series of voyages, with the loss of many lives and ships. Of great assistance in this exploration were the new navigational techniques which were becoming available to the Portuguese. The invention of the magnetic compass made it possible to steer a reasonably true course. The invention of the

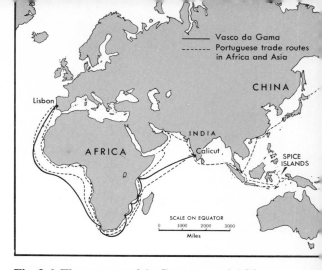

Fig. 2.6. The voyages of da Gama around Africa in search of the Spice Islands, and later trade routes.

keel made it possible to sail against the wind by tacking. Prince Henry the Navigator, who rarely went to sea in person, instigated many voyages of exploration. He combed the libraries of western Europe for information relevant to these voyages.

The discovery of a sea route to India around the south coast of Africa can be divided into five stages. The first stage, 1415-1430, brought the Portuguese to Cape Bojador, south of the Canary Islands, in what is now Spanish Rio de Oro. Twelve years were required to proceed beyond Cape Bojador. During the second stage, 1430-1460, further advances were made along the coast of Africa. Most of this was desert coast, described by the navigators of the time as "no less sandy than the deserts of Libya, where there is no water, no tree, no green herb." Consequently, when the Portuguese caravels sailed beyond the desert coast and sighted the palm trees of the Cape Verde district, they were indeed amazed and pleased, describing the green land as "some gracious fruit garden ordained for the sole end of their delight." The sight of palm trees along the Senegal River caused many to think that they had reached the waters of the Nile at the point "where it floweth into the western sea." Just how they expected the Nile to flow all the way to west Africa and to the Mediterranean at Alexandria was not stated. The third period of exploration along the African coast, 1470-1475, took the Portuguese to a point about two degrees south of the Equator, near the mouth of the Congo River. In the fourth period, 1482-1488, Diaz sailed beyond the Cape of Good Hope for a short distance and then returned to Lisbon.

In the meantime the Portuguese had sent an overland mission to the East by way of Egypt and India; on returning from Calicut, this mission heard of the "Island of the Moon" (Madagascar). Arriving at Cairo, the members of the mission sent word of their discovery to the king of Portugal, urging him to continue the sea voyages around Africa. They assured him that once the Portuguese pilots reached this island they would be able to proceed eastward without further difficulty.

It remained for Vasco da Gama to complete the voyage from Portugal all the way around southern Africa to the Indies. The expedition started in 1497 and reached Cape Verde on July 27 of that year. Continuing on the long and hazardous voyage, da Gama's fleet pulled into Calicut, India, on May 23, 1498—more than 80 years after the original Portuguese attempt to find the sea route to Asia. Da Gama's reception by the Indians was somewhat cool: the first words spoken to him were reported to have been, "May the devil take thee. What brought you hither?" The ships returned to Lisbon on July 10, 1499, thus completing what was in many ways a remarkable voyage. The voyage covered about 24,000 nautical miles and required 630 days, about half of which were actually spent in sailing. The main result of the voyage was the beginning of many trading ventures to the Far East, not only by the Portuguese but also by the Dutch, English, and others.

Meanwhile, Columbus was making his four voyages across the Atlantic, hoping to find a short route to the Indies. A few years later Magellan set sail on what was to become the first circumnavigation of the earth, the avowed purpose of which was to reach the Spice Islands. The details of these voyages are too well known to recount here in detail. Their effect was to add to geographic knowledge and to stimulate further explorations.

The Northeast Passage. After the voyage of Magellan the merchants of western Europe began to seek new and easier routes to Asia. Two possibilities appeared worth investigating: the Northeast Passage around northern Europe and northern Asia to Bering Strait; and the Northwest Passage through Davis Strait and to the north of North America. Little was known about these routes in the middle of the 16th century, but a great many plans were being made to explore them.

Despite the failure of the attempt to find a practicable Northeast Passage from the North Cape of Norway eastward toward Asia, much was learned about the northern lands and peoples. For example, from Burrough's voyage of 1556 comes this description of the Samoyede peoples near the Pechora River:

They have no houses . . . but onely tents, made of deere skins, which they under proppe with stakes and poles: their boates are made of deere skins, and when they come on shoare they carry their boates with them upon their backes: for their carriages they have no other beastes to serve them but deere onely. As for bread and corne, they have none, except the Russes bring it to them.

In modern times, especially since 1933, the Russians have devoted much effort to the sea routes north of Siberia. The routes from the White Sea to the Ob and Yenisey rivers and from Bering Sea to the Kolyma River are now in regular commercial use during the summer; moreover, a number of voyages have been made all the way from Murmansk to Vladivostok.

The Northwest Passage. The French were the first explorers to consider the Northwest Passage seriously. Cartier made three voyages to the Gulf of St. Lawrence region (in 1535, 1536, and 1541) to search for a passage through to China. Although he failed in his objective of discovering a short route to Asia, he did perform a task of the greatest value; by describing the St. Lawrence Lowland as a habitable region, he encouraged the settlement of eastern Canada by the French.

One of the most important voyages in search of the Northwest Passage was made by an Englishman, Martin Frobisher, who sailed from the Thames on June 7, 1576. Passing by the Shetland Islands and Friesland, where he could not land because of the ice, Frobisher entered the large bay on the southern end of Baffinland which now bears his name. There he found Eskimos, whom he described as follows:

They bee like to Tartars, with long blacke haire, broad faces, and flatte noses, and tawnie in colour, wearing Seale skinnes, and so doe the women, not differing in the fashion, but the women are marked in the face with blewe streakes downe the cheekes, and round about the eyes. Their boates are made all of Seales skinnes, with a keele of wood within the skin.

Explorations of the Northwest Passage were continued by John Davis, who set out from Dartmouth on June 7, 1585, and explored the broad strait between Greenland and Baffinland which now bears his name. From his second voyage in search of the Northwest Passage, Davis brought back a cargo of sealskins which more than paid the expenses of the expedition. Later, in 1631 and 1632, Fox and James explored Hudson Bay in the continuing search for the Northwest Passage. Eventually, however, in the face of the difficulties offered by fog and ice, further exploration was more or less abandoned.

Some Results of the Explorations

There is not adequate space here to describe the important explorations of the South Seas by such men as Torres, Tasman, and Cook; nor is there room to discuss the detailed explorations of the interior of the continents. It must suffice to say that the great period of exploration (approximately from the end of the 15th century to the end of the 18th century) expanded two major sources of geographic information.

Material for making maps was painfully acquired through many voyages and expeditions of exploration. As a result, there were significant advances in the techniques of map-making in the 17th and 18th centuries. Made for the first time on the basis of careful instrumental surveys, maps acquired a high degree of accuracy. Also many new techniques were developed for the representation of data on maps. Moreover, new map projections were made for special purposes: for example, the year 1569 saw the publication of Mercator's new map for the use of navigators, on the projection that now bears his name. Unquestionably, the progress of map-making had a profound influence upon all geography, both physical and human.

The tremendous amount of detailed information acquired by the many voyages and travels began to have a direct and vital effect upon the content and organization of geography. The explorers usually had a specific objective—such as the discovery of gold, spices, or a new route—but their curiosity caused them to observe all sorts of geographic phenomena. Native peoples everywhere were accorded close scrutiny in an effort to explain the differences in their physical features and customs; all the observations contributed to the growth of human geography.

For a time information accumulated too rapidly to be systematized critically; but gradually "armchair" geographers began to examine, classify, and organize the information on a scientific basis. A good example of this scientific approach was the work of Bernard Varenius. In 1650 he published his *Geographia Generalis,* dividing the subject of geography into two parts, the general and the special. He defined the first as the science which considers the earth as a whole and explains its properties; he defined the latter as instruction which concerns the constitution of the individual regions. This division of geography into two parts was an idea which had been in existence since the time of the early Greeks; as a matter of fact, the two divisions, general and regional (also called topical and regional), are still valid. Although Varenius did not complete his treatise on regional geography, he outlined its contents under three sections. The first concerned celestial properties, the appearance of the heavens and climate. The second dealt with the terrestrial properties which are observed on the face of every country, such as position, boundaries, shape and size, mountains, rivers, woods, deserts, fertility, minerals, and animals. The third referred to the human properties, the description of inhabitants: their appearance, arts, commerce, cultures, language, government, religion, cities, famous places, and famous men. Despite the fact that the content of the general geography resembled that of the regional geography of Varenius, the treatment of content differed in the two approaches. Varenius preferred general geography to regional because he felt it could more easily be treated as a science. He complained that too much emphasis had been placed upon regional geography, which, in his view, scarcely merited the dignity of being called a science.

Varenius's outline of the content of geography could be interpreted as including a wide variety of subjects, such as astronomy and biology. However, during the 19th century, with the rapid development of the philosophy of geography, there was a tendency to restrict the scope of the study. From this time on, greater specialization was apparent; certain subjects which had formerly been considered parts of geography became sciences in their own right.

Meanwhile, the various aspects of geography, as outlined by Varenius and others, have been cultivated in different degrees in various parts of the earth at different times. During the 19th century major emphasis was on the study of relief features. It was, perhaps, easier to describe the relatively stable relief features than to deal with the more variable cultural features. Relief features were measured and tested in various ways. Many patterns of elevations, depressions, ridges, and valleys were noted; and considerable emphasis was placed upon the processes which modify such relief features. Through this activity a special branch of geography was developed: originally called physiography, under later modifications it came to be known as geomorphology. This field of physiography, or geomorphology, was cultivated in such a way that many other parts of geography were neglected. Although physiography had close connections with geology, it often lost touch with the human element in the geographic landscape.

Human Geography

Partly as a reaction against this school of geography which overemphasized physical features, students began to examine the relationship between man and his natural environment. Thus was originated the school of human geography. Unfortunately, in some cases, human geography was studied more or less in a vacuum, without reference to the other elements in the geographic landscape upon which it depends.

The development of human geography as a special phase of geographic study was stimulated in the last half of the 19th century by Charles Darwin's *Origin of Species*. Moreover, support for the new field could be seen in the fact that Buckle's *History of the Civilization of England* (1881) devoted more than 100 pages to the discussion of the dependence of man upon his environment. Of particular importance was the work of Friedrich Ratzel (1844-1904), a geographer with a special interest in human geography. Trained in the methods of the natural sciences, Ratzel endeavored to apply these methods to the study of human geography. In his first major geographic work.

Anthropogeographie (Geography of Man), he organized the material on the basis of physical features and attempted to link these with cultural or human features. As a result of this approach and the interpretations of his students, Ratzel was given credit by some geographers for the definition of human geography as "the study of the influence of the environment on man"; this definition was to have a strong, but temporary, effect on geographic thought, especially in the United States. The definition was brought to the attention of American geographers by Ellen Semple, a student under Ratzel in Germany, who recast Ratzel's early work and in some ways modified it substantially. She wrote:

Man is a product of the earth's surface. This means not merely that he is a child of the earth, dust of her dust; but that the earth has mothered him, fed him, set him tasks, directed his thoughts, confronted him with difficulties that have strengthened his body and sharpened his wits, given him problems of navigation or irrigation, and at the same time whispered hints for their solution.[2]

This strongly deterministic statement did not correctly represent Ratzel's point of view.

Ratzel's work was scientific in that it was a very orderly and rational approach to the subject; but it was narrow in that it left out some of the factors which are not easily measured or studied. Whatever other features it may have had, Ratzel's work had the merit of reintroducing into geography the human element which had been more or less forced out by the emphasis upon physiography. His writing also raised a great many questions for challenge and serious discussion, not only by geographers but also by anthropologists and sociologists.

One of the most influential students of human geography was Paul Vidal de la Blache, who for many years was Professor

of Geography at the Sorbonne in Paris. Vidal stated that there is no such thing as *necessitism* in geography, only *possibilism.* By this he meant, given a certain environment in which a group of people live, there is no necessity that they should react or be influenced in a certain way; there is only the possibility that they may react in a number of different ways, depending upon their cultural heritage and their group organization. Vidal's approach to human geography was through the comparative study of different parts of the earth. In his introduction to an *Atlas of Historical Geography,* published in 1894, Vidal said:

The field of study *par excellence* of geography is the surface, that is, the ensemble of phenomena which lie in the zone of contact between the solid, liquid, and gaseous bodies which form the earth.

The work of Vidal culminated in the publication (posthumously) of his *Principles of Human Geography* (1921), the first sentence of which is quoted at the beginning of this chapter. In his *Principles of Human Geography* Vidal emphasized the importance of the physical environment but cautioned against "explaining all human facts in terms of environmental control." He also stated that "present forms are unintelligible unless their past evolution is known."

Jean Brunhes, a brilliant pupil of Vidal, was the first to be called to a chair of human geography in either Europe or America. He took the post at Lausanne, Switzerland, in 1907 and a similar position at the Collège de France in Paris in 1912, a post which he held until his death in 1930. Restricting the field of human geography, Jean Brunhes introduced order and classification, the very basis of the scientific approach. The essential facts of human geography, according to Jean Brunhes, are the evidence of human action on the earth's surface; these facts he divides into three groups:

1. The facts of the unproductive occupation of the soil, such as houses and roads.

---

[2] Ellen Churchill Semple, *Influences of Geographic Environment,* p. 1.

2. The facts of vegetable and animal conquest.

3. The facts of the destructive economy in the vegetable, animal, and mineral kingdoms.

Only after these essential facts had been studied would Brunhes include a wide variety of subjects in human geography—subjects such as political geography, social geography, and the geography of infectious diseases.

Other students of Vidal tested his principles by field studies in various parts of France and other countries. Many of these took the form of regional studies, such as *Flanders, Lower Brittany, The Western Alps,* and *The Mediterranean Pyrenees.* In addition, the Vidal school of geography produced what is perhaps the most extensive encyclopedia of world geography ever written: the *Géographie Universelle,* a work of 15 large tomes (some in more than one volume) which required 15 years to complete.

If space permitted, the evolution of human geography could be traced in various countries, notably in Germany, England, and the United States. The general pattern of development was similar to that described above, but the particular development in each country had its individual characteristics. For students in the United States, for example, the story would be incomplete indeed without mention of the contributions by Carl Sauer. One of Sauer's early papers on the method and content of geography, *The Morphology of Landscape,* appeared in 1925 and had a far-reaching effect on geographic thought. Sauer defined the field of geography as the study of landscape: the natural landscape (those natural features which have habitat value) and the cultural landscape, "the impress of the works of man upon the area." The natural landscape includes climate, land surface, soil, drainage, mineral resources, sea and coast, and natural vegetation. The cultural landscape includes population, housing, production, and communication. In the conclusion to his paper Sauer wrote:

This contact of man with his changeful home, as expressed through the cultural landscape, is our field of work. We are concerned with the importance of the site to man, and also with his transformation of the site. Altogether we deal with the interrelation of group, or cultures, and site, as expressed in the various landscapes of the world.[3]

In his subsequent works many of the ideas in "The Morphology of Landscape" were elaborated and illustrated by field studies.

Today human geography is still undergoing some changes, but the hard core of the subject is well established. The most noteworthy changes are in techniques and emphasis rather than in basic content. A high degree of specialization is also apparent, in both method and content. Some workers depend mostly on statistics; others concentrate on aerial photographs. There are urban geographers, rural settlement geographers, agricultural geographers, and geographers who specialize in houses, roads, or place names. On the other hand, there are fewer studies which attempt a complete, over-all coverage of human geography. Each special study, however, contributes something to the main goal of human geography: the description and explanation of the great variety of peoples and cultures, as they exist in highly diversified environments.

Essentially then, human geography is, and always has been, the study of peoples and their works, the place or site, and the specific time. Careful attention is given to the areal distribution of the various factors. Since the time factor is of great importance, human geography is just as concerned with the past as with the present. For this reason the next chapters will deal with the origin, growth, and spread of man on the surface of the earth.

[3] Carl O. Sauer, "The Morphology of Landscape," *University of California Publications in Geography,* Vol. 2, p. 53.

Part II

THE PEOPLE

CHAPTER **3**

The Homeland and Early Migrations of Man

During the last million years a new and incredibly thin layer has spread over a large part of the earth's surface, at the contact of air, water, and land. This layer is the sphere of man and his works—in Pierre Teilhard's phrase, "the mind sphere." At the present time no one knows exactly when or why the development of this thin layer began, and some of the details may never be clear. However, enough is now known to be of great interest and value to the student of human geography. Where, approximately, did the human occupation of the earth originate? Along which routes did man migrate to various parts of the earth? What culture traits did he pick up along the way? How did the various peoples of the earth come to have such different ways of living and sustaining themselves? Fortunately, the answers to these questions need not be quantitatively exact in order to be useful in understanding the role man has played in occupying and changing the face of the earth. For example, despite the lack of conclusive evidence, it is believed that the first human occupation of the earth was probably in a zone extending from equatorial Africa to southeastern Asia. Possibly there was independent development at both ends of this zone, but recent evidence tends to show that Africa is the more likely location of the original home of man. The early development of the hand-ax culture in Africa, as well as the early migrations into Europe and western Asia from Africa, tends to confirm this assumption.

The Ice Age: the Age of Man

Apparently, the first humans date from the early Ice Age (Pleistocene) or from the preceding geologic period (Pliocene), a million or more years ago. For 950,000 years, perhaps, man was distinctly limited in his habitat, as well as in his own development; but 50,000 years ago man broke free from his original homeland, having acquired the requisite tools and abilities. The expansion of man over large parts of the earth was like an irresistible tide. In a few thousand years man reached many parts of the earth which were remote from his original home, including northern Europe, eastern North America, southern South America, and, probably, Australia.

Because the Ice Age was a time of great climatic stress, it is remarkable that man was able not only to survive but also to improve his condition. Four times, at least, ice accumulated on the continents and advanced in slowly spreading sheets into the middle latitudes (Fig. 3.1); four times the earth warmed and the ice melted. Each time plants, animals, and man retreated southward before the advancing ice fronts and then turned northward again when the ice melted. There were climatic changes far beyond the limits of the ice. During the glacial periods lands far to the south of the ice were cooler and moister than they were during the interglacial periods: for example, there

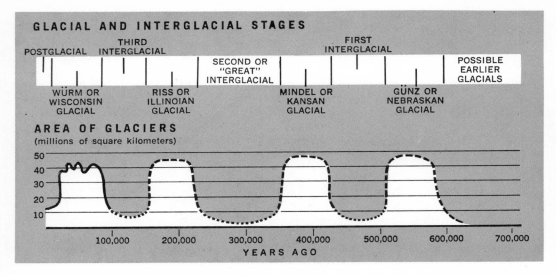

Fig. 3.1. Glacial and interglacial stages in terms of area covered by the continental ice sheets. The figures on the left represent millions of square kilometers.

is evidence that the Sahara was quite cool and humid during the glacial advances.

In northwestern Europe, where man had close contact with glaciation during the Ice Age, the sequence of climatic periods was as follows: Günz glaciation; first interglacial; Mindel glaciation; second interglacial; Riss glaciation; third interglacial; Würm glaciation; fourth interglacial (the present). Some of these glacial intervals were more severe than others; likewise, some of the interglacial periods were warmer than others. The distribution and thickness of the ice was uneven; northwestern Europe and eastern North America, for instance, were much more severely glaciated than Alaska and Siberia.

In western Europe man was able to survive and prosper despite glaciation because he had developed certain peculiarities: some of these had evolved before the Ice Age began; some he acquired rather quickly due to the exigencies of the period. Long before the beginning of the Ice Age, man had learned to descend from the trees (if indeed he ever lived in them), walk erect on the land, and use his hands for a variety of pur-

poses. Of basic importance was man's ability to use tools, many of which were readily available. Perhaps the first tool that man used was a stick sharpened with the broken edge of a piece of flint. As time went on, crude stone implements were greatly improved and elaborated into beautiful examples of knives, scrapers, arrowheads, and spear points.

Because he could use fire, man was able to keep warm as he penetrated into cold lands; with fire, he could make edible foods which he could not tolerate in the raw state. Fire cleared forests and renewed grasslands, thereby attracting wild game, providing pasturage for domestic animals, and supplying land for cultivation. Man probably used fire long before he could make it, since wild fire was available from volcanoes and from forest fires set by lightning. With the careful addition of fuel, man could maintain a fire for his use and even transport it from one camp to another. (This was actually done in pioneer days in eastern United States when matches were very scarce.) Later, of course, man learned to make fire in various ways; the important point, however, is that fire was available to man long before he knew the methods of making fire from flints or from rotating sticks.

Of great value to man in his struggle against his environment was the power of speech. Although the more primitive primates, such as the gibbon and the ape, were able to communicate in a limited way, man was the only creature who learned to convey complicated ideas. By enabling man to communicate the things he had learned, the power of speech facilitated the dispersal of his culture.

Another attribute of man which proved very useful to him was his capacity for eating. With his excellent teeth and good digestion, man was able to chew and digest foods which would cause great suffering, if not death, to most other animals. This ability permitted early man to penetrate into areas where he had never been before and to live on the vegetable and animal fare which he found there.

In addition to these qualities, man developed very freely moving arms; rather delicate but strong, grasping hands; and very sharp-focusing eyes. The ability to focus on nearby objects with a temporarily cross-eyed vision evolved in man to a high degree. Moreover, man could see at great distances, although the sharpness of his vision was not as great as that of some of the other animals. Most important of all, perhaps, was the brain of man, a large brain that made him a reasoning, planning, and inventive creature.

The Early Migrations

From the earliest times man was prone to wander. Evidently, migration is a normal form of human behavior. Man migrates for various reasons, such as the negative pressures of overpopulation and drought or the positive attractions of prosperity in distant lands; sometimes he migrates for no apparent reason. In primitive times, when most of the people were hunters and gatherers, everyone migrated (whereas, in modern times, continuous migration is practiced by relatively few peoples). There were several kinds of migration: in a rhythmic and repetitious movement, a tribe might travel from the sea to the mountains and back again to the coast as the seasons changed; in a more haphazard way a people might wander around searching for water and grass for their livestock or for suitable hunting areas; with still other purposes a people might move far from their homeland and never return. In these early migrations usually only small numbers of people were involved, there being neither very many people in the world at the time nor any great concentrations of population.

Reasons for Migration. No one knows exactly why the early peoples migrated so often. Most peoples, even today, have a strong attachment to their homeland, or their home region. They have a tendency to range a certain distance away from this homeland, but they also have a strong propensity to return to the original home. For the early peoples the pressure to move in many cases overcame the attachment to the homeland. Changes of climate, the advance of enemies, overpopulation, or certain features of the land itself may have encouraged the peoples to migrate. On the other hand, perhaps it was the individual characteristics of some members of the group which inspired the migrations. Just as the migrants from the Atlantic Coast in the early days of the United States were often restive spirits (such as Daniel Boone), so very likely some primitive people had similar adventurous natures.

Besides the individual proclivity to migrate—to find out what is over the next hill —there were a number of other drives which probably played an important role in instigating the early migrations. In the first place, there was the drive for food. Whenever the increase in local population exceeded that of the local food supply, some peoples would range farther afield for their food; finding areas that were less heavily harvested, they were likely to remain in the new location. The distance that peoples migrated in their search for food would depend, in part, on the degree of famine in the original homeland. Another factor in the tendency to migrate lay in the catastrophes which happened to primitive peoples (just as they do to modern peoples). Volcanic activity, earthquakes, fires, and floods caused peoples to seek new homes. Floods occurring at regular intervals would probably show a people that its home site was unsuitable, thus causing it to seek higher ground. Still another factor in the migrations was the interrelationship of different groups. In the course of a war or feud, a strong tribe might drive out a weak tribe, forcing it to find a home in less favorable territory. Generally, then, many of the migrations of primitive mankind were caused by dissatisfaction with the local site and the local environment, as well as by trouble of some kind between groups or individuals. Moreover, during historic times many migrations have also been started because of religious or political suppression.

Evidence of Migration. There is clear evidence of these early migrations, although there was no written record of them. In the first place, the present racial distribution of peoples must be explained in terms of the migrations. The spread of certain physical characteristics, such as color, hair form, and head form, indicates the general direction of many of the migratory peoples. Another line of evidence is language: the use of certain words and certain linguistic structures is, in many cases, an excellent indication of the routes of migration. Further evidence is to be found in a study of the artifacts of man, those objects which make up the material record of the way people lived. These artifacts may be discovered buried in shell heaps and mounds, as well as on the surface of the ground. Still more evidence is offered by the place names which people gave to particular areas as they moved along. In addition, the lines of migration can be traced in the types of houses and their distribution, in the methods of town planning, and in the various systems of land ownership. The study of all this observable evidence offers information about the migrations by analyzing the similar and contrasting cultural traits of many peoples.

Routes of Migration. When primitive man began to migrate from his original zone of development in Africa and southern Asia, many routes were open to him. The very early migrations, both large and small, were necessarily made by land, for they took place before man had any boats for navigating the rivers and seas. However, when boats later became available, migrations occurred along the coastlines, on the rivers, and, in some instances, across rather large expanses of ocean. In most of the migrations man moved along slowly, gradually extending his range of hunting and gathering; these leisurely migrations were in contrast to the occasional hurried ones which resulted from tribal wars and feuds. On the basis of fossils and artifacts, it is possible to trace the routes of many of these migrations in general, if not in detail.

Any consideration of migration routes must deal with the fact of the ancient land bridges. It is now generally believed that during the last ice advance sea level was approximately 300 feet below its present level; as a result, there were land bridges which connected some continents now separated by open water. Presumably, early man could have walked on a land bridge from France to England (across the English Channel) without getting his feet wet. Another likely land bridge was at Bering Strait (Fig. 3.2). Whether this connection between Asia and America was a true land bridge or only a convenient accumulation of ice, it provided a route which was used by primitive man during the period of the early migrations. Also heavily traveled was the route from Asia to Europe across the Strait of Dardanelles; the strait is so shallow even today that it is not difficult to imagine that a

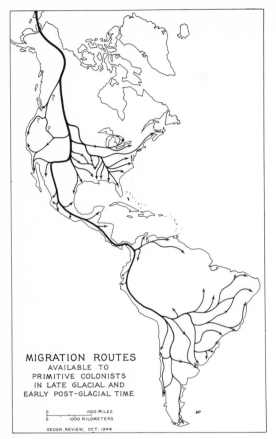

MIGRATION ROUTES
AVAILABLE TO
PRIMITIVE COLONISTS
IN LATE GLACIAL AND
EARLY POST-GLACIAL TIME

1000 MILES
1000 KILOMETERS

GEOGR. REVIEW, OCT. 1944

Fig. 3.2. Prehistoric migrations in the Americas. (Reproduced by courtesy of the *Geographical Review*, American Geographical Society, New York.)

many land bridges that did exist facilitated migrations whose existence has been evidenced by skeletal remains and artifacts. With such evidence of such migrations, it is difficult to verify the theory that man developed independently in several areas of the earth.

A Short History of Early Migrations

The story of man's early migrations is far from complete, but the main outlines are reasonably well known. As the migrations began, a million years or more ago, primitive man faced a changing world, even in low latitudes. As man moved along from one environment to another, he was faced with many problems and opportunities. He encountered many new plants and animals, and he developed new tools and techniques. Most important of all, perhaps, the migrations brought strange tribes together. Undoubtedly, these tribes profited from the intermingling of both their races and their cultures. For the sake of brevity, the migrations of man may be considered under five periods.

From 1,000,000 B.C. to 500,000 B.C. During the first period man emerged as a cultural animal in his original homeland, somewhere in the zone extending from equatorial Africa to southeastern Asia. If the original homeland was in Africa, people soon moved across the Isthmus of Suez and Asia Minor to southeastern Asia; if the homeland was in Asia, people soon migrated to Africa. Whatever the original homeland and the direction of migration, at the close of this first period man also occupied eastern and northeastern Africa, southwestern Asia, India, China, and Java. There is little evidence to show that man reached other regions in the first period, but, on the other hand, there is no clear evidence that he did not. In any event, it appears certain that man advanced from the humid tropical climate of his homeland into the deserts and

land bridge would be exposed by a lower sea level. Likewise, before the eventual rise of sea level, there were migrations of men and animals across the Malacca Strait, which lies between Asia and Sumatra, Java, and Borneo.

The various land bridges made possible many of the early migrations. Of course, not all the narrow straits in the world were land bridges; many straits are far too deep ever to have been rendered land bridges by the lowered sea level (for example, the Strait of Gibraltar between Spain and North Africa, the Strait of Sicily between Tunisia and Sicily). However, the fact remains that the steppes of southwestern Asia and into the temperate climates of China and crossed at least one important land bridge.

From 500,000 B.C. to 20,000 B.C. The second period saw great changes in man and further migrations and settlements throughout southeastern Asia and Africa. It also saw the migration of man to Australia and to North America by way of Bering Strait; new finds of primitive man's skeletal remains and other evidence indicate that this migration was sometime rather early during the second period.

Until about 50,000 years ago man was generally restricted to the low latitudes of his homeland. Before that time he probably made attempts to move into the colder lands of Europe and central Asia during the interglacial periods, when the climate there (in western Europe, for instance) must have been quite pleasant and livable. But with the recurrent advances of the ice early man had difficulty surviving in the north, perhaps because of inadequate clothing, shelter, and tools, in addition to the difficulty of making fire in the colder, wetter conditions.

By the time that the last ice sheet began its retreat, however, man was much better equipped to invade new lands. He was making new tools and weapons from bone, antler, and ivory, as well as from wood and flint. One of his new weapons was the harpoon, consisting of a shaft, a detachable head with barbs, and a line attached to the head. Better spears became available, and a spear thrower was invented which had the effect of lengthening the thrower's arm and thus increasing his power. The fabrication of a single spear thrower or harpoon must have required many hours of patient labor, and each hunter must have spent many days and weeks of practice in learning to use his weapons skillfully.

From 20,000 B.C. to 5000 B.C. As the last ice sheet disappeared, the middle-latitude lands began to be very attractive to primitive man. Primitive peoples advanced into the plains of northern Europe, now occupied by France, the Low Countries, and Germany. Here the hunting was much better than in the tropical lands. For instance, on the grassy plains, where forests later appeared, the woolly mammoth roamed. The killing of the woolly mammoth required the co-operation of many hunters, but each animal provided tons of food. Since the cold climate enabled the people to preserve meat, such a large animal could be consumed over a period of days or weeks. Besides the woolly mammoth, wild animals such as the horse, the cave lion, and the cave bear provided food for man.

This third period of migration saw an increase of population and greater pressure to migrate. There is very clear evidence that during this period man reached the northern part of Europe, including Scandinavia, and moved eastward through Siberia into Inner Asia. Thus, the cool lands of the north and the dry lands of the interior of Asia were occupied. This was also a period of continued migration to North America by way of Bering Strait. Some authorities contend that there were major migrations across the oceans at this time; but the weight of evidence indicates that migrations by land, and perhaps some by small boats along the margins of the oceans, were the principal movements. It is very likely, however, that toward the end of this third period there was considerable migration by boat in short voyages across parts of the ocean: for example, migrations from Asia to Japan, from southeastern Asia to the Philippines, from Asia Minor to Cyprus and Crete, and also to islands like Madagascar, Sicily, Sardinia, and Corsica.

From 5000 B.C. to A.D. 1500. The fourth period was a time of numerous migrations on all the continents. There were also ocean voyages which led to the occupation (at some time during this period) of outlying areas such as New Zealand, the South Pacific Islands, and the Hawaiian Islands. Although numerous, the migrations in the fourth period were mostly on a small scale. Because routes and methods of travel imposed severe limitations, migration was a slow process during which some tribes perished or were forced to abandon areas which they had occupied.

From 1000 B.C. to the beginning of the Christian Era, migrations were accelerated. Although the beginnings of agriculture had reduced the mobility of peoples somewhat, they still had no very permanent habitations. In ancient Greece, for example, the people shifted frequently. It was noted by contemporary writers that the richest soils were always the most subject to changes of master and population. Good land invited invasion; only lands with poor soils and resources were relatively undisturbed. Ancient Rome was an active center of immigration and emigration. People came to Rome from all the known parts of the world; some were reluctant migrants, such as slaves and war prisoners brought in from northern Europe, Africa, and the East. At the same time leaving Rome were Roman military personnel and administrative officials who were moving out to the fringes of the empire, to Africa, Asia, Syria, and Mesopotamia.

The first thousand years of the Christian Era was a period of continued migration; at least, the writers at the time felt that people were moving around with more than their usual facility. Even so, the greatest migrations had still not occurred by A.D. 1000. Germans were on the Rhine, but not at the site of Berlin; Russians had occupied Novgorod and Rostov, but had yet to found Moskva; and not one Hungarian lived in what we now call the Hungarian Basin. Moreover, no white man had yet made a permanent settlement on the soil of the New World.

In the following 500 years (A.D. 1000-1500) there were several important invasions, in addition to the movement of the Mongol peoples into Europe, the drive of the Crusaders to the Near East, and the migration of the Slavic peoples to the north and east toward the Ural Mountains from their original home on the Dnepr River. But even these migrations were small compared to those to come (see Chapter 4).

Some Examples of Primitive Peoples in Modern Times

As the Age of Discovery began (around A.D. 1500), groups of primitive peoples were found in various parts of the earth, living in what resembled neolithic conditions. Although these peoples were living in modern times, they afforded specific examples of how their ancestors lived in the prediscovery period. Outstanding examples of such peoples were the natives of Australia, the natives of Tasmania, and certain pygmy peoples in the Malay Peninsula and in the Congo forest of Africa. With the exception of the Aztecs, the Mayas, and the Incas, most of the peoples in the New World were rather primitive on discovery; but some of the native American peoples were much more primitive than others. Among the most primitive were the Yaghan, the canoe people along the coast of southern Chile; the Ciboney on the southwestern corner of Haiti; the Chichimecs in the north central part of Mexico; and the Seri on the coast of Sonora and on the island of Tiburon. Some of the desert tribes of the Great Basin, as well as most of the California and Oregon Indians, were also living in a primitive state. Space here permits a description of only two of the primitive peoples: the Semang of the Malay Peninsula and the Eskimo of northern Canada, Alaska, and Greenland.

The Semang people had their home in the Malay Peninsula east of Penang, in the densely forested areas where the highest elevation was about 7000 feet. At the time these people were studied in detail in 1927, about 2000 of them were living in small family groups of about a dozen people (Fig. 3.3). The Semang had no broad tribal organization. Each group searched for its own food within a very short distance of its home. This food was derived partly from small game and fish, but mainly from plants such as the durian, which supplied fruits and seeds. Each group gathered all of the edible fruits, leaves, shoots, and tubers that it could find in the vicinity. Dr. Schebesta,

Fig. 3.3. A Semang lean-to hut on the Malay Peninsula. Such crude shelters provide some protection from the heavy rains in the tropical rainforest.

who studied the Semang people, found that they collected an average of a dozen kinds of roots or tubers in one day.

It is worthy of note that these people lived in a very uniform climate with little seasonal change other than slight variations in rainfall. The vegetation grew all the year around and, aside from the fact that certain trees produced fruit or seeds at definite periods, there was little actual seasonal fluctuation in their life. As a result of this, perhaps, there was very little effort on the part of these people to preserve or store food. They went out every day to find their food for that day.

Their houses consisted of walls made of palm leaf branches, which could be raised or lowered to give protection from the sun, wind, or rain. The houses were temporary and were abandoned from time to time as the people sought out other places where more food was available for gathering. The upas tree supplied poison for the Semang

darts and also a kind of cloth from its inner bark. The Semang had bamboo available from which much of their equipment, both weapons and implements, was made. They had the bow and arrow as well as the blow gun (which, as of 1927, they apparently had not had for a very long time).

In strong contrast to the Semang were the Eskimo. The Eskimo, having crossed Bering Strait into Alaska, northern Canada, and eventually Greenland, learned to live in a very cold climate without the aid of firewood. Most of the Eskimo settled in areas close to the sea where they could hunt the large marine game animals—the seal, the walrus, and the whale—as well as many varieties of fish. Since this sea fringe was too far away from the forest for them to have any wood supply except small amounts of driftwood, they learned to burn the blubber of the whale and the fat of other animals in order to maintain fires. They also learned to build snow houses or igloos,

Fig. 3.4. An Eskimo shack near Clyde Inlet in eastern Canada. The house is constructed of odds and ends, including driftwood, pieces of sheet metal, and hides. Note oil drum in foreground.

which in most cases were used only as temporary shelters. An ingenious type of structure, the igloo was formed by blocks of snow or ice carefully tapered to rise in a continuous spiral from the base. The Eskimo were especially clever in developing weapons, such as harpoons and spears, as well as devices for attracting and catching game; they also had the tools to construct boats and permanent houses of driftwood (Fig. 3.4). Altogether, the Eskimo showed a very intelligent approach to the use of their particular environment.

Human Geography of the World about A.D. 1500

The year A.D. 1500, which ushered in the great age of exploration, was a turning point in the geographic development of mankind. Long prior to this time man had spread over most of the inhabitable parts of the earth; no one group of people, however, was then aware that all the world was populated.

The population of the world around A.D. 1500 is estimated to have been about 400 million people, approximately one seventh of the world population today. Of these 400 million, about 80 million lived in Europe, 240 million in Asia, 12 million in the Americas, 70 million in Africa, and two million in Oceania. (These estimates, of course, are based upon data which are subject to considerable error.) The most densely populated areas undoubtedly included the irrigated oases of the lower Nile, the Tigris and Euphrates, and the Indus, as well as the irrigated lowlands of southeastern Asia. Most other parts of the world were comparatively sparsely populated, and some fairly large areas probably had no permanent dwellers at all.

The peoples who occupied the earth in A.D. 1500 belonged to the three major racial groups which are recognized today:

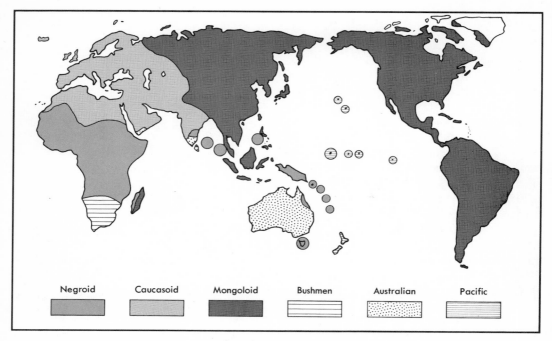

Fig. 3.5. The distribution of races before 1492. (Reprinted from *The Story of Man* by Carleton S. Coon, by permission of Alfred A. Knopf, Inc., and Jonathan Cape Ltd. Copyright 1954, © 1961, 1962 by Carleton S. Coon.)

Caucasoid, Negroid, and Mongoloid. The distribution of these racial groups (Fig. 3.5), however, was quite different from what it is now. In most of Europe, southwestern Asia, and northern Africa, the Caucasoid peoples were dominant. These peoples, often called whites, had straight or ringlet-curly hair and full beards; rather tall, with narrow noses, they had skin which, if not exposed to the sun, ranged from a pinkish white to a deep brown. The Caucasoids varied considerably in size. A fully grown individual, well developed and without excess fat, may have weighed twice as much as some other individual, also fully developed. The range in skin color, eye color, and hair color was also very great. In northern Europe, for example, the Nordic group had very fair skins which would not tan, light hair, and light-colored (often blue) eyes. By contrast, the Mediterranean Caucasoids of southern Europe were shorter, stockier, with straight black hair, dark eyes, and dark brown skins.

South of the middle Sahara in Africa and in various other areas, including southern India and New Guinea in southeastern Asia, the dominant racial group was the Negroid. The Negroids, like the Caucasoids, varied greatly in racial characteristics. Typically, they were black-skinned; many of them had woolly or kinky, rather than curly, hair. Some of them were extremely tall; others were short enough to be called dwarfs or pygmies. Despite disparities in some characteristics, the Negroids were considered to be a valid group, although there were instances in which it was difficult to distinguish among Negroid, Caucasoid, and Mongoloid.

In A.D. 1500 the Mongoloid group occupied the largest area of all. This area included the northern and eastern part of Asia, the land which lies north and east of a line drawn approximately from the northern end of the Ural Mountains to the delta of the Ganges River. The Mongoloid group also occupied all of North and South America; in A.D. 1500 no white man had as yet settled in the Americas. The Mongoloid people had a yellowish skin color which ranged from almost white to coppery. Their hair was straight, coarse, and usually black. Their beards were scanty; their faces were flat; and many of them had the distinctive Oriental eye, known as the almond eye. Their body size varied quite a bit from region to region.

It appears that the various racial characteristics were related in some manner to the environments in which the races developed. For example, the light-skinned Nordics of northern Europe were adapted to a region with a limited amount of sunshine and ultraviolet radiation. Because they did not tan easily, they could not endure long exposure to the sun, especially to the very great ultraviolet radiation in the lower latitudes. On the other hand, the Negroid peoples with their thick, black skin were equipped to resist excessive ultraviolet radiation; really black Negroes did not sunburn. Intermediate in this matter of skin composition were the Mediterranean peoples in the Caucasoid group, who had a pigment in their skin which developed readily on exposure to the sun, thus providing protection against excessive ultraviolet radiation.

The peoples who had spread over the world by the year A.D. 1500 had a variety of occupations and ways of making a living (Fig. 3.6). Most of them were farmers; some were nomadic herders; still others lived by a combination of agriculture and sedentary herding.

By A.D. 1500 groups of people were

Fig. 3.6. Land use in the Old World, A.D. 1500. (Rostlund, *Outline of Cultural Geography*. California Book Co.)

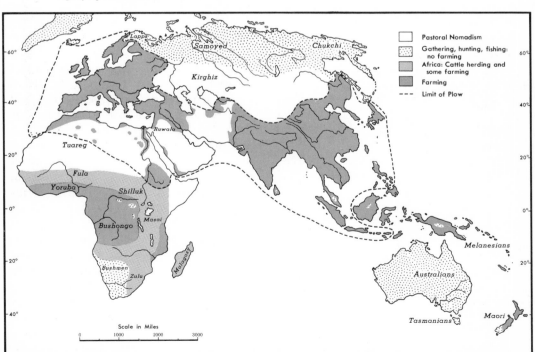

well established in their particular occupations. Some of the farming peoples had invented the plow as an improvement over the hoe, thus taking a great step in the development of agriculture. The plow was in use in Europe, Asia, and the northern part of Africa as far south as Abyssinia and Morocco. Evidence of its use has also been found on the island of Java, but not on Borneo or New Guinea. No evidence has been found of its use in the Americas at this time. In the areas that did not have the plow, hoe culture was the dominant form of agriculture.

In the north of Europe the Lapps, the Samoyeds, and the Chukchi depended upon reindeer herding, hunting, and fishing. In central Asia were nomads, such as the Kirghiz, who lived by grazing their cattle, sheep, goats, horses, and, in some cases, camels and yaks on the arid grasslands of the Old World. They moved about from place to place as the necessity arose for finding new supplies of grass and water. In southwestern Africa the Bushmen and related groups

Fig. 3.7. Land use in the New World, A.D. 1500. (Rostlund, _Outline of Cultural Geography_. California Book Co.)

were living either by hunting or by grazing. Even in areas of the world where agriculture was of central importance, hunting remained a significant occupation.

In the New World (Fig. 3.7) there was a variety of ways of life. In the north the Eskimo were living on the edge of the sea and going inland only occasionally to hunt for land animals. In the present area of the United States the eastern and southwestern parts were occupied by agricultural peoples; the other parts were inhabited by hunters, fishers, and gatherers. In the eastern part the several Indian groups were cultivating a variety of crops, including corn, beans, and squash. In central Mexico the Aztecs developed a complicated agricultural society, as did the Mayas in Yucatán. In South America the Incas, occupying the high valleys and plateaus of Peru and Bolivia, evolved a very complex civilization, characterized by elaborate roads and advanced systems of cultivation. In the tropical parts of South America the Indians were backward, living in the early stages of the Stone Age; in southern South America (principally Argentina) most of the Indians were hunters, specializing in hunting the small deerlike animal called the guanaco.

It is important to note that although man had spread over the earth and had established various forms of society by A.D. 1500, no one realized it. For Europeans the "known world" extended little beyond Europe, northern Africa, and southwestern Asia. A few hardy mariners and land travelers had ventured beyond these limits, but, with the exception of Marco Polo and a few others, the records they had brought back were very meager. North Europeans, for instance, had no definite ideas about central Africa; they were not sure of its existence, much less of its inhabitation. In the years to come, however, the European peoples, particularly those of southern and western Europe, were to extend their sphere of influence over most of the earth, adding greatly to the knowledge of human geography.

When all the world was primarily agricultural,
a destination for the settler was relatively
easy to choose.   Isaiah Bowman

CHAPTER 4

Migration and Growth
of Population in Modern Times

About A.D. 1500, as new lands were being discovered and described, the character of migration changed. Previously, migration had been a slow, step-by-step spreading over the earth. In most cases the migrants themselves had scarcely been aware of there being a migration. By A.D. 1500, however, things were different. Knowledge of new lands was disseminated by books, maps, and word of mouth. Migrations were planned and organized by governments and private companies. Improved transportation, especially by sea, made it possible for migrating peoples to bypass the mountains, swamps, and deserts which were (and still are) effective barriers to land migration. To be sure, the goal of the migrants was more often treasure or trade than permanent settlement, but the effect of their migrations was the establishment of colonies in various parts of the world. For instance, French colonies were founded in eastern Canada; English colonies, among others, in western Canada and the United States; Spanish colonies in Argentina; Dutch colonies in Java; Japanese colonies in Hawaii; and Chinese colonies in Malaya.

Because of favorable circumstances, the migrations of English people to North America were uniquely successful. The migrations were so successful that a new nation was formed of essentially European stock which today has three or four times as many people as the homeland. The English came comparatively late to the business of exploration and settlement in the New World; but, once they had begun, they transported a cross section of their whole culture to the new lands. Although they did not discover much gold or other precious material, the English did find themselves in possession of a vast temperate land, richer in agricultural and industrial potential than any part of Europe.

The Great Modern Migrations

The great migrations since A.D. 1500 originated mainly in Europe and Asia and were directed, for the most part, toward North and South America (Fig. 4.1). Migrations may be classed as intercontinental, international, or internal. (An individual may be involved in all three kinds of migration, step-by-step, before he finds a permanent home.) Some of the important modern migrations are described below.

The Migration from Europe to the Americas. During the last 100 years, more than 65 million emigrants left European countries bound for the Americas. About 45 million of them moved into North America and about 20 million moved into Middle and South America. At first the people com-

41

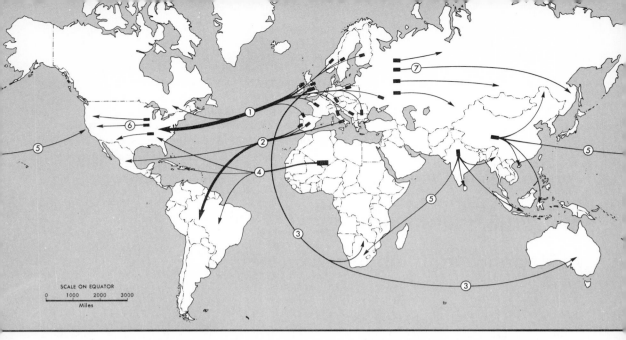

Fig. 4.1. The principal currents of migration in modern times. Since the beginning of the sixteenth century, these have been: (1) from all parts of Europe to North America; (2) from Latin countries of Europe to Middle and South America; (3) from Great Britain to Africa and Australia; (4) import of slaves from Africa to America. Another current (5), partly intercontinental, partly intracontinental, has flowed from China and India. The most important internal migration has been (6) westward in the United States and (7) eastward in Russia. (W. S. & E. S. Woytinsky, *World Population and Production*, The Twentieth Century Fund.)

ing to North America were mostly from the northern European countries; later, however, large numbers came from the southern European countries, especially from Italy. By far the greatest number of immigrants were from the British Isles, but several million came from Germany, Spain, Italy, Russia, and Sweden. Other countries contributed somewhat fewer numbers. Altogether, nearly 34 million European immigrants settled in the United States. Argentina, Canada, and Brazil also received large numbers of European immigrants—somewhere between four and six million.

The great peak of migration from Europe to the Americas occurred in the decade from 1901 to 1910, when 11 million people left Europe (Fig. 4.2). However, the peaks of migration from particular countries occurred at different times. For example, from 1881 to 1890 was the peak for the Irish, Swedes, and Norwegians. The peak of migration to the United States from the southern European countries (Austria, Hungary, Italy, and Yugoslavia) came a decade or two later.

Most of the migrants to South and Middle America came from southern Europe (Spain, Portugal, and Italy), but there were also small settlements by Germans. Approximately 20 million Europeans migrated to South and Middle America; at present, about 50 million people in that area are wholly or partly of European stock. The proportion of people of European extraction varies widely from country to country, but the European migrations have had a profound effect on the culture of every country.

The Migration from Europe to Africa, Australia, and New Zealand. Africa has been colonized largely by Europeans and to a lesser degree by Asians. Northwest Africa has been colonized by peoples from the adjacent European countries of Spain,

France, and Italy. In South Africa the British and the Dutch have been the principal immigrants; large numbers of British have also settled in Oceania. Altogether, about 17 million people have emigrated from Europe to Africa and Oceania, generally moving into areas with rather sparse native populations.

The Migration from China and India. Although only a small percentage of the very large population of China has emigrated, an estimated 10 million Chinese are

now living outside China. Most of these Chinese are in Indonesia, Malaya, Cambodia, Thailand, and Burma; but small numbers of Chinese are also found in North America, South America, Africa, and Europe. More of an internal than an external migration, the great migration from central and northern China into Manchuria moved many millions of people into an area of comparatively thin settlement. Now Manchuria is fairly densely populated, for the most part by Chinese.

Fig. 4.2. Intercontinental migration since 1845. In 1910 nearly 1.4 million people moved from one continent to another.

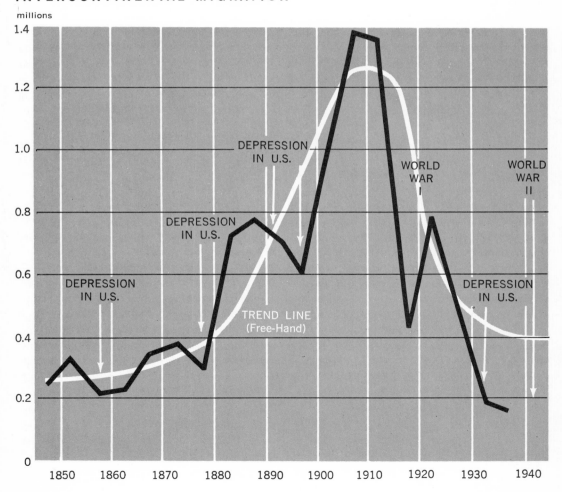

INTERCONTINENTAL MIGRATION

The emigration from India has been remarkably small considering the dense population of that country. Fewer than four million people from India and Pakistan are now living abroad. Most of these are living in Burma, Indonesia, Malaya, and Ceylon; there are also some in British Guiana, Kenya, Tanganyika, and Uganda. In recent years, because of the partition of India, large migrations have occurred between India and Pakistan.

Forced Migrations. Beginning in the 16th century, more than 20 million Negroes were taken from their homes in central Africa to be sold into slavery. They were intended for markets in the Americas, Asia, and Europe, but many died before reaching their destination. About one million entered the United States—the ancestors of the 16 million Negroes living in the country today. The slaves that were brought to America represented a variety of culture groups with different languages and customs. Many of them being skilled in agriculture and metalworking, they made substantial contributions to the plantations, farms, and mines of the New World. Slavery was abolished and forced slave migration was stopped in British possessions in 1836, in French possessions in 1848, in the United States and in Dutch possessions in 1863, in Cuba in 1880, and in Brazil in 1888. Today most Negroes live in the regions of the Americas where their ancestors were originally settled: southeastern United States, the West Indies, northwest Colombia, and eastern Brazil.

Another example of forced migration was the movement of convicts from England to Australia in the early days of Australian settlement. Convicts were also transported from France to Devil's Island on the coast of South America and from England to southeastern United States. There have been many forced migrations in wartime.

Migrations inside Europe. Large-scale migrations began in Europe and adjacent areas during and immediately following World War II. These migrations, some of which were forced, were brought on by various circumstances. Some migrations represented the flight of peoples from advancing war fronts and from bombed-out areas. Some migrations were shifts of workers, from Spain and Portugal into France, for example. After the war, many of the migrations were in the nature of exchanges: for instance, the exchange of people between Romania and Bulgaria after the common border was altered; also, a similar exchange of Turks and Greeks. During the years in which large parts of Russia were occupied by the Germans, a great number of Russians moved toward the Urals; a somewhat smaller number moved into central Asiatic Russia. Altogether, many, many millions of people moved or were deported during the World War II period. Although there have been some subsequent readjustments, the various migrations made a great difference in the population pattern of Europe and adjacent areas.

Since 1949 the most important migration inside Europe has been a voluntary one from East Germany to West Germany. Technically, this is an international migration and a well-guarded international boundary must be crossed, legally or illegally. The emigration from East Germany, in spite of restrictions, has averaged about 230,000 annually; and, until the border was closed, the flow continued at a uniform rate. Of the migrants, 50 per cent were under 25 years of age; 75 per cent were under 45 years of age. East Germany has lost by emigration during the last 12 years more than a million children in the age group of six to 15 years. As a consequence, the East German population has a proportionately large number of old people approaching retirement. This means that the active labor force is in the process of being seriously reduced. On the other hand, West Germany is adding substantially to its effective labor force by welcoming the emigrants.

The Migration of the Jews to Palestine. A migration from Europe which was stimulated greatly by World War II was the movement

TABLE 4.1

JEWISH IMMIGRATION INTO PALESTINE
1923-1960

Year	Immigrants	Year	Immigrants	Year	Immigrants
1923	8,175	1936	29,727	1949	239,424
1924	13,892	1937	10,536	1950	169,620
1925	34,386	1938	12,868	1951	175,095
1926	13,855	1939	27,561	1952	24,369
1927	3,034	1940	8,398	1953	11,326
1928	2,178	1941	5,886	1954	18,370
1929	5,249	1942	3,733	1955	37,478
1930	4,944	1943	8,507	1956	56,234
1931	4,075	1944	14,464	1957	71,224
1932	9,553	1945	13,121	1958	27,082
1933	30,327	1946	17,760	1959	23,895
1934	42,359	1947	21,542	1960	24,510
1935	61,854	1948	119,005		

Total Population of Israel		2,150,400
Jews		1,911,200

of Jews to Israel (Palestine). A century ago there were probably not more than 50,000 Jews in the area (Table 4.1), most of the population there being Arab. This situation began to change, however, when a campaign was started to restore the Jews to their original and ancient home. The resulting migration to Israel, financed in part by private funds from the United States, declined during World War II; but immediately after the war migration to the area increased enormously—the number of immigrants being 240,000 in 1949 alone. This migration to Israel has not taken place without a great deal of stress and strain. For example, it is estimated by the United Nations that about 85 per cent of the non-Jewish population within Israel's boundaries has been displaced, in some cases by purchase of the land held by Arabs. This migration has also required a distinct change in the way of life of the migrants: most of the Jews coming from Europe were city dwellers, tradesfolk, and professional people; in Israel many have become farmers, artisans, and mechanics.

Internal Migrations. In North America internal migration has been, in general, westward from the Atlantic ports, through which most of the immigrants have come. In Canada and the United States many millions of people have moved and continue to move westward. Some of these people are recent immigrants from Europe who are continuing their migration, but some of them are representatives of previously settled "native" stock. Somewhat irregular in quantity, migration is likely to be accentuated in times of economic stress. For example, during the middle 1930's there was great movement from the Dust Bowl of the Great Plains region to the western states, particularly California, Oregon, and Washington.

Although within the United States and Canada the westward migration has attracted the most attention, the migration from the southeastern part of the United States northward has probably involved more people. This migration began with runaway slaves in the pre-Civil War days. It continued after the war and involved both Negroes and whites. Although some of the migrants have returned to their homes, the net movement northward during the last century has involved many millions of people. In most cases this migration has not resulted in population losses in the southern states; the natural increase has been sufficient to maintain the population. (A southward migration of retired people in recent years, especially to Florida, is a reversal of the general trend.) As a result of the Negro migration northward, there are now more Negroes in New York than in South Carolina, more in Illinois than in Florida, and more in California than in Kentucky. But despite this migration, the highest percentage of Negro population is still found in Mississippi, South Carolina, Georgia, Louisiana, and Alabama.

Other important internal migrations include the movements of people from farms to cities, from cities to suburbs; the seasonal movement of cotton and fruit pickers; the northward trek of wheat harvesters from Texas to Canada. Some of the internal migrations are regular and seasonal, some are steadily in one direction, while still others are sporadic and temporary. Most of the people of the United States move every few years; of persons 18 years or older (as of April 1959), only 1.5 per cent had lived in only one house during their lifetime.

In the Soviet Union internal migration has been mostly eastward. At first the migrants traveled from the extreme western part of the U.S.S.R. toward the Urals in the east; later they traveled beyond the Urals along the Trans-Siberian Railway all the way to the Pacific Coast. In recent years the volume of migration has been less than that of North America, but the two movements are similar in many ways.

Restrictions on Migrations. At the present time most countries have some sort of restriction on unlimited immigration. A few generations ago most countries, especially those with large amounts of empty land, welcomed immigrants; however, as the empty spaces were filled up and as economic depressions brought unemployment, there was continuing pressure for the restriction of immigration.

In the United States agitation for restriction began very early; as early as 1836 various states were petitioning Congress to reduce the number of unwanted immigrants. Immediately after the Civil War there was more agitation for restriction, but this was largely offset by the widespread demand for cheap labor. Although the first immigration restrictions in the United States were very limited, they gradually grew in scope. From 1865 to 1875 laws were enacted prohibiting the immigration of prostitutes, convicts, the mentally ill, and any person likely to become a public charge. Later, contract laborers were refused entrance. Still later, admission was denied to illiterate persons over 16 years of age, as well as to most East and South Asians. In 1921 the quota system was inaugurated, limiting immigration from non-American countries to 3 per cent of the number of foreign-born persons of each nationality residing in the United States in 1910. This system had the effect of sharply curtailing immigration from southern European countries and of allowing fairly generous quotas for northern European countries. In 1930 new quotas were established which allowed 150,000 entries a year, prorated among countries according to the number of immigrants from each country living in the continental United States in 1920. (Each country, however, had a minimum quota of 100.) Because quotas were so restricted and requirements were so rigid in the period from 1930 to 1934 (and perhaps because of the Great Depression), fewer aliens entered the United States than left it; and, from 1935 to 1939, net immigration into the United States averaged only 18,000 a year. After World War II, restrictions were relaxed somewhat in favor of war refugees, alien wives and husbands, and children of members of the United States Armed Forces who had married overseas. The admission of

361,000 displaced persons was authorized for the period from July 1, 1948, to June 30, 1951, but qualifications for admission were so difficult that the quota was not filled.

In recent years most other countries have also strictly limited their immigration by the use of quotas and have added other requirements for immigration. Most countries, for example, require that immigrants be financially competent, that they have enough money to support themselves during a period of readjustment. By and large, the countries that are now admitting immigrants in fairly substantial numbers have restrictive demands as to country of origin. Australia, for instance, welcomes English-speaking immigrants from Great Britain and the United States. Similarly, Brazil has decided to admit two or three million immigrants in the near future, most of them from Italy, Portugal, and central Europe. Restrictions on immigration are not limited to the receiving countries. Even though overpopulated, many countries do not like to see their people emigrate, because the emigrants are most likely the vigorous, younger people—those of the greatest economic value to the country. Of the European countries with emigration problems, West Germany and Italy are in the most precarious positions, each having an excess of population, a high birth rate, and an inability to produce enough food for its own purposes.

Cultural Changes Related to Migrations

The last 450 years have been a period of invention, cultural growth, and dispersion of peoples and ideas. In some measure, the diffusion has been brought about by migrations, especially by the contact of Old World peoples and New World peoples. This contact provided for the exchange of crops, livestock, handicraft, and manufacturing skills, as well as political, social, economic, and religious ideas and institutions.

Plants, both cultivated and wild, were ex-changed—some intentionally, others accidentally. European migrants contributed several items to the agriculture of the new lands: small grains, such as wheat and barley; livestock, such as horses, cattle, hogs, sheep, and goats; citrus and deciduous fruits; and a great variety of vegetables. The New World furnished many new crops to Europe and Asia. Crops like corn, for example, were transplanted by returning travelers to southern Europe, as were peanuts, tobacco, and tomatoes. Other crops, such as rubber, cinchona, and manioc, which could not be readily cultivated in Europe, were transported from the Americas to southeastern Asia, where in many cases the crop was more successful than in America. Manioc was carried to Africa and southeast Asia; rubber was taken to India, Java, and Sumatra; cacao was transplanted from Middle and South America to the eastern coast of Africa.

Spanish breeds of horses and cattle were brought to the Americas in very early times. European cattle were in Virginia as early as 1609 and in Massachusetts and New York a little later. The cattle which were introduced at this time were not, of course, the modern breeds of European cattle, such as the Jersey, Guernsey, Holstein, and Hereford. In addition to cattle and horses, the New World also acquired hogs, goats, and sheep.

Of great importance to the New World was the introduction of European handicraft and methods of manufacturing. From these basic methods came modern developments such as iron works, steel mills, advanced mining and smelting equipment, railroads, steamships, the telegraph, and the telephone. European types of clothing were also brought to the New World, but they were modified in many cases to meet new conditions.

Although migration has an important role in the dispersal of culture traits, the fact remains that migrations are special cases; they are neither the only nor even the normal means of cultural diffusion. Sometimes the culture of a migrating people has been so unsuited to the new environment that its way of life has been almost completely rejected. For example, the Mongolian invasion left little permanent effect on most parts of eastern Europe.

The Growth of Population

While the New World was being settled, the population of nearly all parts of the earth was increasing. Even in lands which were losing people through emigration, the total number of people continued to increase. Many factors contributed to this increase. By no means the least of these factors was the great expansion of resources available to man as a result of the discovery and development of new lands. Benefiting by the additional available resources, the human population increased rapidly and filled up the new lands.

No one knows how many people were living on the earth in the year A.D. 1500. For nearly 300 years, however, estimates of the earth's population have been available. Although the older estimates are subject to rather wide errors and even the latest estimates are subject to some errors, the broad picture of population changes in the world is likely to be fairly accurate. The estimated total population of the world in 1650 was about 545 million, in contrast to 2800 million in 1960. The population doubled between 1650 and 1850, a period of 200 years; and it doubled again in the 90 years between 1850 and 1940, when the world population was estimated at 2170 million.

The distribution of population by continents also has changed greatly. In 1650 the population of North America, excluding Middle America, was estimated to be one million; in 1950 the same area was estimated to have 166 million people; in 1960, 200 million people. In 1650 the estimate for North America, including Middle America was 6 million; for South America, 6 million; for Europe, 100 million; for Asia, 330 million; for Africa, 100 million; and for Oceania, 2 million. During the 300 years for which some kind of record is available, all continents have increased their population enormously, but the rates of increase have not been the same. Thus, for example, in 1650 North America had only 0.2 per cent of the total world population, whereas in 1950 it had 6.9 per cent. In the last 300 years North America, Middle America, South America, Europe, and Oceania have gained in terms of their percentage of the world population, while Asia and Africa have lost. The distribution of population in 1650 was thus very different from what it is today.

Striking features of the population changes between 1650 and 1950 were the rapid increase in numbers and the major redistribution of European peoples. Between 1650 and 1950 the total population of the earth increased nearly fivefold, but the European peoples increased eightfold, from 100 million to about 800 million. About 550 million of these 800 million Europeans are now in western Europe and the U.S.S.R.; about 145 million of European ancestry are in the United States and Canada. Latin America has about 50 million; Asia, 40 million; Africa, 7 million; and Oceania, about 10 million.

The population growth of selected countries is even more noticeable than that of the continents. In the period from 1850 to 1960 the population of the United States increased from 23 to 180 million. Canada grew from 1.8 to 18 million; Brazil, from 10 to 52 million. In western Europe the increases were at a slower rate, but all countries showed substantial increases during this period. The United Kingdom grew from 27 to 52 million; France, from 35 to 45 million; Belgium, from 4.3 to 9.1 million; Germany (East and West combined), from 40 to 72 million; and the U.S.S.R., from 60 to 200 million. Similarly, Japan grew from 30 to 92 million.

Increases in a country's population can be attributed to natural causes, an excess of births over deaths; but they can also be ascribed to migration and boundary changes. During the period from 1800 to 1850, for

TABLE 4.2

BIRTH RATES IN SELECTED COUNTRIES, AROUND 1950
(*Births Per 1,000 Inhabitants*)

Country,[a] Year	Births	Country,[a] Year	Births	Country,[a] Year	Births
Trieste, 1950	10.7	United States, 1950	23.4	Panama, 1949	33.0
Angola, 1950	14.3	Paraguay, 1948	23.6	Algeria (Moslems),	
Luxembourg, 1950	14.8	Bulgaria, 1947	24.0	1949	34.1
Austria, 1950	15.8	Finland, 1950	24.0	Colombia, 1949	35.3
United Kingdom, 1950	16.1	Portugal, 1950	24.2	Dominican Republic,	
Western Germany,		New Zealand, 1950	24.6	1950	37.4
1950	16.2	Argentina, 1949	24.9	Puerto Rico, 1950	38.5
Sweden, 1950	16.4	Union of South		Yukon (Canada),	
Belgium, 1950	16.5	Africa,[b] 1950	25.7	1949	39.7
Pakistan, 1948	18.0	Greece, 1949	26.1	Belgian Congo,[b] 1950	39.8
Switzerland, 1950	18.1	Canada, 1950	26.6	Ceylon, 1950	40.3
Denmark, 1950	18.6	India, 1949	26.7	China, 1943	40.7
Hungary, 1948	19.1	Thailand, 1949	27.1	Honduras, 1949	41.3
Norway, 1950	19.3	Indonesia,[c] 1940	28.3	Nicaragua, 1950	41.4
Italy, 1950	19.6	Japan, 1950	28.4	Federation of Malaya,	
Romania, 1945	19.6	Bolivia, 1949	29.0	1949	42.0
Spain, 1950	19.9	Yugoslavia, 1948	30.2	Venezuela, 1950	43.1
France, 1950	20.4	Peru, 1950	30.3	São Tomé and	
Uruguay, 1944	20.7	Gold Coast,[c] 1949	30.7	Principe, 1949	45.2
Ireland, 1950	21.0	Korea, 1944	31.8	Mexico, 1950	45.7
Algeria,[b] 1949	21.4	Chile, 1950	32.4	Singapore,[b] 1950	45.7
Czechoslovakia, 1949	22.1	Burma, 1939	32.4	Costa Rica, 1950	46.5
Netherlands, 1950	22.7	French India,[c] 1949	32.8	El Salvador, 1950	48.7
Australia, 1950	23.3	Israel, 1950	32.9	Guatemala, 1950	48.7

a. Countries arrayed by increasing birth rate.   b. Europeans.   c. Europeans and natives.

example, the United States increased in both territory and population. Decreases in population have generally been limited to rather small parts of the earth's surface. From 1930 to 1940, for instance, France's population fell from 41.8 to 41.2 million. Likewise, during the decade from 1940 to 1950, several states in the interior of the United States lost a small amount of population. Such losses are usually related to migration, but in some cases they are associated with very low birth rates.

The Birth Rate. In any given region the population changes according to the difference between the number of births and the number of deaths and the difference between the number of immigrants and the number

of emigrants. The *crude birth rate*—the number of births per 1000 people per year—varies widely in different parts of the earth and also from year to year. Some students of population prefer to use the *fertility rate* —the number of births per 1000 women of childbearing age (usually considered to be from 15 to 49). The crude birth rate is fairly satisfactory for short-term computations. The fertility rate is more reliable in making long-term studies and in comparing data from different countries.

In 1950 crude birth rates ranged from 48.7 in Guatemala to 15.8 in Austria and 10.7 in Trieste (Table 4.2). In general, the peoples with high birth rates are predominantly agricultural, rural, and non-Euro-

TABLE 4.3

DEATH RATES IN SELECTED COUNTRIES, AROUND 1950
(*Deaths Per 1,000 Inhabitants*)

Country,[a] Year	Deaths	Country,[a] Year	Deaths	Country,[a] Year	Deaths
Belgian Congo,[b] 1950	5.5	Western Germany,		Yugoslavia, 1950	13.1
Angola,[b] 1950	6.3	1950	10.4	Bulgaria, 1947	13.4
Israel, 1950	6.5	Thailand, 1946	10.6	Colombia, 1949	14.0
Panama, 1949	7.1	Greece, 1949	10.7	Honduras, 1949	14.7
Paraguay, 1948	7.2	Spain, 1950	10.8	Algeria (Moslems),	
Netherlands, 1950	7.5	Venezuela, 1950	11.0	1949	14.8
Iceland, 1950	7.9	Japan, 1950	11.0	Tunisia,[c] 1948	14.9
Uruguay, 1948	8.3	Hungary, 1948	11.2	Chile, 1950	15.7
Union of South		Bolivia, 1949	11.3	Federation of	
Africa,[b] 1950	8.6	Algeria,[b] 1949	11.6	Malaya,[c] 1950	15.8
Norway, 1950	8.9	Luxembourg, 1950	11.6	India, 1949	16.0
Canada, 1950	9.0	United Kingdom,		Mexico, 1950	16.4
Argentina, 1949	9.1	1950	11.7	Madagascar,[c] 1949	16.6
Denmark, 1950	9.2	Czechoslovakia, 1950	11.7	Ecuador, 1947	17.7
New Zealand, 1950	9.3	Peru, 1950	11.7	Romania, 1945	20.0
United States, 1950	9.6	Jamaica, 1950	11.8	Egypt, 1948	20.3
Australia, 1950	9.6	Singapore,[b] 1950	12.1	Indonesia,[c] 1940	20.3
Italy, 1950	9.8	Costa Rica, 1950	12.2	Korea, 1944	21.2
Puerto Rico, 1950	9.9	Trinidad, 1950	12.2	Gold Coast,[c] 1949	21.3
Guam, 1949	9.9	Pakistan, 1948	12.3	Guatemala, 1950	21.5
Sweden, 1950	10.1	North Borneo,[c] 1949	12.3	French India,[c] 1949	21.6
Switzerland, 1950	10.1	Belgium, 1950	12.4	Yukon (Canada),	
Finland, 1950	10.2	Ireland, 1950	12.6	1949	21.7
Nicaragua, 1950	10.2	France, 1950	12.6	Burma, 1939	23.0
Trieste, 1950	10.3	Ceylon,[c] 1950	12.6	São Tomé and	
		Austria, 1949	12.7	Principe, 1949	34.0

a. Countries arrayed by increasing death rate.   b. Europeans.   c. Europeans and natives.

pean. The U.S.S.R. is the only nation of European stock that reported a birth rate above 35 immediately before World War II. On a scale of birth rates, the United Kingdom is near the bottom with 16.1, the United States is near the middle with 23.4, and the Latin American countries generally are high on the list. In the United States the birth rate varies widely in different parts of the country, from 35.9 in New Mexico to 21.0 in Massachusetts.

Many countries, including the United States, have shown a rapid increase in the birth rate in recent years. In the decade from 1940 to 1949 the birth rate increased very quickly in the areas with European population. In the United States, Canada, Australia, New Zealand, and the 10 countries of western Europe, there were about 50 million more babies born than would have been estimated on the basis of a study of birth rates in the previous decades. Later data indicate that this increased birth rate is temporary.

The Death Rate. The *crude death rate*— the number of deaths per 1000 persons— also varies from time to time and from place to place. However, as a result of good sanitation and adequate medical care, the death rate has varied less than the birth rate. In

1950 the death rate ranged from 5.5 in the Belgian Congo to 23.0 in Burma and 34.0 in São Tomé (in the Gulf of Guinea) (Table 4.3). In the United States the rate was 9.6; in the United Kingdom, 11.7; in France, 12.6; in Chile, 15.7; and in Indonesia, 20.3. In most of the Western countries the death rate in 1950 was between 9 and 13, a very narrow range.

In the United States the death rate varies from place to place, mainly because of differences in the age composition of the population. The highest death rates are in New England, an area with a fairly high median age. In 1940 Vermont, for example, had a death rate of 13.0 with a median age of 29.9, whereas Utah had a rate of only 8.7 with a median age of 24.3. In connection with the various death rates in the United States, it should be remembered that migrations affect the death rate in the areas of both emigration and immigration: it is customary for people in the median age groups to migrate, taking children with them and leaving large numbers of older people behind.

In other parts of the world, as in the United States, death rates vary with the median age; however, low economic level, poor sanitation (especially with respect to the water supply), and inadequate medical services are also important factors. Whereas the high death rate in France is probably related largely to the age composition, the high death rates in Russia and China are probably influenced by inadequacies of diet, sanitation, and medical care. Although the published death rates of some Oriental countries are to be questioned on the grounds that the estimates of total population may be too high and that many deaths may not be recorded, death rates are probably substantially higher in southeastern Asia than in any other part of the world, in spite of the low median age.

The death rate varies within countries from one population group to another. The death rate is higher for males than for females, higher for Negroes than for whites, higher for the poor than for the rich. Bankers, clergymen, professors, and farmers have a low death rate; bartenders, hotel keepers, glass blowers, and stevedores, a high one.

In what might be called the Golden Age of Migrations, which began about 1500 and is still in progress, great changes have taken place in the distribution and composition of the world's people. From 1500 to the present, the world population has increased fivefold. Migrations to new lands, with resulting expansion of the base of subsistence, have enabled some groups to grow more rapidly than others. This has been especially true of Europeans: in 1500 they made up only about one fifth of the world's people; at present they represent about one third. The cultural impact of these vigorous peoples has been even more important than their increase in numbers. No part of the earth has failed to be affected culturally by contact with Europeans. Natural increase has played a major role in the distribution of population, a role which is particularly noticeable in countries where immigration has not been of much importance in recent centuries. For example, although India, Pakistan, China, Indonesia, and Japan have not experienced large-scale immigration in the last thousand years, these countries have a total of 1000 million inhabitants.

The present numbers, distribution, and character of the world population are changing more slowly than before. Unless there should be war, large-scale migrations are not likely in the immediate future. Therefore, fluctuations in birth rates and death rates, from year to year and from country to country, will probably be the greatest factors in changing the pattern of world population.

CHAPTER **5**

The Present Distribution of Population

The most important single fact of human geography today is the unequal distribution of peoples over the surface of the earth. The more people there are in an area, the clearer and more complex is their mark on the land. The intensity of the development of houses, roads, cultivated plants, domestic animals, pastures, fields, and factories is correlated (sometimes positively and sometimes negatively) with the density of population. Density of population (the number of people per unit area) ranges in rural districts up to 3000 people per square mile and in urban areas up to more than 20,000 per square mile. On the other hand, many parts of the earth, such as the polar caps, some deserts, and the tops of high mountains, have no people at all.

The estimated world population for 1960 is approximately 2.8 billion (2,800,000,000), give or take 100 million. If these people were equally distributed over the land surface of the earth (excluding Antarctica), the density of population would be approximately 54 persons per square mile, comparable to the density of Missouri or to that of the United States as a whole. But much of the land surface of the earth can support only a very few people, if any at all. Therefore, assuming that only one third of the earth's surface can be effectively cultivated (most of the remainder being either too cool or too dry), the average density is about 160 persons per square mile, comparable to the density of Illinois. This generalization is useful mainly as a yardstick for purposes of comparison.

Population is very unequally distributed by continents. Table 5.1 shows the area in millions of square miles, the population in millions, and the density of population for each of the seven large divisions of the earth's surface. The explanation of the inequalities of population distribution, however, is probably not to be found through the study of areas of continental size; it is more likely to be found through the examination of smaller regions, in which such factors as resources and stages of development can be more readily evaluated. Small areas show greater ranges in density of population than those indicated in Table 5.1. A comparison of the following units in the United States suggests the magnitude of the variation in density, in this case expressed as the number of inhabitants per square mile (for additional data see Appendix E).

District of Columbia	13,150	California	67
Rhode Island	748	Alabama	60
New Jersey	420	Texas	30
New York State	309	Oregon	16
Ohio	141	Nevada	1.6
		Alaska	0.1

If geographers from Mars should come to the earth in space ships and make a careful study of the earth's resources, they would

52

TABLE 5.1

	Area in Millions of Square Miles	1960 Popu- lation in Millions	Density of Popu- lation per Square Mile	Rate of Popu- lation increase 1950-1960 (%)
North America	8.2	199	23	1.8
Middle America	1.1	66	60	2.7
South America	6.9	140	20	2.3
Africa	11.7	254	22	2.0
Europe	1.9	427	222	0.8
U.S.S.R.	8.6	214	25	1.7
Asia	10.6	1679	158	1.9
Oceania	3.2	16	5	2.4
World	52.2	2995	57	1.8

Table showing area and population of the earth, by continents, 1960.

undoubtedly conclude that the population distribution is out of joint. Why, they might ask, has Europe 400 million people while the United States, with more coal, iron, and agricultural land, has only 180 million? Does this discrepancy merely represent different stages of development: that is, has the population of western Europe expanded almost to the limit of its resources while that of the United States has not? Why is the population of New Zealand only two million and that of the British Isles more than 50 million when the areas, the climates, and the people are very similar? The Martian geographers would immediately spot New Zealand's isolation, mountainous terrain, and lack of coal as important factors contributing to the population difference. But many of the anomalies of population distribution would be more difficult to explain. Why then do people not migrate from overpopulated areas to under-populated ones? The answer rests in part on the various restrictions to migration and also on the reluctance of many people to leave their homelands and face new conditions of living.

Density of Population

As noted above, population density varies widely from one continent to another; within each continent the range of density is even greater. Moreover, the distribution pattern of each continent is different. In North America the densest population is in the east central portion. In South America, where there are few strong concentrations of population, most of the people live on the highlands and in the temperate southern area. In Africa only two small areas of population density occur, one in Egypt and one in Nigeria, and the deserts have a great sparsity of population. Western Europe is densely peopled, especially in the area extending from England to central Germany. The U.S.S.R. has a small area of population density in the Ukraine. In Asia the north and the interior are thinly populated; even in India and China some districts are almost empty. In Australia most of the people live in the southeast near the coast. It is apparent that any explanation of these various patterns calls for careful study. Distinction should be made between the arithmetical density based upon the total population and the total area, as contrasted with the nutritional density based upon the total population and the productivity of the arable land. It is obvious that the most important tool in the study of population is the map.

Density of population is usually indicated on maps in two ways. One method uses shading: different intensities or colors designate the various categories of population density. A map of the world drawn on this

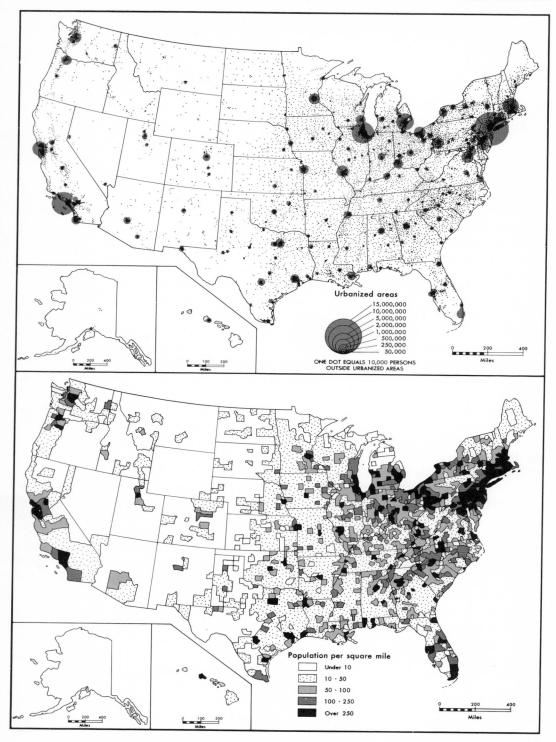

Fig. 5.1. United States dot and density maps of population.

basis (see End Papers) shows the various population densities ranging from fewer than two persons per square mile in relatively uninhabited areas to population densities of over 250, or even over 500, persons per square mile. Since many countries use the metric system, population densities are often expressed in the number of persons per square kilometer; and many maps give a density scale for both square miles and square kilometers. Since a square kilometer is approximately four tenths (.386) of a square mile, it is easy to convert in an approximate manner from one system to another. Population can also be shown by dot maps: one dot stands for a certain number of persons. On a world map one dot may often stand for a million people, whereas on a map of a state a dot may stand for 25, 50, or perhaps 100 persons.

Study of a population map, whether of the dot type or of the density type (Fig. 5.1), immediately shows the great variation in population distribution. Densities range from less than one tenth of a person per square mile in the very cold regions of Greenland and Antarctica to more than 500 persons per square mile in whole countries such as Japan. For purposes of general discussion it is worthwhile to divide population densities into arbitrary categories of a somewhat general nature. Areas with less than one tenth of a person per square mile are considered to be unpopulated; those with from one tenth of a person to 25 persons per square mile are called sparsely populated; those with from 26 to 150 are moderately populated; those with more than 151, densely populated.

The unpopulated areas of the earth include the northern part of North America, Greenland, Antarctica, parts of the Sahara and Arabian deserts, and some of the dry, cool areas in the interior of Asia. A few smaller uninhabited areas are found in the western interior of Australia and on certain high mountains, including parts of the Andes. If more detailed maps were available, many

Fig. 5.2. A sparsely populated area along the Columbia River in the state of Washington. The rugged terrain and the aridity make agriculture difficult.

more small uninhabited areas would be found in various parts of the world.

Sparsely populated areas (Fig. 5.2), with from one tenth of a person to 25 persons per square mile, are very widely distributed over the earth's surface, including more area than any other category. Most of northern and parts of western North America fall into this category, as do the interior of South America, much of Africa, dry Asia, and Siberia.

Moderately populated areas (Fig. 5.3), with from 26 to 150 persons per square mile, include the east central part of the United States, the Middle West, much of the western part of the U.S.S.R., and smaller areas surrounding densely populated zones in various parts of the world.

Densely populated regions (Fig. 5.4), with more than 150 persons per square mile, include Japan, China, Java, much of India, and a large part of western Europe, especially the United Kingdom, France, Belgium, the Netherlands, Denmark, Germany, Poland, Czechoslovakia, Switzerland, Austria, Spain, Portugal, Italy, Hungary, Romania,

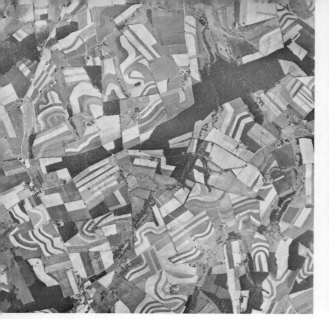

Fig. 5.3. A moderately populated region in southeastern Pennsylvania. The hilly nature of this area is suggested by the strip cropping and the distribution of forest land.

Fig. 5.4. Densely populated area in southern Korea. The small fields, rice paddies, and the close spacing of the houses suggest a high density of essentially rural population.

and a small part of the U.S.S.R. in the vicinity of Kiev.

The largest concentration of population in the world is in eastern Asia. Altogether, more than 625 million people live in this zone on a little more than a million square miles of surface. This means that there is an average population density of more than 500 persons per square mile. In latitude this zone extends from south of the Equator at Java to about 60 degrees north latitude and covers a wide range of climate. Parts of the area are very rugged, although no very great elevations are included. In Japan the population must support itself on about 16 per cent of the land surface of these small islands. So, if population density is stated not in terms of total area but in terms of cultivated land, Japan has a population density (or a nutritional density) of more than 4000 persons per square mile (see Appendix E). Favorable factors in eastern China and Japan are the many small and the few large fertile plains which are highly productive under intense cultivation. The natural setting of eastern China and Japan is similar to that of eastern United States, which is in the same latitude

but only moderately populated. What is the difference? Having studied the environmental factors, physical and cultural, one might conclude that the difference lies in the nature and background of the peoples rather than in the physical environment. If Chinese had settled southeastern United States, it is very probable that the population would have developed higher densities than exist there at present. The case of Java is worthy of special attention. Java lies a few degrees south of the Equator. Most of it is hot and the western end of the island receives quite heavy rainfall. On the two counts of heat and excessive moisture, we should expect Java to be moderately to sparsely populated. However, this small island supports nearly 50 million people and has the highest density of rural population of any part of the world. It behooves us, therefore, to examine very carefully these factors of excessive heat and excessive moisture in connection with the limitation of population. As yet there is no definite proof that any part of the earth's surface is either too hot or too moist to support human life adequately. It is true, of course, that certain sparsely populated areas, such as Amazonia, have high moisture and high temperature; but there is no proof that this is a relationship of cause and effect.

In addition to the large concentration of population in eastern Asia, there is also a great agglomeration in India and Pakistan, in an area which ranges from the Indus eastward to the delta of the Ganges and southward to the tip of the peninsula, including Ceylon. In this area there is a total population of more than 400 million people in approximately a million square miles, or over 400 persons per square mile. This high rate exists in spite of the fact that certain areas in the Deccan Plateau are sparsely populated.

Both the large agglomerations of population in Asia are supported on rice-growing lands. Most of the rice of the world is produced and consumed in these areas; this is true despite the fact that parts of northern China are too cool for rice and parts of western India and Pakistan are too dry for efficient rice production.

The earth's other large agglomerations of population, western Europe and eastern North America, are correlated with the development of manufacturing and cities. Climatically quite different from the Asiatic area, western Europe contains about 375 million people in a little more than a million square miles. Thus, the population density of western Europe is less than that of the Asiatic agglomerations, being about 300 persons per square mile. The smallest of the great agglomerations lies in eastern North America, mainly in northeastern United States and small adjacent portions of Canada. In this area the population of about 100 million lives on about 500,000 square miles of surface, with an average density of about 200 persons per square mile. The most densely populated portion of this area lies next to the seacoast in the vicinity of New York City. There are other areas of concentrated population along the Great Lakes and in the more favored parts of the interior land. Both of the western agglomerations, western Europe and eastern North America,

are correlated with the large-scale mining of coal and the industrial development that goes along with it.

A number of other areas of moderate population density occur in various parts of the world. Contrary to the idea developed in the temperate belt that population decreases with altitude, the highlands of Mexico, Venezuela, and Colombia are much more densely populated than the lowlands. In southeastern Brazil and eastern Argentina there are small, densely populated areas which are associated with three cities of over a million population each. In Africa moderate population density occurs in the northwest, which may in some ways be considered a part of the European world; also there are two heavily populated localities in Nigeria, one near the coast and another in the northern part of the country. Also small areas of moderate population density are found to the west of Lake Victoria, in Nyasaland, and in the southeastern part of the Union of South Africa. The most notable concentration of population in Africa is in lower Egypt along the Nile. Lower Egypt and many other small, densely populated areas outside the great agglomerations depend upon irrigation. In some of the dry regions now sparsely populated, there are temperatures, soils, and other conditions which could support more people if water were made available.

About 1700 million people, two thirds of the world's total population, live on about 8 per cent of the total land surface in an average density of a little under 400 persons per square mile. Of the other 53 million square miles of land surface, one third is moderately populated with an average of about 40 persons per square mile. The remainder, about 35 million square miles, is populated very sparsely, if at all.

Urban Population

The highest local densities of population are, of course, in the large cities (Fig. 5.5). Whereas rural densities rarely reach 3000

Fig. 5.5. A portion of the "Old Square" in New Orleans, Louisiana. This part of the city has a distinct European aspect with steep gabled roofs, numerous dormers and chimneys, and with balconies overhanging the sidewalks.

per square mile, apartment and tenement sections of some cities may reach 25,000. The densities in the business districts and suburban fringes are usually moderate (see Chapter 18).

At present the proportion of the total population living in cities ranges from about 4 per cent in parts of Africa to nearly 80 per cent in Great Britain. As the following samples show, the definition of "urban population" varies somewhat from country to country.

United States: Incorporated places of 2500 or more.

Mexico: Populated places of 2500 or more.

Canada: Incorporated places of all
                   sizes.
Netherlands: Municipalities of 20,000 or
                   more.
Switzerland: Communities of more than
                   10,000.
Japan: Municipalities of 30,000 or
                   more.
New Zealand: Towns of 1000 or more.

As a result of this variation in definition, the following figures, which show the percentage of the total world population living in cities, should be used with caution.

United States	57%	Soviet Union	20%
Mexico	36%	Egypt	25%
Canada	54%	Japan	51%
Argentina	61%	Korea	8%
Brazil	32%	India	14%
Great Britain	80%	Australia	69%
Italy	45%		

Population Patterns

Detailed maps of population show many distinctive patterns and arrangements which are not indicated by the usual density figures. The population density of California and West Virginia, for example, is approximately the same, but the population patterns in the two states are quite different. The people of West Virginia live mainly in the valleys of the Ohio River and its tributaries, which have cut channels in the Appalachian Plateau. As a result, the general pattern of population is dendritic. In California most of the population is clustered (Fig. 5.1) in and near Los Angeles, San Francisco, and the Central Valley. On the whole, other parts of California are sparsely populated. The study of a number of population patterns may uncover useful correlations with other phenomena; in some cases it may seem reasonable to suggest the existence of causal relationships. Some geographers state that parts of the earth's surface are too dry, too wet, too hot, or too cold to support people; others blame poor soil and rugged terrain. In general, such statements are too broad to be of much value and are open to challenge on the grounds of numerous exceptions. In the course of describing the specific patterns which follow, several correlations and possible explanations for the patterns will be given; it is wiser to consider all possible "causes" than to accept the first plausible one presented.

North America (Including Middle America). Much of the population of North America is concentrated in northeastern United States (and adjacent portions of Canada), east of the Mississippi River and south of the Great Lakes and the St. Lawrence River. Specifically, large agglomerations occur also in California and on the Central Plateau of Mexico; these two regions, along with New England illustrate the wide variety of population characteristics on the continent.

CALIFORNIA. The growth and distribution of population in California has been a never-ceasing source of wonder to students of population. Many years ago experts predicted that California had reached its peak of population and could not accept any more. Nevertheless, the growth continues at an accelerated rate, making California one of the most rapidly growing areas in North America. A high birth rate and a large net inmigration contribute to the rapid growth. Every week more than 10,000 persons come to California to live, while around 5000 leave the state during a similar period. Despite the limitations of some areas which are too dry and some which are too high and too cool, from the standpoint of living conditions the California climate is an attraction, especially for people from other parts of North America who have reached the retirement age. The climate is also favorable for many industries, such as the airplane and motion-picture industries. Climatic features induce a great many people to come to California, a prime example of a region that derives a constant source of economic support from outside the state. Many people who have retired to California are living on incomes derived from other parts of the country, such as the Middle West and the industrial East.

In California (Fig. 5.1) the distribution of population is very uneven. There are three clusters of population: the largest in the vicinity of Los Angeles, the second in the vicinity of San Francisco, and the third in the Great Valley. The three districts are quite unlike. The Great Valley has the most level land and the greatest supply of water from the Sierra Nevada and Cascade mountains. San Francisco has the best strategic location with an excellent natural harbor and good access to the Great Valley. Twenty-five years ago it was freely predicted that San Francisco and its satellite cities (Oakland, Alameda, Berkeley, Richmond, and others) would together become the largest urban agglomeration in western United States. Actually, metropolitan Los Angeles now has almost twice as many people as greater San Francisco; it is, in fact, the third largest city in the nation, outranked only by New York and Chicago. With a pleasanter climate than either San Francisco or the Central Valley, Los Angeles makes the most of its mild winters and abundant sunshine to attract both people and industries.

CENTRAL MEXICO. The moderately populated Central Plateau of Mexico supports most of the 34 million people of that country, although by most standards it is too high, too cool, and too dry. The eastern lowland of Mexico appears to be a more favorable place to make a living, but perhaps it is a less pleasant place to live. On the plateau all available water is used to irrigate the semi-arid basins, while the heavy rainfall of the eastern lowland is not utilized to its fullest extent.

NEW ENGLAND. In New England (Fig. 5.1) the population is concentrated largely in the southern part of the region, particularly in Massachusetts, Rhode Island, and Connecticut; in general, the northern part, Maine, New Hampshire, and Vermont, is sparsely populated. Because of a great concentration of manufacturing (particularly light manufacturing) in New England, the proportion of population which lives in cities is greater than that of any other part of North America. Rural farm population in New England is limited by climate and by rough mountainous or plateau land which is difficult to cultivate. Although New England once was self-sufficient in agriculture, it could not compete with the other farmlands opening to the west; as a result, New England agriculture declined in spite of the fact that the population of the region was increasing rapidly. Specifically, the densely populated areas of New England are related to the Connecticut Valley and to the Boston Basin, with the city of Boston as a focus. In order to understand the present distribution of the population, it is necessary to study the historical development of New England. For example, one should take account of the early dependence on water supply and water power for the development of many kinds of mills, especially textile mills; one should also recognize the importance of harbors like Boston Harbor; also one should not overlook the inaccessibility and lack of attraction for industry which characterized some rough, mountainous parts of southern New England.

California, central Mexico, and New England are examples of the variety of population patterns in North America. Population patterns vary from region to region according to factors like production intensity, transport, terrain, and popular preferences. In the most densely populated large area of North America, which can be outlined roughly by drawing a line through Boston, Montreal, Chicago, St. Louis, and Baltimore, there are a number of significant correlations. Population is relatively sparse in the Adirondack Mountains and in some sections of the Appalachians, but high population densities occur in and near the coal fields. Thus, the ridges and valleys of southeastern Pennsylvania are effectively indicated on a detailed population map. The shores of the Great Lakes and the Atlantic Coast north of New Jersey show concentrations of people, but south of New Jersey the coastal fringe supports fewer people than the inland areas.

In parts of western North America the correlation of people and rainfall seems to be quite high: less moisture means fewer people. Exceptions to this correlation are to be found in irrigated lands and mining districts. It is worth noting that the combination of mountain and dry plain, each of which in itself is unfavorable to population, produces an oasis with a local cluster of fairly high population density.

In terms of its resources, North America is underpopulated in comparison with Asia and Europe, each of which has less coal and fewer acres of cultivated land per capita. The greater per capita resources of North America are reasons why its population is increasing rapidly in most parts, the largest increases occurring in the sections already moderately to densely populated. In the United States the center of population has shifted slowly and steadily westward, from the vicinity of Baltimore in 1790 to southern Illinois in 1960, at an average rate of four miles per year. Of great significance is the increasing concentration of people in cities; some rural districts have lost population not because of decreasing productivity but because of the widespread mechanization of agriculture. The mechanization and specialization of agriculture enable many farmers and ranchers to live in town and, at the same time, continue their farm and ranch operations.

South America. In South America the distribution of population is decidedly peripheral. The highland fringe of the continent, with the exception of the northeast coast, the coast of southern Argentina, and part of the dry coasts of Chile and Peru, is moderately to densely populated. Furthermore, this fringe population tends to be concentrated in clusters at particular spots,

sometimes around large cities like Rio de Janeiro, São Paulo, and Buenos Aires, as well as smaller urban centers. Much of South America is hot and moist. Although, as previously indicated, this is not a proven cause of the sparsity of population, the fact remains that the great Amazonian area of South America is both hot and humid and sparsely populated. This fact may indicate an early stage of development; as population pressures increase, it may be that Amazonia, which probably is not prohibitively hot and moist, will be occupied by many millions of people.

If a population map of South America is studied along with a relief map, it will be noted that most of the people of South America live on the highlands, except in Uruguay, Chile, and Argentina. In other words, they may be said to live either in the highlands or in the lowlands of the temperate belt. The highland population is particularly noteworthy in Venezuela, Colombia, Ecuador, Peru, and eastern Brazil. The elevation of the highlands makes possible a temperate climate even in low-latitude tropical areas. The peoples who have settled in these areas have developed a liking for the highlands and a way of life which is related to the highlands. Although they are reluctant to settle the low-lying, humid, tropical areas, there is evidence at present that the highland peoples are beginning to move into these tropical lowland areas, some of which have resources that will become very valuable with the development of transportation lines. Another part of South America that is sparsely populated is Argentine Patagonia, composed of desert and steppe. All in all, it is probably true to say that the sparsely populated areas of South America, generally unattractive to highlanders, are unfavorable for settlement by these peoples. It is difficult to predict, however, what would happen if large numbers of lowland Asians were settled in these areas. Certainly conditions are different from those of southeastern Asia. Specifically, the flood plain of the Amazon

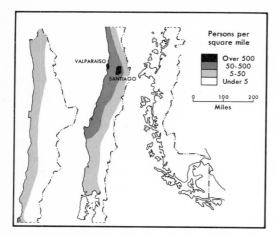

Fig. 5.6. Population map of Chile. Note the concentration of population near the coast in the northern portion, in the interior valley of middle Chile, and the empty areas of southern Chile.

is not so favorable for settlement by rice growers as the lower flood plain of the Yangtze River or the Ganges.

CHILE. Few small countries afford a greater variety of environments for the study of population than does Chile (Fig. 5.6)— a long, slender ladder of a country, ranging in altitude from sea level to over 22,000 feet, in latitude from 17 to 57 degrees south. The climate varies from extremely severe desert in the north to treeless tundra in the south. Most of Chile's seven million people (25 per square mile) live in the middle section of the country where the rainfall and temperature are moderate. The people are approximately 10 per cent pure Indian, 25 per cent of Spanish ancestry, and 65 per cent mestizo. Because it is similar to southern Spain, the Spaniards found Middle Chile to their liking; this liking may account for the fact that 90 per cent of the Chilean people live in this rather small region with a population density of about 125 per square mile. Unlike many of the people of South America, Chileans live at low altitudes, the population being concentrated in the main interior valley and,

to a lesser extent, along the river tributaries. There are no natural harbors in this middle area of Chile and few people live on the coast. Immediately to the south of Middle Chile is a more humid region, similar in climate to northwestern Europe and originally heavily forested. This district was settled by Germans who found it similar to their homeland and cultivated it in the same way. However, remoteness and lack of minerals are severe handicaps to industry and trade, and the population density of the area is low. Similar to the coast of British Columbia or Norway, the southernmost part of Chile has almost no people. Good harbors, many of which are protected by offshore islands, cannot make up for the rugged terrain, dense forest, and low summer temperatures.

The composition of the population of South America is quite different from that of North America. Only a few areas are of predominantly European origin. These include Argentina, the southern part of Uruguay, and part of southern Brazil. The peoples who settled these areas came mainly from southern Europe, especially from Spain, Portugal, and Italy, and, to a limited extent, from Germany. There are also a few areas which have predominantly Chinese or Japanese populations. Notably in eastern Brazil and in Colombia, there are a few small areas where the percentage of Negroes is fairly high. The Andean Highlands from the southern part of Colombia to northwestern Argentina are settled largely by Indians. Most of the remainder of the area's population is made up of mixed peoples, mainly a mixture of Europeans and Indians.

Africa. Most of the 250 million people of Africa live within 20 degrees of the Equator (see End Papers). The most populous political units are Nigeria, Egypt, Algeria, the Congo, Ethiopia, and the Union of South Africa. The highest population densities occur in Egypt and Nigeria. Sparsely populated areas include the Sahara and the dry lands of the southwest, parts of which are uninhabited. Some small areas within the tropics have very little population.

Broadly speaking, the peoples of Africa may be described as Negroes, Arabs and Berbers, and Europeans. Most of the Negroes live south of the Sahara; the Arabs and Berbers occupy the northern third of the continent; most of the Europeans live in the extreme northwest or in the extreme southeast, although a few Europeans are now to be found in all parts of the continent. In general, the Arabs and Berbers occupy the arid and semiarid lands; the Negroes live in the tropical lands, including the tropical highlands; and the Europeans prefer the temperate extremities of the continent. Most of the Negroes are small-scale cultivators; the Arabs and Berbers are pastoral; while the Europeans are engaged in commercial activities, such as large-scale farming, mining, and business. Despite the temptation to establish cause and effect relationships among race, climate, and way of life, it is necessary to realize that detailed investigation reveals many exceptions to the generalizations above.

NIGERIA. Nigeria is the most populous political division of Africa, with more than 30 million people (95 per square mile) living in an area somewhat larger than Texas. There are two densely populated zones (Fig. 5.7), one in the south in and near the delta of the Niger River, the other in the north in the vicinity of the city of Kano. Nigeria can be described briefly in three zones. The southern zone is one of generally low elevation and heavy rainfall, from more than 100 to nearly 400 inches. The middle belt has a moderate elevation of up to 2000 feet, as well as a moderate rainfall of 40 to 60 inches. The northern district is moderate in elevation but has a rainfall of only 25 to 40 inches. A look at Nigeria reveals great contrasts in rainfall and accompanying vegetation: rainforest in the south; in the middle portion savanna consisting of trees and grassland; and thorn bush in the north. Of course,

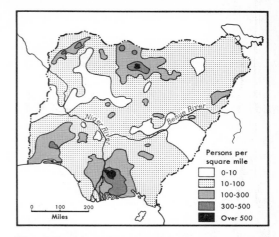

Fig. 5.7. Population density of Nigeria. Note two areas of concentration, one in the north around Kano and the other in the south on the lower Niger River. (After *Focus*, American Geographical Society.)

the natural vegetation has been greatly modified by man through burning, overgrazing, and clearing for cultivation.

Ways of making a living differ in the three zones of Nigeria. In the south the rule is intensive but shifting cultivation of a variety of subsistence crops, in addition to some commercial cultivation of oil palm and cacao. The subsistence crops include yams, beans, melons, cassava, and bananas. Except for goats and chickens, livestock is unimportant; in the absence of draft animals, most of the cultivation is done with hoes and other hand implements.

Although cultivation is scattered, the middle belt produces about the same crops as the south. A distinct difference between the two areas lies in the use of oxen as draft animals in the parts of the middle belt which are free of the tsetse fly. In the northern zone (the largest of the three) there is still more livestock, especially cattle, goats, and donkeys. The northern use of livestock reflects the influence of Arabs and Berbers on primarily Negroid people. Also, millet and peanuts are important field crops in the north.

The distribution of population in Nigeria cannot be explained in simple terms. Although many would say that the southern margin is too wet for optimum living, the density of population is greatest there. Although some would argue that the northern border with its violent summer rains and long drought is not very favorable, it is fairly densely populated in at least the area around Kano. Perhaps the explanation of the population distribution lies in a combination of factors, such as the distribution of the tsetse fly and other disease-carrying organisms, the varieties of soil, the types of vegetation, and the degree of Europeanization.

Europe. In spite of the fact that more people have emigrated from Europe in the last few centuries than from any other area on the earth's surface, Europe is the most densely populated of the large continental masses. (Asia has more people, but it also has a much larger land area.) Perhaps the high densities of population in Europe are related to the lack of dry areas, the rather small area of extremely cold climate, and the great resources of minerals, forests, and soils in the middle-latitude belt.

The population of Europe is unequally distributed, but it appears to be more uniform than that of other land masses because of the relatively small areas of population sparsity. In general, higher density of population is found in western Europe, where the climate offers greater rainfall and milder winter temperatures. However, there is a densely populated zone (over 500 to the square mile) which spans both the western and eastern areas by extending from central Great Britain across northeastern France to the Low Countries and continuing on to the eastern border of modern Europe, which is the western boundary of Russia. There are several other densely populated zones, such as the Po Plain of Italy and the lower Rhone Valley of France. The degree of variation in population density is illustrated by the density rates of various European countries: the most densely populated country is the Netherlands with 800 people per square mile; this is followed by Belgium with about 750, Great Britain with 543, Germany with over 500, Italy with over 425, and France with 203.

The distribution of population in Europe is related to land elevation. The lowlands are evidently the most favorable places for the concentration of population. There is, for example, the great lowland zone running from western France through the Low Countries and northern Germany, including parts of southeastern England. Smaller lowlands, such as the Po Plain, the Rhone Lowland, and the lowlands of southern Spain, are also densely populated areas. The fact that some of the higher parts of Europe are thinly populated may possibly be attributed in part to the limitation on agriculture which results from the relative coolness of the higher elevations. Also, in northwestern Europe there is a correlation of population with coal fields which have good access to iron ore. Most of these coal fields occur in the lowlands.

The sparsely populated areas of Europe are small; some are correlated directly with altitude, others with poor drainage or poor soil. On a good population map one can readily locate such high elevations as the Alps, Pyrenees, Carpathians, and many lesser mountains because of their low population density. It is difficult to determine whether the population density of these districts is related to rugged terrain, cool summer climate, or some other factor. Another example is the Landes Region of southwestern France, which is only sparsely to moderately peopled. This area was once a coastal marsh, fringed with sand dunes; the population increased when the marshes were drained, but it was still not equal in density to the population of adjacent districts. In Spain and Portugal the higher population densities (with the single exception of the Madrid district) are distinctly peripheral, the greatest concentration being in the alluvial lowlands.

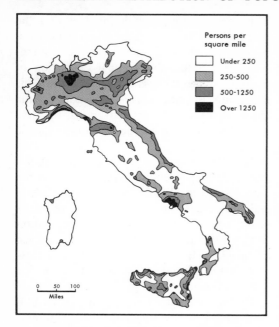

Persons per
square mile

☐ Under 250

▨ 250-500

▨ 500-1250

■ Over 1250

0   50   100
Miles

Fig. 5.8. Population map of Italy. (After *Focus*, American Geographical Society.)

ITALY. Italy is a small, densely populated country (Fig. 5.8) the size of New Mexico, but it has 50 times as many people. The 50 million Italian people (425 per square mile) are unequally distributed over a land which ranges from marshy lowlands to high Alps. Much of Italy consists of rough hill land and low mountains, both of which are ill-suited to intensive cultivation. In spite of limited resources, emigration, and a declining birth rate, the population of Italy continues to increase at the rate of about 10 per thousand per year; if continued, this rate will double the population in about 72 years.

The Italian population is concentrated mainly in the Po Plain to the north, in some of the smaller lowlands to the south (particularly the country around Naples), and in some of the larger cities of Sicily. The pattern of lowlands is important to the distribution of population, but the amount of rainfall and, more especially, of available water is also a vital factor. In the case of the Po Plain, a fairly large alluvial lowland of the

Po River and its tributaries provides a considerable amount of relatively smooth land for cultivation. The total rainfall is greater here than in the peninsular part of Italy; and, most important, there is more rainfall in the summer when conditions for cropping are most favorable. Additional amounts of water from the melting snows of the high Alps are also a great aid to agriculture. The numerous industries in the area are to be explained in part by the accessibility of hydroelectric energy, but there are also other factors, including perhaps the presence of skilled industrial peoples from northern Europe.

It is interesting to note that even in the densely populated area of the Po Plain, which has an average population density of over 500 persons per square mile, there are some small areas which are relatively sparsely populated. Such areas include the immediate banks of the Po River, where the danger of floods and the former prevalence of malaria played a very important role in keeping down the population.

Because of the rapid increase of population and the inability of the land to support very many additional people, Italy has been in the past a region of very large emigration. Migrating to many countries, Italians came in particularly large numbers to the United States, where there are more than a million people of Italian birth and many millions of Italian parentage. Italians have also emigrated in large numbers to such areas as France, northern Africa, Brazil, and Argentina.

In the peninsular portion of Italy and on the islands like Sicily and Sardinia, conditions of life are somewhat different from those in the Po Plain. In these areas of Italy, parts of which have a population density of more than 250 persons per square mile, most of the land is rough or mountainous, and only small areas of lowland near the coast are favorable for cultivation. Nevertheless, these small areas are intensely cultivated and the production of a variety of crops manages to provide most of the food for the people. It is from these less-favored areas that most of the migration has occurred, some of the migration having been directed to the Po Plain as well as to foreign countries.

Particularly in the large cities of the Po Plain Italy is industrialized to a considerable extent, but the country as a whole is less able than some other European countries to support a high density of population. The rapid increase in the Italian population necessitates either a large-scale emigration or a reduced standard of living. Already the standard of living in Italy is low as compared to that of the other countries of Europe, particularly France, Germany, and Great Britain.

The U.S.S.R. The U.S.S.R., with 8.5 million square miles and more than 220 million people, has a very unequally distributed population whose density is only 29 to the square mile. The highest rural density for any fairly large area is in the western Ukraine, the most humid part of western Russia. Moderately high densities extend throughout the middle portions of western Russia and are found also in scattered areas along the eastern end of the Black Sea and in the irrigated areas of Turkestan. There are two kinds of areas in Russia which are sparsely populated because of climate. One kind is composed of the northern lands, including the tundra and a part of the scrub forest; the other kind is made up of the dry lands of Turkestan and of the extreme southeastern part of western Russia. There is a thin band of population extending along the Trans-Siberian Railway from the middle part of the Ural Mountains all the way to the Pacific. In general, the rural population of western Russia is greater than that of comparable areas in the United States, although decidedly less than that of comparable areas in western Europe. The population pattern in western Russia can be correlated with favorable conditions for agriculture and with the location of industrial minerals.

Due to the high birth rate, there has been a rapid increase in the Russian population.

This fact, combined with the fact that the best land of Russia is almost completely occupied, has encouraged the Russian government to promote the gradual expansion of population into the less favorable areas. This expansion is particularly noticeable in the irrigated areas of Turkestan and in the dry-farmed wheat areas all the way to the Pacific Ocean.

THE UKRAINE. The Ukraine Socialist Soviet Republic, extending from Poland to the Don River, is slightly smaller than Texas and has about four and one-half times as many people (Fig. 5.9). The population density (175 per square mile) is the highest in the U.S.S.R., with the highest concentrations in the extreme western part and in the industrial east.

The western Ukraine region is the best part of the U.S.S.R. for agriculture. The rainfall, though light, is heavier than that in most parts of Russia; Kiev, for example, has an average of 24 inches. The temperatures there are the most favorable to agriculture of any in western Russia, since the winters are not very long and the summers are moderately warm; the July temperature of Kiev is 66° F. and thus is comparable to that of Winnipeg. In addition, the western Ukraine has a covering of loess soils which is even more fertile than the black earth farther to the east. The Ukraine produces large quantities of wheat

Fig. 5.9. Population map of the Ukraine.

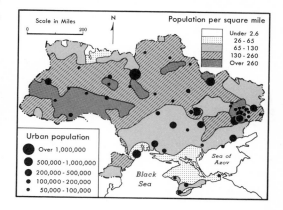

and sugar beets, a very intensive crop. The area of western Ukraine was increased after World War II by the acquisition of territory from southeastern Poland and eastern Czechoslovakia; as a result, additional excellent agricultural land is available to the U.S.S.R. Throughout the Ukraine and the bordering areas, there is a positive correlation between population and intensity of agriculture, except for the industrial regions.

The eastern part of the Ukraine, lying immediately to the north of the Black Sea, is characterized as the Donbas, the industrial region in the basin of the Don River. This region is agricultural as well as industrial and produces large quantities of wheat; however, compared to those of the western Ukraine, the yields are low. The population here is denser than in the heart of the Ukraine because of the development of industry. The great wealth of the Donbas is in the coal fields immediately to the northwest of the lower Don. Iron ore is mined farther to the west in the Krivoi Rog region, near the great bend of the Dnepr River. This region is well served by water transportation, having a system of canals and rivers in addition to accessible sea transportation. The population in the eastern Ukraine tends to be more urban than that in the western Ukraine. West of the Donbas in the great bend of the Dnepr River, the growing industrial district was based originally on iron ores and later on hydroelectric development. This Dnepr Bend industrial district and the Donbas are connected by a double-track, electrified railway, which transports coal, iron ore, and manganese easily and quickly from one site to another. In the U.S.S.R. it is the custom to set up industrial areas both at the iron mines and at the coal mines, whereas in western Europe and the United States the general rule is that the iron ore goes to the coal to be processed.

THE UZBEK SOCIALIST SOVIET REPUBLIC. On the mountain fringe southeast of the Aral Sea, the Uzbek Republic is slightly smaller than California and has about three-fourths as many people. The population, averaging 55 per square mile, is concentrated mostly in the irrigated areas on the alluvial plains. Except for hotter summers, Tashkent is comparable in climate to Salt Lake City with a July temperature of 81° F. and an average annual rainfall of 14 inches. The population pattern of the Uzbek Republic is similar to that of western United States, consisting mainly of a series of population clusters at the foot of the mountains and along the larger rivers.

Asia. Asia has large areas where people are few and small areas where people are many; this is the broad pattern of population. The large areas of few people are represented by the great arid heart of the continent, western China, Mongolia, and the southwestern countries, including Iran and Saudi Arabia. Some of the tropical lands of Asia, such as Borneo and Papua, are also thinly populated. Mongolia has a population density of 1.5 per square mile; Iran, 33; Saudi Arabia, 10; and Papua, 6. On the other hand, there are small areas with many people: Japan, Java, eastern China, the Ganges Plain, and the Malabar Coast of India. Density figures have limited meaning for the large countries, since many countries have both good and poor land. In the table below, the first column represents the average population density per square mile, while the second shows the arable land in acres per capita.

China	156	0.38
Japan	625	0.16
India	300	0.8
Pakistan	212	0.7
Iran	33	2.0
United States	55	2.7
(for comparison)		

Most of the people of Asia live on well-watered plains: some plains are watered by rainfall directly, as in the lower Ganges or the Yangtze; some, like the lower Indus, depend on water from distant mountains. The monsoon climate with its heavy summer rain-

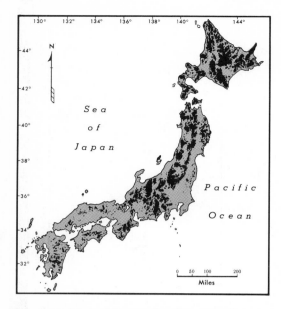

Fig. 5.10. Map of Japan showing sparsely populated areas. (Reprinted from *Japan's Natural Resources,* **by Edward A. Ackerman by permission of The University of Chicago Press. Copyright 1953, by The University of Chicago. All rights reserved.)**

fall is important to the development of the plains, just as the melting snows in the mountains are essential to the life-giving rivers. Plains with plenty of water and a long growing season can produce two or three crops on the same land in one year and thus feed more people.

JAPAN. On a limited scale, the population pattern of Japan is similar to that of the mainland of southeastern Asia. Most of Japan's 92 million people (Fig. 5.10) live on small alluvial plains such as those in the vicinity of Tokyo, Nagoya, and Osaka; the hilly and mountainous land, nearly 85 per cent of the surface of Japan, is thinly peopled. If the population density is computed in terms of total area, it is over 600 per square mile; if it is computed in terms of cultivated land, the figure rises to nearly 4000 (or .16 acre per person). Only about two acres in size, the average Japanese farm must support about 20 people, rural and urban. Such

density of population is a fairly recent development in Japan: a century ago Japan had only 30 million people; 40 years ago the country had less than 60 million.

For the most part, the recent population increases in Japan are associated with industrialization. This association is shown by the fact that the population increases have nearly all been in the cities while the rural population has remained rather constant. The population pressure greatly increased in Japan after World War II, during which Japan lost many of its external territories, among which were Formosa and Manchuria. Since Japan has little more land that can be cultivated, it is necessary for the Japanese to manufacture goods and sell abroad in order to purchase foodstuffs from other countries. Migration is another possible solution to the population problem, but the Japanese have never migrated in large numbers to other countries. There are more than 100,-000 Japanese in Hawaii and a similar number in Brazil; but these numbers are very small in proportion to the total Japanese population, especially considering that the population of Japan is increasing at the rate of more than a million per year.

JAVA. The island of Java is both hot and wet. The western half of the island is in the tropical rainforest and, although the eastern half has a short dry season, it is also hot and wet most of the time. This small island, smaller than Florida, supports 50 million people, more than 1000 per square mile. Obviously, the population of Java cannot be explained in terms of heat and moisture alone. Other partial explanations involve the fresh volcanic deposits which form the basis of fertile soils, the character of the Javanese people with their long-accumulated knowledge of tropical conditions, and the contributions of the Dutch, especially in sanitation and engineering.

As suggested above, the distribution of the world's population is spatially associated with the distribution of a number of physical and cultural elements, each of which varies in relative importance in different parts of the earth. These elements, some of which are listed below, are interrelated in various complex ways.

Location	Soils
Communication	Minerals
Climate	fuels
temperature	metallic
precipitation	non-metals
growing season	Natural Vegetation
Water Supply and	grasslands
Power	forests
from streams	Cultural Heritage
from the ground	political organization
Land Forms	social organization
plains	productive skills
plateaus	industrial develop-
mountains	ment

The interrelations of the above factors may be considered from two points of view: that of dependency, in which one factor is at least a contributing cause of another; and that of compensation, in which an optimum of one factor makes up for a deficiency of another. Thus, from one point of view, water supply and natural vegetation are dependent on climate; climate (locally) is dependent on land forms; soils are dependent on climate and vegetation. On the other hand, climate is not dependent on soil or water supply or cultural heritage.

From the other point of view, however, a favorable climate can compensate for a poor soil, as is illustrated in parts of California and Italy. Water brought by long rivers from distant mountains can make up for the lack of precipitation, as is illustrated by the Nile and the Colorado rivers. Productive skills, highly developed and applied over many years, can improve the soil, drain swamps, roll back the sea (as in the Netherlands), and transform the forest.

Population, when unchecked, increases in a geometrical ratio. Subsistence only increases in an arithmetical ratio. . . . A slight acquaintance with numbers will show the immensity of the first power in comparison with the second.
Thomas R. Malthus

CHAPTER **6**

Future Population

For centuries man has been concerned with the problems of population growth. Even primitive peoples recognized that an increase in numbers often meant lessened individual consumption and forced migrations. Today hundreds of books and articles with divergent points of view reveal the wide interest in the problems of population. Some people are worried over the rapid increase in numbers; others are anxious to have their own numbers increase more rapidly lest they fall behind in the struggle for power. Some of the major population problems can be presented in the form of questions, none of which can be precisely answered. How fast and how much will the world's population continue to grow and where will the growth be the greatest? How will the earth support the peoples of the future and at what standard of living? What will be the needs of the future peoples? Can man establish a balanced relationship to his environment so that resources will not be depleted? The first question is obviously the most critical; if the future population of the world could be foretold with precision, some of the other questions could be answered with more confidence.

More than 150 years ago the pessimistic Reverend Thomas R. Malthus wrote an essay on population which had a profound influence on the thought of his time. He suggested that population tends to increase in geometric progression, while food supply increases more slowly. As a result, barring wars, plagues, and other disasters, the population will increase until finally checked by hunger. Malthus believed at the time he wrote (1798) that this condition would come to pass in Great Britain within 50 years. Although he was wrong in this specific prediction, many students of population believe that his thesis is fundamentally correct. Applying the Malthusian thesis to the modern context, some claim that the industrial nations are currently getting along fairly well only because they are able to obtain raw materials from the nonindustrial nations. Consequently, as more nations became industrialized and process their own raw materials, the standard of living in the present industrial countries must decline. The neo-Malthusians also see a disastrous future for agricultural countries like India and China (Fig. 6.1). Because recent advances in medical science and sanitation have been able to check the death rate in such countries, their rate of population growth has increased alarmingly.

On the other hand, there are those who reject both the past and the present applicability of the Malthusian thesis. Some of these anti-Malthusians deny that there is such a thing

Fig. 6.1. Sampans on the Singapore River, Malaya. These boats function as freight boats and as living quarters.

as a population problem. They point out that every time the earth has been faced with overpopulation, new sources of food have appeared. They regard the sea as a vast storehouse of food which is little utilized today, and they suggest that other new sources of food and energy may be discovered in the future. Perhaps both the neo-Malthusians and the anti-Malthusians have some basis for their positions. But the cold, hard fact remains that today more than half of the world's people are undernourished, ill-clad, and poorly housed; some are actually starving. For them, at least, there is a serious problem, and any denial of the existence of a population problem must seem unrealistic indeed.

Forecasts of Future Population

Forecasts of future population have been made many times during the last 300 years and will continue to be made, in spite of the variability of birth and death rates in various countries from year to year and the tentative assumptions which have to be adopted in order to arrive at a quantitative estimate (Fig. 6.2). Malthus, in effect, made a forecast when he wrote that the population *could* double in 25 or 30 years. If Malthus' hypothetical rate were projected from his time to the present, the earth would now have a population of over 60 billion. Even before Malthus' time William Petty, in his *Economic Writings,* attempted to make a forecast based on the number of years required to double a population, using Noah and his family of seven as the basis of computation. Petty believed that the increase of population was in geometrical progression, but he thought that the rate of increase was declining in his own time. Today, population forecasters have many advantages over Petty and his contemporaries: for one thing, fairly reliable statistics are now available for most countries; also, much more is now known of

PROJECTED WORLD POPULATION TO 2000 A.D.

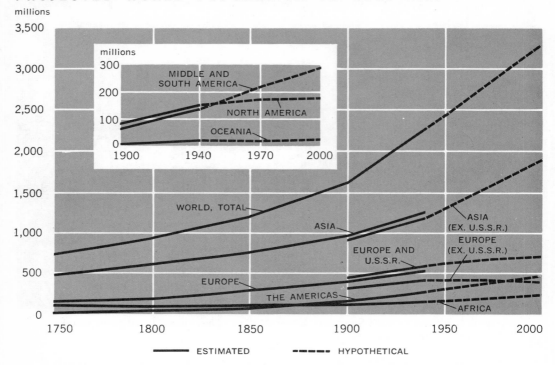

ESTIMATED   HYPOTHETICAL

Fig. 6.2. This conservative projection of population to A.D. 2000 lags behind the actual growth. The estimated population of the world for January 1, 1962, was slightly more than three billion. According to the graph the estimate was about two billion, seven hundred million.

the factors which influence the rate of population growth.

If the current rate of population increase is known, forecasts can be made on a simple mathematical basis. For example, if a country has a birth rate of 25 and a death rate of 15 per thousand persons, the natural increase will be 10 per year (or 1 per cent). Assuming a constant natural increase, the population of any future year can be computed by adding 1 per cent per year. Starting with 1,000,000 people, the number at the end of the first year would be 1,010,000; at the end of the second year, 1,020,100; the third year, 1,030,301; and so on. This natural increase is similar to the accumulation of money from an original investment of $1,000,000 at 1 per cent compound interest. Although this

method of forecast is similar to those of Malthus and Petty, the modern forecaster has the advantage of being able to use reliable data on births and deaths. In 1890 H. S. Pritchett used a mathematical formula to forecast the future population of the United States (Fig. 6.3). His forecast was accurate for the decades immediately following, but his estimates for later periods were too high. For instance, Pritchett forecast that the population of the United States would be 190 million in 1950, whereas the actual figure was 150 million; his predictions of 257 million for 1970 and 40,000 million (40 billion) for the year 2900 seem quite out of line. To be sure, forecasters are sometimes wrong in their predictions. It should be remembered also that their critics are not infallible either

—except, of course, as they are gifted with hindsight.

Since it involves a number of assumptions concerning changes in the birth rate, death rate, size of families, age composition of groups (Fig. 6.4), and other factors, the statistical method of population forecasting is, in essence, more complicated than the simple mathematical method. The statistical method can be used only for countries with good statistical coverage over a long period of time; consequently, it is not suitable for world population forecasts. Realizing that all their assumptions are subject to later modification, some forecasters prefer to predict a possible range rather than a definite figure. Thus, in 1937 Thompson and Whelpton estimated that the population of the United States in 1950 would be from 136 to 144 million, depending on variations in fertility and mortality. The actual count was 150 million. Prepared in 1947, their estimate for 1970 set a range from 151 to 170 million. These forecasts were carefully made by experts who evidently believed in 1937 that the low birth rate was more or less permanent; they apparently considered the much higher rate in 1947 a temporary postwar phenomenon.

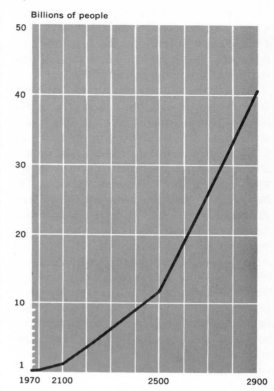

Fig. 6.3. Pritchett's forecast of United States population to the year A.D. 2900 appears to be merely a mathematical projection. It is difficult to imagine what the United States would be like with a population of 40 billion.

Fig. 6.4. Generalized population pyramids of young, aging, and aged populations. The critical age bracket, 15 to 45 years, represents the approximate limits of child bearing.

THREE BASIC AGE POPULATION STRUCTURES

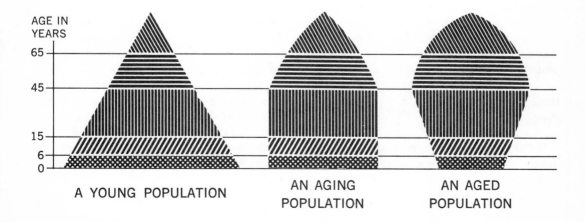

A YOUNG POPULATION   AN AGING POPULATION   AN AGED POPULATION

A forecast of world population is much more risky than one for a single country. In 1945 Notestein made an estimate of 3345 million for the year 2000, a revision of which was published by Woytinsky in 1953.

As a basis of his forecast for the year 2000, Notestein assumed that (1) the population of North America will continue to increase until the year 2000, with increases in Canada offsetting the decreases in the United States; (2) Europe will have slight increases when governmental policies ("bonus for babies," etc.) slow down or stop the current decline; (3) the natural increase in Latin America and the U.S.S.R. will continue to be high; (4) the rate of increase in Asia and Africa will decline; (5) the increase in Australia and New Zealand will be based on both natural increase and immigration. Although it is still too early to set aside Notestein's assumptions, some new trends are to be noted. The recently increased birth rate in Europe and the United States makes it necessary to revise upward the forecasts for these regions. On the other hand, the trends in the U.S.S.R. and Asia suggest a downward revision. Because of such changes, Notestein's estimate may be 100 million high for the world as a whole. Moreover, any major changes in the world economy could call for drastic revisions of the forecast.

Looking back over the record and the forecasts made during the last 300 years, it is evident that the population of the earth fluctuates in an irregular and somewhat unpredictable manner. Even so, forecasts for a few years ahead are fairly reliable and very useful. Generally, the record seems to show that the rate of growth is slowing down and that the world population will be stabilized sometime after the present century.

Basic Needs of the Future Population

If the world population continues to increase at about the present rate, man will need more of everything, especially more food, water, energy, and minerals. Man's needs will increase at an even more accelerated rate than his numbers, since the consumption *per capita* of many resources is growing rapidly. (This is especially true of water supply and energy resources such as petroleum and hydroelectric energy.) Resources formerly considered to be abundant may soon be on the critical list. What are the needs of the future? If an average American were asked to list his fundamental needs, he might reply, "I need an automobile, a television set, and a new house." Somewhere else in the world, the answer might be, "I need six camels, a new tent, and more pasture." In each case basic needs are not even mentioned. The fundamental needs of man are air, water, and food. Such other needs as clothing, shelter, tools, weapons, and machines are of secondary importance. Although it is true that in many parts of the earth man cannot survive without clothing, shelter, and tools, it is also true that in many other parts of the earth primitive peoples did live without any of these aids.

Normally man can live without air for only a few minutes, without water for only a few days, and without food for only a few weeks. Moreover, the quality of the air, water, and food must be within certain tolerable ranges. The air must be neither too dense nor too heavy, neither too cold nor too hot. Without auxiliary breathing apparatus such as oxygen tanks, man cannot live for more than short periods at altitudes of more than 30,000 feet, at which point the air pressure is only one-third that of sea level. Man can live at pressures more than twice that at sea level, such as those encountered below the surface of the ocean, provided that the changes in pressure are not too sudden. Man can tolerate a wide range of air temperatures, from the boiling point to points below freezing. With proper clothing he can live in temperatures lower than −60° F. The humidity of the air is also an important factor since man cannot live long in extremely dry air.

Man's water requirements are highly flexible, but he needs from one to eight quarts of drinking water per day, depending on the air temperature and the nature of his activity. A small amount of dissolved mineral is acceptable in water, but concentrations of 2 per cent or more render the water undrinkable on a permanent basis (see Chapter 9). Sea water, for example, has a concentration of approximately 3.5 per cent.

Of all man's requirements, food probably gives him more concern than any other. Many millions of people are worried because they do not have enough food; fewer millions worry because they have too much and are overweight because of it. How much food does a person need? The answer depends on weight, age, sex, activity, climate, and other factors. Living *without exertion,* an average man requires about 1700 calories per day in order to carry on life processes such as digestion, blood circulation, and maintenance of body warmth. (A calorie is a unit expressing the energy-producing value of food. A tablespoon of honey, for instance, contains about 100 calories.) An average adult performing light physical work, such as housework or office work, needs about 2800 calories per day; this need may range from 2500 or less if the person is small to 4000 or more if he is large. A 200-pound man engaged in heavy manual labor might require 5000 calories per day.

These basic requirements of man—air, water, and food—fix his habitat at or near the contact of air, land, and sea (Fig. 7.1). Most of the people of the earth live between sea level and an elevation of 2000 feet; all people live and work between the level of the deepest mine, about two miles below sea level, and that of the highest mine, about three miles above sea level. Thus, except for brief periods of high-altitude flight, the habitat or environment of man is a layer about five miles or less in thickness.

In addition to air, water, and food, modern man has come to depend on energy from fuels and water power, as well as on various minerals, to supply his needs. But for the exploitation of these resources, the earth could support only a fraction of its present population.

The basic and major secondary requirements for the future may be summarized as follows, with brief comments concerning the scarcity or abundance of resources:

1. *Air.* Air is abundant everywhere at moderate elevations, but it is subject to pollution by smoke and nuclear fall-out. Certain qualities of the air—temperature, humidity, and movement—are limiting factors.

2. *Water.* Water is abundant in some regions, scarce in others. Ocean water can be reclaimed but only at considerable expense. Subject to pollution by mines, factories, and sewage, the future water supply may be the most important factor affecting the distribution of population.

3. *Food.* Food supply is now inadequate in some parts of the earth, although there is surplus food in other parts. The total supply of food can be adequate.

4. *Energy from fossil fuels.* Petroleum and natural gas are adequate for the next half century, but producing regions will change. Coal is adequate for 200 years or more.

5. *Energy from water power.* This energy can be increased in most regions, especially in Africa, Asia, and South America.

6. *Atomic energy.* This energy will be used increasingly but at great expense.

7. *Minerals.* Many minerals are relatively abundant: for example, iron, aluminum, salt, stone, sand, shale, and limestone. Some of the metals are both scarce and critical: for example, tin, chromium, and nickel.

8. *Wood.* Wood is becoming scarce in some regions and costly in most. However, the supply is adequate because of possible substitutes like ceramics, plastics, and metals.

Two of these requirements for the future, food and energy, are discussed below; others will be treated in the chapters to follow.

Food. Man is an omnivore. He will consume almost anything—animal, vegetable, or mineral—from termites to elephants, from grasses to seaweed, from salts to drugs. The three fundamental food elements, carbohydrates, fats, and proteins, vary in amount in

Fig. 6.5. Fruit and vegetable market in Singapore, Malaya. Items include bananas, pineapples, oranges, papayas, mangoes, melons, and sweet potatoes.

different foods. Cereals, sugars, and potatoes furnish carbohydrates; fats are obtained from meat and milk products and from oily vegetables like soybean and oil palm; proteins are obtained from both animal and vegetable products. In regions with insufficient food supplies, the people are likely to suffer most acutely from the lack of proteins and fats (Fig. 6.5). In order to keep in good health, the average adult requires a daily ration of about 150 calories of high-protein food and at least 100 calories of fats. In addition, minerals and vitamins of various qualities are needed, especially calcium, iron, and vitamins A, B, and C.

Not all of the peoples of the world obtain enough food to keep them in good health and to provide them with energy for the work that they do. Nearly half the people of the world have a consumption of below 2300 calories per day. About 20 per cent have a consumption of between 2300 and 2800 calories. Roughly 40 per cent have a daily consumption of above 2800 calories.

The distribution of the calorie intake shows a rather significant pattern in terms of population densities and other items discussed in previous chapters. The highest calorie intakes occur in Canada, the United States, New Zealand, Australia, and Argentina. The European countries have generally high intakes: Scandinavia leads the list with a rate of over 3100 calories per day and is followed by Great Britain with 3050. Eastern and southeastern Europe are comparatively low in calorie intake, and southern Europe is just barely above the minimum for health and energy. Some parts of South America, particularly Brazil, Chile, Colombia, and Peru, have a low calorie intake. The lowest consumption is in India and southeastern Asia, where the calorie intake is barely above 2000 per capita per day. It is obvious from a study of the calorie intake of various peoples that it would be well to increase the total food consumption of the present population by about 20 per cent. At the same time, it would probably be well to reduce the

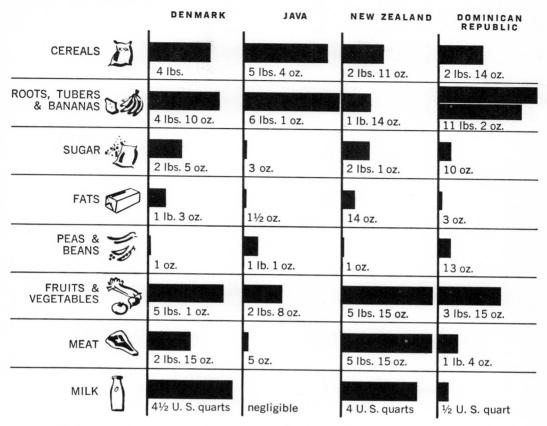

Fig. 6.6. Food patterns for selected countries. The diet of a country is usually adjusted to production, but note the low recorded consumption of sugar in Java and the Dominican Republic. Additional amounts of crude sugar are probably consumed of which there is no statistical record.

calorie intake of particular peoples, especially sedentary peoples in North America, western Europe, and Oceania.

The kinds of food eaten in the various countries depend upon each country's resources. Figure 6.6 shows the amount of food consumed daily by an average family in four locations—Denmark, Java, New Zealand, and Dominican Republic. Denmark and New Zealand have a high calorie intake; Java and Dominican Republic have a somewhat lower intake. It should be noted that Denmark and New Zealand have a definite cool season, while Java and Dominican Republic have no low temperatures. (In winter the consumption of food generally is much higher.) In Denmark the average

family consumes daily four pounds of cereals (mostly wheat and rye), more than four pounds of potatoes, two and one-half pounds of sugar, over one pound of fat, five pounds of fruits and vegetables, nearly three pounds of meat, and four and one-half quarts of milk. In New Zealand the consumption of meat is much higher, that of milk is much the same, as is that of fruits and vegetables; sugar consumption is similar, but there is a lower proportion of potatoes and cereals. This intake pattern reflects the relative abundance of meat in New Zealand. In Java the daily consumption of the average family includes five pounds of rice, six pounds of sweet potatoes and bananas, a large quantity of peas and beans, relatively small amounts

TABLE 6.1

CONSUMPTION OF SELECTED FOODSTUFFS FOR SELECTED COUNTRIES, 1959-60*

	Cereals	Potatoes	Sugar	Meat	Milk	Total Calories
Argentina	115	70	34	109	8	3090
Australia	88	53	50	114	14	3260
Brazil	106	117	31	29	4	2640
Canada	71	63	45	82	17	3150
China (Taiwan)	156	68	9	17	—	2310
Denmark	79	128	47	73	18	3340
France	107	100	32	74	13	2940
West Germany	83	131	29	57	13	2940
India	136	12	14	2	5	1980
Israel	123	41	29	29	9	2780
Japan	151	66	14	6	2	2210
Mexico	124	8	24	12	4	2330
New Zealand	86	55	42	107	22	3450
Peru	89	142	22	17	2	1980
U.A.R. (Egypt)	185	8	12	13	5	2530
United Kingdom	84	88	50	71	14	3290
United States	66	47	41	95	17	3120

* In kilograms per year per capita. Last column shows total calories per day per capita.

of fruits and vegetables, and very little sugar, fat, meat, and milk. In Dominican Republic there is a high consumption of cereals (mostly corn) and of potatoes, bananas, fruits, and vegetables (peas and beans), but the consumption of meat, milk, and fats is low.

The food consumed by peoples is constantly changing in amount and source. During the last 50 years in the United States, for instance, there has been a remarkable change in the diet of the people, even though the calorie intake has remained much the same. In general, there has been a decline in the consumption of grains, white and sweet potatoes, and sugar. Meat and egg consumption has fluctuated but is still at a very high level. The per capita consumption of dairy products has increased, despite the fact that there has been a decline in the per capita consumption of butter as the use of margarine has expanded. The consumption of fruits and vegetables has shown the most consistent increase and now stands at about 160 per cent of the consumption 50 years ago.

In other countries the pattern is similar but not identical. In Great Britain the consumption of wheat flour has declined slightly, but the consumption of potatoes has increased, as has that of meat, eggs, and butter. The use of margarine has also increased in recent years. In addition, sugar consumption has gone up to about 100 pounds per capita per year. In Belgium the consumption of bread has declined slightly, but potato consumption has held up very well. Meat consumption has been much the same over the last 20 years while that of eggs, milk, and sugar has gone up.

The variation in food consumption in various parts of the world is indicated in Table 6.1. It is noteworthy that the largest number of cultivated acres per person occurs in North America and that the smallest number (less than one) occurs in eastern Asia. The most calories per acre are produced in western Europe and the fewest per acre are produced in North America and the U.S.S.R. The highest production of original calories per person, occurring in North America, is nearly 10,000, while eastern Asia produces less than 4000. (Original calories are the total calories produced for each person, whether the person consumes the calories directly or benefits from them indirectly through the consumption of animal products.) This last comparison reflects the fact that North America depends much more on animal products than does eastern Asia.

The sight of fertile fields stretching to the horizon and discussions of the "farm surplus problem" tend to conceal one of the basic facts of world agriculture: little additional good-quality land is available for cultivation. Thus, much of the additional food that will be needed to feed the future population must come from increased yields of acres already under cultivation. In the United States during the first half of the present century, the yield of corn per acre increased 38 per cent; that of wheat, 26 per cent; that of oats, 16 per cent. These increases represent a reversal in trend since, prior to 1900, yields per acre had been slowly decreasing. Improved methods of cultivation, better seeds, and the use of fertilizers contributed to the increased yields.

Various estimates are available as to the possibilities of increasing the production of food in the world. It is well known that some areas of fairly good land are not as intensively cultivated as they might be. Even in countries where the calorie intake is very low, additional food might be cultivated by more efficient agricultural methods and more efficient use might be made of the crops. For example, in India the crops which are now fed to the sacred cattle might be used for human consumption, or the land which is now used to produce forage for the cattle might be used to grow food crops. One estimate suggests that the production of cereals in the world could be doubled by an increase of acreage in the tropical lands: where there is a dry season, wheat could be grown; if there is no dry season, rice could be produced. In the temperate regions the production of potatoes and various other tuberous crops could easily be quadrupled. If properly cultivated, there is no other type of crop

which yields so many calories per acre. The production of sugar, especially cane sugar, in the tropics could be increased many times, as could the production of fats and oils, especially the vegetable fats. Crops such as soybeans and oil seeds (like sesame and sunflower) could be expanded greatly. An increase in meat production is perhaps the most difficult to achieve because any increase involves great expansion in the acreage of forage crops; at present, this acreage would have to be taken from the crop areas producing human food. It is estimated, however, that the present production of meat could be increased by one-fourth to one-third; such an increase could be supported mostly in the tropical belt where grasslands are available for cattle and goats to graze, provided that conditions are suitable and the right breeds of animals are available. Most of the enlargements of production suggested above could be brought about most readily by increasing the yields per acre on lands now under cultivation.

In the future, of course, the total food production of the earth will be limited more and more by the amount of arable land. The total land surface of the earth is nearly 36 billion acres, of which only about 7.5 per cent (2.7 billion acres) is cultivated. This amounts to an average of very nearly one acre per person. With the rapid expansion of world population, it will be difficult indeed to increase the per capita acreage of cultivated land. There may even be a decline in per capita acreage before the world population is stabilized. To be sure, the yields of food per acre will probably be increased in the years to come by improvements in agricultural technology.

Energy. Man has gradually learned to derive energy from a variety of sources other than his own physical strength, but for many thousands of years his only source of power was the food he ate. Fire was the first source of energy beyond himself that man discovered, although at first he used it merely for warmth and comfort. Eventually, man learned to convert the heat from fire into

TABLE 6.2

THE WORLD'S SUPPLY OF ENERGY, BY CONTINENT AND SOURCE

Region	Total	Work Animals	Fuel Wood, Manure, etc.	Coal	Oil and Natural Gas	Water Power
Coal Equivalent, in Millions of Tons						
World	2,895	100	400	1,440	875	80
North America	1,254	10	55	577	580	32
Middle and South America	233	25	55	6	144	3
Europe	694	15	70	568	13	28
USSR	347	10	90	199	43	5
Asia	271	30	100	42	88	11
Africa	72	9	30	29	3	1
Oceania	25	1	—	19	5	—
Percentage Distribution by Source						
World	100	3.5	13.8	49.7	30.2	2.8
North America	100	0.8	4.4	45.9	46.4	2.5
Middle and South America	100	10.7	23.6	2.6	61.8	1.3
Europe	100	2.3	10.1	81.8	1.9	4.0
USSR	100	2.9	25.9	57.4	12.4	1.4
Asia	100	11.1	36.9	15.5	32.5	4.1
Africa	100	12.5	41.6	40.2	4.2	1.4
Oceania	100	4.0	—	76.0	20.0	—
Percentage Distribution by Continent						
World	100.0	100.0	100.0	100.0	100.0	100.0
North America	43.5	10.0	13.8	40.1	66.3	40.0
Middle and South America	4.6	25.0	13.8	0.4	16.5	3.8
Europe	27.4	15.0	17.5	39.4	1.5	35.0
USSR	12.3	10.0	22.5	13.8	4.9	6.2
Asia	8.7	30.0	25.0	2.9	10.0	13.7
Africa	2.6	9.0	7.5	2.0	0.3	1.4
Oceania	0.9	1.0	—	1.3	0.6	—

energy of motion, running the steam engine and the internal-combustion engine on such fuels as wood, coal, peat, petroleum, and natural gas. However, long before he found that fire would supply energy of motion, man had domesticated and used the power of animals like the horse, ox, camel, donkey, elephant, and water buffalo. Later the power of the wind was harnessed to drive wind-mills and sail ships, and water power was used in small mills to grind grain. Today the sources of energy, in order of decreasing importance, are coal, petroleum, natural gas, water power, wood, wind, and animal power (Table 6.2). Human power is so slight in comparison with these that it usually is not included in a list of energy sources. To appreciate the significance of energy resources for the modern world, one needs only to imagine what life would be like without them. There would be no electric lights, no automobiles or forms of transportation other than those provided by the power of humans and domestic animals. Manufacturing, in the modern sense, would be impossible, and the cost of handmade articles would be so high that very few individuals could afford them.

FOSSIL FUELS. Tomorrow may be the age of nuclear energy, but today we are living in the age of the fossil fuels—coal, petroleum, and natural gas. Although no one knows exactly when the fossil fuels were discovered, it is certain that at first they were not used exclusively for fuel. Marco Polo noted the use of petroleum in the dry parts of Asia as a cure for mange on camels. Aristotle mentioned that the ancient Persian kings sometimes had their food cooked in caves where the fires were supplied by seepages of natural gas, continually burning. However, it is known that 2000 years ago the Chinese were mining coal on a fairly large scale and using it as a source of heat. It is certainly true that the use of fossil fuels was greatly stimulated in many parts of the world when the supply of wood for fires was near exhaustion.

Eight centuries ago the forests in parts of Europe and Asia were exhausted; much later some forests in the New World were in a similar condition. In the 13th century the forests of England had already been cut or burned to a very considerable extent, and fuel was very scarce. As a result, the English king, Henry III, gave his permission for the mining of coal, which practice had previously been carried on in Britain to a limited extent by the Romans. Although this permission started the mining of coal on a rather large scale, there was still a good deal of opposition to the practice on the grounds that the burning of coal was unhealthful. Because of such opposition, Edward I, son of Henry III, signed a decree prescribing the death penalty for anyone burning coal in London while Parliament was in session. However, despite the suspicion of coal (which still exists in the current belief that smog and smoke cause certain diseases), England continued to mine and burn more and more coal.

There was little notice taken of coal in the Americas until 1665, when a French missionary made a map of the upper Mississippi Valley on which he marked the word "coal." Later, coal was discovered in a number of places in eastern North America, but it was generally considered to be of little value. Because of this low estimation of its worth, coal was once used in Pennsylvania as a road material, instead of gravel. During the 19th century, nearly 600 years after Henry III had given permission for the mining of coal in England, coal began to be used in eastern United States in some considerable measure. Just as in England, there was a struggle in the United States over the acceptance of coal as a fuel; then, once bituminous coal had been accepted, a struggle was necessary to get anthracite coal into use. At the beginning of the 19th century coal was being imported from Europe to eastern United States in small quantities for the purpose of iron making, but there was little demand for coal for any other purpose. A few years later coal was mined and floated down the Susquehanna River to Lancaster County in Pennsylvania, where the people, never having seen coal, were skeptical about its use. Until a stove or grate was constructed to withstand the heat of the burning coal, there was little success with it as a domestic fuel; but once the grate and stove were introduced, the use of coal spread rapidly in the United States.

About the same time new uses of coal were discovered in western Europe. In London coal gas was developed by heating the coal and driving off the distillate; as a consequence, gas lighting of the streets of London began about 1810, replacing whale oil lamps. About this time in Italy, a kind of kerosene was distilled from petroleum and used for lighting.

Because many advanced industrialized areas of the world did not have petroleum in any quantity, the large-scale use of petroleum as a source of power came somewhat later than the use of coal. Western Europe has never produced large quantities of petroleum and even small quantities were obtained only through deep drilling. By 1830, however, oil wells were beginning to appear in eastern United States. In most cases, the early oil wells, like the one in Burkesville, Kentucky, were discovered accidentally during the process of drilling for water. At first, petroleum was used only for medicinal purposes, but by the 1850's its use as a fuel and source of power became important. Many oil wells were drilled in different parts of the world before the 1850's, and petroleum was obtained from seepages in springs. It remained, however, for the famous Drake well, drilled in western Pennsylvania near Titusville in 1859, to set fire to the imaginations of men concerning the great possibilities of oil. As soon as the Drake well was in production, other wells were drilled in the surrounding country and oil production began on a commercial scale. The discovery of the well in Titusville started eight years of intense oil boom; at first, production soared upward, but then it dropped to a mere trickle as the shallow wells were depleted. It was a period of great violence and lawlessness during which rival organizations endeavored to destroy each other's pipelines and oil tanks.

One of the first large uses of petroleum was for lighting the lamps of the world. Prior to the 1860's, whale oil had been the most important source of light, and whale-oil production in 1859 was 200 times as great as the production of oil. However, many people began to see the advantages of fuel from petroleum, which was both cheap and able to be distributed readily to different parts of the world. Although electric lighting had already appeared and was being used in some places, kerosene was much more widely applied at the time. Kerosene is still used as a source of light in millions of homes.

It is noteworthy that the steam engine, for many years the prime source of power in the world, was developed in the age of wood. Moreover, wood was used for fuel long after coal was known in western Europe and in eastern United States. Large-scale uses of fossil fuels for power (Fig. 6.7) did not get underway until the close of the 19th century, when the production of electric power from coal and the development of the petroleum-fed internal-combustion engine were well launched.

OTHER SOURCES OF ENERGY. Students of population who believe that the earth can support many times the present population are likely to mention sources of energy which have, until the present, been little used. These sources are solar energy and nuclear energy. Water power is also mentioned, especially with reference to harnessing the tides.

Water power depends ultimately on solar energy, as do fossil fuels, wood, and many other fuels. A large part of the energy which comes from the sun to the surface of the earth is used to evaporate water from the oceans, lakes, rivers, soil, and vegetation. This water, carried aloft and dropped on the land in the form of rain or snow, furnishes the basis for hydroelectric energy. At present the distribution of water power, both potential and developed, is uneven: dry or flat lands have little water power; humid, mountainous land has a high potential. The greatest potential water power is in equatorial Africa, which has a heavy rainfall on plateaus and mountains. With a somewhat similar combination of factors, Asia is second in potential water power and is followed by North America, South America, and Europe. In European countries such as Italy and Switzerland, where coal is scarce or lacking, a large proportion of the potential power has been developed. North America is in an intermediate position in terms of developed power, while Africa and Asia are low. Water power is a permanent source of energy in the sense that it is constantly renewable as long as energy comes from the sun to the earth.

Man is just beginning to make direct use of solar energy. It is estimated that in three days the earth's surface receives as much energy from the sun as could be produced by burning all of the coal, petroleum, and

Fig. 6.7. A steam power plant on the Ohio River near Moundsville, West Virginia. The river and its tributaries provide cheap transportation for coal. A stockpile of coal can be seen behind the smokestacks.

natural gas existing in the crust of the earth. In regions with long hours of sunshine, it is not difficult to heat a house with solar energy, and small solar batteries can be used to energize small electrical devices like radios. But the large-scale installations needed to power a factory or light a city are both difficult and expensive. In addition, the fact that solar energy is interrupted by clouds and nighttime presents a serious handicap. Nevertheless, if coal, petroleum, and water power were unavailable, solar energy might be used much more than it is at the present time.

The world is just on the threshold of great developments in nuclear energy. Various radioactive substances have the property of generating heat which, if controlled properly, can be used to produce steam and thus pro-vide a long-lasting source of energy with very small bulk and weight. One of the first large-scale examples of the use of nuclear energy was the atomic submarine *Nautilus,* which cruised around the oceans of the earth for 350,000 miles without being recharged. The simplest form of nuclear energy is derived from Uranium 235 atoms, which, if bombarded by neutrons, split into two fragments with a resulting release of a great amount of energy. One pound of Uranium 235 produces as much energy as could be obtained by burning about 1500 tons of coal. Unfortunately, ordinary uranium contains only a small amount of Uranium 235 and elaborate processes are necessary in order to make the conversion.

CONSUMPTION OF ENERGY. About 3000 or 4000 calories of food are utilized per capita per day in the United States, but the total energy consumption of a person in the United States is about 200,000 calories per day. These calories are derived from all sources of energy, but mostly from coal, petroleum, natural gas, and water power. The amount of nuclear energy used per capita is still quite small. The uses of energy vary in different parts of the world, but there is a general pattern of use which is similar to that of the United States. About 20 per cent of the energy is used for space heating (heating houses and enclosures of various kinds); a little less than 20 per cent goes directly into electrical power; about 40 per cent is used for industry, including the production of iron and steel; and the remainder is used largely for transport—for the driving of locomotives, ships, automobiles, trucks, and airplanes. Of the energy used in the United States, about 45 per cent comes from coal; about 18 per cent, from natural gas; about 10 per cent, from water power; and the remainder comes from petroleum.

It is impossible to forecast with any exactness the future demands for energy. The present trend is toward a greater consumption of energy per capita; this trend, in combination with population increases, indicates a very much larger production for the whole world. There is enough coal available in the world to last at least 200 years, even with a constantly increasing rate of production. Some of this coal is deep and some is of rather low quality, but it can be mined and used. At the present rate of consumption, petroleum (Table 6.3) will probably be exhausted in about 50 years; natural gas may be expected to have somewhat the same life. The difficulties involved in using the more permanent sources of energy, particularly solar energy and nuclear energy, will restrict their development for many years to come. In any event, the future development of energy will play a very important part in determining the numbers and distribution of the peoples of the world, as well as their standard of living and way of life. The amount and nature of the energy provided in the future will have a bearing on the techniques used in agriculture and manufacturing and on the nature of transportation systems on the earth and in space.

It is difficult to contemplate the human scene without thinking of the future and its population problems. Even in the more stable countries there is abundant evidence of change, while in others the rate of change is appallingly rapid. The question, however, is not merely one of what will happen to particular communities and nations. Rather, the question is, What is in store for the

TABLE 6.3

ENERGY PRODUCED, 1960*

	Total	Coal	Oil	Gas	Hydro	Per Capita
World	4311	2204	1399	622	86	1082
North America	1441	401	508	500	32	7802
Caribbean America	263	5	237	20	1	893
Other America	34	4	23	4	3	519
Western Europe	563	499	20	16	28	2565
Middle East	351	5	345	1	0	264
Far East	165	115	36	5	9	242
Oceania	31	30	0	0	1	2947
Africa	58	43	14	0	1	310

* In millions of metric tons coal equivalent. Per capita consumption in kilograms.

world? A study of human geography does not provide the answer to this question, but it can contribute to an understanding of the world's problems.

The Western way of life, which was developed in Europe and transmitted to the New World, has now penetrated most areas of the earth in some measure. This penetration has been accompanied by a great increase in mechanization and industrialization. Western agriculture, for example, is little concerned with the simple methods of last year: the bulldozer, the tractor, the gang plow, and the combine have replaced the hoe, the spade, and the sickle. Likewise, the assembly line has replaced the craftsman and mass advertising is taking over the function of the individual salesman. People are inclined to contemplate the modern scene with a mixture of wonder and anxiety, marveling at the recent inventions and discoveries (such as nuclear energy), yet deploring the congestion of our cities, highways, and schools. It is obvious to such observers that, although some lands may have too few people, more lands will soon have too many. The future world situation with respect to population is well stated by Harrison Brown in *The Challenge of Man's Future:*

. . . we see that, although our high-grade resources are disappearing, we can live comfortably on low-grade resources . . . that, although a large fraction of the world's population is starving, all of humanity can, in principle, be nourished adequately . . . that, although world populations are increasing rapidly, those populations can, in principle, be stabilized. . . . But it is equally clear that the achievement of this condition will require the application of intelligence, imagination, courage, unselfish help, planning, and prodigious effort. . . . Man is rapidly creating a situation from which he will have increasing difficulty extricating himself.[1]

[1] Harrison Brown, *The Challenge of Man's Future*, p. 265.

Part III

THE PLACE

*Our environment is at any moment of human history
the product of a perennial revolution, of a
continuous process of change.*
Erwin A. Gutkind

CHAPTER 7

Environment: The Importance of Place

Nearly three billion people live in a shallow zone at the surface of the earth. It is a zone of moderate temperature and moisture, with rain and snow; rivers, lakes, and oceans; mountains, plateaus, and plains. This life zone extends about three miles above and a few hundred feet below sea level. To be sure, man can reach slightly beyond this zone: he has climbed to a height of many miles in the air and promises to go much farther; he has descended several thousand feet beneath the land and the sea. But these have been special, temporary migrations which up to this time have not permanently extended the zone of human occupation.

Within this thin life zone, which is comparable in thinness to the rubber of a toy balloon that has been inflated to a diameter of several feet (Fig. 7.1), the specific place or environment in which man lives is of great importance. Among the elements of environment are location, altitude, landform, soil, climate, drainage, natural vegetation,

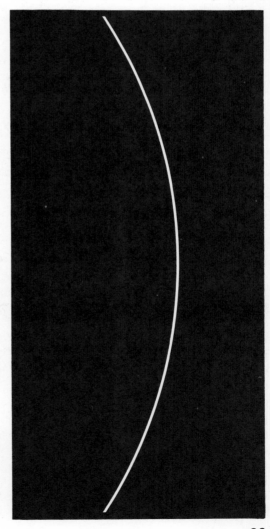

Fig. 7.1. This arc of the earth's circumference represents approximately 3400 miles and its width, less than one millimeter, represents 15 miles. The width of the line encompasses the highest mountain on the earth and the lowest depth in the ocean. Almost all the activities of man take place within this thin layer.

and useful minerals, all of which occur in various combinations. Man has adapted himself to a great many combinations of these environmental factors, as have plants and animals. Thus, if the Eskimo, accustomed to the cold of the northern latitudes, was suddenly transported to the tropics, he might perish because of his lack of resistance to tropical diseases. Likewise, the dweller of the tropics, a native of Java perhaps, would quickly perish if he were placed in the habitat of the Eskimo. It is apparent that men, plants, and animals have gradually learned to adapt themselves to a great variety of conditions. They can even tolerate changes, provided the changes are not too abrupt.

Man plays a unique role in all parts of the life zone; unlike the plants and other animals, he has a positive place in the economy. He plants trees and cuts down forests; he fixes shifting sands by planting dune grass and starts dust storms by plowing semiarid grasslands; he cultivates plants and domesticates animals.

Horizontal Distribution

Within the thin life zone there are restrictions on the horizontal distribution of human occupation; as a result, a large part of the earth's surface is empty (see End Papers). Some of the restrictions to human occupation can be overcome through the application of certain techniques of living, but others are more difficult to surmount. In visualizing the limits of mankind's distribution, a globe is of great use. If a globe is rotated with fingers placed at the parallels of 60 degrees north latitude and 60 degrees south latitude, the approximate limits of effective settlement are indicated. A few permanent settlements have been established at higher latitudes, but these settlements are of negligible size and, furthermore, are unable to exist without the support of lower-latitude economies. Observation of a globe should also make apparent the fact that a large proportion of the earth's surface be-

tween the polar circles is water. Although man uses this area, he does not occupy it.

As indicated in previous chapters, man is distributed unevenly within the occupied lands. What are the chief limiting factors in the environment which affect this distribution? Two sets of factors, one natural and one cultural, are more or less intermingled in the complex which we call "environment." In addition to the physical factors mentioned above, there are cultural factors such as the nature of cultivated plants, the techniques of cultivation and processing, and various other cultural traits of different peoples, as well as such negative factors as the presence of parasites and disease. Before entering upon a detailed discussion of physical and cultural factors in the chapters to follow, it will be well to discuss briefly the meaning of the more important environmental factors. This brief discussion must of necessity be suggestive rather than definitive.

Climate

Man may not be able to affect the climate very much, but the climate certainly affects him in a variety of ways. Not only has it limited his distribution but also it has apparently brought about, over a long period of time, certain physical changes in his skin color, body weight, and body measurements (Fig. 7.2). Although man may not be able to modify climate very much, he has made many adaptations or adjustments to climate by means of houses, clothing, irrigation, windbreaks, air conditioning, and other devices. Man is certainly less restricted by climate today than he was a thousand years ago.

Climate affects the human animal in much the same way it affects other animals, except that man is able to modify many of its effects. The physical character of man varies from climate to climate—especially in skin color, body proportions, and body weight—but careful study is necessary to determine how much of the difference should be

Fig. 7.2. Racial types: (a) Zulu from Dundee, South Africa; (b) shepherd boy from Korinthos, Greece; (c) Indian woman from Yukon Territory, Canada; (d) Chinese from Hong Kong.

ascribed to climate and how much to other factors such as race, diet, and ways of living. Three ecological rules, derived from the study of animals, apply in some measure to man.

GLOGER'S RULE

In mammals and birds, races which inhabit warm and humid regions have more melanin [dark] pigmentation than races of the same species in cooler and drier regions; arid regions are characterized by accumulation of yellow and reddish-brown . . . pigmentation.[1]

Examples come easily to mind: blond Scandinavians, dark Italians, swarthy Arabs, and brown Hindus are all Caucasians. To what extent are these physical differences based on racial inheritance and to what extent are they attributable to climate? Whatever the answer, there is clearly some correlation with climate.

BERGMANN'S RULE

The smaller-sized geographic races of a species are found in the warmer parts of the range, the larger-sized races in the cooler districts.

Coon's Comments on Bergmann's Rule

In Europe the Irish have a mean of 157 pounds, the Finns of 154, and so on down the temperature cline to the Spaniards with 132 and the racially white Berbers of Algeria with 124 pounds. In Asia the Mongoloid peoples are graded from the North Chinese with 142 to the Annamites with 112 pounds, and the Siberian peoples of the far north are probably heavier than the North Chinese, although no figures are easily available. Their neighbors across Bering Strait, the Eastern Aleuts, run to means of 150 pounds. . . . In South America there is every evidence that the rule holds true, with bulky Indians at the cold end, and smaller ones in the forests, while up in the chilly altiplano they again grow bulky. In Central America we find a mean of 119 pounds for the Maya of Yucatan, which rises as one goes northward into the United States and Canada to a peak in the 160's.

Low figures are obtained from people like the Andamanese, whose male population averages only 98 pounds, and the Bushmen of the Kalihari, with 89. Even the Baluba, an equatorial Negro tribe, weigh only 118 pounds, and the Australian aborigine around the Gulf of Carpentaria, 123. In Polynesia, where offshore breezes make heat loss no problem, peoples of tropical provenience, the Hawaiians and the Maori, living at 20 and 40 degrees from the equator respectively, weigh from 140 pounds

upward, much more than the means for the inhabitants of Java and Sumatra, whence their ancestors are said to have come. Their islands are larger and hotter.

Man's size is as plastic as his tannable skin color, and as automatic. Anyone who has visited the Lower Amazon country has seen that the Brazilian citizens in that tropical forest are of one size, whatever their color, hair form, or cast of facial features. At least three racial stocks are concerned, the Mediterranean, the Negro, and the American Indian. All come out the same. Farther south, representatives of these three stocks are much larger.

ALLEN'S RULE

Protruding body parts, such as tails, ears, bills, extremities, and so forth, are relatively shorter in the cooler parts of the range of the species than in the warmer parts.

Coon's Comments on Allen's Rule

One of the racial peculiarities of Negroes is long arms, with particular emphasis on the length of the forearm, and large hands, with long fingers. Forest negroes often have relatively short legs, but we have seen that the legs have much less to do with heat regulation than the arms. The Nilotics, Somalis, Masai, and other black-skinned peoples of the Sahara, Sudan, and the Horn of Africa, have long skinny legs as well, and long gracile necks; no case of adaptation to a given environmental situation could be clearer. The same is true of South Indians, the Ceylonese Vedda, most Melanesians, and the Australian aborigines of the desert, as well as white Australians from Queensland. The Bushman of the Kalahari is extremely slender. On the inhabitants of the American deserts information is defective. At any rate, as far as we know, the desert portion of Allen's rule holds for man, for obvious reasons. The mechanism of change is less obvious. If it is Darwinian selection, it is hard to see how it applies to white Australians.

Polar and subpolar peoples are invariably described, in the prime of the individual, as well equipped with subcutaneous fat. This fat is especially developed on critical spots, such as the cheek, wrists, and ankles. One centimeter of fat is given the same insulation rating as a complete suit of winter clothing. The healthy Negro living in a hot country carries almost no sub-

[1] Carleton S. Coon, "Climate and Race" in Harlow Shapley, ed. *Climatic Change*, p. 15.

a

b

c

d

Fig. 7.3. Types of clothing: (a) Eskimo winter outfit of sealskin with quiver and bow; (b) Zulu ceremonial dress, South Africa (with closeup view of huts similar to those in Fig. 1.4); (c) a variety of boys' clothing in Le Havre, France; (d) a Maori fur cloak, New Zealand.

cutaneous fat. His superior performance in the desert, compared with that of whites of the same age and weight, has been demonstrated.[2]

[2] *Ibid.*, pp. 16-30.

Unable to change the climate in any fundamental sense and with only a limited capacity for physical adaptation, man has developed over the years many protective and modifying devices and practices to enable him to endure and even to enjoy the climatic hazards. Only two of these "inventions" are discussed here: clothing and shelter. These are merely examples; others will be mentioned in the chapters which follow.

Man uses a variety of material and fashion in clothing (Fig. 7.3) in order to keep himself dry in wet climates, warm in cold lands, and protected from the sun and wind in hot, dry regions. Man has directed much effort toward the perfection of garments which give protection from the elements without interfering with activity. The Ona Indians of Patagonia have solved this problem by the use of a large fur garment, fastened loosely at the throat, which can be discarded quickly by a hunter when he spots his quarry. Obviously this solution would not be satisfactory for an Eskimo. Furs, skins, the hair and wool of many animals, numerous vegetable fibers, bark, grasses, and many other materials are used for garments, in addition to the modern synthetic materials. Clothing is not only a protection against the climatic elements; it also protects the delicate human hide from abrasion, and, perhaps most important, it is a major form of adornment.

Like clothing, shelter takes form (Fig. 7.4) according to need, materials available, and habits of the people. In the rainy tropics a native, in order to shelter himself against the heavy rains, may mount a thick thatch on poles. With such a roof, he would omit walls, since a free circulation of air is desirable. In the same environment a transplanted European might use sheet metal for a roof and metal screens or Venetian blinds for walls. In the hot, dry lands where wood is scarce, some sort of earthy material is often used; such materials as mud, adobe, and stone provide a certain amount of insulation against the extreme heat of the day and the cold of the night. In and near the forested regions, wood is the most important building material for a great variety of

structures. In the cold regions of heavy snow a steep-sloped gable roof prevents the accumulation of snow that might crush the structure. Adaptation to climate is also seen in the location and orientation of houses: for example, houses are built on the north slopes in the hotter lands of the Northern Hemisphere, on the south slopes in the cooler lands, and on the leeward side in the lands with high wind velocities. Storm cellars, below ground, are special shelters against a very specific kind of climatic hazard—the tornado.

Shelters built by man are showing constant improvement in construction, but the greatest advances in recent years have been in controlling the temperature and moisture content of the air inside the shelters. From the open fire at the entrance of a cave to the latest air-conditioning units, there have been constant efforts to create an artificial climate inside shelters. What is required of the inside air varies from climate to climate and from season to season. In the cold-winter climates of the higher latitudes, for example, it is desirable to warm the air (in extreme cases, as much as 70 to 100 degrees) and to add moisture for greater comfort. In the lower latitudes it is necessary to cool the air and to extract the surplus moisture for maximum comfort.

Landforms

The life zone, which seems so thin in proportion to the size of the earth, appears thick to a man climbing a lofty mountain. Variation in altitude, expressing the detailed shape of the earth's surface, is one of the limiting factors in man's occupation of the land. It should be noted, however, that some of the limitations which are apparently related to landforms are also related to climate. For instance, the plateaus of Tibet are thinly populated not merely because they are high and rugged but also because the climate at these altitudes is too cool and dry for crops to grow.

Fig. 7.4. Materials used in housing: (a) house near Taos, New Mexico; timber is used for door, window frames, and roof supports; the remainder, including the roof, is of adobe; (b) houses in a Batak village in Sumatra; bamboo and other timbers are used for wall supports, and the roofs are thatched; (c) home in the Black Forest, western Germany; walls are of timber and stone, and roof is thatched; (d) Indian tepees in Glacier National Park, Montana (erected as a tourist attraction, but similar in form to those formerly used by the Indians of this area); tepee frame is made of small lodgepole pines; covering on the original tepees was made from hides.

To be sure, high altitude is a limiting factor in itself because of the low oxygen content of the air. Workers in the tin mines of Bolivia have performed manual labor at 17,000 feet, where the air is extremely thin and low in oxygen. To be able to work at such an altitude, however, these highland Indians have to have a very large lung capacity enabling them to breathe more air, as well as a very large proportion of red corpuscles in their blood. It should also be noted

that people could scarcely exist at this altitude unless supplied with food and other necessities from the lower regions.

Broadly speaking, the major landforms of the earth's surface can be classified as plains, hill lands, plateaus, and mountains. Since definitions of these forms vary in different parts of the world and since it is not easy to define these forms sharply, map designations are not always consistent.

Plains. Most of the world's people live in

Fig. 7.5. This smooth plain in Central Illinois is broken only by a few small stream courses. This is in the heart of the Corn Belt.

plains: the Interior Plains of North America (Fig. 7.5), the Pampa Plains of South America, the Northern Plain of Europe, the Ganges Plain of India and Pakistan, and the North China Plain, for example. People live in plains because of the ease of movement and the ease of cultivation and because the plains are warmer than the adjacent plateaus and mountains. A comparison of a world map of plains with a world population map reveals that people are concentrated in

certain parts of certain plains. Many plains, such as the arctic plains of North America and Siberia, are too cold to support many people. Some plains are too arid, like those in central Australia and the southern Sahara. The warm, humid plains are often moderately to densely populated. The marginal plains of southeastern Asia and some of the plains of equatorial Africa fall into this category. (There are exceptions, of which Amazonia is a striking example.) It is safe to say that all the warm, well-drained plains with moderate rainfall are either well-peopled or in the process of becoming so. Some plains, such as those in the interior of the United States, would be more densely populated if there were no restrictions to immigration.

Plains have an advantage over plateaus, hill lands, and mountains in that they have room for settlement to spread out continuously—room for farms, cities, roads, and factories. Often used for navigation, the rivers of plains may also bring water from distant mountains to supplement the rainfall. On the other hand, some parts of plains are subject to floods and tsunamis; some parts are swampy and difficult to drain, a fact often associated with the prevalence of disease.

Hill Lands. Adjacent to the plains in many parts of the world are the hill lands (Fig. 7.6). Hill land can be defined simply as area which has both a local relief (differences in elevation) of less than 2000 feet in one mile and land that is nearly all in slope. According to this arbitrary definition, many mountain margins are classified as hills: the margins of the Appalachians, the Ozarks, the Coast Ranges of California, the Pennine Range of England, the Jura Mountains of France and Switzerland, the Apennines of Italy, and many others.

Usually the result of the erosion of plains, plateaus, or the margins of mountains, hill lands shows a great variety of shapes and patterns. The western part of the Appalachian Plateau in Pennsylvania, West Virginia, southeastern Ohio, and eastern Kentucky may be described as hill land, a classification that is much more meaningful than the term "plateau." The hills in this land vary in height and shape, but most of them are either ridges or knobs with limited summit areas. The valleys between the hills are narrow, except where a large river like the Ohio has formed a flood plain. The slopes of the hills are generally steep, often as steep as 45 degrees. These slopes were originally forested, but many parts have been cleared and some have been cultivated.

It is apparent that these hills have a significant effect on the human patterns in the area. Roads follow the narrow, winding valleys, and the courses of the railroads are especially tortuous as they attempt to avoid steep slopes by finding a way around the hills. The road patterns of plains are likely to be rectangular, or at least very straight and regular; but here roads are irregularly patterned according to streams and ridges, often in a tree-like arrangement. Although relatively sparsely populated, these hill lands do not lack population. (In some parts of the world, hill lands are densely populated.) Cultivation on the hill slopes does encounter the hazard of severe erosion, especially in regions where the rain falls in torrents. As

a result, cropping is likely to be shifted from one small "patch" to another as the soils become impoverished. Some of the hill lands have been completely abandoned because of severe erosion.

Plateaus. In adjacent parts of four states —Utah, Colorado, Arizona, and New Mexico—lies one of the best examples of a plateau in the world, the Colorado Plateau. Briefly described, the Colorado Plateau consists of relatively smooth upland surfaces at elevations of one mile or more (Fig. 7.7), below which the Colorado River and its tributaries have cut deep canyons and above which stand a few small volcanic peaks. The peaks are not an essential quality of the plateau, just an added decoration.

The fact that not many people live on the Colorado Plateau is related more to its coolness and dryness than to its plateau nature. Nevertheless, because of its plateau nature, it is somewhat isolated; also, although movement of people is relatively easy on the smooth uplands, it is not easy to cross the plateau as a whole or move from one segment to another. In addition, since the plateau is generally too high for ordinary cultivation, human activities are limited largely to grazing, mining, and recreation.

Not all plateaus are sparsely populated— at least not in comparison with the plains adjacent to them. The plateau areas of South America and Africa, for example, have densities of population greater than those of the adjacent plains. In tropical lands the people prefer the cool, temperate character of the plateaus and mountains to the hot, steamy lowlands. Moreover, the plateaus, especially those in the tropics and elsewhere at low altitudes, enable people to live by agriculture. Despite this, almost no plateaus are densely populated, and those which are very dry, like the ones in the Sahara, or very cold, like those in Inner Asia, support very few people indeed.

Mountains. Since they occur in such variety of form and origin, the most complicated of all the major landforms are the moun-

Fig. 7.6. Foothills of the Front Range in Colorado. The smoothest land is cropped. Many of the hills take the form of cuestas or hogbacks.

Fig. 7.7. The Grand Canyon, in the Colorado Plateau, looking toward the north rim. The horizontal sediments and the even skyline are typical of plateau regions. Human access is difficult in the canyon areas, but easy on the uplands.

tains. Briefly and arbitrarily described, a mountain is a region of high relief (differences in elevation of at least 2000 feet in one square mile) which has a limited summit area. Most of the major mountains of the world occur in the World Ridge, which extends from the southern tip of South America through Central America and North America to central and southwestern Asia and southern Europe. The World Ridge, stretching from the southern Andes to the Pyrenees, includes, among other ranges, the Sierra Madre of Mexico; the Rocky Mountains, Sierra Nevada, and Cascade Range of the United States; the Rocky Mountains and Coast Mountains of British Columbia; the Alaska Range; the Stanovoy Range of Siberia; the Himalayas of Asia; the Caucasus of the Soviet Union; and the Alps of Europe.

Although all mountains differ in detail and have been occupied by different peoples, the significance of mountains in human life can best be described in terms of a specific mountain area. The Front Range of the Rocky Mountains in Colorado exemplifies the major characteristics of mountains (Fig. 7.8). From the Great Plains on the east, where the elevation is about 5000 feet, the Front Range rises to more than 14,000 feet in the form of a long, narrow ridge. The summits consist of either horn-like peaks or knife-edge ridges; actually, in many parts there is scarcely room to stand on the summits. From the crest the slopes drop off steeply for 2000 feet or more and then fall less steeply to the foothills and plains below.

The Front Range of the Rocky Moun-

Fig. 7.8. A view of the Rocky Mountains near Banff, Canada; Lake Minnewanka in the foreground. This range is important for water supply and recreation.

tains was first visited by white men for the purpose of fur trapping. The "mountain men," as these trappers were called, had no thought of settling permanently. They visited the Range in the summer, trapping beaver and other animals, and then either "holed in" for the winter in one of the valleys or returned to the nearest fur market on the Mississippi River. Except for their implements, guns, and ammunition, these men and their pack animals were able to live off the land.

Later, the Front Range was used for grazing, mining, and recreation; its favorable valleys were used for agriculture; and it served as a source of water for the cities and the irrigated lands in the plains. Grazing continues to utilize the mountain pastures above the timber line (about 11,000 feet) during the short summer season. Summer is also the chief season for tourists. Both the grazing animals and the tourists descend to the plains when the snow begins to fly. The snow which accumulates during the winter melts slowly during the spring and summer and affords a steady supply of water to the plains. Mining, once the most important activity in the region, has declined as the minerals have been exhausted, but mining has left a permanent imprint on the region; more than one old mining town with its characteristic atmosphere has been converted into a summer resort for tourists.

Like most long, lofty ranges, the Front Range is a barrier to routes of travel. From southern Wyoming to northern New Mexico, no low pass affords an easy east-west route; the major transcontinental routes, the Overland Route to the north and the Santa Fe Trail to the south, avoid the Range. However, since the Range is in the direct line from Chicago to San Francisco, much thought and effort have been expended in trying to find an easy route across it. One railway line crosses the Rockies at more than 11,000 feet, an unusually high elevation for railroads in North America, but finds a burdensome expense in "boosting" the trains across the pass. A tunnel, nine miles long and carved mostly in granite, affords a more direct route at a comparatively low elevation.

Most of the people who derive benefit from the Front Range do not live in the mountains. (In fact, some of them have never even seen the Range.) For instance, such nearby cities as Denver owe much of their importance to the Front Range.

Water

Water is an important environmental factor in many ways distinct from climate. In the form of rain, snow, hail, dew, or fog, water is a climatic phenomenon; but the quality and supply of water running on or beneath the ground depend on the nature of the earth's crust—on the slope, structure, and porosity of the land. Water, referred to by Jean Brunhes as the "supreme economic wealth," is a complicated phenomenon which varies in its occurrence and quality but remains of constant interest to man. As Professor Brunhes remarked:

There is no house or human habitation in the building of which man has not taken into account the proximity of water. The smallest chalet in the mountains is situated primarily near a streamlet or a spring, and a village has of necessity its spring or well. In countries where the climatic conditions include a longer or shorter dry period, the roofs and terraces are so constructed as to collect all the rainwater in tanks.[3]

[3] Jean Brunhes, *Human Geography*, abridged edition, pp. 39-40.

Whereas climate may limit settlements to specific regions, the water supply often pinpoints the exact spot for a settlement.

Water is significant in so many ways that few communities find their own supply entirely satisfactory. Thus, in many communities people refer to the water "problem" instead of the water "supply." Although water is essential to the everyday acts of drinking, washing, and sprinkling the lawn, its chief uses are in crop irrigation (the largest use of water in the United States), industry, transportation, recreation, and the production of hydroelectric energy. The usage of water varies from place to place according to the needs, the nature of the supply, and the customs of the people. For instance, in some humid regions very little water is needed for irrigation; similarly, in flat plains it is not feasible to develop water power. Often, one use of water interferes with another. Certain industrial uses, for example, pollute the water and make it unfit for drinking and washing. Irrigation increases the silt content of many rivers below the point at which irrigation ditches are discharged, sometimes killing the fish and creating mud flats which interfere with navigation. Dams for hydroelectric power may help or hinder navigation according to the nature of the structures and the stream.

There are few better illustrations of the varied uses of water than the St. Lawrence —Great Lakes Seaway (Fig. 7.9). The Seaway's greatest assets are numerous lakes (both large and small), a moderate precipitation (some of which is snow which melts slowly in the spring), and a step-by-step drop to the sea through a series of falls and rapids. First of all, the waterway provides nearby cities with enormous supplies of water for domestic and industrial uses. In spite of the large amounts of water withdrawn from the Seaway, its levels have been little affected. An exception to this general statement concerns Chicago, which, because of a lowered water level, has had to restrict the use of water for sewage-disposal purposes.

Fig. 7.9. St. Lambert Lock at the east end of the St. Lawrence Seaway near Montreal, Canada. This is the first of a series of locks which bypass the rapids of the St. Lawrence River.

Although many dams have been constructed in the Seaway, there are also available thousands of natural power sites, such as Niagara Falls. (In the particular case of Niagara Falls, use of its water power has been limited in order to preserve its scenic value.) The transportation potential of the waterway is just beginning to be realized. This waterway has been a highway for freight transportation ever since the days of the fur traders with their large freight canoes, and its shores have provided water-level routes for rail and highway. Rapids and falls hinder water transport somewhat, but these can be bypassed by means of canals with locks. Comparatively little of the Seaway's water is used for irrigation since the region is humid (with fairly adequate summer rain), but as cultivation becomes more intensive it is likely that more supplemental irrigation will be used. The flood hazard in the area is comparatively small since the numerous lakes serve as reservoirs to regulate the flow of water.

Many parts of the earth's surface are favorable for human occupation in all respects except in that they lack water. The obvious remedy for this deficiency is to bring water to the dry lands from adjacent mountains (where temperature and terrain are unfavorable for human occupation). Such a transfer of water makes posible the irrigation of many dry areas; in addition, many large cities obtain their water supplies from a similar process. For centuries man has been working out the details of this process. In Egypt, Mesopotamia, and the Indus Plain, for example, the rainfall is almost negligible. Water from humid regions brought to these lands by great rivers—the Nile, Tigris, Euphrates, and Indus—makes parts of these regions highly productive. However, irrigation is needed not only by the very dry lands; it is also important in making regions with moderate rainfall even more productive. As a result of irrigation, two crops instead of one may be grown and periodic drought may

a

b

c

Fig. 7.10. Vegetation types: (a) Douglas fir forest of western Washington, including cedar and an understory of hardwoods; (b) chaparral, including red shank, Ceanothus, and sage, on the margin of the Cleveland National Forest, California; (c) semiarid grassland in the panhandle of western Oklahoma; shrubs in the foreground and trees along the stream in the distance, otherwise grass; (d) desert landscape, Clark County, Nevada, showing creosote bush and yucca (Joshua trees).

d

be ameliorated. Elaborate systems of dams and canals are necessary to control the irrigation water so that it can be applied in the correct amount at the right place at the proper season. The planning and organization which are required for the control of irrigation have had a profound effect on the habits and social organization of peoples throughout the centuries. Irrigation is discussed at greater length in the chapter on Water.

Natural Vegetation

Just as the water supply depends in some measure on the climate, so the zones of natural plants, with their special demands

and limitations in terms of temperature and moisture, follow the major climatic regions. Within these regions local vegetation varies greatly, depending on slope, soil, and the activities of man. The broad types of natural vegetation include forest, brush, grass, and desert vegetation (Fig. 7.10). Except for the ice caps, there is no part of the land which is entirely devoid of vegetation.

102

So great is the variety of natural vegetation that most geographers usually prefer to discuss "plant associations" rather than individual species. (Of course, in dealing with the adaptation of plants for cultivation, one would consider specific plants.) Forests are divided into two broad groups, evergreen and deciduous; these in turn are divided into tropical and mid-latitude groupings. Often occurring in regions of moderate moisture, the brushlands with their low growth of woody shrubs have different names in various lands: chaparral in western United States; *maquis* in France (hence the name for the French Underground during World War II); thicket in many English-speaking countries. The grasslands are of three broad types: steppe (short grass) in the semiarid lands, savanna in the tropical lands with a dry season, and prairie in the humid regions. Deserts, too dry for trees and grass (except in favored places), support a variety of thorny shrubs like cactus, agave, and yucca.

Natural vegetation as an environmental factor may be considered briefly under three headings: (1) natural vegetation as a source of cultivated plants; (2) the effect of natural vegetation on the distribution of settlement; and (3) the present direct use of natural vegetation. (All three of these aspects will be treated in greater detail in subsequent chapters.) All the plants cultivated by man had their origin in natural vegetation. Many of these plants—the Brazilian rubber tree, for example—still grow in their wild state, but many others were domesticated so long ago that their natural ancestors no longer exist. Maize or Indian corn, for instance, is not known in the wild state, and much research has been necessary to determine the nature of its wild ancestor. As man has adapted plants to cultivation, he has transported them, sometimes even making them grow in conditions quite unfavorable to the original plants; as a result, the present distribution of cultivated crops bears little relation to the distribution of natural vegetation.

Historically, natural vegetation has been both a help and a hindrance to the dispersion of peoples. For example, the forests of central Europe discouraged the early settlers who came from the grasslands of Asia. Their folklore testifies to their fear of the forests and their reluctance to live in them. On the other hand, once the people became accustomed to the forests, they began to distrust the grasslands. There was a strong feeling on the part of the people who settled eastern United States that only land which would grow trees was fertile. Although mistaken, this belief certainly affected the settlement pattern of the United States.

The direct use of natural vegetation plays an important role in the world economy. The forest furnishes lumber (from balsa to mahogany), pulpwood for paper, and a variety of fibers, fruits, nuts, dyestuffs, and tanning materials. New wood products are constantly being developed. Forest lands serve as watersheds for the water supply of adjacent plains, and brushland is used to protect watershed slopes. Grazing animals like goats and donkeys thrive on brush, although it is not favorable for cattle and sheep. The grasslands, more or less modified by man, provide an enormous acreage for grazing animals. This acreage is found especially in the steppe lands and the lofty mountain pastures which are, respectively, too dry and too cool for cultivation. Man, sometimes unconsciously, has made tremendous changes in the natural vegetation; but large areas of the world remain, if not untouched, at least in a condition resembling the original state.

Although by no means all-important, place is a significant factor in human affairs. This chapter's brief discussion of some of the place phenomena suggests that man reacts to his physical environment in various ways and to various degrees. Place phenomena are interconnected. Soil and vegetation, for example, depend on climate as well as on each other. Some aspects of place limit man in his activities; others suggest activities to man; still others have no discernible effect on man at all.

In the descriptions and explanations of human geography, it is not safe to confine one's attention to a single element or even a few elements. One should develop the habit of considering "multiple hypotheses," or several possible explanations. In the field of human geography the phenomena are complex and difficult to measure and analyze. Although it is to be assumed that relationships exist between the factors in the natural environment and the patterns of human geography, this does not mean that simple cause-and-effect connections can be established. Most explanations of relationship are likely to be partial ones; man can hope only to narrow the gap between his own understanding and the ultimate truth as he increases his knowledge of the individual factors. In the chapters which follow some of the elements of the environment will be discussed in more detail. Meanwhile, a partial list of the major elements is inserted in the next column for consideration and reference.

It will be worthwhile for the reader to apply this list to some small part of the earth which he knows firsthand. Let us assume for a moment that he lives in a small

NATURAL ELEMENTS	CULTURAL ELEMENTS
CLIMATE	POPULATION
LAND	Density
Form or shape	Mobility
Soil	Cultural Heritage
Drainage	HOUSING
Minerals	Material
Vegetation	Form and Structure
Sea and Coast	Function
Location	PRODUCTION
	Pastoral
	Agricultural
	Mining
	Manufacturing
	COMMUNICATION
	Roads and Railways
	Waterways
	Airlines

locality in the Corn Belt. Why is the area a corn belt? Is it a result of the climate? Or has it been determined by the soil, the nature of the plain? Does the natural vegetation of the land, which was originally a prairie, have a particular importance? Are the natural factors causal or just favorable in regard to the production of corn? What is the significance of the nature of the people, their cultural heritage, and their nearness to manufacturing and large centers of population?

CHAPTER **8**

Man's Adaptations to Climate

To paraphrase an old and famous quotation, people have been talking about climate for a long time but have been able to do very little to change it. Probably the first people to study the subject of climate, the ancient Greeks used the word *klimata* for the zonal divisions of the earth which they had designated according to the length of day in midsummer. Although limited in observation to the environs of the Mediterranean and hampered by having none of the instruments considered necessary today for measuring the elements of weather and climate, the Greeks arrived at some interesting and worthwhile conclusions. In the first place, they decided sheerly by reasoning that the earth was a sphere because no other shape was worthy of the earth! Their method of reaching this conclusion was unscientific, but the conclusion was essentially correct and was later confirmed through observation. From the seasonal behavior of the sun the Greeks deduced that the axis of the earth was inclined to the plane of its orbit around the sun—a fact of primary climatic importance. With this in mind, they divided the earth into zones, separating these zones by what are now called the Tropic of Cancer, the Tropic of Capricorn, the Arctic Circle, and the Antarctic Circle (see Fig. 2.2). The Greeks believed that the winterless zone, from latitude 23° 27′ north to 23° 27′ south, was so hot that the ocean boiled there. The temperate zones, from latitude 23° 33′ to 66° 33′ both north and south, were considered to be suitable for human life. The polar zones, from latitude 66° 33′ north and south to the poles, were thought to be uninhabitable.

The Greeks based their system of climates on the length of the longest day and the height of the sun at various latitudes. They numbered the climates at half-hour intervals; thus, Climate No. 1, for example, with a longest day of 12.5 hours, extended to approximately 8° 34′ north and south of the Equator. Below is a partial list of the Greek climates.

Climate No.	Longest Day (hours)
1	12.5
2	13
3	13.5
4	14
5	14.5
6	15
7	15.5
8	16

It is evident that this system of the Greeks applied only from latitudes 0° to 66° 33′ north and south since the length of the longest day within the polar circles does not vary. The system set up a series of parallel bands in which each band represented a uniform climate. The Greeks failed to consider variations in rainfall, altitude, distance from the sea, and other factors which bring about differences in climate in the same latitude.

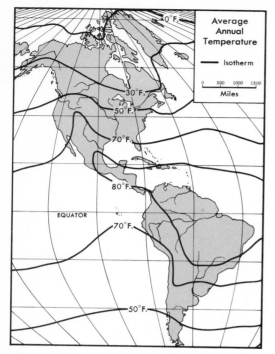

Average Annual Temperature

— Isotherm

0   500   1000   1500
Miles

30°F.

30°F.

50°F.

70°F.

80°F.

EQUATOR

70°F.

50°F.

Fig. 8.1. Average annual temperatures of the western hemisphere. Note the effect of the continents on the isotherms. These isotherms divide the surface into zones; equatorial, temperate, and polar.

Consequently, they did not realize that climatic regions are irregular areas rather than latitude belts (Fig. 8.1).

Modern Concepts of Climate

Climate is the average condition and the usual seasonal change of the weather. Climate is made up of many elements; these elements can be isolated and studied separately, but they must be integrated in order to understand their meaning for human life. The elements of climate are interdependent and may be grouped in pairs in which interdependence is clearly indicated. The first pair of climatic elements consists of *solar radiation* and *temperature*. The temperature

of the earth's surface depends more upon the sun's radiation in various forms of heat and light than upon any other factor. A second pair of elements is made up of *pressure* and *wind*. Changes in temperature and different temperatures in various parts of the earth bring about different pressures. These pressures lead to winds, movements of air in a horizontal direction. The third pair of elements consists of *moisture* and *precipitation*. This moisture includes that in the air as well as the moisture which falls to the ground in the form of rain, hail, sleet, and snow. The climatic elements that concern man most frequently are temperature and precipitation, especially the temperature of the warmest month and the coldest month and the precipitation of the wettest month and the driest month. The average annual rainfall is also of great concern, but the mean annual temperature is usually of less significance.

In modern times numerous systems have been devised to describe the climates of the earth; most of these systems are based on extensive records of temperature, rainfall, and other phenomena. One of the best of these systems is that of Wladimir Köppen, first published in 1918 and later revised. The fact that the Köppen system has been used, copied, and modified widely is a tribute to both its logic and its flexibility. The bare outline of the system is presented in this chapter; additional details can be found in Appendix C.

In the Köppen system, quantitative definitions, without which any descriptions are vague and ambiguous, are made largely in terms of temperature and precipitation; subdivisions are marked out mostly on the basis of the season of precipitation. On the map (see Figs. C.1, C.2, and C.3) the boundaries between adjacent climates are mostly *isotherms* (lines of equal temperature), *isohyets* (lines of equal precipitation), or some combination of the two. The letters in parentheses in the following sections refer to the Köppen climates (see Appendix C).

The Tropical Lands (Af and Aw)

The *A* climates, representing the winter-less zone, are defined by the isotherms (one in each hemisphere) of 64° F. for the coolest month. Although the *A* climates are humid, with sufficient moisture for tree growth, some areas have a distinct dry season; consequently, there is a basis for subdivision. The tropical rainforest (*Af*) has rain in sufficient quantities for tree growth in all seasons, although there may be periods of heavy rainfall and lighter rainfall. On the other hand, the tropical savanna (*Aw*) has a dry season at the time of low sun (winter). Actually, *w* stands for winter dry, but it is used to indicate low sun rather than a cold season. As a matter of fact, in some places near the Equator the season of low sun is warmer than the season of high sun.

The Rainforest Lands (Af). The characteristics of the rainforest are well known, but its exact quantitative limits are not so familiar to the average person. First of all, the climate is always warm; specifically, the average temperature of the coldest month is above 64° F. As a result, there is no winter, although there may be some slight fluctuations in temperature from season to season. On the other hand, the temperatures are not usually extreme; very high temperatures, such as those found in the deserts of the world, are unknown in the rainforest. The maximum temperature in the rainforest rarely rises above 100° F. and the minimum does not fall below 50° F. The temperatures can be described as very monotonous, with most stations showing little variation from month to month. A sample of the temperatures in Belém, Brazil, on the Amazon River illustrates this monotony.

Belém, Brazil

	Temp. ° F.	Rainfall (inches)
Jan.	78	12.5
Feb.	77	14.1
Mar.	78	14.1
Apr.	78	12.6
May	79	10.2
June	79	6.7
July	79	5.9
Aug.	79	4.4
Sept.	79	3.5
Oct.	79	3.3
Nov.	80	2.6
Dec.	79	6.1
Year	79	96.0

(*Average temperatures are listed to nearest degree Fahrenheit and rainfall to nearest one-tenth inch*)

It is evident that Belém has an even temperature all year, but it should be added that the daily range (the difference between the temperatures of day and night) is much greater than the annual range. The daily maximum often exceeds 90° F. and the minimum sometimes falls below 70° F. The rain is lightest in September, October, and November; during these months the rain is so light that the period is called a dry season by the natives, if not by the climatologists. Other rainforest stations differ very little from Belém in temperature, but they do show variations in the rainfall pattern. Libreville in Gabon has light rains in June, July, and August; Colón, Canal Zone, has them in February and March; Singapore in Malaya has no month with light rains, the driest month having over six inches.

The rainfall in the tropical rainforest is almost as monotonous as the temperature. Every month of the year there is usually rain enough to support a dense vegetation (see data above on Belém). The rains usually occur in brief, heavy downpours with thunder and lightning, often during the same time of day at a particular station. The total rainfall over most of the rainforest ranges from 40 to 100 inches per year.

Because of the heavy rainfall, high atmospheric humidity, and high temperatures all year, the vegetation of the rainforest is luxuriant and varied, one of the most complex combinations of plants to be found any place in the world. Conditions are so favorable for the growth of plants that several layers or "stories" of plants occur in many parts of the rainforest. The most conspicuous plants are the tall trees, the crowns of which are often a hundred feet above the forest floor. There is also a layer of shorter trees which depend on the light that filters through the tall trees. Near the ground in many places there is another layer of plant growth which can survive with even less light. In spite of the dense canopy of vegetation, some light and heat penetrate to the very floor of the forest. The humidity of the air is so high that many vines grow upon the trees, using them for support, sustenance, or both.

Specific records of climatic data have the virtue of going far beyond vague climatic terms, which have quite different values in various parts of the world; but climatic data alone cannot take the place of carefully written descriptions. The description below of Belém and vicinity was written more than a century ago by Henry Walter Bates in *The Naturalist on the River Amazons:*

A little difference exists between the dry and wet seasons; but generally, the dry season, which lasts from July to December, is varied with showers, and the wet, from January to June, with sunny days. It results from this, that the periodical phenomena of plants and animals do not take place at about the same time in all species, or in the individuals of any given species, as they do in temperate countries. Of course there is no hybernation; nor, as the dry season is not excessive, is there any summer torpidity as in some tropical countries. Plants do not flower or shed their leaves, nor do birds moult, pair, or breed simultaneously. In Europe, a woodland scene has its spring, its summer, its autumnal, and its winter aspects. In the equatorial forests the aspect is the same or nearly so every day in the year: budding, flowering, fruiting, and leaf shedding are always going on in one species or other. The activity of birds and insects proceeds without interruption, each species having its own separate times; the colonies of wasps, for instance, do

not die off annually, leaving only the queens, as in cold climates; but the succession of generations and colonies goes on incessantly. It is never either spring, summer, or autumn, but each day is a combination of all three. With the day and night always of equal length, the atmospheric disturbances of each day neutralising themselves before each succeeding morn; with the sun in its course proceeding mid-way across the sky, and the daily temperature the same within two or three degrees throughout the year—how grand in its perfect equilibrium and simplicity is the march of Nature under the equator![1]

The rainforest, always warm and always moist, is not generally considered a favorable site for human settlements. It is true that large areas of the rainforest in South America and central Africa are sparsely populated. However, it is also true that some of the more favorable parts of the rainforest (such as western Java, eastern Madagascar, and the eastern coast of Brazil) are moderately to densely populated (Fig. 8.2). A statement often made with reference to the rainforest is that it is unsuitable for white settlers. According to this view, some of the colored races can survive in the rainforest, but the whites cannot. This position is of doubtful validity. To be sure, most of the white people from the temperate belt do not *like* to live in the rainforest, but it does not follow that they are *unable* to do so. There are, in fact, many instances of white people living and working at hard manual labor in the tropics. Of course, there are some hazards to human occupation in the tropics. Tropical diseases (including dysentery, yellow fever, and many others) and disease-carrying fauna both thrive in this climate. The great strides which have been made during recent years in controlling tropical diseases are having an important effect on the settlement of the rainforest.

In spite of the handicaps of life in the rainforest, human activities are varied and

[1] Henry Walter Bates, *The Naturalist on the River Amazons*, pp. 31-32.

Fig. 8.2. Workmen unloading bamboo along the Cauca River near Cali, Colombia. This is on the drier margin of the rainforest.

widespread there. The cultivation of many crops is quite feasible. Rice grows well if the soils are at all favorable and if conditions are satisfactory for the flooding and draining of the rice paddies. The banana, which produces fruit every month of the year, is quite an important food crop, especially in Amazonia and equatorial Africa. Manioc (cassava), from which tapioca is derived, is also a favorite crop. The large manioc root may be dried and ground into flour for bread making, or it may be eaten boiled in the same way that people of the temperate belt eat white potatoes. Also, many wild fruits and nuts are gathered by the inhabitants of the rainforest.

The Tropical Savanna Lands (Aw). In the tropical savanna the temperature conditions are similar to those of the rainforest, but there is a dry season which ranges from a few months to six or seven months. Man-

dalay, Burma, represents a somewhat dry aspect of savanna climate.

Mandalay, Burma		
	Temp. ° F.	*Rainfall (inches)*
Jan.	69	0.1
Feb.	74	0.1
Mar.	82	0.2
Apr.	89	1.1
May	89	5.9
June	85	5.5
July	85	3.3
Aug.	85	4.6
Sept.	83	5.7
Oct.	83	4.7
Nov.	76	1.6
Dec.	69	0.4
Year	81	33.2

The dry season, beginning in December and ending in April, lasts five months; of these

Fig. 8.3. A landscape on the dry margin of the savanna in Bechuanaland, South Africa. The grasses, shrubs, and scattered trees are adapted to a long dry season.

five months, only April has as much as one inch of rain. The dry season is also the cool season. The seasonal variation of the tropical savanna has a profound effect upon the landscape and also upon the people who live in this area, which is much more densely populated than the rainforest. The seasonal changes in precipitation affect the streams, causing many of them to dry up for several months. The effect upon vegetation is even more striking: the long dry season makes it difficult for large trees to grow and encourages grasses, shrubs, and scrubby growths of trees to take over the landscape (Fig. 8.3). Any larger trees usually grow along the stream beds, where there is a supply of ground water to support them during the long dry season.

The savanna climate of southeastern Asia might well be called the rice climate par excellence. It is true that rice will grow in other climates, but the moist summers and dry winter periods of the savanna are especially favorable; the savanna provides both abundant moisture in the period of growth and a favorable season for harvesting and drying the rice. It is rather curious that rice production has not spread on a large scale into such savanna areas as those of Africa and South America, which offer conditions favorable for rice production. Favorable conditions involve a nearly level alluvial plain which can be watered with additional moisture from nearby lofty mountains.

Found especially in India and southeastern Asia, the monsoon climate (*Am*), with its heavy summer rains and short dry season in winter, is a transition between the *Af* and *Aw* climates. In India the monsoon is the main dependence of the many millions who live by agriculture. If the monsoon rains are abundant and evenly spaced, the crops are reasonably good, and most of the people have enough to eat. If the monsoon is late and the rains are deficient, there can be starvation and death. The first report of the

Fig. 8.4. Sheep grazing on the steppe lands of Outer Mongolia near Ulan Bator.

coming of the monsoon is from the island groups to the south of India, from the Seychelles or Mauritius. When the first heavy rain denoting the arrival of the monsoon reaches the Malabar Coast of India, the country is filled with rejoicing. The soil, which was parched and cracked, quickly absorbs much of the rain, and with unbelievable rapidity the natural vegetation bursts into life. Now the rice paddies can be flooded and the various summer crops can be seeded.

The Dry Lands (BS and BW)

The distinction between the dry *B* climates and the humid climates cannot be made in terms of temperature or of seasons of rainfall. The *B* climates are distinguished by their particular combinations of moisture and temperature; by definition, the dry climates are those in which moisture is deficient, in which evaporation is greater than precipitation. The dry climates are classified

on the basis of severity of drought. The most severe drought is found in the desert (*BW*), which, in general, is too dry for grass to grow. Less severe drought is found in the steppe (*BS*), which is semiarid in character; it has enough moisture for grass to grow, but, in general, it cannot support trees. It should be noted that the dry climates are further divided on the basis of winter temperatures into cold deserts, cold steppes, hot deserts, and hot steppes. Any quantitative definition of the dry climates must deal with the various combinations of moisture, temperature, and evaporation. For example, there will be rapid evaporation of any rainfall which occurs mostly in a warm season; thus any given amount of moisture will be less effective falling in a warm season than falling as winter rain.

The Steppe Lands (BS). The steppe climate (Fig. 8.4) is found in various parts of the world, in both high and low latitudes. Many well-known steppes have specific regional names: the Great Plains of Canada and the United States, the Dry Pampa of Argentina, the Veld of South Africa, and the Gobi of Inner Asia, for example. In many ways the steppes are favorable for the settlement of man in moderate numbers; when irrigation is available, they can support even large numbers. Steppes were especially selected by the pastoral people of early times as very favorable locations for their grazing animals. Likewise, steppes are favored by the hunting peoples because of the abundance of wild game. The grasses which grow in the steppe lands are tall and thick on the humid margins, scattered and sparse on the dry margins; thus the possibilities of utilization vary from place to place on the basis of moisture, as well as on the basis of temperature. The steppe lands vary in temperature from areas which are always warm, such as the southern border of the Sahara, to areas with cold winters, such as the Canadian Plains and the plains of central Siberia. In the steppe lands with a long cold season, less moisture is needed to provide for the grassy vegetation (see example of Calgary, Canada).

Calgary, Canada

	Temp. ° F.	Rainfall (inches)
Jan.	13	0.5
Feb.	17	0.5
Mar.	26	0.8
Apr.	40	1.0
May	50	2.3
June	56	3.1
July	62	2.5
Aug.	60	2.3
Sept.	51	1.5
Oct.	42	0.7
Nov.	28	0.7
Dec.	19	0.6
Year	38	16.7

In general, it can be said that the amount of annual rainfall on the humid edges of the steppes varies from 15 to 30 inches, while on the dry margins the variation is from 8 to 20 inches. Because of the low humidity of the air, evaporation is very rapid; as a result, a given amount of rain is less effective in the BS climate than in the moist climates.

The steppes have played a very important part in the development of human history. In the first instance, they provided good hunting grounds for the nomadic hunting and gathering peoples. Game, consisting especially of the large herbivorous animals, was abundant and easily discovered on the steppes, which have little cover to hide large animals. When the steppes were invaded by people who had developed domestic animals in more humid regions, the pastoral stage followed the hunting stage there. The pastoral stage was succeeded in the more favorable parts of the steppes by the cultivation of crops not requiring large amounts of moisture, particularly the small grains like wheat, barley, and rye. These plants originated in the steppes and were domesticated there. Special varieties of the small grains have been developed which are better adapted than most other plants to growing in areas with limited rainfall. It should be noted, however, that wheat, barley, and rye grow even better with the greater rainfall of the humid regions. Of course, in the more humid regions these cereals must meet the competition of other plants which may yield more food value per acre.

Some of the hazards of human occupation of the steppe lands are described by Jan O. M. Broek in the U.S.D.A. Yearbook, *Climate and Man:*

The rainfall in the semiarid fringes, although meager on the average, may in some years be considerable. These variations make the steppe a far more hazardous land with which to deal than is the desert. As far as climate is concerned, successful occupation depends upon how well the farming methods are adapted to these special conditions. These problems have been discussed in a preceding article on the Great Plains. It may be noted that substantially the same struggle characterizes settlement in the steppes of Argentina, South Africa, southern Australia, Manchuria, Mongolia, and south-

Fig. 8.5. The All-American Canal carrying water from the Colorado River through the desert to the Imperial Valley.

ern Siberia. These semiarid regions, formerly the habitat of the roaming hunter or herdsman, have for the greater part been settled during the last century. This has been made possible through modern means of transportation and cultivation. In some of these areas the frontier is still moving forward, but in general it can be said that already the best steppe lands are occupied. The main task now is to consolidate the conquest in terms of a better adjustment to the peculiar environment. It is even quite likely that the forward surge into the dry realms has gone further than is wise under present conditions. Wherever further advance is possible it will require heavy capital investment. Clearly it is not production per acre that counts here, but production per man. Settlement, therefore will always be sparse.

The Deserts (BW). The deserts, the lands of little rain, would seem to be some of the least favorable for human occupation. As was indicated at the beginning of this chapter, some lands are too dry to support human beings. But the ingenuity of man, which enables him to obtain water from sand dunes, wells, springs, and distant mountains, has made it possible for certain limited areas of the desert lands to be densely populated. In lower Egypt, for example, 20 million people live in a very small region near the Nile. Benefiting from a local water supply, areas like this are called oases; some other outstanding examples of oases are the Imperial Valley of California and Mexico, the lower Indus Valley of Pakistan, the Euphrates Valley in Iraq, and the Mendoza Oasis of Argentina (Fig. 8.5).

Some desert areas have very little rainfall indeed. In some areas, years may pass without any rain falling and then a heavy downpour may bring the average annual rainfall up to one or two inches. A good example of an area with little rainfall is Touggourt, Algeria.

Touggourt, Algeria

	Temp. ° F.	Rainfall (inches)
Jan.	51	0.2
Feb.	60	0.4
Mar.	61	0.6
Apr.	70	0.1
May	77	0.2
June	87	0.1
July	92	0.0
Aug.	90	0.0
Sept.	84	0.0
Oct.	72	0.2
Nov.	61	0.6
Dec.	53	0.4
Year	71	2.8

Some other desert areas, especially those bordering on steppes, have an annual rainfall of as much as 10, 12, or even 15 inches. If the rainfall in the desert occurs in the warmest season, its effectiveness is limited. On the other hand, in the dry lands of the San Joaquin Valley of California, eight inches of winter rainfall is sufficient to produce a crop of wheat.

The vegetation of the desert is characteristically not grass. Instead, the desert produces a great variety of plants that are especially adapted to aridity. Very few parts of the desert are entirely without vegetation, only the rapidly moving sand dunes being entirely naked. The vegetation of the desert varies widely with the temperature conditions: in the lower-latitude deserts grow varieties of cactus, agave, creosote bush, and similar plants; in the higher latitudes sagebrush and salt bush are common and various other plants are also found. The desert plants are adapted to a short growing season, for rain and moisture may appear for only a very short period and then be

followed by a very long dry season (perhaps of several years). The adaptation of the plants to the desert climate is both varied and ingenious. Some plants have adapted themselves to aridity by growing large rootstocks or bulbs which are deep in the ground and protected from the high rate of evaporation which occurs on the surface. Another adaptation to dryness is the absence of leaves or the growth of very small, glossy leaves which keep evaporation at a minimum.

Settlement in the desert is dependent upon the available sources of water—rivers (with their headwaters in humid regions), springs, and wells. In some cases water can be obtained from shallow wells, but in other cases it must be drawn from deep wells. In many instances occupation of the desert has had to wait for modern drilling apparatus. Whatever its source of water, a desert settlement is usually an isolated but densely populated oasis, surrounded by empty lands. Kashgar in the Tarim Basin is such an oasis (see description by Marco Polo in Chapter 2). Lower Egypt, the Imperial Valley of California and Mexico, Mesopotamia (Iraq), and many other famous oases have been described in detail by geographers.

The Mesothermal Lands (Cf, Cw, and Cs)

The mesothermal lands are defined as humid areas with the average temperature of the coolest month between 32° F. and 64° F.; they are subdivided according to the season of rainfall:

Cf	Humid Mesothermal	Uniform rainfall
Cw	Temperate Savanna	Winter dry
Cs	Mediterranean	Summer dry

The quantitative distinction between the dry seasons is as follows: in the Cw climate the rainfall for the wettest month of summer is at least 10 times that of the driest month in winter; in the Cs climate the rainfall of the wettest month in winter is at least three times that of the driest month in summer. These definitions are general rules to which there are some exceptions.

The Humid Mesothermal Lands (Cf). There are two broad locations in which the *Cf* climate appears: one location is on the eastern side of continents, as in southeastern United States, southeastern China, east central Argentina, and southeastern Africa; the other location is on the west coasts of continents, as in northwestern Europe, the Pacific Northwest in the United States, southern Chile, and New Zealand. In general, the areas on east coasts have hot summers and are designated *Cfa; a* indicates that the average temperature of the warmest month is above 72° F. On the west coasts of continents and also at higher altitudes in tropical areas (in the Andes, for example), the climate is *Cfb; b* indicates a cooler summer. The difference between the climates *Cfa* and *Cfb* is very important for human life; for example, corn grows well in *Cfa* and *Dfa,* but it usually will not mature in *Cfb.* So, from the standpoint of human occupation and uses of the land, this is a significant subdivision, which is illustrated by Charleston, South Carolina (*Cfa*), and Dublin, Ireland (*Cfb*).

Charleston, South Carolina

	Temp. ° F.	Rainfall (inches)
Jan.	50	2.4
Feb.	52	3.0
Mar.	58	2.7
Apr.	65	2.3
May	73	3.0
June	79	3.8
July	82	6.1
Aug.	81	5.6
Sept.	77	4.3
Oct.	68	2.8
Nov.	58	1.8
Dec.	51	2.3
Year	66	40.3

Dublin, Ireland

	Temp. ° F.	Rainfall (inches)
Jan.	41	2.3
Feb.	41	1.8
Mar.	42	1.9
Apr.	45	1.8
May	51	2.1
June	55	2.0
July	59	2.7
Aug.	58	3.2
Sept.	54	1.9
Oct.	49	2.6
Nov.	43	2.8
Dec.	41	2.5
Year	48	27.6

In the humid mesothermal lands the original vegetation was forest, with some areas of grassland or prairies which were probably culturally induced (that is, they were produced by man through burning or clearing). In many instances the natural vegetation has been cleared for the purpose of cultivating the land or of producing lumber and other wood products. In general, the forests tend to be broad-leaved, deciduous types (Fig. 8.6), but in many places coniferous trees grow—particularly on the west coasts with cool summers (*Cfb*). It is worth noting that, although northwestern Europe and

Fig. 8.6. Sugar cane fields and forest near Baton Rouge, Louisiana. This region receives more than 50 inches of rainfall, evenly distributed.

northwestern United States have similar climates, their natural vegetation is quite different. In western Europe, hardwoods are common, with oak the dominant tree; in the humid parts of the Pacific Northwest, on the other hand, coniferous trees are predominant.

The humid mesothermal lands are quite favorable for human occupation and support many millions of people. Agriculture is common, particularly in the areas that have been settled by Europeans. Various crops are cultivated: corn, cotton, and tobacco in the areas with hot summers (*Cfa*); the small grains; hay and forage crops; and many other commercial crops. Livestock thrive in these regions.

The Temperate Savanna Lands (Cw). The temperate savanna climate, with mild, dry winters and hot, rainy summers, occurs in the subtropical belts. In many respects this climate is similar to the tropical savanna climate (*Aw*), but the temperate savanna climate has a definite cool season and a warm season which is somewhat modified, particularly in the higher altitudes. The principal regions of the temperate savanna are the Chaco of South America, the Coffee Belt of southeastern Brazil, the Highland of Ethiopia, and some of the temperate lands of India and southern China. Because there is heavy evaporation during the warm season, crops and natural vegetation require more rain than they would if the rain fell in the cool season of the year. This climate is sometimes referred to as the "coffee climate" because it is so well suited to the growth of coffee, with heavy rainfall in the season when the coffee is growing most rapidly and a dry season in the cooler period when the coffee can be harvested and dried in the open air. An example of this climate is Benares, India.

Benares, India

	Temp. °F.	Rainfall (inches)
Jan.	60	0.7
Feb.	65	0.6
Mar.	77	0.4
Apr.	87	0.2
May	91	0.6
June	89	4.8
July	84	12.1
Aug.	83	11.6
Sept.	83	7.1
Oct.	78	2.1
Nov.	68	0.2
Dec.	60	0.2
Year	77	40.6

The Mediterranean Lands (Cs). The Mediterranean lands have warm, dry summers and mild, rainy winters (Fig. 8.7), during which seasons the periods of precipitation are interspersed with times of sunshine. The Mediterranean climate, with its sunny skies and mild seasonal changes, is preferred by the people who spend their lives studying climates; it is for this reason often called the "climatologist's climate." It occurs both on the west coasts of the continents in the lower-middle latitudes and around the Mediterranean Sea.

Because the dry season comes at the warmest time of the year (as shown by the data for Naples, Italy), the natural vegetation is forced to grow either in the wet season with comparatively low temperatures or in the dry season with a very limited amount of moisture. The crops grown by man must either be adapted in the same manner or be provided with water during the dry season by means of irrigation.

Naples, Italy

	Temp. °F.	Rainfall (inches)
Jan.	47	3.7
Feb.	48	2.9
Mar.	51	2.8
Apr.	57	2.6
May	64	2.0
June	70	1.4
July	75	0.6
Aug.	75	1.1
Sept.	71	2.9
Oct.	63	4.6
Nov.	55	4.5
Dec.	49	4.4
Year	60	33.4

Fig. 8.7. A Mediterranean landscape at Arcos de la Frontera in southern Spain. Compare the site of this fortified town with that of Carcassonne, France (Fig. 1.2.). Olive trees are in the foreground, with vineyards on the right slope.

Natural vegetation in the Mediterranean lands consists of three main types: forests, shrubs, and grasses. The forests, which are in some cases very dense (like the redwood forests of California), usually occur in the most favorable localities. Scrub oak is prevalent, however, in less humid localities. Another type of vegetation, classified generally as brush or shrubby vegetation, has specific names in different Mediterranean regions; thus, in France it is called *maquis* and in California it is referred to as chaparral. In each case the reference is to a vegetation formation which consists of a number of herbaceous plants with adaptations for living during a dry season. Grass, the third type of natural vegetation, is found in the driest localities, such as the southern Coast Ranges of California and the plateaus of southern Spain.

The cultivated plants which man has developed in the Mediterranean lands over the centuries are those which were originally adapted to some limitations of moisture. These plants include the olive, the almond, the citrus fruits, the vine, and the small grains. The tree crops, with deep roots which reach into the ground water, are able to live through the long summers without irrigation. However, all of these tree crops produce better if irrigation is provided, as it usually is. The winter grains (wheat and barley, particularly) which grow in this climate throughout the winter season are usually sown in the early winter or late autumn and harvested in the following summer. Because the temperatures during this period are somewhat lower than those of the rest of the year, the winter grains have a long growing season.

In the parts of Europe, Asia, and Africa which surround the Mediterranean Sea, man developed a complex civilization at a very early date. The Mediterranean region was the cradle of European culture, from which grew the Western culture that has penetrated into so many parts of the earth. The people who moved into the Mediterranean area from the steppes and drier lands to the south and west found that, in addition to being able to graze animals, they could also grow a variety of crops. As a result, their culture expanded and they developed techniques and methods that were to have a profound effect, not only in the Mediterranean region but also in other parts of the world.

The areas of Mediterranean climate which are not in the region of the Mediterranean Sea were settled much later. These areas include a part of California, Middle Chile, the Cape District of Africa, and two areas in Australia, one in the southwest and one in the southeast near Adelaide.

The Humid Microthermal Lands (Df, Dw, and Ds)

In the interior of the northern lands of North America, Europe, and Asia, the humid areas are characterized by warm summers and severe winters. This combination is found only in the Northern Hemisphere, where large land masses occur at high latitudes. The D climates are subdivided in the same manner as the C climates, but the subdivisions Dw and Ds are less significant than Cw and Cs. In the Dw areas the winters are so severe that the drought loses a large part of its meaning. The great variations within the type can be seen in the range of temperature and rainfall of two stations: Chicago, Illinois, with warm summers and moderately severe winters; and Chita, east of Lake Baykal in Asiatic Russia, with long, very severe winters and much less precipitation.

Chicago, Illinois

	Temp. ° F.	Rainfall (inches)
Jan.	24	1.7
Feb.	26	1.6
Mar.	36	2.7
Apr.	47	2.6
May	57	3.4
June	67	3.4
July	73	3.1
Aug.	71	3.3
Sept.	65	3.5
Oct.	54	2.4
Nov.	40	2.1
Dec.	29	1.9
Year	49	31.9

Chita, U.S.S.R.

	Temp. ° F.	Rainfall (inches)
Jan.	−17	0.1
Feb.	− 7	0.1
Mar.	10	0.1
Apr.	32	0.4
May	46	1.1
June	60	1.8
July	66	3.3
Aug.	60	3.3
Sept.	47	1.2
Oct.	29	0.5
Nov.	6	0.2
Dec.	−12	0.2
Year	27	12.3

The D areas are forested, with coniferous trees in nearly all parts. On the northern margin the forest is very stunted and worthless from the standpoint of lumber (Fig. 8.8); on the southern margin, in many cases, there are hardwoods as well as conifers. The forests are the most valuable natural resource of the inhabitants. These forest lands also support fur-bearing animals such as beaver, fox, mink, otter, martin, and wolf, all of which develop pelts of high quality because of the coldness of the winters. On the southern margin, where the summers are the warmest and longest, crops such as potatoes, sugarbeets, small grains, and hay

Fig. 8.8. A pine and birch forest at Lake Itasca, Minnesota, in the humid continental climate.

will mature. However, the abundant forests, water power, and mineral wealth of certain parts of the *D* climate are more important than agriculture, especially in the Great Lakes-St. Lawrence region of North America and the Scandinavian-Finnish region of northern Europe.

Primitive man was able to settle in the *D* climate only after he had acquired fire, adequate clothing, and skill in building shelters. The forests provided him with wood for fuel and for the construction of houses; the animals were a source of both food and clothing. It is probable that man first invaded these lands in summer and returned to warmer lands in the winter. Gradually, man became a more permanent resident as crops and livestock were introduced. It then became necessary for him to prepare for the long winters by hoarding food and fuel; even though he hoarded, however, the winters were often times of starvation and misery.

Nowadays, thanks to modern heating and air conditioning, people can live comfortably in the *D* climate—indoors, at least; but even a few years ago they were not able to do so. The following description is from Graham Hutton's *Midwest at Noon*:

It is the core of the Midwest which has the worst weather: the area east of the Mississippi including the northern halves of Illinois, Indiana, and Ohio, the Michigan peninsula, and

Fig. 8.9. Hilly tundra country on the border between Alaska and Yukon Territory of Canada near Dawson. In this area some trees will grow in lower altitudes.

southern Wisconsin. This is the coastal area of the Great Lakes, which here exercise an attraction on the transcontinental lines of temperature and pressure and form a kind of water pocket around which the great winds sweep snow, rain, and cold spells.

Dwellers in the belt that runs from Milwaukee to Chicago, the big cities along the Indiana-Michigan coastal rim, Detroit, Toledo, Cleveland, Erie, and Buffalo and a long way inland, during the ferocious winters are weighed down by a cold humidity and blasted by icy winds reaching gale dimensions. They are snowed-in frequently by blizzards that blacken noonday and paralyze all forms of traffic. They are exposed to the packing of snow into miniature but almost as deadly Himalayas of solid black ice on every path from the home driveway to the side-walks of the metropolis. Blizzards snow-in the suburbanites to this day; and the normal snows are heavy enough to make shoveling and cleaning, overshoes and snow boots, an indispensable part of every midwesterner's winter. Rare, indeed, in any winter in this wide core of the Midwest is an ideal winter-sports day: clear, dry air, bright-blue skies, hard, strong sun, no wind,

and zero or subzero temperature. When such a day dawns, everyone talks about it: commuters and housewives and store-keepers and school children.

In defense against the bitter winds and cold the Midwest has developed artificial heating in its houses, offices, and vehicles to a point at which its people are alternately baked and frozen a dozen times a day.[2]

The Polar Lands (ET and EF)

On the polar margins in both hemispheres are the tundra (*ET*) and the frost (*EF*) climates. In general, these lands are too cool for forests or crops to grow. The tundra lands (*ET*) are the regions in which the temperature of the warmest month lies between 32° F. (freezing) and 50° F. (Fig. 8.9). The frost lands (*EF*) are those areas where the temperature of the warmest month averages below freezing. In both of these climates the precipitation is low, but since evaporation is also low they are in effect humid. At least,

[2] Graham Hutton, *Midwest at Noon*, pp. 8-9.

there is humidity and moisture during the short summer season or during the periods of thawing.

In the tundra the vegetation consists largely of dwarfed plants, grasses, mosses, lichens, stunted species of certain trees (such as the birch), and many types of boggy plants that grow in the low, flat, moist regions. The tundra of North America is occupied by Eskimo, who depend more upon the sea animals than upon the browsing animals which feed upon the tundra vegetation. However, some Eskimo do depend upon domestic browsing animals; the Lapps and other peoples of northern Europe depend upon the reindeer. Attempts have been made to produce reindeer meat in large quantities for export to the temperate lands, but these attempts have not been sucessful since the tundra region is very remote, the transportation of the meat to market is very difficult, and the people of the temperate belts are not accustomed to eating this particular kind of meat. The areas of frost climate are lands of snow and ice where no effective thawing occurs. They are almost without vegetation, except for very low forms of life such as algae.

In recent years various military and scientific posts have been established in the polar lands in northern Canada, Alaska, Siberia, at the South Pole, and even on the polar sea ice. Supplied by air and equipped with scientifically designed clothing and the best of modern shelters, man can live indefinitely in the polar regions. Some of the reasons for the military and scientific "settlements" will be discussed in later chapters.

The Perfect Climate

No climate on earth is perfect from the standpoint of human comfort and productivity; it is either too hot or too cold, too wet or too dry, too foggy or too windy at some season of the year. Man likes to be comfortable when out-of-doors, whether he be at rest or engaged in strenuous physical activity; he also likes a climate in which he can produce the things he needs, especially food. No place on earth fulfills these two requirements entirely; if one requirement is reasonably well met, the other requirement is not. The Mediterranean climate comes closest to many people's ideal of a livable region, but from the standpoint of productivity its long, dry summers and the variability of its winter rains are serious handicaps. Doubling its rainfall would increase productivity, but at the same time it would reduce the comfort factor. The humid mesothermal lands are very favorable for crop production; but their hot, humid summers, so necessary for the maturing of corn, are by no means pleasant. The "ideal climate" is often mentioned, but the fact remains that every climate has its disadvantages as well as its good qualities. Migratory birds have the best solution; they enjoy the best season of several climates during the course of a year.

Man's Effect on Climate

Man has made some slight changes in climate, but they are so slight in some cases that special instruments are needed to measure them; moreover, most of the changes have been unintentional. The clearing of forests has undoubtedly brought about slight local increases in temperature and decreases in humidity. Because large cities are constructed of great piles of steel and masonry, which absorb and radiate large quantities of heat, the average summer-noonday temperature of each city is increased by one or two degrees. The winter temperature of a city is increased slightly by space heating and by the heat from factories and thousands of automobiles. On the other hand, smog over a city may reduce the midday temperature slightly. Altogether, the unintentional changes which man has made in climate are like those which he might experience in changing his altitude a few hundred feet or in moving from the north side of a steep hill to the south side.

Fig. 8.10. Super-cooled clouds that have been seeded with dry-ice pellets from a plane. This operation has produced a more than three-mile-wide hole in the cloud layer, causing the cloud droplets to coalesce and often producing rainfall.

Man has also made deliberate attempts to change the climate. Snake dances and the firing of cannons have been tried. However, his most successful efforts in modifying climate have been in cloud seeding, a process designed to increase precipitation (Fig. 8.10). The usual method of cloud seeding involves the dispersal of fine particles of silver iodide, dry ice, or water directly into a cloud from a plane or from a suitable apparatus on the ground. These particles are the nuclei around which raindrops or snow crystals form. If conditions are favorable, precipitation occurs; but the method is not successful with all clouds. Good results are obtained where moisture-laden winds with clouds are moving up mountain slopes; in such cases precipitation is increased by cloud seeding. But in very dry regions, where the need for additional rainfall is greatest, rain making is not usually feasible.

The Changing Climate

Man may be able to change the climate very little, but *the climate is constantly changing.* During man's brief existence he has probably never known a uniform, "normal" climate. He is now living either at the end of an ice age or in an interglacial period in which the atmosphere, as well as the crust of the earth, is unstable. The frequent periods of drought (like the great "dust bowl" period in the Great Plains in the middle 1930's), the recent occurrence of numerous tornadoes in the Middle West, and the cool summers of northern Europe all attest to the great variability of climate in our own century. It is by no means easy to explain these variations or to forecast them, although many have attempted to do so. If the causes of these changes (which have the appearance of being entirely matters of chance) could be determined, it might be possible to forecast the weather for several years in advance. It must suffice here to suggest the amount of variation for one station, Syracuse, New York, and to warn the reader that the "average climate" is merely a mean, around which the climate fluctuates from season to season and from year to year.

Syracuse, New York (54-Year Record)

	Temp. °F.
Mean annual	47.8
January mean	24.7
January, 1932	37.2
January, 1920	13.9
Absolute maximum	102.0

	Temp. °F.
July mean	71.4
July, 1921	76.6
July, 1925	67.8
Absolute minimum	−26.0

Precipitation (inches)

Mean annual	35.84
Wettest year, 1922	48.17
Driest year, 1908	26.96
January average	2.76
Wettest January, 1925	5.87
Driest January, 1933	1.00
July average	3.29
Wettest July, 1928	6.14
Driest July, 1933	0.30

Man lives in the air and is much more aware of the changes in it than of disturbances in the crust of the earth or in the bodies of water. In a thousand different ways man's adaptations to climate have been made and new adaptations continue to appear, some of which are obvious and some of which are subtle. Clothing nowadays is designed partly for ornamentation, but basically it is intended to protect man from the hazards of the particular climate in which he lives: from heat, cold, rain, wind, and sun. Houses in cold lands are built almost airtight and have thick insulation, while in warmer lands houses may not even have walls, needing only a roof to keep out the rain. Farming, logging, fishing, hunting, and the gathering of wild fruits and nuts are all geared to the march of the seasons. Even vacations are planned with the weather in mind. And those who can afford it travel thousands of miles in search of a better climate, only to find, perhaps, that the people who stayed at home enjoyed a period of unusually fine weather. Man can change the climate very little and his forecasts are imperfect, but he has learned to live in moderate comfort with the many aspects of climate, in spite of its fickle variations.

CHAPTER 9

Water

Even more than air, water sets limits on the development and continued existence of human agglomerations. Air is abundant in all parts of the usual human environment, but water is unequally distributed; consequently, water exerts a greater influence on the location of human settlements and on the way people live. The quantity of water needed by modern man is an index of its importance. If the average person in the United States were asked how much water he uses per day, he might guess that he uses a few pints for drinking, a few gallons for washing, and a few tens of gallons for watering the lawn. If the manager of a city water-supply system in the United States were questioned, he might state that a city of 50,-000 population requires about 25 million gallons of water per day, or 500 gallons of water per capita. It is thus obvious that most of the water used is not used directly *by* the individual but indirectly *for* him, in industry and elsewhere (Fig. 9.1).

The average, moderately active person can get along with about three quarts of drinking water per day, if the temperature is moderate; however, in a hot desert the amount demanded by such a person would jump to about 12 quarts. In primitive villages about five gallons of water per day are used per capita for drinking, cooking, and washing. In addition, the millions of homes all over the world which do not have running water require about 10 gallons per person; those homes with running water use

directly about 60 gallons per person. In the United States the average per capita use (both direct and indirect) of water is about 1200 gallons per day. About half of this amount is used for irrigation, and most of the remainder is used by industry. A single irrigated acre may require more than a million gallons of water during a crop season, and a single medium-sized factory may require 10 million gallons per day.

An indication of the importance of water is the fact that human habitations are rarely built without consideration being given to the availability of water. Of course, it is true that some settlements do not have a local supply of water and must haul water for many miles. It is also true that many habitations have been abandoned because of inadequate or failing water supply (Fig. 9.2).

The Water Cycle

The waters of the earth are in constant circulation; in using water, man merely interrupts a small portion of these waters at a convenient point in the water cycle (Fig. 9.3). The water cycle involves the movement of water from the ocean to the air, from the air to the land, and from the land back to the ocean. Through evaporation, moisture is picked up from the surface of the oceans and, to a lesser extent, from the land. The water in the air, in the form of either transparent vapor or clouds, moves in large air masses over the continents, where

124

Fig. 9.1. Abundance of water is shown by this power development on the Saguenay River, Quebec, Canada. Moderate rainfall, melting snow, and numerous lakes contribute to this abundance.

it is warmed by radiation from the land. Warming causes the air mass to rise; when it rises high enough, condensation occurs and the water falls—usually in the form of rain or snow. The water then runs slowly off the land and back to the oceans.

Actually, the water cycle is much more varied and complicated than this simple description would indicate. A large part of the water which is evaporated from the ocean does not reach the land; it falls back directly to the sea. Nearly 100,000 cubic miles of water are evaporated annually from the surface of the earth, 80 per cent of which water comes from the oceans. Only about one fourth of the precipitation (about 24,000 cubic miles) falls on the land. If all this water fell on the United States in the form of snow, it would reach a depth of over 500 feet in a year, provided there was no melting.

Fig. 9.2. Water is scarce in the Sahara, central Algeria, but obviously at times heavy downpours occur.

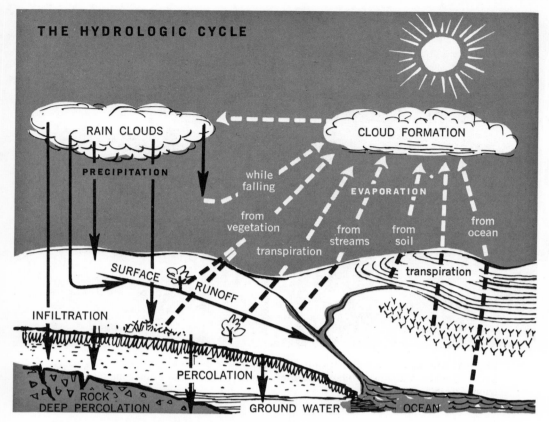

Fig. 9.3. A simplified diagram of the hydrologic cycle. Water evaporates from the ocean (lower right) and, to a lesser extent, from the land. Of the precipitation falling on the land, some evaporates, some runs off, and some soaks into the ground.

On the land the water cycle is subject to many natural interruptions. Some of the water falling from clouds evaporates before reaching the ground; some falls on vegetation and evaporates from its surfaces. Water that reaches the ground may run off quickly to the sea, or it may be absorbed by the soil and thence reach the bedrock underneath as ground water. The water in streams may be stored temporarily in lakes, or it may seep through the porous beds of the streams into the ground water.

Man takes advantage of the natural interruptions in the cycle and also makes his own interruptions. Both kinds of interruptions can be illustrated by tracing an imaginary

drop of water through the water cycle (Fig. 9.4). This droplet of water falls from a cloud onto the land, enters a stream, flows with the stream for some distance, and then is interrupted in its course by a dam which provides a reservoir. This particular droplet seeps through the bottom of the reservoir, penetrates to greater depths, and enters the ground water. The movement of this drop brings it to a spring. The spring flows into a stream which is regulated by a small dam, and the drop is introduced into the water supply of a small city. The drop is chlorinated and filtered so as to improve its quality and make it safe for human consumption, although it may be used for industrial pur-

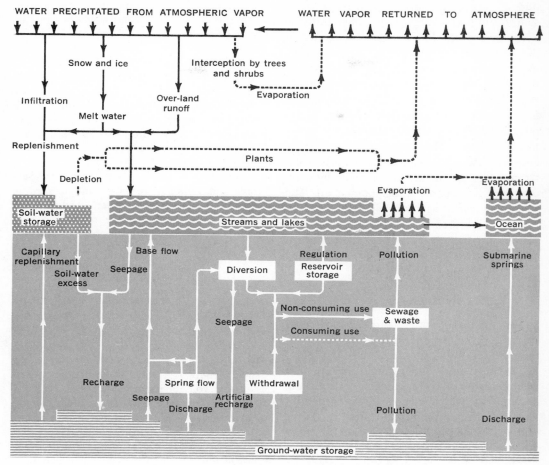

Fig. 9.4. Some of the complications of water circulation, including human uses, are indicated in this diagram. It shows the interchange of water stored in the soil, ground lakes, streams, oceans, and man-made reservoirs.

poses in which purity is not very important. The drop then enters the city. It may be used up and returned to the atmosphere by evaporation from plants (if, for example, it has been sprinkled on lawns), or it may be used for industrial purposes, for cooling perhaps, and returned to the stream.

Another drop of water accumulating from rainfall in a shallow basin may sink into the ground and enter the ground water. This particular body of ground water is about 100 feet below the surface. Beneath the

ground water is a hard, impervious layer of rock which prevents further sinking of water. Several wells tap this ground water, and the water is used for irrigation. The droplet is carried across the field. It may join the surplus water, laden with silt perhaps, and flow off into an adjacent stream; it may enter a plant from which it is transpired into the atmosphere; or perhaps it will remain in the plant until the plant is consumed by man.

The movement of water through the very complicated water cycle takes various forms and is subject to various influences. It is safe to say that wherever man interrupts the hydrologic cycle, he changes the quality of the water and the direction of its movement. He may use the water up, turning it back to the air so that it is not immediately available; he may add something to it in the form of silt from irrigation, sewage, or industrial waste; or he may change the water in other ways. The hydrologic cycle in its entirety is so complicated, particularly when we consider the modifications made by man, that very few people understand it all. The science of hydrology is a highly specialized branch of research, with specialists in ground water, in irrigation, and in sewage treatment and waste disposal.

The Water Balance

The amount of water available for human use in a given region depends on precipitation and on evaporation and run-off, including seepage and underground losses. The water balance may be compared to a bank account in which deposits (precipitation) and withdrawals (run-off in streams, evaporation and transpiration, seepage, and other losses) are made irregularly. When a surplus of precipitation occurs, water can accumulate in the soil, in the streams, and in the reservoirs. Some of the withdrawals represent the water used by man, who merely interrupts the water cycle slightly; the water man uses is lost by evaporation, transpiration, and run-off.

The following account of the water balance at Berkeley, California, and at Seabrook, New Jersey, is taken from *The Water Balance*, by C. W. Thornthwaite and J. R. Mather, Laboratory of Climatology, Centerton, New Jersey, 1955:

. . . at Seabrook, New Jersey, the potential evapotranspiration is negligibly small in winter but in early spring it begins a rapid rise which reaches the high point of the year of more than 150 mm in July. It falls rapidly during the au-

tumn months. The corresponding precipitation is far more uniformly distributed through the year, being very close to 90 mm in nine of the twelve months. The rainiest months are July and August, each of which receives more than 110 mm; November, the driest month, has only 70 mm.

In Berkeley, California, in a different climatic zone, nearly all of the rainfall comes in winter and there is almost no rain in summer. Here the winter water surplus is 107 mm and the summer water deficit is 184 mm.

A comparison of the water balance for Seabrook and Berkeley reveals some interesting facts. Both places have water surpluses and deficits during the year. The surplus at Seabrook is considerably greater than at Berkeley however. In addition, the net water balance shows an annual surplus of 358 mm at Seabrook and −77 mm at Berkeley. Thus at Seabrook and in other areas with similar water balances there is a large supply of readily available water which may be stored in the water table beneath the earth's surface—a supply which can be used for widespread irrigation and which will be replenished each year. On the other hand, at Berkeley water taken from the soil water reservoir for irrigation is not all replaced and there would be a year to year decline in the surface water table. Full irrigation of all land in such areas would not be possible. These two stations are illustrative of two different situations; in one area widespread climatic changes can be brought about through irrigation, but in the other, the influence of irrigation is of only local significance.[1]

It should be pointed out that the water balance (or water budget, as it is sometimes called) is of great significance not only to the natural vegetation of an area but also to the cultivated plants. It had been assumed that if a region received a summer maximum of rain, there was a surplus of water available in the soil; however, measurements made in the soil and the computation of precipitation and evaporation have proved otherwise. This discovery has led to

[1] C. W. Thornthwaite & J. R. Mather, *The Water Balance*, Publications in Climatology, Vol. 8, No. 1, p. 27.

Fig. 9.5. Water taken out of a river for power purposes, re-enters the river lower down. On the St. John River in New Brunswick, Canada, a wide meander of the river makes it easy to take the water across the narrow neck.

increased irrigation in areas formerly considered to be humid during the entire year.

Water in Streams

Across the length and breadth of the land, most of the people live on or near streams (Fig. 9.5), the most important sources of water. Three fourths of the water used by cities and towns and by farmers for irrigation, 90 per cent of the fresh water used by industry, and nearly all of the water used for the generation of electricity comes from streams or from lakes and reservoirs which are associated with streams. Streams represent the run-off of the precipitation which falls on the land; because of the irregularity of the precipitation and the nature of the land itself, the flow of streams is variable—much more variable in some regions than in others. A stream may flood in one season and go dry in another.

Because of the variability in stream flow, it is highly desirable to study streams and to measure their flow; such measurement has been carried on for many years. Two aspects of the flow of a stream are measured: the height of the stream at various stages and the velocity of its flow. The height of a stream can be measured by a simple float gauge which records on a revolving drum. The velocity of flow can be measured by placing in the stream a meter which consists of revolving cups. Some-

HYDROGRAPH OF STREAM FLOW (Muskingum River at Dresden, Ohio)

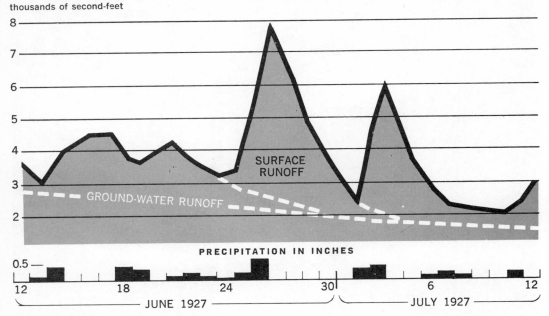

Fig. 9.6. Flow of the Muskingum River, in Ohio, for one month (in thousands of second-feet), showing two flood peaks. The ground-water runoff is quite constant even during floods.

times, simultaneous measurements are taken in different locations in order to get an idea of the average velocity of the stream. Most streams have a decided seasonal variation in flow as well as a variation from year to year. The difference between the low-water stage of a stream and the flood stage is often very great. The stream flow in the Muskingum River (Ohio) is highly variable (Fig. 9.6). In this graph the flow is expressed in thousands of cubic feet per second and ranges from about 2000 to 8000 "second feet" over a period of a few weeks. The fluctuation in stream flow is directly related to the fluctuation in precipitation, but the peaks in stream flow often lag behind the peaks in precipitation because of the slowness with which water is delivered from the small tributaries into the main stream.

The amount of water poured into streams varies widely in different parts of the United

States. In the Olympic Mountains of Washington about 80 inches of precipitation annually pour into the streams; by contrast, in the Arizona desert less than one inch of precipitation runs into the streams. The higher temperatures in the latter area cause such active evaporation that little water remains to run off into streams. The higher the temperature, the greater the loss by evaporation. Also, many features on the surface of the land affect the stream flow. The slope of the land itself is a prime factor: steep slopes are associated with rapid runoff, gentler slopes with gentler run-off. However, many other factors are involved, especially the character of the soil and the character of the natural vegetation.

For the people who live near streams, it is a simple matter, in principle if not in practice, to obtain a supply of water. Many of these people pump water out of rivers,

Fig. 9.7. Springs flowing from horizontal lava beds into the Snake River in the Thousand Springs region near Twin Falls, Idaho. Some of these springs are used to generate power.

pass it through filtration plants, and then pump it into elevated reservoirs in order to provide pressure for water systems. Some rivers must be dammed and their water stored so that cities may have sufficient water in periods of low run-off. Most large cities have a series of dams on various streams to supply their needs, some of these cities using reservoirs a few hundred miles away.

Ground Water

In many parts of the world where run-off is very slight, people depend upon ground water for their water supply. Ground water occurs in the pores of the bedrock some distance below the surface and is not to be confused with soil water, which is very near the surface. The amount of ground water withdrawn daily in the United States is about 30 to 35 billion gallons, which amount represents about 15 to 20 per cent of all water used.

Ground water is obtained from springs and wells. A spring occurs when slight pressure causes ground water to emerge at the surface (Fig. 9.7) and re-enter the surface drainage. At first, man's use of ground water was confined to his use of the springs which, in many lands, provided a more dependable supply of water than streams; early man found it a simple matter to dig around a spring and convert it into a crude well. Some springs have a flow of many thousands of gallons a minute and are sufficient to operate hydroelectric plants and supply water for cities of considerable size.

Ground water is more commonly available in some form of well. Wells have been dug for many centuries, and those that have yielded a large amount of water have often become central points of settlement. In some places it is not easy for man to dig a well

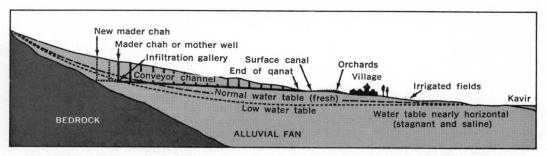

Fig. 9.8. This horizontal well (qanat) allows the water to flow by gravity to the irrigated fields.

if he has only primitive tools. In the sandy deserts, for instance, water can be found not far from the surface of the dunes, but it is not possible to dig and maintain a deep well in sand without constructing some sort of supporting lining to prevent cave-ins. As a consequence, there are only shallow wells in the sandy areas occupied by primitive peoples, and these must be constantly redug. It is likewise difficult to dig a deep well in areas of hard rock. Thus in many regions ground water did not become available until modern well-drilling techniques were introduced.

Water does not occur at all places in the ground in sufficient quantities to justify the digging of wells. Since ground water is very irregular in occurrence, the first problem in digging a well is to find the water. Many methods are used to find water, including the "doodle bug" or so-called water-witching method, which is accepted by a surprising number of people; according to this method, a "gifted" person simply carries around the branch of a tree which, when water is reached, supposedly twists down toward the earth and points out the location of a well. Scientific methods of locating wells are based on a thorough knowledge of the underlying rocks, the use of dyes to trace the movement of underground water, and a complete record of nearby wells. With modern well-drilling machinery a well of several hundred feet in depth can be drilled

in a short time, and some water wells are now drilled thousands of feet in depth. It is interesting to note that drilling for water has sometimes helped in locating oil wells. (An example of this occurred in western Pennsylvania in the early days before the oil booms started.)

The peoples of the Old World deserts, especially in northern Africa and southwestern Asia, learned centuries ago that it was easier to drill a horizontal well than a vertical one. Starting in the loose alluvial material near the foot of a hill or mountain, these peoples used their simple tools to dig wells at a gentle upslope; when they encountered water, sometimes many thousands of feet from the initial opening, gravity would bring the water to the surface where it could be used for irrigation in the fields (Fig. 9.8). These peoples also found that it was more feasible to put timber supports in the roof of a horizontal well than to dig a vertical well and hoist the alluvial material out. (Even in horizontal wells, however, some vertical shafts were provided for the removal of debris.) Furthermore, the vertical well required continuous and burdensome lifting or pumping of water—sometimes to a height of several hundred feet.

On tropical islands today a variant of the horizontal well is sometimes used; this variant consists of an inclined shaft which is driven down to the ground water at about 30 degrees to the horizontal. In the Hawai-

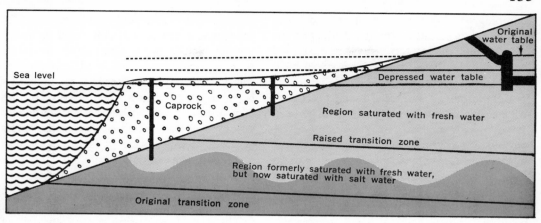

Fig. 9.9. The Maui well, indicated by the heavy black line, is driven at an angle to the top of the fresh water level. Both the fresh water and the salt water are contained in the porous rock of the old volcano. The caprock on the left holds the fresh water in and keeps the sea water out at the upper level. This represents conditions in the vicinity of Honolulu, Hawaii.

ian Islands this type of well is called the Maui well or the skimming well (Fig. 9.9) because it skims the fresh water off the top without reaching the salt water at greater depths. Large shafts are driven so that these wells can accommodate pumps at the bottom. One well pumps about 13 million gallons of water per day to supply a part of Honolulu's needs.

The supply of ground water in any one locality can be quickly reduced by over-pumping. In fact, in some parts of the world pumping has been so excessive that the ground water has been exhausted and the surface streams have dried up. In one Middle Western state in the United States, so many wells were drilled in one locality that the river, a good-sized stream originally, went completely dry and the water table was lowered by hundreds of feet. Reservoirs of ground water have accumulated over many years; the withdrawal from them must be somewhat in proportion to their renewal by precipitation and infiltration. To be sure, the withdrawal from these reservoirs may be temporarily stepped up in cases of emergency; but if pumping continues at excessive

rates for a long time, disaster faces the dependent settlements.

A special kind of well is the artesian well, which taps water in artesian basins in many parts of the world. Artesian water is contained in a porous layer of rock, or aquifer, which is capped by an impermeable layer of rock. Such water is found in the northern Great Plains of the United States, in the eastern basins of Australia, and in many smaller artesian basins in various parts of the world. In the Great Plains the Dakota sandstone, a thick porous formation, is capped by a watertight shale. These rock formations dip gently to the east, while their higher western extremities are exposed to the infiltration of water. A water pressure is thus created in the lower eastern elevations. When wells are drilled through the capping layer into the sandstone, the water spurts several feet into the air. The artesian well, of course, has the advantage of requiring no pumping. Many so-called artesian wells, however, do not flow enough to make all pumping unnecessary; the term is sometimes applied to deep wells in which the water comes up from the bottom partly without pumping. Artesian supplies of ground water can be easily exhausted by the drilling of too many wells or by too heavy pumping of existing wells; as a result, many states have enacted laws restricting the pumping.

Compared to surface supplies, ground-water sources have certain advantages and some disadvantages. In the first place, ground water is usually deeper and, except in a few instances where springs or artesian wells have considerable pressure, must be pumped up some distance. Ground water, however, usually occurs in large storage reservoirs which have a much greater capacity than man-made surface reservoirs. Furthermore, ground water can be obtained in many instances from wells which have been drilled in the most convenient places. For example, a well in South Dakota was drilled on the top of a hill so that the water would flow by gravity into the large agricultural area at a lower elevation. The quality of ground water is usually much more uniform than that of surface streams and, in general, does not need so much filtration and chlorination. Ground water is also likely to be uniform in temperature and in the content of soluble minerals.

Water from the Sea

Since most of the world's water is in the oceans and the oceans are close to many areas with a deficiency of fresh water, it is natural that a great deal of attention should be given to the reclamation of sea water for general use—for domestic purposes, for irrigation, and for industry. The reclamation process is more expensive, however, than the purification of fresh water. It is usually easy enough to filter out sediment in river water and remove some of the soluble minerals, but it is more difficult to purify sea water and water from salt and brackish lakes because of the amount and complexity of the salts.

The simplest method of purifying sea water is often called conversion and in-volves evaporation and condensation. The sea water is heated and converted to steam, leaving behind the soluble salts; the steam is then cooled and condensed into distilled water. Although this process is simple, it is by no means cheap when large quantities of water are to be converted. Distillation of water has been carried on for many, many years on a small scale in laboratories and, on a somewhat larger scale, aboard passenger ships, which find it cheaper to convert sea water than to carry large quantities of fresh water all the way across the ocean.

The cost of converting water from the sea depends, of course, upon the cost of power or energy. At present, the cost of converted sea water is at least 10 times the cost of water obtained from sources on the land. Therefore, sea water is not used generally, and its use may not be feasible on a large scale for some years to come. All the available methods of converting sea water, including distillation, are expensive either in the amount of energy required or in the amount of materials involved. Cheaper power, especially nuclear power, may change this picture within a few years. It should be noted that in some cases sea water can be used for certain purposes without conversion. For example, sea water has been used for cooling furnaces after special provision has been made in the pipes to avoid excessive corrosion.

Major Uses of Water

Irrigation. Man's water supply goes for irrigation, industrial uses, and domestic uses (in that order). In addition, there is a very important special use of water in the generation of power, but the water so used is not "consumed" and thus is usually available for other purposes also. In the United States irrigation accounts for more than half of the total water consumption. Most of this irrigation occurs in the western part of the country, but irrigation is also used in the humid areas to supplement the rainfall and to bring

Fig. 9.10. Irrigation ditches in a field, Pinal County, Arizona. These ditches and furrows are arranged to move the water more or less across the slope, rather than down the slope. This field is normally planted in cotton.

about more even crop growth. The large industrial farms in the humid areas make a careful check of the rainfall and add predetermined amounts of water by irrigation to keep the crops growing at the optimum rate.

Water for irrigation comes from a variety of sources. Most of it comes from surface streams which have been dammed up in order to provide a more uniform rate of water supply. Characteristically, the large irrigation projects, not only in western United States but in many other parts of the world, are related to high mountains which collect snow in the winter; as the snow melts in the spring and early summer, a constant supply of water goes down to the lowland

to be used for irrigation. Irrigation water is also obtained from ground water; although this source is used less extensively, in some areas it offers the principal supply for the irrigated fields.

Irrigated areas are limited not only by the water supply but also by the terrain. For example, even though there is an abundant water supply deep in the Colorado Canyon, the lofty Colorado Plateau is not irrigable because it is many thousands of feet above the water supply. The best site for irrigation is a lowland to which water, diverted from a stream or obtained from wells or springs, will flow by gravity (Fig. 9.10). Water can be pumped up a few hundred feet without too great an expense, but in every case there is a point beyond which the cost of pumping is no longer commensurate with the value of the crop. Land for irrigation should also be nearly level, with a very gentle slope in one direction; on such land the water can run slowly across the fields and then off into drainage ditches. Where land is irregular, sprinklers are often used for irrigation; however, these involve additional expense in the purchase of equipment and in its maintenance, moving, and tending.

Irrigation is a very old practice; in some places (the lower Nile, for example) it is more or less of a natural process. The Nile rises in the high plateaus and mountains of eastern Africa, where there is heavy rainfall at the time of the high sun. From this area water flows slowly northward down the Nile and reaches lower Egypt in middle or late summer. There it spreads over the flood plain and soaks the soil well, after which it recedes. Formerly, crops were planted after the natural flood waters of the Nile had receded. A similar schedule is now followed in many other parts of the world: once a flood or high stage of a river has given the flood plain a good soaking, the crop is grown mostly on the basis of the water retained in the soil. Of course, in modern times the construction of dams has regulated the flow of the Nile so that the water can be used much more efficiently. Many of the irrigated oases in the world are fundamentally like the area of the Nile: their water comes from distant mountains, is regulated by dams and reservoirs, and is applied to the land by means of a system of branching ditches. Other examples of such irrigated areas are the Imperial Valley of California and Mexico at the lower end of the Colorado River, the Peruvian coast, western Argentina, and certain parts of Inner Asia.

When irrigation is practiced in more humid regions, the methods are likely to be a little different. The humid regions are more likely to have a constant supply of ground water, and the irrigation in those regions is likely to be based on generally shallow wells, from which water is pumped to supplement the rainfall. A typical example of such a system of irrigation may be seen in southern New Jersey, where vegetables of various kinds are grown for freezing and canning. The rainfall in this area is normally adequate for the growth of crops, and for many years the crops were not irrigated. It has been found, however, that supplemental irrigation will protect the crops from drought and, furthermore, that the water supply to the plants can be carefully regulated to produce an increase in the yield and the quality of the crops. The rains throughout the year keep the water supply in the ground replenished, so there is little danger of its being exhausted.

Industrial Uses. Next to irrigation, industry is the greatest user of water in the industrialized countries. Many industries consume large quantities of water; that is, they use it and leave it in a state not altogether satisfactory for other uses. The simplest industrial use of water is its use in cooling; a great deal of water is needed by steel mills and other factories which employ heat in metallurgical or chemical processes. In some cases water used for cooling is slightly polluted; in other cases it is unchanged. Another major industrial use, particularly important in textile and paper production, is the use in washing, during which process water is likely to be polluted by chemicals. Water is particularly affected in paper production, where the use of quantities of sulfur results in polluted water which has the foul smell of rotten cabbages. In many cases the location of an industry is decided by the availability of water. Some industries require pure water, while others can use water of low quality or water that contains some impurities. Frequently, water must be filtered before it can be used in critical industrial processes.

Domestic Uses. Although the quantity of water used for domestic consumption is relatively small, it is in many cases the most critical. The water supply for cities, towns, and individual water systems of isolated houses and communities must have high quality. People prefer a soft water free from disease-carrying organisms, with a good taste and a reasonably clear color. If the supply of water is from a protected stream or from ground water, very little purification is necessary. However, the many cities which obtain their water supply from rivers polluted by industries and sewage-disposal plants must subject it to a great deal of chemical treatment and filtration.

Water Power. As soon as man invented the wheel, he began to use the power of running or falling water to turn his implements. The first wheel known to archaeology was a potter's wheel, dated from 3200 B.C., and the first water-powered wheel was used in approximately 100 B.C. A Norwegian farmer may use water power to turn his grindstone and sharpen the scythes which he needs on steep, rocky slopes that do not lend themselves to machine cultivation or harvesting; he uses water power by directing a small waterfall to the wooden blades of the wheel which turns his grindstone. For centuries man has used water power in various ways to turn the stones that grind his grain. A swift stream can turn a large wheel from below or by pouring water on it from above. In some cases streams have been diverted into canals or millraces before being applied to paddle wheels.

In modern times most water power is used to generate electricity (Fig. 9.11). However, there are only a few sites available in various parts of the earth which are suitable for the increasing number of large-scale power developments. The conditions which affect the development of a water-power site are various. In the first place, the stream that is to be used should be located near areas of power demand; many excellent water-power sites in remote parts of the world are not developed because there is no nearby demand. The stream should have a moderate to large volume of water and little

variability of flow—that is, it should not go dry during any season. It should have a local fall or steep gradient; it should have a low sediment load so that the reservoir will not become silted; and, preferably, the stream should not freeze over. Lastly, if there is not a natural waterfall, the stream should have a good dam site in a narrow valley with hard rock on the sides and bottom so that the dam may have a firm foundation. The principal water-power sites of the world are developed in mountainous areas of moderate to high precipitation. They are also limited to regions that are densely or fairly densely populated, or to the vicinity of such regions.

Conditions favoring water-power development can be illustrated by Niagara Falls, where the Niagara River plunges over a cliff of limestone and produces a head of water of about 160 feet. Above the falls is a series of

Fig. 9.11. Hoover Dam and power plant on the Colorado River. The narrow canyon in hard rock favors the building of a high dam. The main purpose of this dam is power and flood control.

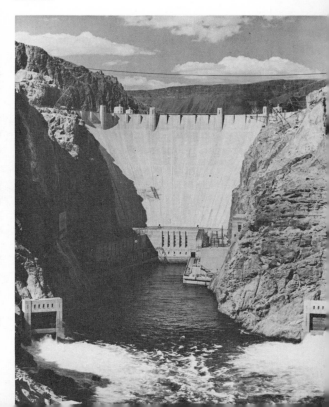

lakes—the Great Lakes—which serve as natural regulating reservoirs and make the flow of water in the Niagara River remarkably uniform; fluctuations in the levels of the Great Lakes occur over a period of years rather than seasonally. It is a simple matter to divert a part of the water of Niagara River into large pipes or tubes, called penstocks, and to take the water in these tubes to generators at or near the base of the falls. It should be pointed out that below the falls the rapids produce an additional head of water, with the result that the total available head between Lakes Erie and Ontario is more than 300 feet. The power from Niagara Falls and from the other sites along the river is fed into a system of transmission lines on both sides of the boundary between Canada and the United States, which lines supply power to Hamilton, Buffalo, Rochester, and many other cities. A number of industries have been located near the falls because of the cheap, abundant power. The generation of power at the falls is restricted somewhat by the demands of recreation; by international agreement, only a limited amount of water may be diverted, lest the beauty of the falls be diminished.

Until recently, water-power development was carried on at individual sites more or less independent of each other. At first, water power in the form of electricity was used locally; later it was distributed more broadly by interconnected power lines. In recent years the tendency has been to develop the water power of a whole river system or of a whole region in one co-ordinated effort. It is obvious that the construction of a dam on one part of a river will affect the construction and the functioning of a reservoir on another part.

A large-scale example of a regional development is the Tennessee Valley Project, in which the waters of the Tennessee River and its tributaries have been developed as a whole. This project actually began during World War I with the construction of a dam in northwestern Alabama at Muscle Shoals.

This dam and its power plant were constructed in order to fix nitrogen from the air and thus alleviate the scarcity of nitrate which existed in the United States because of war conditions. Since the war ended before the power plant was finished, the plant was not, at once, used for nitrogen fixation; but it constituted the beginning of the power system known as the Tennessee Valley Project. In 1933 the Federal government set up the Tennessee Valley Authority with a plan to develop the whole watershed of the Tennessee River. In the first part of the program nine dams were constructed on the main river and 12 on the tributary streams. These dams have enabled the Authority to control the water more or less throughout the whole system and to provide, in addition to a large amount of power, considerable flood control and some improvements for navigation. Needless to say, the development of hydroelectric energy on such a scale has had a great impact upon the lives of all the people in the area. New industries have been set up, and the standards of living of all the people have changed as cheap hydroelectric energy has become available. There are now 34 major hydroelectric power plants and 12 steam power plants which contribute to the power pool; there are over 10,000 miles of power lines serving more than 1,300,000 customers. In 1929 the per capita income in the region was only 44 per cent of the national average; by 1954 it was 62 per cent of that average. Only 3 per cent of the farms had electricity in 1933; in 1954, 93 per cent were electrified.

The Tennessee Valley Project set the stage for many similar developments in different parts of the United States. In the northern part of the Great Plains, the Missouri Valley and its tributaries include a wide area of the plains and the eastern flank of the Rocky Mountains. The Missouri Basin Project is set up in somewhat the same manner as the Tennessee Valley Project, but it has the additional object of irrigation. Since the Missouri River is subject to flood, flood control in the downstream areas (especially between Sioux City, Iowa, and St. Louis, Missouri) is an important part of the program. Finally, there is power development, not quite so centrally important as it is in the Tennessee Valley but nevertheless a significant item. The Missouri River and its tributaries, such as the Milk, the Yellowstone, and the Platte, have their headwaters in the Rocky Mountains. Thus their heaviest flow occurs with the melting of snow in spring and early summer. The rivers flow through areas which, though normally called plains, are in many cases actually hilly plateaus. The only level land near the rivers is the flood plain, some of which has been irrigated for a long time on a small scale. The construction of several dams at strategic points has built up reservoirs of water at higher levels and has enabled the farmers in the vicinity to irrigate much more land than they had irrigated before. Although the Missouri River was used for the navigation of small boats in pioneer days, the use of the river for transport declined when larger river boats began operating on the Mississippi and the Ohio. The construction of the dams has made it possible to use barges on the lower part of the river and has extended the usefulness of the river in this respect.

Throughout the world many types of power sites have been developed or are under construction. In the Alps, the Pyrenees, and other mountain ranges of western Europe, many of the valleys have a series of relatively small dams and power plants that are placed on a river, one after the other, like beads on a string. In this type of development the water is used several times, the reservoirs are small, and parts of the valley floor are available for human occupance. In recent years many large dams have been constructed and many more are planned, notably in India, China, Egypt, Australia, and Canada. The large dams provide more power than smaller dams, but the reservoirs behind them flood out the agricultural land in the valleys, as well as the towns, villages, railways, and roads.

World Distribution of Water-Power Resources

The hydroelectric resources of the world are very unequally distributed and developed. One of the fundamental requirements of water power is that heavy precipitation fall on elevated land. Many regions with a heavy rainfall and a good supply of surface and ground water lack elevated land and thus do not have power potentialities. In Louisiana, for example, there is little fall to the rivers, and the banks and bottoms are too soft to provide good dam sites.

Western Europe has a greater percentage of its power developed than any comparable area in the world. Mountainous areas, such as the Alps, Pyrenees, and Carpathians, receive heavy precipitation in the form of snow and rain; and the rivers flowing from these mountains have an even regime which makes for very satisfactory power development. In some of the areas involved, such as Italy, Switzerland, and southern France, the scarcity of coal has greatly stimulated the development of water power. In western Europe the typical power plant is small and was developed early in terms of the modern industrial age. The output of several small plants is usually combined to supply energy for light manufacturing and railway operation as well as for domestic uses. Eastern Europe, including Russia, has comparatively little of its power potential developed, although Russia has been making great strides in recent years.

South America has a much greater potential than Europe, but only a small part of its power has been developed. The heavy precipitation on the east side of the Andes and on the Brazilian Plateau means a great potential of power; but since many of these power sites are in remote, sparsely populated, and nonindustrial areas, the need for their development is not very great at the present time. The principal power developments which have occurred in South America are in the densely populated areas of eastern Brazil and northwestern Argentina.

North America has the highest per capita development of water power in the world. The greatest potential in North America lies in the lofty western mountains, which have heavy precipitation, and in the plateau region of eastern Canada, where there is a series of natural lakes that are used as reservoirs. The greatest need for power in North America, however, occurs in the eastern part, in the highly industrialized areas, where most of the power used is derived from coal and petroleum.

The U.S.S.R. has a somewhat greater potential than North America if both the European and Asiatic portions of the U.S.S.R. are included in the comparison. The greatest power developments are in the large rivers, such as the Dnepr and the Volga, and in the rivers which flow down from the high mountains, such as the Amu and the Syr. Since the latter areas were somewhat remote from the early industrial centers of the U.S.S.R., their development languished for many years.

In Asia the greatest power potential is in the lofty mountains (the Himalayas, for example), but only a small part of this potential has been developed. India and China are just beginning to develop their tremendous water-power potential. Only in Japan is there widespread use of hydroelectric energy.

The greatest potential of all for the development of water power is in Africa, especially in that part of Africa which is south of the Sahara. This very great potential is a result of the combination of a number of factors. South of the Sahara, Africa is a plateau with a very heavy average rainfall. The run-off of the large rivers and their tributaries (the Congo and the Zambezi, for example) over many cataracts and waterfalls creates a large power potential. The region has been slow to develop because of its inaccessibility; the waterfalls that are so favorable for power also serve to hinder transport, even in the lower parts of the rivers. Now, however, development is going on very rapidly. A number of new dams are being constructed, and Africa may soon realize at least a reasonable proportion of its power potential.

Water Problems

The major types of water problems are three in number: problems related to water supply, which may be concerned with either scarcity or excess; problems related to the quality and pollution of water; and problems related to the allocation of water rights.

Floods. All parts of the land, except those that are perpetually frozen, are subject to floods (Fig. 9.12). Even the driest part of the Sahara may have a flood; likewise, a flood may occur in a region where the rainfall is ordinarily uniform. However, some districts are naturally more subject to floods than others. The most vulnerable spots are those close to high mountains which have large amounts of snow in winter: if the snow melts quickly in the spring, at the same time that heavy rains occur, the run-off may be so excessive that the streams are not able to contain the water; it may overflow the flood plains and perhaps even the higher levels. The Nile in Africa, the Ohio and the Mississippi in eastern United States, and the Sacramento in California are prime examples of river systems that are subject to annual flooding.

The damage done by floods costs hundreds of millions of dollars yearly and calls for flood control and protection. The details of flood control vary from place to place. One method of flood control requires a series of dams in the main stream and in the tributaries so that in times of heavy run-off the gates of the reservoirs can be closed and the water held back until the danger of flood has passed. Since the reservoirs must be partially empty when the run-off begins to be heavy, this system of flood control interferes somewhat with the use of some reservoirs for the storage of irrigation water or for hydroelectric development. Another method of flood control requires that a flood wall or levee be built along the banks of a river to keep the

Fig. 9.12. Airphoto of a flood near Salina, Kansas, on the flood plain of the Smoky Hill River. Only a few patches of land remain above water.

water out of certain areas. Many cities along the Ohio and the Mississippi have flood walls or levees for this particular purpose. Whether they are simply banks of earth or are made of concrete, these walls entail some difficulties, particularly since they prevent drainage of the areas *to* the river. Gates in the flood walls are used in many places to allow for this drainage.

Water Supply. Although there are many kinds of water problems, most water problems revolve around the question of scarcity. As the population increases and the per capita use of water increases, the water supply of some communities begins to fall far below their needs. This scarcity demands that the communities reach out farther and farther to supplement their local water supply. Los Angeles, for example, brings some of its water from the Owens Valley and from

the Colorado River, both of which are a few hundred miles from the city itself. As the area continues to grow, water may have to be brought from even greater distances. New York City gets a part of its water from the Adirondacks; London takes a part of its supply from Wales; and Moscow taps the upper Volga River. The practice of supplementing the local water supply is not new; the peoples of ancient Rome, Greece, Egypt, Israel, and Babylonia built long aqueducts for this purpose, as well as reservoirs and irrigation canals (remnants of which works are still to be seen).

Water Quality. The waters of the earth vary widely in a number of qualities; some of these qualities are critical for certain purposes while others are of little consequence. The soluble mineral content (hardness), the amount of suspended matter, and the organic content are likely to be the most significant qualities. Such qualities as the color (of clear water) and the temperature are not so likely to be critical.

Hardness may be defined as the proportion of dissolved mineral, usually expressed in parts per million (ppm). Soft water has up to 50 parts of dissolved mineral per million; medium-hard water has 50 to 100 parts; hard water has more than 100. A rough indication of hardness is the amount of soap required to make a permanent lather; for example, 10 grains of soap to a gallon of water indicates a hardness of 171 ppm, an amount just tolerable for domestic uses. Hard water may leave a "scale" in pipes and cooking utensils; on the other hand, very soft water may be corrosive. Hard water can be softened by precipitation of the soluble minerals and by filtration. Associated with the hardness of water is its acidity or alkalinity, a quality measured by the pH factor. A pH value of 7 indicates neutral water; more than 7 indicates alkaline water; less than 7 indicates acid water.

Water usually contains minute traces of many minerals which are necessary to human health; in certain areas, however, minerals other than those found naturally in the local water supply must be added to the human diet to avoid deficiency diseases. Iodine, for example, is necessary for the proper functioning of the thyroid gland. It was noted many years ago that goiter, or enlargement of the thyroid gland, was common in the interior of the United States and other regions where the iodine content of the water was low. On the other hand, people living near the ocean were essentially free from goiter, especially if they ate sea foods. Once the relation of iodine to goiter was clear, it was easy to add minute quantities of iodine to the diet of people living in critical areas, usually by adding it to table salt.

The case of fluorine is a little more complicated. Small quantities of a soluble fluoride are needed to minimize tooth decay in growing children. However, too much fluoride produces spotted teeth (a highly undesirable condition from the standpoint of beauty) and perhaps other undesirable effects. Individual doses of fluoride may be added to the milk or drinking water of children, but this individual application is considered a nuisance and many cities add small quantities of fluoride to the entire water supply. In other communities the addition of fluoride to the entire water supply has been called "mass medication" and has resulted in bitter arguments.

Although minute quantities of many trace elements are necessary for the health of plants and animals, a little too much of them may be very harmful. For example, although the element boron is essential for the proper growth of plants, serious damage to plants is likely to result if the concentration of boron exceeds one part per million.

Organic matter, living and dead, may affect the quality of water to a critical degree. Water derived from swamps, lakes, or sluggish streams may be brown in color, have an unpleasant taste and odor, and be difficult to filter; but it is the living organisms in water which cause most concern. In populated areas the surface waters and in some cases the ground water may act as carriers for organisms associated with typhoid, dysentery, and other diseases. Proper chlorination kills most but not all of these organisms.

The Ownership of Water. The problem of the ownership and allocation of the surface and ground waters of the world is very complicated, involving conflict between individual owners of land and also between states and nations (see Chapter 25). The common-law water rights, often known as riparian rights, are recognized in many parts of the world; thus, if an owner's land includes the bank or banks of a stream, he is recognized as having certain privileges in regard to the water in that stream. He can use the water for various purposes—for power, for domestic use, for irrigation—but he is expected to pass the water on in a usable state to the owners of the land below. Obviously, many disputes are likely to arise about the uses and ownership of water. Those who do not have land touching a body of water may not have any rights to surface water. In some cases streams have been diverted, with resulting effects on water rights; ordinarily, streams cannot be diverted from one watershed to another without special legal action.

The development of large irrigation projects in various parts of the world has led to special kinds of ownership. In addition to individual ownership, there is community ownership and ownership by corporations and so-called land companies and water companies. In many cases ownership of land is involved with the ownership of water; in other cases it is not. In the United States the early western settlements assumed their ownership of water. The Mormon settlements along the west side of the Wasatch Range were examples of communal ownership centered in a particular religious group. Many Mormon settlements were successful because the Mormons migrated to the region early and selected the best land that was readily and inexpensively irrigable without too much construction of dams and ditches. More recently many of the large irrigation projects, as well as the hydroelectric projects, have been sponsored by the Federal government; such projects are usually too difficult for small groups of private citizens to finance or are planned on unusually difficult terrain. In the Federal projects, the ownership of the land and the water is vested in a Federal agency, such as the United States Reclamation Service.

The rights of ownership of ground water are quite different from those of surface water. In the common law developed by English jurists, no real provision was made for the contingencies of ownership of underground water. In the common-law system that is in effect in the United States and elsewhere, it is generally considered legal for a property owner to drill a well and pump out as much water as he can, even though it is known that by so doing he is taking water from underneath the adjacent owner's land.

In some localities the pumping of large quantities of water from the ground has resulted in considerable damage to adjacent properties, including subsidence of the land. Excessive pumping of ground water also depletes the supply and often increases the mineral content of the water to the point where the water is not satisfactory for some domestic and industrial purposes. Excessive pumping has also led, in places near the coast, to the invasion of salt water into the fresh ground water underneath the land.

The Demand for More Water. Most of the water problems—supply, pollution, flood control, cost, and ownership—are intensified by the continually increasing demand for water. In the United States the population has doubled since 1900, while the per capita use of water has quadrupled. The use of water in the United States is not distributed in proportion to population, however, and the water problems are not of equal intensity in all sections of the country. In the 17 western states, with about 40 million people, the average daily use of water is 85 billion gallons, or about 2150 gallons per capita per day. Fully nine tenths of this amount is used for irrigation. The 31 eastern states, with 130 million people, use about 80 billion gallons per day, of which amount 65 billion gallons are used for industry and three billion gallons are used for irrigation.

As the demand for water increases, the cost per unit rises. The annual water bill in the United States is in excess of three billion dollars, or about 18 dollars per capita. City people pay about one sixth of this bill, farmers pay one tenth, and most of the remainder is charged to industry. The investment in dams, reservoirs, filtration plants, and pipelines totals about 50 billion dollars. As more and more water is needed and more radioactive waste materials are added to the usual pollution, the cost of a clean, pure water supply must increase. However, since such a water supply is both necessary and convenient, the consumers will probably bear the increased cost with little complaint.

Every nation is a portion of soil and humanity.
Friedrich Ratzel

CHAPTER 10

Growth of the Soil

In Knut Hamsun's book entitled *Growth of the Soil,* a man named Isak trudges through the forest and grassland with a pack on his back looking for a place to build a home. He has a careful eye for the features of the land—its slope, exposure, water supply, and native vegetation—as indicators of fertility. He digs in the soil at intervals until he is satisfied with the leafy mold and then selects a plot of ground which includes both woodland and grassland. Here his home grows, eventually complete with family, livestock, and some of the blessings of civilization. Just as a plant grows in the soil while owing its fundamental character to its ancestry, so Isak and his family grow on the land. There are some important differences, however, between the plant's growth and Isak's growth: Isak is not literally attached to the land, even though he is dependent on it; his heritage includes a great deal of know-how passed down by word of mouth from generation to generation; and Isak and his family, in the course of a few years, will make profound changes in the environment, including the soils.

In a very real sense man is a growth of the soil, that upper, weathered part of the earth's crust which supports plant life and is the fundamental source of man's food and much of his clothing and shelter. Plants and animals supply many of man's needs, but they, in turn, are dependent on the soil. The soil is seen by many but understood by few.

HYPOTHETICAL SOIL PROFILE

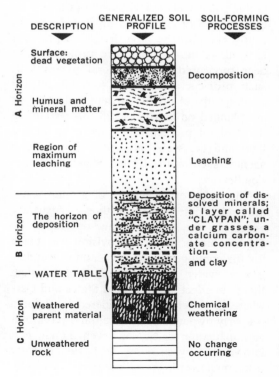

Fig. 10.1. Right: A hypothetical soil profile. At a given moment the water table may be at any level or it may be absent. Far right: (a) red-yellow podzolic soil near Ruston, Louisiana; (b) brown soil near Akron, Ohio; (c) sierozem or gray desert soil near Minden, Nevada; and (d) chernozem in Spink County, South Dakota. Measurements are in feet.

144

a

b

c

d

Even the people who are "close to the soil" rarely appreciate its variety and complexities. To the casual observer, all soils may appear alike, but the soil of any region is a composite expression of many landscape elements—rock type, slope, climate, vegetation, and (last but not least) the work of man. Since each of these factors is variable in both space and time, the number of soil types is legion. As Karel Capek says, "Not even the clouds are so diverse, so beautiful and terrible as the soil under your feet . . ." (Fig. 10.1).

Just as man benefits by interrupting water at some point in the hydrologic cycle, so he feeds himself by using the weathered rocks and minerals on their way to the sea. These rocks must be dissolved and their nutrients collected in the soil complex and held there for exchange with the roots of plants; only through this process can life survive on the earth. If man removes the nutrients from the soil faster than they are restored, the consequence is not only hunger in the usual sense but hidden hunger that is based on soil deficiencies.

Where the population pressure is so great that the soil has no opportunity to rebuild its fertility, or where the farmer undergoes social pressure to produce not merely for necessities but also for luxuries, the basic fertility of the soil is pushed to lower and lower levels. On some of the small farms of China fertility has been maintained for 40 centuries; on some of the wheat farms of the newer lands serious depletion has occurred in the last half century. The world has sufficient knowledge of soil to balance use and depletion, to manage soil so that both quality and quantity of production are maintained. It is sad, therefore, that soils in the United States have been rapidly depleted at the same time that large agricultural surpluses were being piled up, many of which surpluses have been eventually lost through spoilage.

Man has lived so long in intimate touch with the soil (although often unaware of its qualities) that each has had a profound effect upon the other. Man has done much to modify the soil from the time he first scratched it with a stick to transplant a few cuttings or to plant a few seeds. He has cleared steep slopes, plowed progressively deeper, destroyed the natural vegetation, and introduced crops and weeds which have had varying effects upon the soil. The interaction of man and soil varies widely in different parts of the earth, depending upon the quality of the soil and upon the characteristics of the people who till it.

The Development of Soil Science

During the long course of agricultural history, from the time that he first began to cultivate plants, man's knowledge of soil has grown. Much of his knowledge has come about as the result of trial and error, and his progress has at times been very slow or even nonexistent. However, as long as 40 centuries ago the Chinese made a soil map which was used for tax purposes and the administration of agricultural affairs. Prior to that time people learned to use the soil in a variety of ways. They discovered the use of manure and lime; they built terraces on steep hillsides; and they practiced crop rotation and irrigation. It was not until the Industrial Revolution began, however, that soils came to be studied systematically and scientifically. Field experimentation in the use of soils began about 1834 in western Europe, and soon several experiment stations were started.

It came to be recognized that the soil was a very complex material consisting of various elements or parts, all of which parts had to do with fertility. Early recognition of the variety of soil texture—the difference between the light, sandy soils and the heavy, clay soils—enabled farmers to choose better sites for their crops. It was also noted that the mineral content of soils varied widely and that it had a profound effect upon fertility. In fact, the great German soil scientist,

Fig. 10.2. Types of plows: (a) a wooden plow with a single handle and a metal point, Pakistan; (b) a wooden plow formerly used in Europe and America; (c) an all-steel plow developed in 1849; note the alternate hitching holes which regulate the plow depth; (d) a modern, tractor-drawn five-bottom plow from Wisconsin.

Justus von Liebig, thus stated the theory of plant nutrition: ". . . the crops on a field diminish or increase in exact proportion to the diminution or increase of the mineral substances conveyed to it in manure." Although this arbitrary statement overemphasized the importance of mineral content, the use of mineral fertilizers to supplement manures on the soils of northern Europe did much to improve the crop yields.

Liebig was more or less unaware of the importance of other elements in the soil: the bacteria, which play a significant part; the fine colloids, which are critical in the retention of the soil water in which soluble minerals are held; the organic content of the

soil (often referred to as humus), which is present usually in the upper layer of the soil.

As methods of cultivation improved, especially with deeper plowing, knowledge of the soil increased (Fig. 10.2). The distinction between topsoil, subsoil, and bedrock was noted. At first, the topsoil was defined as the plow depth; but since total soil depth varies from a few inches to 20 feet or more in various parts of the world, this was obviously an arbitrary and unsatisfactory definition. A new definition based on texture, mineral content, and color was devised: the topsoil was renamed the *A* horizon; the subsoil, the *B* horizon; and the bedrock or parent material, the *C* horizon. The role of the rock from which soil was weathered became more clearly defined; because this role had been greatly exaggerated, it had formerly been customary to classify soils simply as "sandstone soils," "limestone soils," "shale soils," "granite soils," and so on. By this system one could convert a geologic map to a soils map with a few strokes of the pen, but nothing of value was added.

The correlation of soil and vegetation was recognized very early. Since the farmer did not ordinarily see more than the surface of the soil and its covering vegetation, it was natural that he should judge the soil in terms of the vegetation cover. He learned that certain types of natural vegetation, such as oak forests, indicated soils of fairly high fertility and that other types of vegetation, such as dwarf oak or scrub pine, suggested low fertility. Even though such generalizations were by no means reliable or applicable in all areas (since climate rather than soil is responsible for some differences in vegetation), a fund of knowledge was built up relating vegetation cover to soil fertility. Modern soil science has rejected some of these generalizations and modified others.

About 1870, Russian soil scientists brought forth a theory with reference to soils which changed the approach to soil study. The Russians confined their studies mostly to what was formerly called European Russia, an ideal place to study soils from a broad point of view. The land is level and has great uniformity in rock (parent) material. The country has a gradual change in climate from the cold tundras of the north, through the intermediate humid climates, to the dry climates of the south near the Caspian and Black seas; vegetation also changes gradually within the same area. From a study of the soils in this area the Russians concluded that given enough time for a soil to weather to a mature state, all soils, regardless of the parent material, will take on certain aspects depending upon the climate alone. In other words, the Russian soil scientists believed that the great factor was cli-

mate; parent material, slope, and vegetation were of minor importance. Like many useful generalizations, this one was too sweeping to be entirely true; but, on the whole, it was a great contribution to soil science all over the world. Its influence was delayed somewhat by the fact that in 1870 few soil scientists outside of Russia could read the Russian language. The full effect of the theory was felt later when the studies were translated into German and English.

Many types of scientists, including geologists, hydrologists, bacteriologists, chemists, and geographers, are now engaged in studying soils in many parts of the world. The goal of most of their studies is to determine the fertility of the soil and to devise methods of maintaining the fertility and improving it under various conditions of cultivation.

The Soil Profile

One of the significant contributions which has been made to soil science within the last half century is the definition of the soil profile (Fig. 10.3). The differentiation between the topsoil and the subsoil was noted very early, but it remained for modern soil science to define them scientifically. The topsoil is called the *A* horizon. The essential feature of the *A* horizon is that some material, including soluble mineral matter, has been and is being removed from it. Rain falling on the topsoil dissolves some of the mineral matter and carries it away, either to the streams or to the subsoil or ground water below; the trickling of water through the *A* horizon also removes some of the finer insoluble material. Because of this loss of mineral and fine clay particles, the *A* horizon becomes somewhat coarser and takes on a different structure. The top of the *A* horizon usually includes some organic matter, more or less decomposed. In the forest this organic matter may take the form of forest litter, including leaves and twigs which fall from the trees. In the grasslands this organic matter may consist of remnants of blades and roots of grass, partially decomposed. The color of the *A*

COMPARISON OF SOIL PROFILES

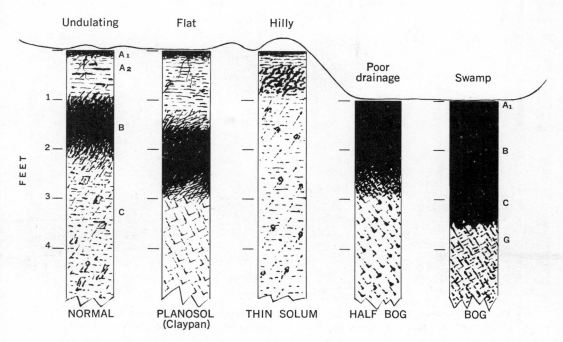

Fig. 10.3. The nature of the soil profile depends partly on the surface. All the profiles above are from the same parent material.

horizon—typically dark grey or chocolate brown—is usually affected by both organic content and mineral content and varies in different climates and, to a certain extent, with different parent rock materials (see Appendix D).

The subsoil has come to be called the *B* horizon. It is made up of weathered material from the parent rock, plus soluble minerals and fine particles washed down from the *A* horizon. The *B* horizon is characteristically finer in texture than the *A* horizon, tends to be almost plastic in character, and is also likely to contain much more moisture. Its color—often brown or red—is likely to be more representative of the climatic conditions and of the parent material than is the color of the *A* horizon.

The *C* horizon is the bedrock or parent material and may consist of anything from

sand or gravel to granite or lava. It is partially weathered and partially broken up by the effect of weathering, but it is not completely converted. In some cases the contact of the horizons is sharply defined; in others it is transitional. If surface conditions are stable long enough, all soils tend to become mature and to show a definite profile consisting of *A*, *B*, and *C* horizons.

Soil Fertility

The fertility of the soil depends upon many qualities. First of all, at least a moderate depth of soil is essential since a thin soil cannot supply sufficient water and soluble minerals. The depth is related to such factors as climate, rock material, degree of slope, length of slope, exposure, and vegetation. In warm, humid climates chemical

Fig. 10.4. Soil erosion of the "shoestring" type developed along plow furrows in a Nebraska field. Some of the soil accumulates in the low area in the foreground.

weathering is rapid, and soil on gentle slopes may reach a depth of 20 feet or more. Soft rocks weather readily and are often associated with thick soils; hard rocks, such as granite, are accompanied by thin soils. Steep slopes are less likely than gentle slopes to accumulate thick soils; in middle latitudes soils are generally thicker on the poleward slopes (the northern slopes in the Northern Hemisphere) than on the slopes toward the Equator. Forested regions often have thicker soils than grasslands, but this difference may be an expression of climate rather than vegetation. Deep soils tend to develop where weathering is rapid and removal by erosion is comparatively slow. It should be noted that soil erosion, the removal of soil from the surface, is a perfectly normal and natural phenomenon and is, indeed, very necessary for the maintenance of soil fertility. If soils did not erode at all, the soluble mineral and

the organic content of the soil would be exhausted and, as a result, the soil would fail to produce (Fig. 10.4). Normal soil erosion on most slopes is slow, but erosion is often greatly accelerated by man. What is ordinarily referred to as soil erosion is generally the accelerated soil erosion that is brought on by cultivation, grazing, or deforestation. Accelerated erosion is a very complicated problem, and studies in various parts of the world suggest that generalizations about it are likely to be unsatisfactory (Fig. 10.5).

Another factor influencing the fertility of the soil is its texture, which is determined by the size of the particles of which it is composed. Some soils are very coarse and "light," while others are very fine and "heavy"; most soils are made up of mixtures of fine and coarse particles in various proportions. The coarsest soils are gravelly and sandy, with limited amounts of silt and clay.

The relative amounts of gravel, sand, silt, and clay have a good deal to do with fertility: they affect the capacity of the soil to absorb and hold water; they also affect the amount of soluble mineral that can be retained in the soil for plant food. Coarse-textured soils absorb water readily but do not hold it well. Soils which contain large amounts of sand and silt are often called "warm" soils, or light-textured soils, whereas the ones with high concentrations of clay are called "cold" soils, or heavy soils.

The fertility of soils also depends upon their chemical composition, especially the amount of certain soluble minerals present in the soil waters. Although many minerals are necessary for soil fertility, only a few of them are likely to be in short supply. Attention, therefore, is focussed largely on the minerals that are likely to be deficient—nitrates, phosphates, potash, lime, and other minerals in particular areas—and less attention is given to those minerals that are usually present in sufficient quantities. Of all the soluble minerals in the soil, the nitrates and the phosphates are most likely to be deficient. In some soils the amount of phosphorus is so little that it is absolutely necessary to add it in the form of mineral fertilizer before satisfactory crops can be grown or satisfactory grass can be grown for the pasturing of livestock. Somewhat less critical is potash, or potassium, but in many cases small amounts are added to improve fertility. Calcium, represented by lime, is less critical, but it is often deficient in humid regions. It requires quite a bit of persuasion to convince farmers who live on soils underlain by limestone that their soils need lime. To the farmer who sees solid limestone a few inches below his soil, it seems a bit strange that the topsoil is deficient in lime, but such indeed is the case. The fact is that heavy rains dissolve lime and remove it from the topsoil. At the present time tremendous amounts of lime are added to soils in various parts of the world.

Soil usually contains small quantities of numerous chemical elements (commonly called trace elements, rare elements, or minor elements) which are necessary in small amounts for the growth of plants and for the health of the animals that feed on the plants. In addition to the minerals mentioned above, it is generally agreed that small amounts of the following elements are needed in the form of suitable compounds: carbon, nitrogen, oxygen, magnesium, sulfur, iodine, iron, manganese, copper, zinc, and cobalt. In most cases only a few parts per million of these elements are needed, but a deficiency of any of these elements is likely to cause a very specific reaction, either on plants or on animal life. It is well known that a deficiency of iodine is associated with human goiter. It is less well known that where copper and iron are deficient in the soil cattle growth is not normal. In New Zealand low cobalt content results in the bush sickness of sheep. Fortunately, it is frequently easy to add minerals to the diet of livestock (usually by using salt blocks).

Another group of elements often found in soils may become toxic, even at very low concentrations: aluminum, arsenic, barium, chromium, fluorine, lead, selenium, and thal-

Fig. 10.5. Strip cropping in Texas. Alternate strips of row crops and grass, laid out along the contour lines, help to prevent erosion.

lium. Some of these elements tend to accumulate in the tissues of plants and animals; plants usually have a high tolerance for them, but the animals eating the plants may not. In certain parts of the Great Plains selenium salts (metallic selenium is used in photoelectric cells) tend to accumulate in the grasses in much greater concentrations than in the soils, and the livestock feeding on the grasses suffer severely.

Another factor in soil fertility is humus. Humus is partially decayed organic matter which is derived from the vegetation growing on and in the soil. Humus has two main functions: it is a plant food in itself; it also adds weak acids to the water which percolates into the soil from rainfall, thus making possible the more effective solution of the rocks. Although the importance of humus has led to the assumption that black soils are always fertile, such is not the case. In some instances the black color of the soil is derived from the nature of the rock material and not from the supply of humus. Furthermore, humus content alone is not a satisfactory indicator of fertility.

Bacterial content and foreign material in the soil are also important for fertility. The function of bacteria is to bring about physical and chemical changes in the soil: one effect of bacteria is to break down very complicated chemical compounds of an organic nature; another effect is to furnish nitrogen for plant growth. However, there are some bacteria in the soil which are harmful and which must be eliminated in order to improve fertility. Also found in the soil are various organisms, including worms, algae, and many kinds of fungi. Altogether, the soil is a very complicated substance composed of chemical, organic, and a great many insoluble materials of various sizes and textures. These materials are tied together in numerous kinds of structures—some soils are very loose and friable, while others are so hard that they can scarcely be crushed with the fingers.

Soil Types

The major soil types, which are discussed here only briefly, include: the soils of the humid tropical lands and savannas; the soils of the humid mild-winter lands; the soils of the humid cold-winter lands; the soils of the dry lands; and the soils of the tundra, including the frozen soils. It is obvious that these are very broad classifications which must be subdivided if any detailed studies are to be made. The great variety of soils is based upon varying conditions of rainfall, temperature, natural vegetation, slope, and, to some extent, parent material.

The Soils of the Humid Tropical Lands and Savannas. The soils of the humid tropical lands have long attracted the attention of soil scientists, partly because of their inherent qualities and partly because of the potentialities of the humid tropical regions for human settlement. For several centuries certain parts of the humid tropical lands have been used for plantation crops. These parts, in general, are the most favored places and are specially adapted to such plantation crops as rubber, rice, sugar cane, bananas, cacao, and coffee. In recent years attention has been called to these tropical areas as possible sites for resettling large numbers of people from the very densely populated areas of southeastern Asia and elsewhere (Fig. 10.6).

The soils of the humid tropical areas have developed under optimum conditions for chemical weathering but have undergone little mechanical weathering. High temperatures and abundant moisture have brought about very deep chemical weathering and, in many instances, soil profiles have a depth of 25 or 30 feet. However, since a very complete leaching, or dissolving-out, of the soluble minerals has been associated with the heavy rainfall and high temperatures of the humid tropical lands, the tropical soils are of low fertility. What remains after this extreme leaching consists mainly of compounds of iron, magnesium, and aluminum—a mass which is almost completely insoluble. In many cases these tropical soils are slightly cemented or indurated and are difficult to cultivate. The soil structure is often porous, and the minerals ordinarily thought of as the fertilizer minerals are present in very small quantities or are completely lacking.

Many people believe that the tropical soils have a high potentiality for fertility and are only awaiting the efforts of energetic people who can work in the humid tropics to produce an abundance of food and other crops. However, according to Robert L. Pendleton, who worked with tropical soils for many years, not more than 5 per cent of these soils can be cultivated satisfactorily without considerable use of mineral fertilizers and other materials. The soils considered to be readily cultivatable are derived from recent volcanic or alluvial deposits which have not had time to weather or leach out as completely as the soils in surrounding areas. The alluvial areas are very subject to flood, however, and are not always suitable places for cultivation. The tropical soils are especially difficult to cultivate over a long period of time if the crop involved leaves the soil exposed to sun and rain for many months after harvesting. Most successful cultivation of the tropical soils involves crops which shade the soil or which themselves grow in the shade of trees. For example, the banana gives continuous shade to the soil all the year around, and coffee is often grown in the shade of larger trees.

Outside of southeastern Asia, which has the most favored areas of tropical soils, most of the agriculture of the humid tropical lands is of a shifting nature and is usually known as shifting-field agriculture or hoe culture. Such an agricultural system is perhaps the most satisfactory use of the soils by primitive peoples or by any peoples who live mainly on a subsistence basis. The system involves the clearing of a small portion of virgin forest, the cultivation of crops favored

Fig. 10.6. Pulling up rice plants from the seed bed for transplanting to rice paddies near Tokyo, Japan.

in the area (such as manioc and bananas), and then the shifting of cultivation after a few years to an entirely new location. Since weeds can still grow and compete with the crops in fields that have been cleared, it is considered easier to clear new fields than to maintain the old fields. Fertilizers are seldom used in the shifting economy of the tropical areas. In some instances attempts have been made by governments to bring modern agriculture into the areas of the tropical soils: experts come in, select the best areas, and direct the farmers in the planting of crops and the use of fertilizers, insecticides, and so on. These attempts have been only partially successful and, in spite of all efforts, fertility has declined.

The descriptions above apply to the tropical areas that have heavy rainfall all year and uniformly high temperatures. On the margins of these tropical areas are the savannas, which have dry seasons at the time of low sun. The savannas are less subject to leaching and are, therefore, much more favorable for cultivation, even though savanna soils are often porous and require irrigation in order to produce good crops, especially in the drier areas. Rice, sugar cane, and wheat are grown extensively on the humid margins of the savannas, and grazing is important in some savanna areas. It should

153

Fig. 10.7. White Dutch clover on clay soil in the Black Belt, Sumter County, Alabama. This field formerly produced cotton.

be noted that the choice of crops is not dictated entirely by the climate and soil; the living habits and preferences of the people are also important.

The Soils of the Humid Mild-Winter Lands. The soils of the humid mild-winter lands differ from those of the tropics in several respects. In the first place, since leaching is moderate, the organic and soluble-mineral content is higher. Also, the topsoil under natural conditions is usually dark chocolate brown, while the *B* horizon is brown, red, or yellow. These soils are cultivated widely in southeastern United States (the Cotton Belt), in western Europe, and in eastern Asia (southern China and Japan). Some of these soils were developed in forested areas; some others in grasslands or prairies.

A description of a few specific localities will serve to illustrate the variety of soil qualities within this soil group and will also suggest the variety of man's use of the soil. In western Europe, where soil science developed early (with great emphasis on the chemical aspect of soils, the use of fertilizers and manures, and careful cultivation), there

has been distinct improvement in the quality of the soil. Notable in this regard is the development of the plains of northwestern Europe, and a very special case is the reclaiming of the salty soils in the lands recovered from the sea in the Netherlands and the building of these soils into a condition of great fertility. On the other hand, much cultivation has taken place in areas where there is a problem of low initial fertility because of low mineral content, as well as a risk of slope wash due to heavy rains, particularly at times when there is no crop or other cover on the land.

In the Cotton Belt of southeastern United States certain areas have been cultivated rather intensively for nearly 200 years. One of these areas is the Black Belt of Alabama (Fig. 10.7), so named because of the dark, almost black color of the soil. This area was originally an area of high fertility with a cover of tall grass and groves of trees, in contrast to the densely forested areas which surrounded it. Like many other fertile areas, it was taken over by plantations very early and was cultivated intensively for the production of cotton and other crops. Soil fertility in the area has declined throughout the years, although in recent years production has been improved by modern methods of cultivation, including the extensive use of fertilizers. Some of the characteristics of the soil in this area are undoubtedly due to the parent material, a chalky limestone, which outcrops in a broad crescent in central Alabama and northeastern Mississippi. Because of the intensive use of this area for plantation agriculture, there is a great concentration of Negro population; some counties have a predominance of Negroes, while in most counties nearly half of the population is Negro. The plantations have given way in many cases to tenant farms, but the cultivation of cotton continues, even though some of the land has been abandoned because of low fertility.

Not all soils developed on limestone are alike. A quite different soil type is repre-

Fig. 10.8. A smooth portion of the Kentucky Blue Grass in Fayette County. Most of the area is in pasture, but there are a few small fields of tobacco and other crops.

sented by the Blue Grass Region of Kentucky (Fig. 10.8). Most people think of this region as a broad, fertile land with very gentle rolling slopes on which thoroughbred horses graze in lush pastures dotted with oak trees for shade, while white wood fences separate the various fields. Such landscapes do exist, particularly in the central part of the region, but the more usual type of land use is the cultivation of tobacco, corn, hay, and other crops. A part of this region has quite steep slopes and, consequently, problems which are in contrast with those faced in the Black Belt of Alabama. The soils of the Blue Grass are derived mostly from impure limestones which are high in phosphate. This high phosphate content, together with the high content of other soluble minerals, makes for the very fertile soil which has stood up under continuous cultivation for nearly 150 years. This record of cultivation is particularly remarkable because tobacco is a very exacting crop which tends to use up soluble minerals rapidly. Also, when tobacco is harvested, the land is

left bare and is subject to erosion by the winter rains. Nevertheless, even in many areas of steep slopes, cultivation has continued without serious loss of fertility for 150 years. It appears that some quality of the soil makes it highly resistant to erosion, even on slopes of up to 30 degrees. This quality of the soil was supplemented by the fact that some of the farmers who came to this region originally had some experience in hillside farming and used various simple methods to control erosion and thus minimize soil losses. In instances where methods of cultivation were not so careful, serious erosion has resulted in the removal of the entire soil profile and the exposure of the bedrock.

The type of soil that exists in the Blue Grass Region exists under different conditions in the Balkan country of Yugoslavia. In Yugoslavia too the underlying rock is limestone, but it is a very pure variety which dissolves readily, with the result that the soluble material (but not the soil) passes away through underground channels. This

Fig. 10.9. A podzol profile and landscape near Antwerp, Belgium. Note the dark layer of vegetation at the top and the leached, ash-colored layer in the A horizon.

region was originally forested, but it was cleared very early to provide lumber for ships and fuel in the days when the Romans ruled the Mediterranean. The cleared land became highly subject to erosion, and eventually nearly all of the surface soil was removed from many areas. However, since the drainage is such that all of the larger streams are underground and the soil washed from the slopes of the depressions accumulates in the low-lying areas, the small lowlands are very fertile, although many of them are too small to support a farm family.

The Soils of the Humid Cold-Winter Lands. The conditions in the humid cold-winter lands differ from those in the humid mild-winter lands: the winters are severe, the soil freezes, there is a snow cover, and there are lesser amounts of precipitation. The soils of the humid cold-winter lands are cultivated very widely in northeastern United States, Canada, northern China, Manchuria, and many parts of northern U.S.S.R. The soils vary in terms of parent material, which includes sedimentary, igneous, and metamorphic rocks, as well as glacial deposits which

are too young to have developed mature soils.

In general, two broad types of soils occur in the humid cold-winter lands: the grey forest soils, associated with broad-leaved deciduous trees; and the podzol soils, associated with pines, spruces, firs, and other varieties of coniferous trees. Both of these soil types tend to be grey in the A horizon and to have various colors in the B horizon, depending on the rainfall and the parent material. The podzols (Fig. 10.9) are especially grey (their name is derived from the Russian word for ashes). Both the grey forest soils and the podzols tend to have a low mineral content and to be acid; they profit by the application of lime and other soluble minerals. Widely cultivated (especially by northern Europeans) for pasture and various root crops, these soils are leached on the surface but are not subject to severe erosion during the winter because of the freezing of the soil and the presence of a snow cover. The frozen soil, though, may be hazardous if a quick thaw in the spring results in the rapid melting of the snow before there is opportunity for the water to soak into the soil. Rapid melting brings about extensive run-off and sometimes severe erosional damage. Throughout the area of the humid cold-winter soils there is wide distribution of dairying and cultivation (particularly in Europe) of small grains, potatoes, sugar beets, and many other crops. Some of these soils are closely associated with the industrial areas of North America and Europe, and the abundant market provided by these industrial cities stimulates agriculture on soils that otherwise probably would not be cultivated.

The Soils of the Dry Lands. In the dry lands, the steppes and deserts, soil conditions are in many cases the reverse of those in humid regions. The rainfall is light or even deficient, and there is very little leaching of the soil. On the other hand, there is an accumulation of soluble materials in the soil

156

which in some cases prohibits agriculture. Two general types of dry-land soils are recognized: the chernozems and the chestnut brown soils. The chernozems occur in areas of moderate rainfall of from 15 to 25 inches. The chestnut brown soils occur in areas where the rainfall is from approximately 5 to 15 inches. The chernozem soils are the "black earth" soils of the U.S.S.R., the subhumid portions of the United States, and the Pampa of Argentina. The dark color of the chernozem soils is due to their high humus content, which is derived from grass roots; these soils are found in grassland areas with a very thick growth of grass. From the standpoint of cultivation, the characteristics of chernozem soil are very favorable: it is a crumbly soil which generally stands up well under long, continuous cultivation because of its high mineral content. However, in the U.S.S.R. almost three centuries of cultivation have brought about a definite decline in fertility. There is a slight decline in fertility in some of the newer lands, such as the chernozem areas of the United States and Argentina (Fig. 10.10). All in all, the chernozem soils are fertile and stand up for many years without the addition of fertilizer. They do suffer, though, from the hazard of drought.

The soils of the deserts and the drier parts of the steppes are generally thinner and lighter in color than the chernozems. One group, called the chestnut brown soils, has a humus zone which is thin and light in color and underlain by a thin leached zone. The zone of accumulation, or calcium layer, is close to the surface and is usually from one to three feet in thickness. Chestnut brown soils occur in the drier parts of steppes, including the Great Plains, the Dry Pampa Region of Argentina, the Sudan of Africa, and the Caspian Sea-Lake Balkhash Region of the U.S.S.R. The rainfall of these regions, about 5 to 15 inches, is generally too light for agriculture without irrigation, but where water is available cultiva-

Fig. 10.10. Chernozem soil landscape in eastern South Dakota. Corn and wheat are the crops. The climate of the chernozem area can be described as subhumid.

Fig. 10.11. Desert soils are often derived from the weathered material of the adjacent rock masses. Monument Valley, Arizona.

tion is intensive. Because of their high mineral content, these soils must be handled carefully to avoid the accumulation of soluble mineral (alkali) at the surface. In the heart of the desert (Fig. 10.11) the soils are generally only a few inches thick, or they may be entirely missing. In many places the absence of a continuous vegetation cover permits the soil to be removed almost as fast as it is formed. With proper irrigation, however, the desert soils produce well.

The Soils of the Tundra. On the poleward margin of the forest lands are the soils of the tundra, with light rain and snow, low evaporation, and low average temperatures. Decay of vegetable matter is slow, and the surface of the tundra is usually covered with a thick mat of partially decayed leaves and twigs from the ground cover. Underneath this mat is a thin grey layer of leached soil mixed with organic material. Millions of acres of tundra soils are permanently frozen, thawing out only a few inches on the surface during the short summer. Permafrost, as this phenomenon is called, often reaches to a depth of a few hundred feet. Cultivation of the tundra soils is possible for such fast-growing plants as white potatoes, cabbages, and carrots; long hours of sunshine offset in part the shortness of the summers. Most of the tundra areas are used for pastures, furnishing forage for such browsing animals as reindeer, caribou, and moose.

The above descriptions of soil types are much too brief to do more than suggest the variety of soils used by man. Even within one type, soil qualities may vary widely. Climate does not differ appreciably between adjacent farms, but rock type, slope steepness, slope length, vegetation cover, and human factors may be quite different. Climate is the best basis for soil classification where brevity is necessary, but it covers only one phase of the soil complex.

Some Problems of Soils and Men

Enough has been said to show the great variety of soils. Perhaps the fundamental soil problem is this diversity and the necessity for man to modify it and adjust to it. Many mistakes have been made in soil use by assuming that procedures found successful in one region can be applied to another. Certainly, the individual farmer's lack of knowledge of specific soil qualities has resulted in the misuse of soils; however, even if every farmer in the world understood the qualities of his soil, social and economic pressures would probably prevent his putting his knowledge into practice. "Keeping up with the Joneses" often necessitates purchasing a new automobile instead of cutting down the acreage of row crops, or buying a new television set instead of seed for a cover crop.

Proper soil use has been hampered by the idea current in some countries, including the United States, that every man has the right to do as he pleases with his land (whether it is his "in fee simple" or only temporarily in his charge as a tenant or renter). This idea was accepted in pioneer days in the United States when good land was abundant, but it did result—and still results—in the settlement of poor land not at all suited to continued cultivation. In the United States settlers took up homesteads in the Great Plains, and the topsoil took flight as soon as it was plowed. Settlers in hill lands, especially the southern Appalachians, cultivated steep slopes from which the soil promptly washed into the nearest valley. Some modern farm owners look upon the land as a means by which to make a quick profit and get out; others are resigned to living poorly on a farm which has been in the family for several generations. On the other hand, millions of well-tended farms bear witness to pride of ownership. Why do some farmers give the soil loving care while others are indifferent to its maintenance? It would be easy to say that the good farmers are on good soils and the bad farmers are on poor soils, but such is not always the case. Good farms and poor farms often exist side by side on the same kind of soil. Good farmers, those who love the soil and intend to make their permanent home on it, do tend to seek out the better soils, but their search is made difficult by the fact that most of the good land has been occupied.

Ownership encourages good farm practices and tenancy often does not. More than one third of the farms of the United States are operated by tenants, most of whom are under pressure to produce as much of a cash crop as possible on a small amount of land. The result of such pressure is rapid soil depletion. Even more detrimental, perhaps, is the fact that most tenants move from farm to farm and, therefore, have little incentive to improve the land. Where land is high in price, it is often more profitable to be a tenant than an owner, especially if as an owner the farmer is saddled with a heavy mortgage.

The practice of granting governmental subsidies to farmers has not always improved the soils, especially on distressed land that is plagued by recurring floods or drought or on land where the soils are inherently poor. The effect of crop loans, seed loans, direct relief, work relief, and various rehabilitation schemes has often been to keep people on land which should never have been used for farming.

The Balance Sheet

Day by day, partly because of accelerated soil erosion and rapid population growth, we have less and less good soil under our feet to support us. Accelerated soil erosion and the resulting disturbance of vegetation probably represent the greatest impact man has made on the earth. However, that both man and nature have enormous powers of rehabilitation, especially if they work together, is illustrated by the fact that many soils yield twice as much today as they did a generation ago, thanks to better seeds, fertilizers, and improved methods of cultivation. The exploding population of the earth presents a hazard even more serious than soil erosion. The improved techniques of agriculture are keeping up with population in a few countries; in some there is an even race; in others the techniques are falling behind. Where peoples are living on a bare subsistence level, a built-in balancing mechanism is provided—a higher death rate slows down the population increase.

Some students of population and resources are optimistic about the future, believing that the Nuclear Age will somehow provide us with everything we need without depending on soil and climate. Perhaps it will, but probably not in the next few generations. In the meantime one can take either an optimistic or a pessimistic view of the balance sheet between soils and population. As is often the case, the most tenable view is probably somewhere between the extreme views.

Part IV

MAN'S USE OF THE EARTH
AND THE MARK HE MAKES ON IT

CHAPTER 11

Living Off the Land:
Fishing, Hunting, and Gathering

The idea of "living off the land" still arouses a deep response in the human family. Many people get a thrill out of shooting a deer or a pheasant, catching a lively sporting fish, gathering blueberries or other fruits or nuts in the forest, or digging clams on the coast. Although primitive hunting, fishing, and gathering support very few people today, several thousand years ago many people lived entirely by these means; the fact that our ancestors lived in this manner has left a deep impress on us, not only on our material culture but also on our habits.

Centuries ago a large part of the earth's surface was occupied by primitive peoples who lived, without benefit of agriculture, on whatever they could pick up from the land. Some were primarily hunters; others were fishers; still others gathered wild fruits, edible roots, and nuts; some practiced a combination of these various methods. The plants and animals that were accessible to primitive groups varied from place to place according to the environment, but all of the primitive groups had some characteristics in common. Although the primitive peoples had, in many cases, a knowledge of plants

that would rival the learning of a modern gardener, they did not sow or cultivate to any extent. Even though they hunted various kinds of wild animals, they did not domesticate any, other than the dog. These primitive peoples usually had some sort of house or shelter; in most cases the shelter was not permanent, but one that could be carried from place to place according to necessity.

The primitive population was sparse in most instances and, although the people hunted and gathered over large areas, many parts of the land were not noticeably modified by their occupation. Early travelers who encountered primitive peoples often concluded with no basis for comparison, that the primitive inhabitants did not change the character of the land. There is some evidence, however, that the effect of their occupation was significant, especially with respect to the natural vegetation. It is clear that the hunting-gathering peoples had the means to alter the landscape. In many parts of the world primitive man learned the use of fire very early, perhaps from the natural blazes set by lightning. Another possible source of fires was the eruption of a volcano. In modern times a forest fire set by hot ash or lava often burns many miles from the origin; there is reason to believe that such fires were common in prehistoric times also. A variety of tools, including knives and axes, were in use for cutting and pounding; these, as well as bows, arrows, and spears, were also used for killing animals. Small trees were felled, perhaps with the aid of fire, for the construction of shelters; clearings were established and trails marked out. An unconscious scatterer of seeds, man, together with the birds, was no doubt responsible for the accidental transplanting of many living plants. The occupation of the earth by primitive peoples was not intensive and took place over many thousands of years (whereas only a few centuries were required for modern man to spread over the earth). Although the effect of the prehistoric peoples on the land was significant, it was slight compared with the changes which took place in man himself. Nature has often erased the mark left by man on the land and has restored the landscape to nearly its original condition, but the changes in man have been cumulative and have endured to the present day.

The hunting-gathering peoples learned to eat a great variety of foods. The use of fire for cooking made it possible for them to use materials which would otherwise have been either completely or nearly inedible. Acorns, for example, a common source of food for primitive peoples, were scarcely edible until they were steeped in hot water to remove the excess acid. Driven sometimes by famine and other times by curiosity, primitive peoples must have tried everything that seemed edible. One can only speculate concerning the failures and the resulting stomach-aches and fatalities, but from this process of trial and error the peoples developed a remarkable knowledge of what plants, animals, and fishes were edible and at which season. The fact that modern man (considered in general) eats almost everything is related, at least in part, to the experiences of primitive man. No other animal consumes such a weird variety of foodstuffs. For instance, the dog, oldest of the domesticated animals, will not eat some of man's foods, perhaps because he cannot digest some of them. Only the pig is a near rival to man in his digestive capacity. Man's omnivorous quality has made it easier for him to occupy much of the earth's surface.

Distribution and Environment

Many thousands of years ago primitive hunters, fishers, and gatherers dominated the inhabited earth, leaving a record of their life in old kitchen middens, shell heaps, and burial grounds; they maintained themselves in forest, grassland, and desert by means of the great variety of animals and plants which they caught or gathered. By A.D. 1500, however, agriculture and herding had spread over much of the land, and the primitive hunters and gatherers occupied somewhat peripheral regions (see Figures 3.6 and 3.7), mostly in the colder and drier climates. Of course, hunting and gathering continued as secondary productive activities in the farming and grazing regions.

By A.D. 1500 in Europe and Asia only the northern fringe, the tundra, and the edge of the taiga were still occupied by hunters and fishermen, and even here the reindeer had been domesticated. In southeast Asia, in the interior of Malaya, Borneo, and Papua, pygmy and pygmoid peoples lived by hunting and gathering (as they have continued to live almost to the present). In Australia, at the time of discovery early in the 17th century, all of the 300,000 natives lived by hunting and gathering; perhaps 50,000 of this group survive there today, but only a few can be classified as primitive hunters.

In North and South America the population at the time of discovery was probably no more than 25 to 30 million people; of these only two or three million were true hunters and gatherers, while the majority practiced agriculture. In North America the Eskimo occupied the arctic fringe; salmon-fishing

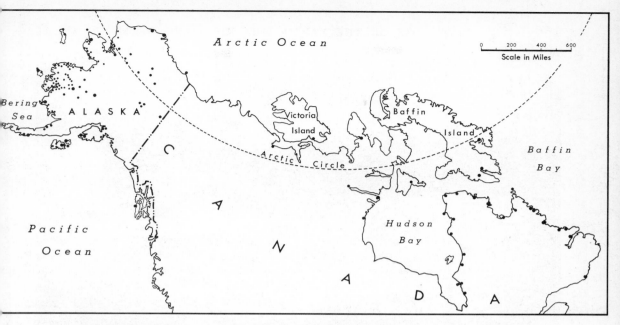

Fig. 11.1. Distribution of the Eskimo. Each dot represents an Eskimo community. (After Sol Tax's map of the distribution of the North American Indians.)

Indians were found along the northern Pacific Coast; and shell fishermen lived farther south. In the interior (especially in the Great Basin and the Great Plains) hunting and gathering were important, but at least some of the people were sedentary agriculturists. With the coming of the horse from Europe via Mexico, some of the sedentary agriculturists became nomadic buffalo hunters. In South America guanaco hunters occupied the southern regions, living mostly on this small wild relative of the llama. In the tropical interior lived some of the most primitive Indians of the continent, hunting with implements of the Stone Age and poisoned arrows and spears. Perhaps they had been forced there by more powerful neighbors.

The interior of Africa was discovered by Europeans much later than North and South America. Most of the natives there were eithers herders or farmers; however, a few primitive hunters and gatherers lived in the tropical interior and in the dry southwestern area, where the pygmoid Bushmen lived by hunting and gathering despite their contact with the pastoral Zulus.

Space permits detailed description of only five primitive groups, each in a different environment: the Eskimo, the salmon-fishing Indians of the northern Pacific Coast, the Semang of Malaya, the Australian aborigines, and the South African Bushmen. The descriptions which follow, based mostly on observations made during the last 100 years, are in the past tense since few (if any) of these peoples live today under primitive conditions. The present tense is used for strictly contemporary descriptions and for reference to natural features which have changed little in the last few thousand years.

Eskimo. For 3000 years the Eskimo people have occupied the arctic fringe of North America from the Bering Sea, west of Alaska, all the way to Greenland. The total area they occupy is well over a million square miles, but much of this territory is barren and is not actually used by the Eskimo at all. The Eskimo live mostly on the margin of the sea, where sea animals provide food and materials for clothing and shelter (Fig. 11.1). In this area the climate is too severe for any kind of agriculture. The

165

Fig. 11.2. A portion of the modern settlement at Pt. Barrow, Alaska. The occurrence of oil in this area has led to the construction of modern frame buildings.

land is treeless with shrubs, grasses, mosses, and lichens; summers are not warm enough or long enough to allow trees to grow.

Prior to the advent of the white man, the use of the environment by the Eskimo varied with the two seasons, summer and winter. In summer the people went inland to hunt, lived in skin tents, and traveled in boats where possible. They hunted caribou and fished in the inland lakes (sometimes through the ice during the early part of the season); they often ate birds' eggs and collected any other edible material. In other words, they lived almost entirely off the land. In the winter the Eskimo lived on the coast (Fig. 11.2) in crude huts or, when traveling, in igloos, sometimes actually on the sea ice several miles from the shore. The winter food consisted principally of the seals that were harpooned when they visited the breathing holes in the ice. Seals, walrus, polar bears, whales, and other animals were also hunted in summer by means of the kayak and harpoon. Fishing was common, particularly fishing which used the method of

gigging (whereby fish attracted by a lure were caught on hooks moving up and down in the water). The Eskimo apparently did not use nets for fishing until the coming of the white man.

The Eskimo developed a remarkable set of implements and a variety of clothing in order to live in the severe winters of the tundra. Clothing was mostly obtained from the skins of such animals as the caribou and the seal, but other animal skins were used also, including that of the polar bear. Clothing was made by the women, who cut skins into appropriate patterns and sewed them together with a needle or an awl and thread made of animal sinews; the work of making and keeping clothing in good repair was the major occupation of the women. For the extreme winter weather the clothing made from caribou skins was the best. Hunters who were out-of-doors for long periods often wore two suits of caribou skin, an outer suit with the hair on the outside and an inner one with the hair on the inside. Lighter clothing made from the short-haired summer coat of the caribou was used in milder weather. In the summer, work clothes were made from the strong and windproof skins of the harbor seal. The usual garments were a tunic coat or parka, which reached just below the top of the thighs, and a long pair of leggings. Footgear included waterproof knee-length boots made of sealskin. Gloves and mittens were worn commonly, and in winter fur socks were worn inside the sealskin boots.

The Eskimo usually lived in semipermanent camps of a few families each. They never had a very strong tribal organization, but some camps may have had as many as 100 people. These camps were not villages in the strict sense of the word, but merely groups of houses. The winter camps were located in the coastal area so that the hunters could go out on the sea ice and harpoon or shoot seals at the same time that they maintained trap lines on land during the season from November to the end of March.

In modern times, of course, the life of the Eskimo has been greatly changed by contact with the white man. For example, the summer tents formerly made of caribou skins are now apt to be manufactured in Seattle and purchased at the trading post. The Eskimo now use a variety of household utensils, and the men have metal knives, scrapers, drills, and other implements with which to make their kayaks and sleds (Fig. 11.3). (Most of the tools used to be of stone, bone, or ivory, and sometimes copper tools

Fig. 11.3. An Eskimo of one of the Diomede Islands using a bow drill. The hacksaw at upper left and the metal vise at the lower right suggest that some modern tools are being used.

Fig. 11.4. Indian netting sockeye salmon from a creek on Attu Island, Alaska.

were used where native copper could be found.) The Eskimo household now has lamps, cooking pots, and wooden tables made from driftwood; the women have skin scrapers, awls, and lacing needles. Many Eskimo now manufacture clothing and trinkets for sale to tourists.

In moving into the difficult environment of the tundra, the Eskimo showed a remarkable adaptive ability. The movement of the Eskimo into the tundra from eastern Asia was probably gradual, but the skill with which clothing, tools, and techniques were made to fit harsh conditions is without parallel. The Eskimo were unable, however, to make any important changes in the environment: since it is difficult or impossible to burn, the tundra vegetation remained substantially intact. Also, although some species of hunted animals (such as the caribou) were greatly reduced in numbers, there is no record of their extermination. Only with the advent of the white man in the last few centuries have significant changes occurred: the introduction of reindeer, fur trapping and gold mining on a commercial basis, salmon canning, and exploration for minerals and oil. These innovations have brought about profound changes in the way of life of the Eskimo—changes to which he has adapted readily, just as he adapted to the original natural conditions of the tundra.

Salmon Fishermen. When white men first appeared on the coast of Oregon, Washington, and British Columbia, the Indians lived by fishing, gathering, and hunting. In general, fishing was most important; the gathering of edible roots, nuts, fruits, and berries was secondary; and hunting was of least importance. In the coastal zone there were many tribes of various cultures, such as the Nootka of Vancouver Island, the Siwash of Puget Sound, and the Chinook of the lower Columbia River. Altogether, this area probably supported about 200,000 people; although the Indians were scattered widely over the whole region, not all of the land was actually occupied by the tribes.

The land in which these Indians lived has a great variety of surface and climate. It is hilly and rugged, and the coast line for the most part is difficult so far as use of the sea is concerned. The climate is mild and rainy along the coast, with an annual rainfall of over 100 inches in many places. The Indians, who lived on the coast in winter, usually migrated inland in summer, at least for short distances, to gather berries and to hunt. In the inland area of the Willamette Valley there were some prairie lands where wild grazing animals were probably quite abundant, whereas in the coastal areas game was scarce. In addition to the larger game animals, ducks, geese, and various other waterfowl were obtained.

The plant food was very plentiful and was widely used. Such common plants as the squaw root, the arrowhead, and the camas root grew widely over the area from British Columbia to California, as did many kinds of berries (including wild huckleberries) and some quantities of nuts and acorns.

The major sources of food, though, were the sea and the rivers. During the salmon run in late summer and early autumn, the Indians caught large quantities of salmon by spearing, netting, and various other devices (Fig. 11.4). They often channeled the narrow or shallow parts of the streams in order to catch the fish, which were preserved by smoking or drying, depending upon the weather and the preference of the individuals concerned. One of the most common methods of preserving salmon was to dry and smoke the fish and then grind it into meal, which was stored in baskets sealed over with fish skins. Fish pemmican, as this meal was called, would keep for several years in a dry, cool location.

To the Indians living along the coast, the sea furnished a great variety of food, especially in the intertidal zone; in this zone at low tide the Indians could gather shellfish of various kinds, especially clams, mussels, and abalone. The sea also furnished seal, sea lions, and occasionally whales (the Indians were quick to take advantage of stranded animals such as whales). Other fish that were taken included the halibut, cod, herring, and candlefish, which last was used largely for the preparation of oil because of its high fat content.

Unlike many primitive hunters, fishers, and gatherers, the Indians of the Pacific Coast had permanent dwellings made of split cedar planks. They also usually constructed temporary houses of mats when they made their short migrations to remote fishing places or to places where they picked berries or gathered food away from their main houses. They had a rather large variety of material possessions, perhaps the most important of which were the large, sea-going dugout canoes made from cedar logs (Fig. 11.5). Many of these canoes were large enough to carry 50 or 60 men, who, sitting two by two and wielding paddles, navigated the marginal seas with a great deal of skill and courage. In addition, the Indians pos-

Fig. 11.5. Dugout canoes are common in various parts of the world. These thin-shelled canoes on the Congo River are used mainly to transport firewood. Note cultivation on the river bank at the right.

sessed various kinds of spears, harpoons, traps, fishhooks, and nets, including dip nets for salmon fishing. Food containers of various kinds made from wood were also very common.

The concentration of salmon fishing in the lower courses of the rivers and in the shallow edge of the ocean permitted the Indians to live in moderately dense population clusters. As a result, their impact on the land was more pronounced than that of the Eskimo. They cut the forest for fuel and building material and sometimes burned it. Their gathering and scattering of roots, berries and acorns brought about noticeable changes in the vegetation pattern. Today, few of the salmon-fishing Indians are left. Those who still fish are likely to do so with outboard motors and modern nets, and their catch probably goes to a nearby cannery.

Australian Aborigines. The Great Australian Desert (Fig. 11.6) is the second largest desert in the world (after the Sahara), occupying well over a million square miles. Like much arctic land, parts of this desert are completely unproductive, even in terms of primitive people. Temperatures in the Great Australian Desert are high most of the year, and the rate of evaporation is also very high, with the result that even where the rainfall appears to be moderate the climate is actually very dry. For example, Alice Springs, in the central part of the Australian Desert, has an altitude of about 1800 feet, an average annual temperature of 68° F., a rainfall of nearly 10 inches, and a potential evaporation of 110 inches; in effect, a severe desert exists. The Australian Desert, like other deserts, varies a great deal in the character of its relief and soils. Part of it is covered with dunes, and a much larger part is covered with rocky materials which are usually known by the general term of hamada. Much of the desert has no streams at all; where rivers or streams do flow occasionally, they flow usually only once in several years. In this environment the Australian aborigines learned to live by hunting and

gathering, and they devised tools and implements of a very primitive character to help them in their way of life.

When Australia was discovered early in the 17th century, it was a museum for the study of primitive men, animals, and plants, most of which had undergone little change for thousands of years. Nine tenths of the plants did not grow elsewhere, and the animals made Australia a land of living fossils. There were 50 kinds of marsupials in Australia, from the kangaroo to the opossum, only one of which was known in other lands. An egg-laying mammal (the platypus) and flightless birds (the emu and the cassowary) were discovered, and koalas played in the eucalyptus trees like animated teddy bears.

The Australian aborigines, cut off from other lands when the sea level rose at the end of the glacial period, at first had an easy time. Game was abundant, and few of the animals were dangerous. Australia, however, like most low-latitude continental interiors, gradually dried up, and living became much more difficult. The population decreased and became concentrated in the northwestern part of the continent, leaving only a few areas of concentration on the more humid east coast. Perhaps the hot, dry interior

Fig. 11.6. Australian desert, distribution of aboriginal reserves.

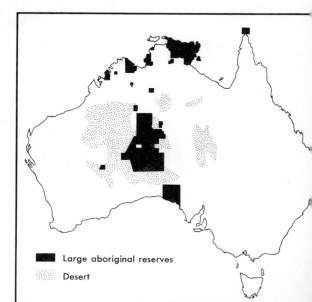

■ Large aboriginal reserves

░ Desert

Fig. 11.7. Australian aborigines dressed up for a corroboree (native celebration). The culture of these Negroid peoples is adapted to life in the desert.

trapped the western people; more likely, their way of life, adapted to the dry lands, made it difficult for them to invade the humid fringe.

The primitive Australians had no agriculture or domestic animals. They had no pottery and no bows and arrows; they did not even have harpoons. In a sense, their culture was as primitive as any found in the Age of Discovery (Fig. 11.7). Their houses, clothing, weapons, tools, and boats were very scantily developed, despite their access to a variety of materials. An unusual development in the evolution of weapons was the boomerang, which grew out of the throwing stick or flat club used by many primitive peoples. Crescent-shaped throwing sticks have been found among primitive people in both Asia and America, but the Australians were the only ones to add a particular bend and give the boomerang its peculiar flight.

Perhaps the Australians developed a proficiency with the boomerang because they lacked other weapons such as the bow.

Today there are fewer than 25,000 primitive Australians (it is estimated that there were 300,000 at the time of discovery). Some of these are still nomadic, living somewhat in the manner of their ancestors; but few have been untouched by white settlement. Thousands are regularly employed on ranches and farms, and many are living in organized camps. The transition from primitive to civilized life was by no means easy. As soon as white settlers arrived, the black men began to die off, exposed as they were to new diseases and new ways of life. Their hunting skills were lost and, in spite of new clothes, shelters, and means of obtaining water, the race dwindled and withered. They had been able to adapt to the slow drying of the land; they were less able to adapt to the cataclysmic changes brought about by white settlement.

South African Bushmen. The Bushmen of South Africa resemble in some ways the Australian aborigines, but have many distinctive characteristics. Their appearance, environment, and ways of living are graphically described by Elizabeth Marshall Thomas in *The Harmless People:*

Physically, the Bushmen are a handsome people, though short of stature—a man being a few inches over and a woman a few inches under five feet—and a little swaybacked of carriage, which makes their bellies stick out. . . . Bushmen have long, slender arms and legs, and the men are built for running, all lean muscle and fine bone, and consequently they often seem younger than they are.

Bushmen dress themselves in the skins of animals, a man wearing only a leather loincloth and a woman a small leather apron and a big kaross, a leather cape made from a whole animal hide, belted at the waist with a sinew cord, knotted at the shoulder, forming a pouch in back where a baby can ride, and where the woman carries her blown ostrich eggs, which are used as water containers.

Culturally and historically, the Bushmen are an interesting people, for they and the Hottentots, who belong to the same racial and language groups, are the earliest human inhabitants still living in southern Africa.

The Bushmen are one of the most primitive peoples living on earth. Although most of their groups own some metal objects, Bushmen do not smelt or forge metal, but get it in trade from their Bantu neighbors. They use soft metal in the making of a few tools such as knives, arrowheads, and little axes, cold-hammering the metal into shape themselves. Bushmen make the other tools they use from wood and bone, grass and fiber, the things of the veld. They dig roots and pick berries to eat because they have no crops. The desert is too dry for anything but desert plants to grow naturally, and Bushmen, who quickly consume all the wild food available in one place, cannot stay anywhere long enough to tend crops or wait for them to grow.[1]

[1] Elizabeth Thomas, *The Harmless People,* pp. 6-9.

Semang. The Semang were primitive hunters and gatherers who lived in the tropical rainforest of the Malay Peninsula inland and at elevations up to a few thousand feet. They were probably much more numerous at one time, but in recent years the population has declined to less than 2000. The Semang lived for a long time in small family groups of a dozen people or so, each group occupying an area of from 15 to 20 square miles and seeking its food from small animals and from edible fruits, nuts, leaves, shoots, roots, and tubers of the rainforest. Visiting a Semang camp one day, Schebesta, an anthropologist, counted 12 different kinds of tubers and roots being prepared and eaten. Some of the plant foods they used contained poison, but the Semang had learned how to remove it. Trees were very important to the Semang. The ipoh tree, for example, supplied poison for blowgun darts, as well as a kind of cloth made from the inner bark. In the Semang economy each person owned one ipoh tree and took a protective interest both in that tree and in several durian trees, which supplied fruits and seeds for food. The owners' visits to the durian trees scattered through the forest were important events. Since small animals, fruits, and nuts were available all year in the rainforest, the Semang had little notion of the preservation and storage of food. They had few storehouses, merely gathering what they needed from day to day and consuming it.

The Semang house was usually constructed with an arched framework that was made by bending small trees or saplings; these bent saplings were held together at the top by a crosspiece which also formed the roof support. Small logs were laid on the ground lengthwise of the hut, and smaller branches or split bamboo were laid across these to form a rude flooring on which sleeping mats could be spread. Fire pits were located at each end of the hut for the purpose of furnishing heat, making a smudge to protect against insects, and cooking. The houses were placed in a crude row or in a small circle in an open space. The open space had no relation to cultivation of plants, but served as a protection against tigers and pests such as leeches. The house furnishings consisted of mats, baskets, and pots. (The pots were usually obtained from other tribes.) Leaves were used for dishes, and gourds and bamboo tubes were used for containing water and also, to a certain extent, for cooking. Bamboo tubes could be filled with food, leaned near the fire, and heated just enough to prevent burning. Rattan with thorns was used (as a grater) in preparing roots and tubers, as were small wooden mortars and pestles obtained from neighboring tribes.

Semang implements were made mostly of wood, split bamboo, and coconut shells. Originally the Semang had no stone tools, but they obtained metal materials from the Malayans once the Malayans had obtained these materials from the Europeans (Fig. 11.8). Bamboo scoops and traps were used by the Semang for fishing until such modern implements as fishing nets were acquired from other peoples.

The weapons of the Semang were originally the bow and arrow; later the blowgun was acquired from a neighboring group of people. Nowadays the Semang are familiar with cotton cloth, rice cultivation, metal implements, and fish nets; their way of life has changed materially by contact with Europeans and other native peoples in Malaya. Originally they had no domesticated plants and thus depended on wild plants; and they had no domesticated animals, with the exception of the dog. They sometimes did catch and tame wild pigs and monkeys to keep as pets, but these animals did not become domesticated in the real sense of the word.

Although hunting was important to the Semang, the gathering of tubers, fruits, nuts, and other edible materials was even more important. The men did the hunting and gathered the edible shellfish and grubs, locusts, snakes, frogs, and small rodents, while

Fig. 11.8. Semang father and son in Upper Perak, Malay Peninsula, using both primitive and modern implements. The father is giving the son a drink by pouring from a teakettle into a bamboo tube.

the women dug for tubers and gathered other edible vegetables. Very little edible material available in the rainforest failed to reach the stomachs of the Semang. Altogether, the Semang, at the time of their discovery by Europeans, represented a fine example of primitive peoples living almost entirely by hunting and gathering in the rainforest—an environment which furnishes a variety of possible foods and also presents many difficulties in terms of disease and other hazards.

The Effect of Primitive People on the Land

In the eyes of the white people who first discovered them, the primitive peoples seemed to be making a very slight impact on the land. However, since the primitive peoples had been occupying the land for thousands of years, it is probable that their total effect on it was rather great.

The greatest change made by the primitive

173

peoples was brought about through the use of fire. It was common practice in many parts of the world to burn the natural vegetation each year, particularly during a dry season when burning was easy. This practice was carried on for various reasons in the Pacific Northwest, in the eastern part of the United States, and, in fact, in all the areas occupied by primitive hunters, gatherers, fishers, and herders. Where grazing animals (such as deer or buffalo) were present, the natives burned the forest in order to improve the grass and thus make the areas more attractive to the game. The effect of this burning over thousands of years was, in many areas, to destroy the forest and replace it with grasslands. The primitive peoples also burned areas in order to facilitate the gathering of nut or root crops. It was easy for the natives to start fires or to spread fires that had been started naturally by lightning; of course, the primitive peoples did little to prevent the spread of forest fires. One effect of fire was to change the nature of the forests. Some trees could withstand fires and some could not; even the forests which we think of as primeval have probably been modified to a considerable extent by the use of fire.

The modification of flora took many forms. Primitive peoples were constantly modifying the plant associations. They girdled and felled trees and cleared the floor of the forest, often removing logs, brush, and undergrowth for fuel purposes. Such small clearings let in sunlight and changed the plant environment. The peoples dug roots in various places, harvested seeds, and carried these materials to their camping sites or their living quarters. Thus materials were shifted or transported, and the plant associations, particularly around home sites, were markedly changed due to the spreading of garbage and other refuse.

There are many well-known instances of the effect of primitive peoples on the distribution of plants. For example, when the sour Seville orange was brought to Florida early in the 16th century by the Spaniards, the Indians obtained a few of the fruits. They unwittingly dispersed the seeds of these oranges, and in a few years orange trees were growing wild around various Indian camping sites along the rivers. In California the buckeye and walnut became associated with Indian camp sites, as did the chinquapin. In various parts of eastern and central United States, edible plants, particularly such tree plants as the wild plum and the crab apple, were found near old Indian camp sites. In the drier parts of Arizona and New Mexico, mesquite trees were found near sites formerly occupied by primitive peoples. The plants which are associated with camp sites are called "camp followers."

Although the effect of primitive peoples on the fauna was also extensive, it was by no means cataclysmic. There is no real evidence that any species of animals was completely destroyed by primitive peoples, perhaps because their methods of catching and hunting wild animals were not conducive to extermination. For every Indian hunter chasing buffalo in the Great Plains there were perhaps hundreds of buffalo (it was only the white hunters who slaughtered buffalo by the thousands), and there was a similar relationship between fish and birds and non-agricultural peoples. There is even evidence that the activities of primitive peoples tended to keep the population of fish and game to a point where the most vigorous animals would survive within the limits of the food supply.

Cultural Differences

A thousand years ago the primitive hunting, fishing, and gathering peoples occupied a very large part of the earth's surface. They lived in various environments, and they had a great many cultural differences. To be sure, they had a great many characteristics in common, particularly their lack of crops and domesticated animals; but their differences were perhaps more striking than their similarities.

Some of the differences can be attributed

to environment. It is no accident that the Indians of the lower Columbia River depended on the salmon or that the Eskimo depended on the seal. It would have been surprising if the Semang had neglected the durian tree or if the Australian aborigines had failed to capture the kangaroo. Primitive peoples, driven by hunger and cold, did not fail to try out any resources of the environment which would contribute to their food, clothing, and shelter.

However, many cultural differences cannot be explained in terms of the environment. That the cultural heritage of peoples may be a much stronger factor than environment is suggested by the fact that significant differences existed between different groups living in similar environments. The Eskimo living on the coast of Alaska developed warm clothing; the Yaghans on the southern tip of South America, also living in a cold climate, wore scarcely any clothing. The Indians east of the Rocky Mountains lived in tepees; those west of the mountains did not, although the same building materials were available to both groups.

In general, cultural differences are to be explained by three factors: independent invention, diffusion by migration, and diffusion by borrowing. A good example of independent invention is the boomerang in Australia. Diffusion by migration is a very simple means of culture dispersal, but it is much less important than diffusion by borrowing. When migrants crossed such great barriers as the Bering Sea and the English Channel, they undoubtedly carried many culture traits to new lands; nevertheless, many great migrations failed to result in significant diffusion. On the other hand, diffusion by borrowing, the transfer of ideas and culture traits from tribe to tribe and from group to group, was constantly going on. Individuals who were transferred from one tribe to an-

other as prisoners or slaves often had a strong influence on the life of their captors. Diffusion by borrowing also commonly occurred through trade. For example, when the English settlers came to the eastern coast of North America, they introduced in trade with the Indians a tomahawk pipe made of iron which presumably could be used as both a weapon in war and a symbol of peace. A few pipes passed from tribe to tribe through trade; and soon the Indians in the remote interior were making tomahawk pipes of stone, since the demand for the iron pipes exceeded the supply.

Certain traits were common to most of the hunting, fishing, and gathering peoples.

A. The distinguishing traits were largely negative:
   1. lack of crops and knowledge of cultivation.
   2. lack of domestic animals, except the dog.
   3. no permanent settlements.
   4. no high population densities.

B. Some traits were positive and were shared with other peoples:
   1. the use of fire.
   2. cooked food and the means of preserving and storing food.
   3. a house or shelter of some kind, fixed or portable.
   4. tools and weapons for a variety of purposes.
   5. language, religion, and some sort of tribal organization.
   6. a good working knowledge of plants, animals and (to some extent) minerals, with many skills in using these materials to supply their needs.

All of these positive traits were involved in the next great advance in human culture, the domestication of plants and animals, a great forward leap which would have been impossible without the contribution of the hunters and gatherers.

CHAPTER **12**

From Weeds to Crops to Livestock

The long, long road from ancient weeds to modern cultivated plants and from wild to domesticated animals leads through many thousands of years and through many obscure lines of dispersal from places of origin. Altogether, more than 300 species of cultivated plants and more than a dozen types of domesticated animals have become important to the economy of the world. Many other plants, including various ornamental trees, shrubs, and flowers, are used casually with little or no alteration. Some plants are important only in very restricted localities, as is *yerba maté* in Paraguay; likewise, some domestic animals have a very limited distribution, as does the yak in Tibet. It should be noted that domestication involves the alteration of plants and animals by selection, hybridization, and other methods. In the early days this domestication and alteration was casual or even accidental, whereas today it is highly organized, scientific, and quite complicated. Although cultivated plants and domesticated animals are often closely associated, it is simpler, at first, to discuss them separately.

Early Domestication of Plants

The cultivation of plants apparently began around the dump heaps of the hunting, gathering, and fishing peoples. In the modern dump heaps around our modern towns and cities, there are often strange weeds which have been brought in by chance from distant places. Particularly around the kitchen middens of primitive fishermen, seeds, roots, and parts of plants that were brought in for food could have rooted, grown, and later suggested cultivation and care. In many cases, to be sure, cultivation did not develop. Thus, although the salmon fishermen of the Pacific Northwest gathered plants and ate various root plants and some seed plants and although some of these plants undoubtedly were accidentally transferred to the dump heaps around their villages, these Pacific Northwest Indians never really became cultivators of plants. Given more time, perhaps, and the stimulus of changing conditions, these Indians might have turned more and more to agriculture.

In general, the domestication of plants marked a great step forward in man's use of the earth. The domestication of plants enabled man to produce much more food from a given area and to insure a supply of food that was steadier than that gained from hunting, gathering, and fishing. In some cases plant domestication also led to greater leisure for the new agriculturists, some of which leisure could be used in collecting, selecting, and improving the plants with which they were already familiar.

A number of conditions were necessary for the domestication of plants. First of all, some form of sedentary life was almost a necessity. Since migratory hunters and gatherers did not have an opportunity to stay very long in one place, they could not become familiar with the local plants and their usefulness for food and other purposes; also they could not follow up the planting from season to season and from year to year in order to develop a successful transplant from a wild species. It is most likely that sedentary fishermen were the first people to domesticate plants. In many parts of the earth where fishing was especially good, it was possible for the people to live most of the year in one locality and develop permanent habitations that were often fairly substantial. Such people modified the local vegetation by burning and clearing, cutting out trails, trampling down the earth, and digging for roots, thus disturbing and cultivating the soil. This situation was most favorable for the domestication of useful plants (Fig. 12.1).

In addition, it was necessary to have a favorable climate so that domestication could be accomplished without danger from excessive frost or drought. In many parts of the world it was easy to convert wild plants to crops, either by seeding or by inserting plant cuttings into the ground. These two types of reproduction, seed reproduction and vegetative reproduction, posed somewhat different problems. It is probable that vegetative reproduction was utilized first by the primitive farmers, who could easily transplant the roots and plants that they brought from the forests by inserting them in the ground or simply by throwing them on dump heaps. Since the primitive farmers would not have had the knowledge to irrigate young plants in the early stages of their growth, adequate rainfall at the time of greatest growth was a necessity.

Another favorable condition for the domestication of plants involved the nature of the wild flora itself. Since some plants are more easily transplanted than others, only a few of the many plants that the primitive farmers tried to transplant grew successfully. This variation in plants became important as domestication proceeded. The primitive

Fig. 12.1. Primitive plow cultivation in southern Mexico. The oxen are yoked to the horns and the single-handled plow is made of wood, except for the point.

farmer must have noticed early that some individual plants produced larger seeds or larger, sweeter fruits and that by simple selection he was able to improve the quality of the plants under cultivation. There must have been a great stimulus to the development of agriculture when the primitive farmer discovered that his cultivated plants were larger and in many ways superior to the wild plants still growing in the forest nearby. The improvement of a plant from season to season was significant, but it was also important for man to be aware of this change. Finally, much later, hybridization and selective breeding were developed, partly through rules of thumb and fortuitous selection.

Homelands of Cultivated Plants

The cultivation of plants began in several places on the earth's surface between 10,-000 and 20,000 years ago. Because of the wide distribution of peoples at that time, it would seem logical to suppose that cultivation developed independently in many parts of the world; the evidence, however, though not complete, suggests the contrary.

177

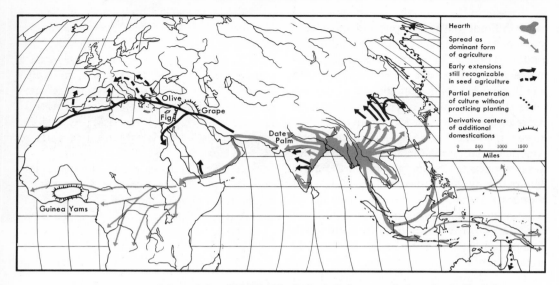

Fig. 12.2. Plant origins of the Old World. (Adapted, by permission, from Carl O. Sauer, *Agricultural Origins and Dispersals*, American Geographical Society.)

The existing evidence indicates that most of the important cultivated plants, as well as the idea of domestication itself, occurred in southeastern Asia (Fig. 12.2). Southeastern Asia, an area including India, Burma, Indochina, southern China, and Indonesia, was a favorable place for the development of domestication. The climate was mild, with little or no freezing; and the rainfall was abundant, particularly during the summer season when most crops grow at a maximum rate. From this area came rice (which was probably first grown in India as a cultivated crop), sugar cane, bananas, yams, breadfruit, and taro. In China (somewhat beyond the limits of southeastern Asia) some varieties of barley and millet originated, as did the peach, the soybean, various varieties of tea, and citrus fruits including the citron. It should be pointed out here, perhaps, that most of the cultivated plants are "sun lovers" in that they thrive under maximum heat conditions in full sunlight rather than in the shade. Of course, a few crops like coffee and cacao grow better in the shade than in the sun, at least in some climates.

Another center of domestication was northeastern Africa, where some forms of such grains as barley, wheat, and millet apparently originated. This region also was the original home of the sorghums, the modern varieties of coffee, and the excellent food and animal feed known as cowpeas.

Some kinds of barley, wheat, and millet originated in southwestern Asia, which is drier than southeastern Asia. A few of the tree crops, such as the apple and the cherry, also had their source here. The grape probably had its start in this area, as did certain varieties of peas and lentils. The Mediterranean region of Europe, of Africa, and possibly of Asia was the original home of the olive and the fig, while in north central Europe rye and oats were developed.

In the New World there were three principal areas of plant domestication: the Andean Region of South America, the plateaus and associated lowlands of Middle America, and the mid-latitude regions of North America (Fig. 12.3). In South America on the high Andean plateau, where a very highly developed civilization existed when the area was discovered by Europeans, a number of crops originated, including the white potato in high altitudes and the sweet potato in lower altitudes. The peanut, the pineapple, manioc (cassava), and cacao were also cultivated. Tobacco (at least the present commercial varieties) probably originated in South America also, although there was another kind of tobacco growing in North America at the time of Columbus. In the higher plateaus of Mexico and Central America a number of crops, some of which were apparently native to the area, were being grown at the time of the European conquest. Perhaps the most important of these crops was maize (corn); although maize was being grown very widely in both North America and South America, its original homeland was on the high plateaus of Middle America. Beans, particularly kidney beans and lima beans, probably originated in these lands, as did squashes, tomatoes, peppers, and avocados. Of course, at the time of European settlement, many of these crops were much more widely cultivated than a map of their homeland location would indicate, and some were being cultivated in environments in which the climates and soils were not at all favorable for high yields.

The only crops that were domesticated in North America, north of Mexico, were the sunflower and the Jerusalem artichoke. Although neither of these crops is now grown commercially to any great extent in North America, each is of some commercial importance in foreign lands: the sunflower is important especially in the U.S.S.R. and the Jerusalem artichoke is important in parts of western Europe.

It is convenient to group the most important crops of the world in a few simple categories similar to those in Table 12.1. Of course, the listings in Table 12.1 are obviously both arbitrary and incomplete. Maize, for example, could be listed as a feed crop as well as a grain, and flax could be listed as an oilseed as well as a fiber crop.

TABLE 12.1

Cultivated Crops

Grains		Root Crops
wheat	millet	white potato
barley	sorghum	sweet potato
oat	rice	yam
rye	maize (corn)	manioc
		beet

Citrus Fruits	Deciduous Fruits	Salad Vegetables
orange	apple	tomato
lemon	pear	avocado
grapefruit	cherry	lettuce
citron	peach	cabbage
		carrot

Fiber Crops	Feed Crops	Oilseeds
cotton	hay	rape
hemp	alfalfa	olive
jute	clover	sesame
abacá	timothy	oil palm
flax		poppy
		sunflower

Miscellaneous

peanut	melon	banana	pea
sugar cane	tea	soybean	tobacco
cacao	coffee	bean	rubber
squash	grape		

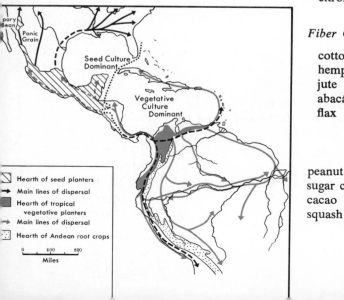

Fig. 12.3. Plant origins of the New World. (Adapted, by permission, from Carl O. Sauer, *Agricultural Origins and Dispersals,* American Geographical Society.)

pary Bean

Panic Grain

Seed Culture Dominant

Vegetative Culture Dominant

Hearth of seed planters
Main lines of dispersal
Hearth of tropical vegetative planters
Main lines of dispersal
Hearth of Andean root crops

0   400   800
Miles

TABLE 12.2

Homeland of Plants

New World	Old World	

North America

sunflower
Jerusalem artichoke

Middle America

maize (corn)
tomato
squash
lima bean
kidney bean
red pepper

South America

white potato
sweet potato
tobacco
manioc (cassava)
peanut
cacao
pineapple
rubber
quinine

Northeastern Africa

coffee
sorghum
barley
wheat
millet
cotton
sesame

Southwestern Asia

wheat (some forms)
barley (some forms)
millet (some forms)
apple
cherry
grape
pea
poppy
melon
flax
hemp

Southeastern Asia

sugar cane
yam
taro
breadfruit
rice
banana

China

citrus fruits
peach
soybean
tea
millet (some forms)
barley (some forms)

Europe

rye
oat

In Table 12.2 some of the most important crops are listed according to their place of origin. The accompanying maps (Fig. 12.2 and 12.3) also show the distribution of these crop origins, as well as the chief areas of crop cultivation at the present time.

Dispersion and Present Status of Cultivated Plants

Many of the crops listed in Tables 12.1 and 12.2 have reached their greatest commercial importance outside their homelands. Coffee originated in Ethiopia, but most of it is grown in Brazil. Rubber and quinine are natives of South America; as cultivated plants, they thrive in southeastern Asia. Maize originated in Middle America, but it grows better and in much larger quantities in eastern United States, Argentina, and

Hungary. Certain varieties of bananas are much more important in Middle America and central Africa than they are in their homeland, southeastern Asia.

The shift from homeland to commercial region is no accident. In many instances a new area of cultivation offers more favorable conditions for a crop than its homeland does. The hot, humid summers of Iowa are certainly more favorable for the growth of maize than the cool, semiarid plateaus of Middle America. Also, in the homeland where a crop was first domesticated, it is often beset with a great number of pests and diseases, each of which has a peculiar ability to feast on this particular plant. In the newer areas of cultivation the environment is frequently unfavorable for most of these parasites.

The region in which a cultivated crop

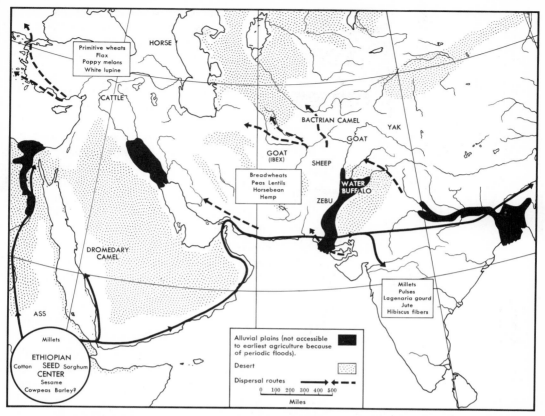

Fig. 12.4. Origin of seed plants and domesticated animals in southwestern Asia and northeastern Africa. (Adapted, by permission, from Carl O. Sauer, *Agricultural Origins and Dispersals*, American Geographical Society.)

ultimately reaches its greatest importance depends on a number of complex and related factors. A favorable environment is important, of course, but not necessarily an environment exactly like that of the plant's homeland. A need for the crop must be felt, either for local consumption or for sale. The habits and the cultural heritage of a people suggest the extent to which a crop is cultivated in a given area. Tea could be grown in large quantities in southeastern United States, but most Americans prefer to drink coffee. Even if Americans did prefer tea, the high labor cost of growing and processing the tea would make it difficult for a tea farmer in the United States to compete

with those of India, Pakistan, and Ceylon. In tracing briefly the domestication, alteration, and migration of some of the cultivated plants, it becomes evident that many factors, both natural and cultural, are involved.

The Grains. Wheat, barley, rye, maize, sorghum, millet, oats, and rice have each played an important role in the life of man (Fig. 12.4). Each grain has its own optimum environment and its own special uses. Wheat makes the best bread; rice keeps the best in hot, humid lands; barley makes the best beer and ale; and oats will mature in the northern areas, such as Scotland, where most other small grains will not. The development of special varieties has enabled the various

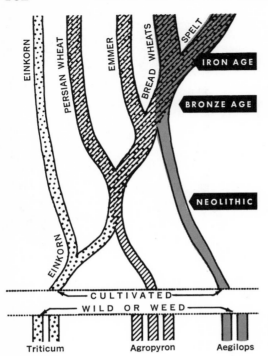

Fig. 12.5. Family tree of the wheats. (From Edgar Anderson.)

The modern bread wheats, of which there are many varieties, probably originated in Kashmir, Turkestan, and Ethiopia. Wheat is the bread grain par excellence. Breads made from other substances—rye, barley, maize, potato, or cassava—are generally considered inferior and are produced only in regions where, for reasons of climate or soil, good bread wheats are difficult to grow. (This is not to say, of course, that everyone prefers wheat bread.) Anderson's diagram (Fig. 12.5) shows the ancestry of the bread wheats and indicates that the relation of the wild weeds to the cultivated varieties is not yet entirely clear. The bread wheats have been improved slowly over the centuries by selection and crossbreeding designed to increase yield, develop certain qualities (such as high gluten content), and increase resistance to disease. Macaroni wheats have been developed for the manufacture of macaroni, spaghetti, and other pastes.

Barley is probably the oldest of the cultivated grains of any importance today. From centers of dispersion in Ethiopia, Tibet, and Nepal, cultivated barley moved westward and became probably the first grain to be grown in the Mediterranean lands. Barley does not make a good bread and is consumed mostly in the form of porridge, soups, and such malt beverages as beer and ale. Most people have eaten barley in some form, since it is common in many prepared and canned soups.

Oats also originated in the old lands and are now dispersed in many wild varieties in different parts of the world. Oats were probably derived from some wild, weed-like crop that was first discovered in the fields of the ancient varieties of wheat.

Rye is one of the newest of the grain crops to be developed on a large scale. Probably a weed in the grain fields of southwestern Asia, it was developed into a commercial crop in central and northern Europe. Rye has the advantage of producing a fairly good crop under temperature and moisture conditions that would decrease the yields of wheat and other grains. Rye flour is used in

grains to grow in many different environments. The large grains, with the exception of maize, play relatively minor roles.

In Neolithic times the hybrid of a weed and a variety of quack grass yielded Emmer wheat, which was once widely cultivated in central Europe and Egypt. A bearded, flat-eared variety, it is grown today, mostly for cattle feed, in only a few out-of-the-way places. Einkorn (one grain), also an ancient variety of wheat, is still cultivated in southwestern Asia and Morocco.

Wheat is grown today in many lands and in a variety of climates. It grows near the Equator at high altitudes; it grows far to the north near the fringe of agriculture; it is a second (winter) crop in many rice-growing regions. Most of the world's wheat is grown today in the middle latitudes, between 30 and 55 degrees north and between 25 and 40 degrees south, where rainfall is from 12 to 45 inches. Canada, the United States, Argentina, the U.S.S.R., India, and Australia are the largest surplus producers.

breads in various parts of the world, particularly in central and northern Europe.

Rice, one of the oldest crops grown by man, originated in southeastern Asia, probably in India (there are widespread weeds in this area which resemble rice). Rice grows in wild varieties in various parts of the world; it also grows in cultivated varieties, including large-kernelled forms, small-kernelled forms, and glutenous forms. Some varieties are adapted to marshy lands, while some thrive in upland or hillside cultivation. The best environment for rice is the tropical savanna, where high temperatures and heavy summer rains are followed by a dry season during which the grain may ripen. Since much of the rice crop is irrigated, it is desirable to have a tight subsoil to conserve water (Fig. 12.6).

All parts of the rice plant are used: the straw is twisted into rope or woven into a variety of useful articles; even the husk and the sheaves are used in the rice mills for fuel. Much of the rice consumed today is milled in a process which removes the outer husk and some or all of the bran. This milling process improves the keeping qualities of the grain, but it also removes most of the vitamins unless the rice is first boiled to drive the vitamins into the kernel. A diet which consists largely of milled rice may lead to the deficiency disease known as beriberi.

The first cultivation of upland rice probably involved clearing the land by fire and scattering the seeds in the ashes. The development of the plow made a profound change in the method of cultivation, as did the introduction of irrigation. The first plows were probably drawn by women; later, draft animals, such as cattle, water buffalo, and horses, were introduced. Of these draft animals, the water buffalo proved to be the most efficient for plowing the flooded paddies.

Maize (Indian corn), the *grain sorghums* (such as kafir corn), and the *millets* are used for both food and feed. Of these grains, maize is the most important today. In North America the Indians were growing maize

Fig. 12.6. A four-horsepower diesel rototiller in a rice paddy, Toyama Prefecture, central Japan.

widely when the first Spaniards arrived. The colonists took over its cultivation, and it was soon introduced to the Old World and adapted to many varieties of climate and cultivation methods. Since the natives in the New World had little livestock, they used maize primarily as a food; however, when the settlers from Europe discovered that it was a good fattening feed for cattle, they increased its production enormously. Maize requires more rainfall than wheat, needs a longer growing season, and is more sensitive to frost. However, in the lands of long, warm summers and adequate rainfall, the yields of maize are very high, and the dollar value of an acre of maize is greater than the value of an acre of wheat (Fig. 12.7).

The manner of using maize varies in the different parts of the world where it is cultivated. In the northern lands it is grown for fodder only, since the grain will not mature. In the middle latitudes, where it is used chiefly for livestock feed, the emphasis is on large ears of full grains; in these areas maize is fed to the animals either in the ear or shelled. Sometimes the animals are allowed to harvest the maize in the field. As a human food, maize is often consumed in corn bread made from coarse meal or is eaten as a vege-

Fig. 12.7. An experimental maize field in Chile. In many parts of Latin America maize is grown under unfavorable conditions. Efforts are being made to improve the crop by seed selection and improved methods of tillage.

table. In Mexico maize is soaked in lime water and then mashed into a paste which is patted into thin cakes and cooked as *tortillas* (unleavened little cakes). Maize flour is sometimes used in small quantities in wheat bread, but it is not a satisfactory substitute for wheat flour. Maize meal is eaten in the form of mush or porridge, and maize is used in the manufacture of starch, alcohol, and vegetable oil. The maize grains can also be parched or roasted, and a special variety can be popped. Altogether, maize is a very valuable and versatile crop; if a satisfactory bread could be made from it, maize might be used even more widely for food.

The sorghums and the millets, species of grass with many characteristics in common, have been cultivated since prehistoric times in Egypt, Ethiopia, and Arabia. As the culti-

vation of these grains spread to other parts of Africa and Asia and, lately, to America, a number of varieties and uses appeared. The grain sorghums and the millets are grown for the seed in the head of the plant. The great Indian millet is an important food crop in India, where it is known as *jowar*. A similar variety of millet feeds millions in the Sudan region of Africa. Today the grain sorghums and the millets are grown for food in many areas where rice will not yield well, including northern China and Manchuria. The sweet sorghums are grown for their sap, which is used to make molasses in lands where sugar cane will not grow well. Millets and sorghums are also used widely as forage crops or fodder. Some sorghums have been selected for cultivation in the semiarid regions of Asia, Africa, and the Americas; still another sorghum produces a long, stiff straw which has been used for centuries in making brooms and is, therefore, called broom corn.

In summary it may be stated that most seed crops appear to have originated in the Old World (Fig. 12.4). Three principal centers of origin may be recognized: Ethiopia, whence came some of the millets and the sorghums, cotton, sesame, and coffee; Persia (Iran), which produced the primitive wheats, the poppy, the melon, and flax; and north-western India, which cultivated the bread wheats and hemp. It is by no means certain that these areas served as the original homes for the crops mentioned, but they undoubtedly were places of important early development. Likewise, the New World was an area of early development for maize and some of the beans.

The Root Crops. When South and Central America were discovered, the root crops— the white potato, sweet potato, cassava, beet, peanut, and many others—were probably of more importance than the seed crops. Once early man became familiar with the food value of a root, it was an easy matter for him to transplant it and protect it. Of course, the harvesting of the root crops required digging, while the seed crops were easily seen and harvested.

The *white potato,* grown widely in the temperate belts and at high altitudes in the tropical latitudes, is one of the most interesting of the root crops. Several species of potato were being cultivated in the highlands of Mexico, Central America, and South America (as far south as the Chilean Andes) when the first Europeans came to the New World. The white potato was transplanted to Europe early in the Age of Discovery and was cultivated in Ireland, hence the name Irish potato; but it became an even more important crop in Germany, Poland, and the U.S.S.R., where it serves mainly as a feed crop for livestock but is also used for food and as a source of starch and alcohol.

The *sweet potato* also originated in the New World (specifically South America) and spread from there as far as New Zealand in very early times. In the Philippines the sweet potato is called by the Mexican name of *batata* or *camote.*

The *yam,* which resembles the sweet potato in appearance, originated in southeastern Asia. More starchy than the sweet potato and with a lower sugar content, the yam grows widely in tropical and subtropical lands, especially India and China. It was commonly cultivated in Polynesia before the introduction of the sweet potato.

Cassava, also known as manioc or mandioca, is a root crop of great importance from which tapioca is manufactured. The bitter manioc is poisonous, but it can be eaten after suitable grinding, leaching, and squeezing. The roots of the sweet cassava can be sliced, dried, and ground into a meal from which bread can be made. Cassava grows well in the humid tropics, where bread grains give a poor yield; it also is a valuable crop in regions subject to drought, since its long roots enable it to mature when other crops fail.

Although many details of man's conquest of the plant world are unknown today and may never be known, many of the relevant facts are fairly well established. The first cultivation of plants began about 20,000 years ago in and around the homes of sedentary fishing peoples who were also gatherers. Fire was important in clearing the land and cooking plants which would otherwise have been inedible. Once cultivation had been begun, the next step was plant selection, first of the vegetative types and later of the seed types. Diffusion of the improved plants often brought them to more favorable areas for cultivation. By A.D. 1500 the selection of cultivated plants was nearly completed, and few plants have been domesticated in the last 450 years. In the last century great improvements have been made in cultivated plants by the scientific selection and breeding of species already domesticated. Special hybrids of maize, for example, have been tailored to specific parts of the Corn Belt, with the result that yield has been increased as much as 50 per cent. New varieties of grain sorghums have been developed which are suitable for machine harvest. Soybeans with high oil content have been cultivated as an industrial crop. With the main objective of higher yields of better-quality crops, plant breeders select varieties which will resist disease and drought and also mature in a short season. In short, they try to develop plants that are adapted to the local conditions under which they are grown. (Additional material on the dispersion of cultivated plants is found in Chapter 26.)

Origin and Distribution of Domestic Animals

As plants were slowly being domesticated through many centuries, the major domesticated animals were gradually being introduced to the agricultural economy. Such household animals as the dog, cat, pig, chicken, duck, goose, and turkey were probably domesticated by the vegetative agriculturalists. Such herd animals as cattle, the zebu, horse, ass, sheep, goat, camel, llama, carabao (water buffalo), yak, and a few others were introduced by the seed agriculturalists.

It was formerly thought that animals were domesticated by hunters who captured young animals, brought them into hunting camps, and gradually found uses for them. However, it seems more likely, as Sauer suggests, that the principal herd animals could not have been tamed by hunters or by any kind of wandering peoples. Their taming would have required a sedentary group which had both leisure and plenty of food, since hungry people would have eaten the young animals before there was time for them to become domesticated. It should be noted that all herd animals listed above are now milked.

It is probable that the domestication of both household and herd animals came about when agriculturalists, occasionally encountering the young of wild animals, brought them into the home site and added them to the household, either for the purpose of entertainment or for some religious ceremony. It is likely that these young animals were nursed by the women of the household and then cared for by the children, led out to graze, tethered, and thus brought into an adjustment with the household. Undoubtedly, the animals were kept at first more or less as curiosities rather than as sources of food. Gradually, however, as the production of milk became important, there was further domestication and further selection and development of animals in order to find the ones that would furnish the most milk and the ones that could also be used for meat animals, riding animals, or draft animals.

Man's choice of which animals were to be domesticated throws a very interesting light on man's agricultural origins. Many types of wild animals were available to the primitive agriculturalists of the Old World, including various kinds of deer, antelope, gazelle, wild cattle, bison, buffalo, camels, elephants, goats, sheep, horses, and asses. It is significant that the animals which were domesticated were not the easiest to tame. For example, although deer are very easy to tame as household pets (a fact which is illustrated by many modern examples along the margins of settlements), of the deer family only the reindeer became a domestic animal. Cattle, goats, sheep, and horses, which are very difficult to capture and tame, were widely selected for domestication.

Domestic cattle originated from the wild species which ranged from the Atlantic portion of Europe into southern Asia. Among the fiercest and most savage of animals, these cattle in the wild state could easily protect themselves against all predatory animals. There is no evidence that any of these wild cattle were tamed in the adult state; rather, they were taken as very young animals, brought up in the households of the

Fig. 12.8. Two varieties of camels: left, the dromedary from lower Egypt; above, the Bactrian from central Asia. The longer hair of this camel is an advantage in the cold areas of central Asia.

seed agriculturalists, and used first of all for ceremonial purposes.

The ceremonial use of cattle gradually developed into the use of them as draft animals; cattle were probably the first plow animals to be used extensively. For many centuries the use of cattle for milk or for meat purposes was decidedly minor. More recently, in Europe, in East Africa, and then in many other parts of the world, beef has become an important food of man.

The camel was widely used in past times in parts of southwestern Asia and in northern and central Africa. Two varieties of camels were known: the Bactrian, with two humps, and the dromedary, with one hump (Fig. 12.8). Camels were apparently on the verge of extinction as wild animals about the time that they were domesticated. The Bactrian camel and the dromedary camel were probably domesticated separately, since crosses between these animals are sterile.

The horse has been studied perhaps more completely than any other of the domesticated animals. On the basis of fossil remains, it is evident that the horse was widely distributed at the time that the domestication

of animals was taking place. The ancestor of the modern domestic horse was the tarpan.

The horse was probably originally domesticated near the Caucasus Mountains, from which area it gradually moved out into other sections. The horse was particularly associated with the expansion of peoples and their military movements, serving as a means of transportation, an important draft animal for war chariots, and a necessary mount for cavalry units. In some places the horse was endowed with sacred qualities; it was sometimes sacrificed and eaten during festivals. Only after the horse was domesticated completely by the seed agriculturalists was it transferred to the nomadic peoples who lived on the fringe of the agricultural settlements.

Closely associated with the domestication of the horse was the use of the ass or donkey. A great many wild asses and zebras ranged from the southern part of Africa to southwestern and central Asia, but the wild ass of Nubia was very likely the one that was domesticated. The ass was presumably easier to domesticate than the horse and probably was domesticated somewhat earlier. It was

Fig. 12.9. A zebu bull from Agra, India. This breed has been crossed with western cattle to produce an animal more resistant to hot weather.

used very early as a riding animal and as a source of milk, but it did not become an important draft animal.

Goats and sheep probably originated in the western Himalayas or in other nearby mountains. Both goats and sheep were difficult to domesticate because they generally tended to avoid human settlements; but, once domesticated, they became both household and herd animals and were incorporated into the religious life of the early peoples, especially as sacrifices. Goats were particularly well adapted to the dry country of southwestern Asia since they could feed on coarse vegetation, and sheep could also feed and live in areas where cattle and horses would not fare so well. Sheep and goats provided meat and milk for the early peoples, but they were of limited use as pack animals or draft animals. Later, as breeds were improved, the wool of the sheep and the hair of the goat were used to make clothing and tents; as a result, these two animals became very popular and attained a wide distribution.

It may be inferred from the discussion of the development of agriculture and the use of domestic animals that the progress of man, at least in the early days, may be measured not by his use of primitive tools but by his skill in the domestication of plants and animals and by his adaptation of these to his own particular uses. The discoveries and developments of the early, primitive peoples still play a very important role in our lives today.

Recent Developments in Domesticated Plants and Animals

It is significant that few new species of plants and animals have been domesticated in recent centuries; man has been occupied for the last 500 years or more with the improvement of plants and animals previously domesticated. For example, man has continued to improve varieties of wheat so they will resist disease, ripen in a shorter period in marginal lands, and provide a good yield in areas of very low rainfall. In recent years special varieties of hybrid corn have been developed to fit varying environments in the corn-growing regions: some for the drier regions, some for the wetter; some for the cooler regions, some for the hotter. As a result, productivity has increased by as much as 50 per cent without improvements in soil, fertilizer, or tillage. Many new varieties of other plants have been introduced, and man has continued to improve different strains to meet the demands and conditions of modern life. Likewise, domestic animals have been selected and, by careful breeding, greatly improved. Some specialized dairy cattle (Jerseys, for example) have been bred for very high butterfat content of milk; others have been bred for a large volume of milk production. Special kinds of beef cattle have been bred, some of which can survive in tropical lands that are not ordinarily very favorable for cattle. An example of such breeding is the crossing of European cattle with the zebu of southeast Asia (Fig. 12.9). Many kinds of horses have been developed—specialized race horses, draft horses, and short and quarter horses, for example. Breeds of sheep have been introduced which produce a high quality of wool, meat, or, in certain cases, a combination of the two. The list could go on and on, especially in the field of plant development.

A little reflection will reveal the tremendous effect that the domestication of plants and animals has had on modern life. Numerous changes have been made in the natural vegetation cover of the earth. The overgrazing of some areas has resulted in the conclusion, probably erroneous, that the climate has become drier, since the long-term effect of overgrazing is not immediately apparent. The forests have been cleared, natural grasslands modified, and brushlands burned to provide more land for crops and livestock. As population pressure has increased, hunters and gatherers have been pushed into very remote localities and have become of minor importance.

The very form of agricultural settlements suggests the importance of domestic plants and animals; central in any agricultural settlement are such structures as barns for the storage of grain, hay, and tobacco and animal shelters, from hog houses to dairy barns. In the many places where game animals have been protected and preserved for the continued satisfaction of man's hunting instinct, the management of man is very clear. Even these wild herds of deer, elk, buffalo, and other animals are domesticated in the sense that they are guarded, protected by the limiting quotas set on hunters, and in other ways looked after very carefully by government or private agencies.

Diversification of Farms

By A.D. 1500 man had acquired a great variety of domesticated plants and animals. These plants and animals were living in many different environments and man himself was differentiated into many tribes and nations. In addition to the various crops and livestock, man had acquired a variety of tools and implements that were simple compared to the large machines used today but quite effective in the agricultural production of the time. In A.D. 1500 man had hoes, plows, digging sticks, axes, and many other implements which aided him in his efforts to produce a living from his environment. With this complex of crops, livestock, and tools, many peoples have toiled in different parts of the earth and have developed many ways of living, from nomadic herding to dairy farming, from hoe culture to machine culture, from the small subsistence farm to the huge commercial plantation.

CHAPTER **13**

The Alteration of Grasslands and Forests

After a brief consideration of the domestication of animals and the development of various crops, it is appropriate to examine another aspect of man's occupation of the earth—the changes he has made in the grasslands and forests. In many ways these changes have been incidental to man's occupation of the earth and have been so slow that people have often been unaware of their significance.

There are two distinct phases or aspects of man's alteration of the earth: the extensive and the intensive. Extensive alteration is often peripheral and may come about through temporary or partial occupation during which large portions of the natural vegetation suffer little change. Extensive changes have been brought about by grazing or browsing animals, by the selective cutting of certain forest trees, and by "patch" cultivation. However, the time factor is important: if even partial occupation is continued long enough, there may be lasting changes. If bison, for example, invade a forest periodically and continuously for a century, browsing and trampling the young shoots so that young trees cannot grow, in the end the forest may be destroyed. Also, if shifting "patch" cultivation is practiced long enough for each plot to be cleared several times, the natural vegetation may be completely changed.

Intensive occupation, on the other hand, brings drastic changes almost immediately, especially if plow agriculture is involved. If a forest is completely cleared, with stumps removed and land plowed, the alteration is nearly complete. Even if the field is later abandoned for a time, any wild plants which appear often bear little resemblance to the original vegetation. Intensive occupation has a similar effect on grasslands; once the sod is broken by the plow, change is likely to be marked and long continued.

Fire

Man and nature have collaborated in many ways to alter grasslands and forests. Fire, both of natural origin and man-made, has been of primary significance in the process. Fire has been used by man since very ancient times, and early literature is full of records of primitive peoples' burning and leaving fires to burn. One of the oldest historical records, the *Periplus* of Hanno (5th century B.C.), describes fires in Africa: ". . . by day we saw nothing but woods but by night we saw many fires burning . . . going along four days, we saw by night the land full of flames and in the midst was a lofty fire, greater than the rest and seemed to touch the stars." There is also evidence of man's use of fire in prehistorical times. Deposits in the caves occupied by Peking man indicate that he used fire more than 200,000 years ago, even though he may not have been able to make it himself. The use of fire is one of the main criteria which distinguish

190

Fig. 13.1. A fire in a bluestem grass pasture in Kansas. For many centuries it has been customary to burn grasslands in autumn to remove the dead material and to encourage growth of a new crop.

man from the other primates. (The other criteria include the development of language and the manufacture of tools.)

It is reasonably certain that fires caused by lightning, volcanic activity, and other natural phenomena occurred long before the advent of man. It remained for man to adopt nature's fire, learn to make fire himself, and use it for his own purposes. Ancient or primitive man did not attempt to put out fires set by lightning, nor did he bother to put out his own campfires. It was often an advantage to him to have fires spread, since a closed forest does not have large numbers of game animals. It is known that hundreds of primitive peoples in various parts of the world set fires and encouraged existing fires in order to clear the land, attract game animals (to the new grass which followed), and drive game dur-

ing hunts (Fig. 13.1). Then, just as today, when campfires were fanned by winds in dry weather, great modifications occurred in the natural vegetation.

Primitive man also allowed fires to burn in order to destroy the protective cover of vegetation which might hide enemies. This motive was also often present in the minds of the pioneers of North America, especially where there was danger of Indian attacks. One pioneer noted that it was very common for a traveler to set fires wherever favorable conditions permitted. In drier weather it was easy to ignite bits of brush or leaves and start many fires. Sometimes it was possible from a point of vantage to trace the journey of an individual by the fires that he lighted; the arrival of a neighbor who lived many miles away was often announced several

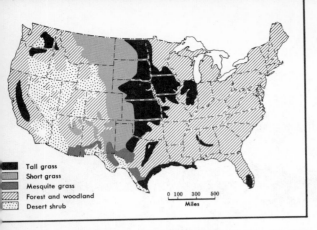

Fig. 13.2. Natural vegetation of the United States, showing the tall grass prairie regions in black. The prairie vegetation is quite distinct from the short grass of the Great Plains and from the forested land to the east.

Tall grass
Short grass
Mesquite grass
Forest and woodland
Desert shrub

0   100   300   500
Miles

hours ahead by the fires he started along the way.

The burning of natural vegetation—forest, brush, and grassland—seems to have been a habit common to both primitive peoples and modern peoples. Altogether, burning has been the most important method of clearing land and changing natural vegetation. In very recent times, perhaps, the bulldozer has been a rival of fire, but in the past as a whole fire has been the most important tool in changing the face of the land.

Modification of the Grasslands

Since the natural grasses are valuable to man only after they have been converted by animals into high-protein foods, the grasslands were first used by hunting peoples; later, the grasslands were used by agricultural and pastoral peoples who did some hunting in the margins of the agricultural areas. In North America the first hunters to record their contact with bison were the pioneers who crossed the Appalachians and moved into Kentucky and Tennessee. The bison occupied the forest, but they grazed mostly in the large clearings which had originally been produced by the Indians' burning of the forest and brush in order to improve game conditions. Since the pioneers had few

domestic animals and lacked sufficient domestic cattle for meat, they killed the bison in large numbers and, in a matter of a few years, drove them out of the grasslands on the forest margins.

As the settlers moved west, they encountered two distinct types of grassland: the humid prairie and the semiarid short-grass country. The prairie was the first of the grasslands to be altered on a large scale, as farms were established in such states as Indiana, Illinois, and Iowa (Fig. 13.2). Although the tough sod of the prairie was initially difficult to plow, such plowing was easier than the clearing of forest land. The settlers were surprised to find that when a field was plowed and then abandoned, it had a succeeding growth which consisted largely of shrubs and small trees rather than grass. Defined as a grassland in a forest climate, the prairie supported forest trees along its stream valleys. Although the principal result of the occupation of the prairie was the replacement of grass with cropland, a further result was the conversion of parts of the prairie into woodland.

Beyond the prairie were the Great Plains, the short-grass country, where buffalo grazed on the grama grass which grew in bunches with bare ground between (Fig. 13.3). That this region was often called the Great American Desert is attributable to the fact that some of the early surveys of the area were made in drought years; in humid years the Great Plains did not resemble a desert. A century or more ago many people thought of all treeless regions as deserts and so called the Great Plains a desert; others thought the presence of grass indicated that it was a more humid region. Those who opposed western settlement for political reasons called the region a desert; those who stood to gain by settlement (railroaders, for example) were sure this region would blossom as soon as settlers moved in. Today the region is a land of ranches, wheat farms, and smaller irrigated areas, but in 1800 it was the domain of bison or American buffalo and Indians.

192

Fig. 13.3. A virgin grassland in the Great Plains near Great Falls, Montana. Although this grassland has been grazed heavily, the land has never been plowed.

The bison migrated with the season, more or less at random, and the Indians followed. As the animals grazed and trampled the earth in great, closely packed herds, they damaged the grass; but in succeeding years they avoided the areas visited in previous years and thus afforded the grass a chance for regrowth. Some of the natural grasses, including buffalo grass and grama grass, were actually improved by moderate grazing and were thus referred to as increasers. Since, in addition, other grasses, mainly those which stood higher above the ground, were decreased by grazing, the whole nature of the grassland was gradually changed. The carrying capacity of the grassland depended on the rainfall, the species of grass concerned, the soil, and, of course, the local and temporary weather conditions. In general, the character of the tall-grass prairie was degraded by intensive grazing. The grasses and other plants which had the highest demands for moisture and growing space were likely to be eliminated by the grazing process, particularly if the grazing was intensive.

There were also profound alterations in the natural animal life of the grasslands. Man made quite a few changes in the grassland animal population, especially among the meat-eating predators which preyed upon the grazing animals. The coyote in the Great Plains was hunted out, poisoned, and otherwise attacked by man because of its despoiling of livestock. As a result, there was an increase in the rodent population, which included rats, gophers, field mice, prairie dogs, jack rabbits, and other animals which were normally the prey of the coyote.

Man also inadvertently introduced animals into grasslands, often with very profound effects. Because there were none of their natural enemies (such as the coyote) in the area, rabbits spread so quickly in the Australian grasslands that they began to eat up all the vegetation, with great losses resulting for the ranchers. Man also unintentionally brought about other changes in vegetation. For example, when he introduced the prickly-pear cactus to Australia, it spread very rapidly, taking over the grassland and making grazing very poor indeed. Great efforts have been made in recent years to combat both the rabbit and the prickly pear in the Australian grazing areas. After much experimentation, a moth was introduced from Texas which has destroyed nearly all the cactus in Australia. The rabbit problem has proved to be more difficult; the construction of thousands of miles of rabbit-proof fences has been only partially effective.

In those grasslands that were humid enough for cultivation, the conversion to crops was much more complete than it was in forest areas. The relatively level, even nature of much grassland made it easy to put almost all of the land into cultivation, whereas much of the forested land was hilly or had valleys with steep local slopes which were not so readily cultivated. The grassland in many parts of the world escaped complete elimination largely because certain areas were set aside by man to remain uncultivated. For instance, the railroad rights of way were fenced to keep the livestock off the tracks. Growing here in essentially their natural condition, the grasses were subject to occasional fires, sometimes fires set by locomotives in the days of steam. Nowadays, working crews periodically burn the vegetation along the rights of way in order to maintain grass where trees and shrubs would otherwise grow.

Modification of the Forests

The modification of the forests of the earth has varied from place to place and from time to time. It will be possible here only to note some of the changes brought about in the mid-latitude and northern coniferous and deciduous forests. In many cases man's exploitation of the forest began with the use of the forest animals. An example of this initial exploitation is the early fur trapping in North America, particularly in northeastern United States and Canada. In the process of trapping beaver, the principal source of furs, the fur trappers made only slight modifications in the forest. Undoubtedly they occasionally set fires, but their chief use of the trees was for birch bark for their canoes and fuel for their campfires. Some modifications were made along the trails, particularly the portage trails between the lakes and streams, but these alterations were minor.

Large-scale alteration of the forest began with the actual use of timber in some quantity. At first the effect of this use was decidedly peripheral. In New England they began to use the forest for ship masts, spars, and shipbuilding timbers in general. The spruce was used for masts and spars, and the birch, particularly the knees of the birch, was used for ship timbers. There was a more complete exploitation of the forest land as the population increased and lumber was used in large quantities for the construction of houses and furniture. The New England forest was a mixture of coniferous and deciduous trees. Some deciduous trees later considered valuable were not used much in the early days; one of the trees neglected in the early days was the sugar maple, which later came to be used both for its syrup and as a furniture wood.

In the coniferous forests of northeastern United States and the adjacent parts of Canada at the time of active lumbering operations more than a century ago, the principal tree was the white pine. The white pine occurred in nearly pure stands and could be cut cheaply in large quantities and readily sawed into lumber and other products. The widespread logging of this tree, however, resulted in permanent change in the vegetation (Fig. 13.4) because the pine did not reseed itself very well when large areas were cut. The successive vegetation was likely to be brush, consisting of quaking aspen, scrub oak, and various shrubs. Later, when large quantities of spruce were cut for pulp in the

Fig. 13.4. Cut-over and burnt-over land near Cadillac, Michigan. The land is now being used for pasture.

more northern forests, other trees growing along with the spruce (such as the balsam) were left standing. This practice resulted in a permanent change in the forest but not in its complete destruction.

Clearing of the Forest for Farms

As man expanded into the forest areas in greater numbers, he caused major changes in the vegetation by clearing land for agriculture. He usually cleared limited areas almost completely, leaving isolated bits of forest to serve as wood lots for fuel supply. Clearing of the forest was selective since certain types of forest were regarded as indicative of certain qualities in the land. For example, the pioneers crossing the Appalachians from Virginia and the Carolinas brought with them a general notion that the most fertile land was indicated by the presence of hardwoods, particularly the black walnut and the white oak. As a result of this belief (which had some truth in it), the large hardwood trees were cut in many places and were destroyed by burning, there being little demand for the lumber in the particular localities. One common method of beginning a clearing was to girdle the trees by cutting through their bark a few feet above the ground, causing their death. Crops could be cultivated among the dead trees since they would have no leaves and, therefore, would cast little shade. Such a clearing is called a deadening (Fig. 13.5).

In recent years the rapid destruction of the forests has been offset by tree farming that is designed to bring about a sustained yield. Tree farming has been going on for several generations of trees in western Europe and Japan, but the practice is just getting under way in the United States. Tree farming may be carried on in various ways: it may include careful planting, pruning,

Fig. 13.5. A "deadening" in the Mark Twain National Forest of Missouri. The trees have been killed by girdling to avoid shade which would interfere with the crops growing beneath.

thinning, and harvesting; it may often be only carefully planned cutting, in conjunction with fire, insect, and rodent control (Fig. 13.6); in other instances it may include seeding, transplanting, and even irrigating. Obviously, the methods used in tree farming must vary with climate, terrain, soil, and species of trees.

The great increase in tree farming in recent years has come none too soon. About half of the world's forests have been cut over; some of the land is now in farms and some is being reforested, but large areas consist of cut-over waste land in which little or no regrowth occurs. It is estimated that there are three billion acres of potential forest land in the world, including tropical forests and inaccessible forests in isolated regions. Tropical forests are so extensive that they seem to offer the greatest resource of usable trees, but many authorities insist that the broadleaf forests of the tropical lands contain only a

Fig. 13.6. Strip logging on forest land in Colorado. This method makes for favorable reseeding conditions and tends to prevent excessive run-off.

small percentage of usable trees and that these are scattered through the tropical swamps and uplands, making logging very expensive except near navigable water. In this century at least, it may be more feasible to grow timber by careful management in the mid-latitudes than to harvest it in the tropics (Fig. 13.7).

Consequences of Man's Alteration of the Land

Man's occupation of the land and the consequent modification or destruction of the natural grasslands and forests have had far-reaching effects, some of which are not completely understood. Man's effect on climate, for example, is a controversial subject. Debate centers around such questions as whether or not the destruction of forests has any measurable effect upon climate. It has been contended that forests increase rainfall and that the destruction of forests decreases rainfall. This contention is difficult to prove, however, and evidence indicates that if rainfall is increased by forests, the amount of increase is probably slight. This question was argued during the middle 1930's with reference to the Dust Bowl in the Great Plains. It was proposed at that time to construct a shelter belt of trees, from the Canadian border to the Mexican border, which would, according to its proponents, increase the rainfall, decrease the dust storms, and have many other beneficial effects. It is true that in forests temperatures vary somewhat from those of adjacent grasslands presumably receiving the same amount of energy or insolation from the sun; it is also true that snow remains on the ground in forests longer than in open lands; but the total effect of such variations is probably not very great. However, in areas of thin soil, where bedrock is at or near the surface, temperatures during the warmest part of the day are notably higher than they are in forests. The result is increased evaporation, a drier environment, and a quite different vegetation pattern.

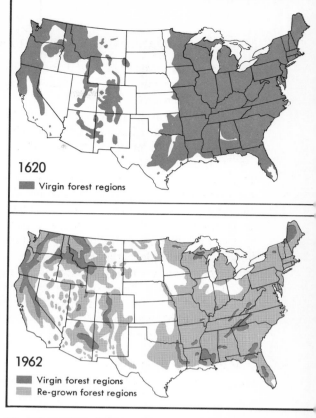

Fig. 13.7. United States forest regions in 1962 compared with those in 1620.

Another effect of vegetational changes concerns the rate of run-off of streams. It is generally conceded that the destruction of natural vegetation, particularly the forests, tends to increase flood hazards. However, it should be pointed out that destructive floods occurred long before any great changes in the vegetation cover were made. For example, the greatest recorded flood in the Willamette Valley of Oregon occurred in 1861 before any substantial settlement had been made in the watershed of the river or any clearing of the forests had been made on a large scale. The flood was probably caused by the combination of unusually heavy rainfall and rapid melting of a heavy snow cover in the adjacent mountains. Undoubtedly, however, when forest cover is removed (particularly when litter on the floor of the forest, including the upper part of the soil, is removed), run-off becomes more rapid. By and large, the flood hazard is increased by the destruction of the forest and the grass-land, but by how much it is increased is very difficult to determine.

The soils themselves are affected by the activities of man and animals. Grazing animals, wild or tame, trample the soil and scar it with trails. The bison actually picked up great quantities of soil in their thick fur and carried it away, producing shallow depressions known as buffalo wallows. (These depressions are visible today in many parts of the Great Plains.) Cattle grazing on steep slopes produce little paths, called cow contours, that modify the soil substantially. In the cut-over forest lands the soil is often disturbed by the very operation of logging; the dragging of logs to the nearest road-way may make permanent gashes in the soil.

Man has changed the face of the earth in many ways. Although his changes have af-fected much more than the grasslands and forests, many of them have been unplanned and even unintentional. Many people consider that it is possible to alter the landscape wisely only in those areas with surplus raw materials or some other kind of surplus wealth. However, even in the richest of lands there is little evidence that man is inclined to alter the landscape wisely until most of the original natural resource has been destroyed. On the other hand, in lands where the pressure of population is great and increasing rapidly, where every scrap of wood and blade of grass is hungrily consumed, conservation measures are indeed difficult to put into practice. Everywhere the resource of grass and forest is changing, occasionally increasing but mostly decreasing. In the end, the criterion of wise change must be: does the change maintain or increase the productivity of the land on a permanent basis?

CHAPTER 14

Houses and Settlements

To many people a house, especially one constructed of brick, stone, or concrete, seems permanent. However, all houses are temporary, only some last longer than others; in some parts of Europe houses over 400 years old are common, while in the United States few houses are more than 100 years old. Structures are constantly being revised as new techniques of building are developed and as houses are expected to perform different functions; as a result, houses, taken together, form a changing but continuing feature of the landscape. Houses are as varied as the peoples and environments with which they are associated. Houses are of all shapes and materials and serve many functions. In the broad sense they include caves, tents, and trailers, as well as the more traditional shelters; they may be either more or less temporary and they may be either fixed or movable.

Houses reflect the nature of a region since their character is related to the environment and to the cultural heritage of the people who build them (Fig. 14.1). Houses reflect the nature of the rock material or the vegetation which is the basis for their construction. They reflect the climate in the protection they offer against cold, wind, or heavy rain.

In a manner of speaking, the house is merely an extension of the cave. Finding shelter in caves, primitive man often extended them, especially the shallow ones, into constructed shelters. In some parts of the world men still live in underground caves, either natural or man-made (Fig. 14.2). One of the most famous examples of such housing is in southern Spain in the town of Guadix, where more than 3000 people live in caves hollowed out in the sides of the cliffs. The material of the cliffs is strong enough to withstand crumbling but easy to excavate with a pick and shovel. A door is made by cutting an opening in a cliff and facing it up with masonry; excavation provides a chimney to carry out the smoke from fires; and the interior is often enlarged, through excavation, to suit the convenience of the dweller.

The major characteristics of houses are form, function, material, and pattern. As varied as the geography of the world, form includes such features as the number of stories in a house, the shape of its roof, and its floor plan. The function of the house, the uses to which it is put, also varies widely. The most simple function of the house is to shelter people from the weather, but the house also has other functions. In some parts of the world the house shelters livestock and feed for livestock; in other words, the barn is built into the house. (Some very elaborate houses in western Europe were built upon this model, although the livestock may now have separate shelters.) Some houses make provision for recreation, storage, cooking, and even for light manufacturing.

The materials used in building houses include almost all of the structural materials available to man. A modern frame house in a new subdivision in the United States, or in

Fig. 14.1. House types: (a) the restoration of a log house used as a store in New Salem, Illinois; the chimney as well as the walls and roof are made of wood; the log house usually had a rectangular pattern and a gabled roof; in some cases two log houses were built some distance apart with a covering roof between them; (b) this tent house in Mongolia is a substantial, permanent installation; the frame and the felt covering are held together by ropes; the stovepipe at the peak is a recent innovation; (c) typical suburban house near Ann Arbor, Michigan; single-story houses with overhanging, low-pitched gable roofs are common; most of these houses are of wood frame construction; (d) trailer houses, either on wheels or mounted on more permanent foundations, provide homes for many thousands of people; many trailerites live in the same location for many years.

one of the housing projects of western Europe, is constructed of a great variety of materials. Concrete, reinforced with steel, has in many cases taken the place of stone as a foundation material. The main part of a house may be of wood, stone, or brick, but it is likely that all of these materials will be used in some part of it. (Even if the frame and the walls of a house are mostly of wood, the chimney will be made of brick or stone.)

Some very important parts of the modern house are made of metal: hardware with which to lock and hinge doors and windows; metal pipe—copper or steel—for the circulation of water; wiring made of copper and other materials. A great many of the labor-saving devices built into houses are also made of metal. Glass plays an increasingly important part in the construction of houses in the modern manner. By and large, however, the materials used most extensively in houses throughout the world are wood, stone, and mud (adobe).

The pattern of houses, their arrangement in groups and their orientation, varies widely in different parts of the world. Some houses, like American farmhouses in many parts of the Middle West, are widely and evenly scattered. On the other hand, houses may be grouped in small clusters, called hamlets, or large clusters, called villages. In villages the arrangement may vary from the long, narrow groupings found in street villages to the very compact groupings found in the agricultural villages of western France.

Wooden Houses

Wooden houses are very common in many parts of the world. Originally most common in forested regions, the wooden house in re-cent years has been enabled, through the development of easy transportation of lumber and logs, to extend far beyond the forested belt. In general, however, the wooden house is most important in northern Europe, particularly in northern U.S.S.R. and the Scandinavian countries, and in North America, especially in Canada and the northern part of the United States; these areas either are in the forest or have ready access to forest products. One of the many kinds of wooden house is the log house, a very early type that is still used. The frame house is a very widespread form that has many varieties, including the modern, functional variety so popular in western Europe and the United States today.

The log house probably had its origin in northern U.S.S.R., Finland, and Scandinavia. It was developed in an area where the trees, growing tall, slender, and straight, could be

Fig. 14.2. The masonry tenements in this view are the outgrowth of cave dwellings at Medenine, Tunisia.

readily cut and notched to form the individual logs of the house. Cut to an even length and notched at each end, the logs were laid up in a square or rectangle to form a log house. The log house was brought to America by the first settlers from northern Europe. Although the native Indians of North America had all the necessary materials, they did not build log houses; instead, they used the materials—the long, slender, straight logs—to construct the conical tepees used in various parts of eastern North America.

The log house has many refinements. In Scandinavia it is common to square logs before they are placed in position, thus reducing to a minimum the crack or chink between individual logs and making a much more pleasing house. It is common in Scandinavia today to paint a log house, just as it is common in the United States to varnish or otherwise decorate the exterior of a log house constructed as a summer cottage on a lake or stream.

The log house survives in many parts of the forested belt of the Northern Hemisphere because it is both traditional and easy to construct. An ax is the only tool that is really needed in the building of a log house, although the more elaborate log houses require additional tools and materials. Both the nature of the log house and its ease of construction are well shown in the traditional barn-raising of eastern North America, a practice still carried on in some remote places. During a barn-raising, neighbors gather at the spot with axes and perhaps a few other tools (including the adze), cut down the nearby trees, trim off the branches, cut them to lengths, and lay up the logs of the house or barn. It is possible for a few men to build a good-sized log house in a day, taking time out for some recreation.

The stockade method is another simple way of building houses from logs. The logs are cut to the desired length and then driven or placed vertically in the ground as close together as possible. Usually they are fastened together at the top to make the structure a little stronger. The stockade method was used in New England in the early days and in other frontier lands in the United States. (The fort at Boonesboro, Kentucky, for example, was constructed in the stockade method.) The stockade method is still commonly used in many other parts of the world. By and large, however, it is easier and usually cheaper to build a satisfactory house of sawn lumber than to build one of logs; a good log house today is something of a luxury.

Frame houses, made largely of wood, are today numerous, and perhaps more widespread, than log houses. The frame house, as the term implies, is essentially a frame of wood; the standard members—the horizontal joists and the vertical studs—are nailed together and braced appropriately to make a strong frame to which the walls, floors, and roof are fastened. The exterior walls usually consist of vertical boards nailed to the frame. The frame house depends upon dimension lumber, boards sawn to specific sizes and lengths: the joists are usually about two inches by eight inches and of various lengths; the studs, also used for bracing, are usually two by four. Unlike the log house, the frame house calls for the use of nails, and it requires a little more skill in construction. The frame house permits a great variety of shapes and floor plans. In its simplest form, the frame house is a rectangular box with either a shed roof (which slopes in one direction) or a gable roof (which slopes in two directions); the ridge of the roof, whether shed or gable, is commonly parallel to the length of the house. Attached to the house there is usually some kind of porch with a roof. There are many variations of the simple frame house: for instance, the ridge of the roof may be parallel to the width of the structure rather than to the length; a room may be added to the house by means of a simple shed roof; the roof may take any one of many forms (a pyramid, for example).

More elaborate frame houses generally

have two stories, rarely three, with a variety of floor plans and roof types. The form of the roof gives more variation to these frame houses than any other characteristic, although differences in the floor plan are also important. A very common plan is the T-shape; another is the L-shape. The frame house lends itself very readily to enlarging and remodeling as a family grows larger or as additional functions are taken on by the house.

The frame house is very common in western Europe. One of the many interesting varieties is the Basque house, in which the asymmetrical gable roof (oriented to the width of the structure rather than the length) shelters both the residence and the barn (Fig. 14.3).

One of the common varieties of frame house in the United States is the bungalow. The bungalow is usually one story high, two rooms wide, and two or more rooms deep; in some cases, dormer windows make part of the attic space usable. Bungalows were built in large numbers during the last 50 years. Somewhat similar to the bungalow and perhaps earlier in origin is the Cape Cod house.

So-called colonial houses of various kinds have been constructed in many areas of the United States. They are usually classified according to roof form or forms of ornamentation such as pillars, columns, doorway carvings, windows, and eaves. The more elaborate form of colonial house may be seen on southern plantations; examples of this form are Mount Vernon, Monticello, and the Hermitage (the home of Andrew Jackson near Nashville, Tennessee).

Particularly during the last 25 years, the so-called modern house has come to be very common. Difficult to define precisely, the modern house usually is designed particularly for functional effectiveness. It is likely to have a simple shed roof rather than a gable roof. It may have an attached or built-in garage and may utilize very large areas of glass, its windows often reaching from the eaves to the floor. The roof is likely to overhang the house frame by several feet in order to provide protection from the sun, particularly on the sides with the largest expanses of glass. In structure, the modern house does not differ fundamentally from some other frame houses. The modern house has had great vogue in western Europe and in many parts of the United States.

Houses of Earth and Stone

In the many parts of the world where there is not enough timber or wood for the construction of houses, people use local materials like mud, sod, and stones of various kinds (Fig. 14.4). The resulting structures have disadvantages as compared to log or frame houses, but they also have some advantages.

A good example of the mud or earth house may be found in lower Egypt, where very few trees are grown and where conditions of life are very different from those of the forested regions. The Egyptian lives out-of-doors most of the time and uses his house only for a shelter at night. His shelter needs to protect him against extreme heat only, not against extreme cold. Since he has very little timber or stone for use, the Egyptian builds his house of mud that has been

Fig. 14.3. A Basque house in southwestern France. The asymmetrical gable is characteristic. The left-hand section of the house is ordinarily used as a barn.

Fig. 14.4. This sod house in Sherman County, Kansas, has door frames and corner posts of wood. The walls and roof are of sod. Such houses were usually constructed in areas where timber was very scarce.

cast in the form of crude bricks and allowed to dry in the sun. Laying the mud bricks, he uses mud for mortar. For a roof, he may make a wood frame from tree branches found along the irrigation ditches, place a network of straw over this wood frame, and then plaster the wood and straw with mud. This kind of house is satisfactory except in periods of heavy rains. The lower Nile rarely has heavy rains, but occasionally a cloudburst or thundershower will completely demolish a mud hut. Although Egyptians build elaborate houses and structures of stone for their dead, very simple and very temporary mud houses are considered to be adequate living quarters. Since stone is available in upper Egypt, houses of stone (often constructed without mortar) are available there. These houses may be roofed with timbers and some sort of thatch material taken from the rushes or reeds that grow along the Nile. Since rains are so rare, however, many Egyptian houses have no roof at all; their walls protect against wind and give shade except at the time of highest sun. Like the houses in upper Egypt, houses in other very dry areas of the earth's surface are sometimes constructed without roofs.

The adobe house of Mexico and southwestern United States is similar fundamentally to the Egyptian mud house. Large, flat bricks are made by forcing mud into molds, allowing it to dry slightly, removing it from the molds in the form of bricks, and stacking the bricks in the sun to dry for a period of several days. Sometimes, straw or some other material is added to the mud for reinforcement. These adobe bricks are easy to lay and make a very satisfactory wall in a dry climate; they are also adequate in a humid climate if sufficiently protected by an exterior coating and an overhanging roof. Adobe houses commonly have roofs of tile or sheet metal supported on a wood frame.

It is an easy transition from the house of mud bricks to the house of stone, provided that satisfactory stone is available. In some areas, only rounded stones are present, and these are hard to use. However, if flat stones or stones that can be split along lines of cleavage are available, construction is easy. Usually soft enough to be worked readily and yet hard enough to resist weathering, limestone and sandstone are perhaps the most satisfactory for construction. (Some varieties of sandstone and limestone, of course, are not satisfactory since they weather quickly and disintegrate.) Since a stone house requires more labor than either a wooden house or a mud house, its use is somewhat restricted. Stone, like brick, is used as facing for frame houses in some places; but since the use of stone requires a great amount of labor, it is relatively expensive, particularly in urban locations where modern labor costs are in effect. Stone has the advantage of greater permanence and great strength, but it has some disadvantages in terms of insulation and earthquake hazards. Stone or masonry buildings of any kind are likely to crack and disintegrate during severe earthquakes, killing many people with falling fragments; frame houses, on the other hand, may suffer some structural damage, but they are not likely to cause much loss of life.

Portable Houses

A special kind of housing is the portable house, represented particularly by trailers of various kinds, houseboats, and prefabricated houses that can be easily knocked down, transported, and set up again. The trailer is a very old institution. In early times the nomads of southwestern Asia had a trailer which was essentially a mud hut constructed with a framework of twigs and set upon a large cart. The nomads could carry this hut with

them on their migrations in search of grass and water. In the U.S.S.R. a century or more ago small portable frame or log houses were constructed in the northern forested regions. These houses were transported by river on barges or flatboats for use in the dry regions of southern U.S.S.R. Phenomena of recent housing, modern house trailers are usually made of steel, aluminum, or plywood and vary in size from small camping trailers to large, three-room trailers that are somewhat difficult to transport, even along modern highways. The increase in the use of trailers in recent years is associated with the migration of labor and also reflects the shortage of housing in general.

Prefabricated houses of metal or plywood came into use in association with wartime industries and military establishments and made it possible to set up elaborate housing areas in a short time. These houses were manufactured in sections, and the units (often consisting of complete walls) were shipped by rail or truck from the factories to the housing sites and quickly assembled. In some cases concrete foundations were laid for the houses; in other cases the houses were set upon concrete blocks or stones. When a wartime industry was closed, the prefabricated houses in the area were often knocked down, transported, and set up again on the margins of cities where the demand for housing exceeded the supply. Prefabricated houses are widely used today.

Another variety of the portable house is the houseboat which is very common in eastern and southeastern Asia and is also frequently found in some areas of the Western Hemisphere. Houseboats are essentially houses of small size which have been constructed upon flatboats so that they can be towed from place to place by some kind of motor power. Some houseboats have built-in motors, and some have facilities for attaching outboard motors. The houseboat usually reflects a shortage of housing or a shortage of land upon which housing can be constructed in densely congested areas.

The house is a very widespread type of shelter which includes everything from railroad roundhouses and airplane hangars to courthouses, office buildings, and air-raid shelters. The houses that have been discussed in this chapter are mostly small houses that are used primarily for residential purposes. Space does not permit more than a mention of such elaborate types of houses as public buildings and skyscrapers. Stone and many other common building materials have definite limitations in terms of very large or very tall buildings. Since the structural strength of stone is not great enough to support a very tall building without steel reinforcement, the modern building, particularly the modern office building or skyscraper, has a basic frame of very strong steel members. The steel frame is covered with either stone, brick, concrete, or some other material.

Settlements: the Grouping of Houses

The term *settlement* has two distinct meanings in geographic literature. It may refer to the colonization of new territories by migrating peoples; or it may refer to the grouping of peoples and houses into hamlets, villages, towns, and cities. It is with the second of these meanings that we are concerned here.

Throughout the world, the degree of dispersion (or scattering) of nonurban houses varies radically. At one extreme are the very compact rural settlements of the Orient, particularly of China and Japan but also of India and Pakistan. These highly nucleated (or grouped) settlements are usually associated with population density and fairly intensive activities, such as irrigation farming. At the other extreme are the widely scattered farmhouses of Middle Western United States, the Argentine Pampa, and many other areas, where each farmer traditionally lives on his own farm and where the farms are sometimes large, each consisting of several sections of land. The distribution of houses, the pattern of settlement, depends upon the size of the holdings of land: if the farms are large, then the houses are far apart. Between these two extremes are areas of western Europe which have both strongly nucleated settlements and highly dispersed settlements. The degree of dispersion in a settlement depends upon the nature of the land, the particular function of the settlement, and the cultural heritage of the people who have formed the settlement. Inertia often causes the form of a settlement to outlast its original function. For example, a settlement shaped by the need for defense may retain its original form long after the need for defense has vanished. Likewise, the traditional Russian street village continues to exist even though communal farms have taken the place of the individual peasant holdings in the U.S.S.R. (A discussion of urban distribution occurs in Chapter 18.)

Any grouping of houses is likely to have a purpose of some kind, whether simply the desire of people to get together or some other reason. Every grouping of houses is likely to have a function beyond that of the individual houses composing it. The grouping may maintain a community ownership of goods (the products of the fields perhaps) or it may serve the purposes of trade. For trading purposes, even the smallest grouping of houses may include a store, perhaps in one of the dwellings of the group.

The grouping of houses into settlements has its origin in population increases and in the diversification of the functions of houses and people as a result of the complication of civilization. Settlements are likely to be located at certain strategic points. The fact that one of the commonest locations is at (or near) the intersection of two or more roads suggests that trade and communication play an important part in the grouping of houses. A settlement may also be located near a supply of a needed commodity, such as water or wood, or at a place where the land is especially rich and productive. Very often a settlement develops at a point where it can take advantage of the introduction of a new form of transportation. A settlement is also likely to be established at the ford of a stream, where eventually there will probably be a bridge or a ferry site.

Since one of the most important functions of the settlement is that of providing a market for both the individuals living in the settlement and those passing by or coming from outlying houses or settlements, every grouping of houses is likely to be along some line of communication—a navigable stream, a trail, or a road. As soon as a settlement develops on a trail, communication and travel become more intense and the travelers who pass by avail themselves of some of the local products. A small hamlet or village which grows up at a crossroads soon has two primitive streets which may develop into a square or a local market; such a settlement may later become the site of a fair and continue to grow until a city develops. Of course, not all settlements develop into cities. Some remain small because of the limitations of the site and the surroundings and because of the competition of other nearby settlements.

Although the functions of each small settlement (whether hamlet or village) are likely to be similar to those of every other small settlement, there is wide variety in the plan or arrangement of houses, the materials and characteristics of houses, and the relationship between the settlement and land forms, drainage forms, and vegetation. The pattern of a settlement is influenced by its site. For example, settlements in narrow valleys tend to have string-town shapes, and settlements on steep slopes are likely to have arrangements of streets and houses which conform to the contours of the slopes. Likewise, a small village in rural Japan is usually oriented to rice paddies, but it may have a very distinct relation to nearby hill slopes. Because good land is at a great premium in Japan, the village is tightly pressed into a very small space, usually in the center or near the center of a basin. Rice paddies, crisscrossed by narrow roads and irrigation ditches, cover the sur-

rounding area of the basin. Adjacent hill slopes, connected by trails to the village, are used for upland rice, tea, and other crops.

In hilly or mountainous land, settlements are often located with respect to the slopes. For example, a hamlet or village may be originally established on a hill top for reasons of defense and then maintained there long after the disappearance of the necessity for defense. Also, the location of a settlement may be dictated by the availability of sunshine. In the deep valleys of the Alps the maximum amount of sunshine is received by a settlement on a south-facing slope; a settlement on the other side of the valley would receive only a few hours of sunshine, even in summer.

Even small differences in terrain may effect substantial differences in settlements. For example, in France there are two broad types of landscape (involving the pattern of vegetation, roads, and houses) known as *bocage* and *campagne*. Although it is generally a wooded, hilly country, the *bocage* supports houses and farms. The area is characterized by a great many hedges, and there are many small areas of woodland. From a distance the *bocage* looks like a forest, but it actually supports a great many people, usually in isolated farmsteads. The *campagne,* on the other hand, is very open country, smoother than the *bocage* and with very few trees. The houses are grouped in agricultural hamlets or villages, which often have stone walls around them, and the fields are marked out with stone walls rather than hedges. Nearly every bit of the land, other than that occupied by roads, fences, and houses, is under cultivation.

Types of Settlements

Settlements are of various sizes, from the hamlet of four or five houses grouped closely together, to the village of perhaps a few dozen houses, to the town and the city. Although these classifications have not been exactly defined, the hamlet is generally considered

to consist of four or five houses; the village may contain up to 25 houses; and the town is considered to be a settlement with some urban qualities but less than 15,000 population (Fig. 14.5). These arbitrary classifications may have to be modified in some cases, but they provide a rough basis for discussion.

The grouping of houses takes many forms. One of the simplest forms is the street village, or street hamlet, in which all of the houses are arranged along one street or road. The street village develops where there is essentially no crossroad or other strong focus of settlement. The street village is associated with the system of landholding in which the fields of the individual farmer are scattered throughout the surrounding country. Since the ownership of the land shifts frequently, it is more satisfactory for the

Fig. 14.5. Hamlets, villages, and towns; top, the structures in this small hamlet in the Swiss Alps are built of local wood and stone; center, this Korean village on the Han River is located in an intensively cultivated plain; straw is used in thatching the roofs; bottom, this town, Ferrera, on the Island of Minorca, Spain, is quite compact in order to leave as much land for cultivation as possible.

Fig. 14.6. The streets of this cooperative town, Nahalal, Israel, are arranged in a circular and radial pattern. The business district is at the center, surrounded by residences. The cultivated fields are on the margins.

farmer to live in the loose cluster of houses in the street village than to live on his land.

The crossroad village, or crossroad hamlet, is slightly more compact than the street village. The houses, residences, stores, or markets, are located as close to the crossroads as possible in order to take advantage of traffic going both ways. A modern crossroads hamlet may consist of a filling station, a grocery store, and a few other shops built on adjacent corners of a rural intersection. The crossroad village tends to develop in a more or less irregular rectangular pattern as additional streets are laid out approximately parallel to the original crossroads (which are, of course, probably neither straight lines nor at right angles to each other).

An early version of the compact settlement was the round village, in which the houses were arranged in a radial pattern. Developed for protection, the round village was often encircled by a wall; then, as the settlement grew and new walls were constructed farther from the center of the vil-

lage, the original wall would become a street. The resulting pattern of these villages (which were very common in the Slavic portions of eastern Europe) consisted of radial streets which led out from a central square or market and were connected by crude circular streets. Modern equivalents of the round villages are to be found in some of the new planned cities, one of which has recently been constructed in Israel (Fig. 14.6). The radial plan lends itself to a satisfactory modern settlement, provided that it makes appropriate provisions for such necessities as market area and recreational area.

Most of the descriptions in this chapter refer particularly to agricultural settlements, but they apply equally well to mining settlements, logging settlements, and settlements based on other kinds of human activity. An important modern type of rural settlement is to be found in the vicinity of large cities. Called suburbs, these settlements include both widely dispersed and intensely nucleated examples.

CHAPTER **15**

Ownership of the Land

Types of World Tenure

On a day in June, when geography students are looking forward to the end of the term and to summer vacation, four farmers in different parts of the world are worrying about their wheat crops.

On the high plains of East Africa, overlooking Lake Victoria, a farmer is wondering if the rains that are falling will be enough for a good crop, so that he can make an offering of wheat-beer to his chief. Thousands of miles to the north, where the gently rolling plains of the Ukraine are green with growing wheat, the farm manager is calculating how the crop will be divided if—as he hopes—his assigned quota is overfulfilled.

Halfway around the world, in the Willamette Valley of Oregon, another farmer looks over his field of ripening wheat and ponders on how much of his profit will be used to make the final payment of the mortgage on his farm. A fourth farmer is standing in a newly plowed field in Chile, wondering if the wheat he is about to plant will yield enough to buy his wife a new dress and permit his son to attend school in a neighboring town.

Each farmer is concerned with the amount of wheat that will be taken from the fields; but each plans to use the harvest in a different manner, according to the ownership, or *tenure,* system under which he operates his farm. Since he cultivates them by hand and hoe, the wheat plots of the African cultivator

are small. That they are also new is indicated by the fact that the beer he plans to give his chief symbolizes his gratitude for permission to open the brushland to cultivation. The land has been his tribe's permanent location since Europeans in the 1890's stopped intertribal warfare and put an end to the slave trade managed by Arab raiders. This tribal farmer may take the products off the land as long as he maintains crops upon it, but if he moves away he cannot sell his holding. His holding reverts to the tribe, and the chief may allot it to another cultivator if the farmer fails to return after a season or two.

In the Ukraine the manager of the collective farm, or *kolkhoz,* will deliver the grain to the nearest city and will receive cash in return. He will divide this money among the farm residents according to their work record for the season. Since the money each family receives is limited, they must add to their larder from "private" plots of vegetables and from "private" animals.

The Chilean farmer is a tenant upon a large estate owned by an eminent family. The farmer spends much of his time working the landlord's fields and the remainder of his time cultivating his own smaller plots. He has no choice regarding the disposal of these plots, which he may not be permitted to farm the following year.

The Oregon farmer, working in the shadow

of the Cascades, will own his farm in *fee simple* when he pays off the mortgage. The farm will be his to do with as he pleases: he may, for example, raise wheat or other crops on it the following year; he may sell it outright; he may will it to his heirs.

These farmers operate their plots under four different systems of land ownership. (There are, of course, more than four possible systems.) The majority of the world's people—its farmers—live under some one of the four dominant forms of land ownership, or tenure: *tribal* tenure; *communal* tenure; *tenant,* or sharecropping, tenure; or *freehold* tenure. The existence of any one of these tenure types in a region depends, to a greater or lesser degree, on the type of economy which prevails in that region. The system of tenure in a region is also related to the pressure of people on the land, the types of tools and machines used for cultivation, and, of course, the history of the area. Some possible relationships, by no means present in all cases, are shown in Table 15.1.

Early in the occupation of an area the population density is generally fairly low. There are not many more people living on the land during the first stage of migratory agriculture than were there during the hunting and gathering stage. In the practice of migratory agriculture people go into an area of virgin forest, cut down the bushes and trees, and burn them to provide fertile ash and sunlight for growing two or three harvests before moving on. Since migratory agriculture makes a more reliable source of food readily available, the population increases gradually over what it was in the gathering stage; also, the need for labor to care for the fields may induce the cultivators to have more children. During the practice of migratory agriculture land is considered to be available for use by all without restraint; when the fertility of an area is exhausted after a year or two, the cultivators move on, generally as a small clan of three or four families. In areas where the population density remains low it is possible that a clan

will never return to lands it has once abandoned.

In many areas the people "fill up the land," relatively speaking, and once-cleared fields that have since grown up in bushes and small trees are cut and burned again. Clans stop migrating aimlessly and settle down in villages of perhaps three or four clans which consider themselves to be part of a tribe. Fields are used, retired from use, and eventually used again in a system of "bush fallowing" developed under tribal rules. Although the rules for the use of available land are generally simple when tribes are small and "bush fallowing" has just begun, it eventually becomes necessary for the tribal chief to make decisions as to the proper use of the land. In general, the complexity of customs and laws connected with land tenure is directly related to duration of settlement; that is, the longer an area has been settled, the more complex its system of land tenure is likely to be. This rule is true of both tribal areas and more developed regions.

It is evident that attitudes toward the use of a resource tend to vary with the amount of the resource available. Examples illustrating this tendency may be found in many areas of the world. Among the Tolowa Indians of California, anyone could fish freely along the ocean beach; along the much more restricted river banks, however, no one could fish outside of his allotted stretch of bank. Fishing in the ocean was communal and unrestricted among the Kiwai of New Guinea, but definite property rights were applied to their limited agricultural land. Most nomadic herding groups hold their pasture in common and may even regard it as being free, like the air. However, although Kirghiz nomads of southern Siberia are "communists" in summer when the pasture is abundant, they become quite "individualistic" in their attitude when they descend to their winter quarters where grazing land is limited and they use both natural and artificial boundaries to mark off private property. Among

TABLE 15.1   **A Typology of Old World Agricultural Types**

Agricultural Types	Common Tools	Crop Emphasis	Typical Crops	Land Pattern
Migratory Agriculture.	Digging stick.	Individual plants of few varieties; leisurely experimentation with camp-follower plants and individual "found" trees.	Yams, upland rice; breadfruit, banana.	Amorphous.
Bush Fallowing (shifting agriculture with a definite base; *chena*).	"Primitive" hoe.	Individual plants of more varieties. Mixed planting; individual planted trees.	Upland rice and yams.	Garden.
"Savage" Fallow.	Developed hoe and mattocks.	Field crops, clear-planted with no inter-row cropping.	Millets, buck-wheat.	A few scattered fields.
European Manorial System.	Iron-tipped plow of wood.	Three-field system; rotation of grain crops, pasture and fallow.	Wheat, rye.	Many scattered fields; fragmentation.
Oriental Rice Farming with Dry Winter Grains.	Wooden harrow; iron-tipped wood plow.	Intensification of plant yields; winter grains intercropped with vegetables, later with cash crops.	Paddy rice, taro; barley, wheat.	Many scattered fields; fragmentation.
Mixed Farming.	Iron plow with share.	Efficiency of farm unit (betterment of the individual unit)	Potatoes and other root crops; maize, wheat.	Compact farm unit; distinct fenced fields.
Tropical Plantation.	Steel plow; few other tools.	High yielding perennial plant types.	Rubber, sugar cane, coffee, bananas.	Large blocks, bounded by selva.
Mid-latitude Monoculture.	Steel plow, discs, mechanical harvesters.	Hybridization, emphasis on annuals; scientific experimentation.	Wheat, maize sorghums.	Large blocks, joining each other, not separable by the eye.

(with Suggested Relations to Life and Economy)

Dominant Animals	Ownership Pattern	Settlement Type	Economic Stage	Population Density
Dog.	Nuclear family; clan.	Temporary scattered huts.	Subsistence.	2-3 per sq. mile.
Dog, pig, chicken.	Tribal. (emphasis on use-occupation)	Loosely nucleated village.	Barter; proto-feudal.	15-20 per sq. mile.
Oxen, goat, horse.	Extended family.	Tightly nucleated village.	Early feudalism.	50-100 per sq. mile.
Oxen, sheep.	Communal, with periodic redistribution; latifundia.	Manorial cluster.	Late feudalism.	100-150 per sq. mile.
Bullocks, horse, water buffalo.	Communal with periodic redistribution; *shōen* (manorial system)	Nucleated villages along break-of-slope.	"Centralized" feudalism.	200-600 per sq. mile.
Dairy cattle, horses, oxen, pigs.	Individual freehold; tenant-at-will.	Individually dispersed, or where nucleated, wet-point (well) or high-point (defense) emphasis.	Small-scale capitalism (emphasis on individual effort)	150-300 per sq. mile.
None	Corporate.	Workers' permanent dormitories.	Corporate capitalism.	50-100 per sq. mile or variable.
None	Large private operation under government subsidy.	Shelters for migratory workers; crop processing and storage sheds.	Private large-scale capitalism.	Serves urban populations exclusively.

the Rwala Bedouins of Arabia, there are no rules about the ownership of territory or the inheritance of land, but there are elaborate rules governing the inheritance of camels.

These examples illustrate man's attempt to divide the land and its resources in a manner considered both right and proper. Man's ideas about what constitutes a just division are complexly interwoven with other aspects of his life, as the following sections of this chapter will show.

Tribal Tenure

Ancient Hindu law states that ". . . he who clears a piece of land is the owner of it" and that ". . . sages who know the past declare a field to belong to him who cut away the wood or who cleared and tilled it." These quotations from the ancient Hindu folk code, the *Law of Manu,* state the general tribal attitude of tenure through use, or use-occupancy. Since the clearing of woodland and brushland is an arduous task, it is not surprising that, where tools are primitive and few, the labor of preparing a new field for cultivation carries with it fairly permanent rights to the produce of that field.

Tribal land systems predominate in the cultivated but otherwise primitive areas of Asia and Black Africa. All tribal systems of landholding have two main aspects: the relation of the cultivating family to the tribe; the ownership and labor allocation within the family.

Relation of Cultivating Family to Tribe. Where ownership consists only of the right to occupance during use, failure to utilize the land often results in its being returned to the status of public or tribal property. The period of noncultivation which must elapse before the change of title occurs differs from area to area. In much of East Africa, where population pressure on the land is rather high, the required period of noncultivation is only one season. In New Zealand, on the other hand, Maori custom required that there be three generations of "no fires on the land" before title reverted to the tribe. All land, whether acquired by conquest, by gift, or by right of ancestry, was subject to reversion under Maori law.

The Yoruba of the Niger delta area have religious sentiments and magical beliefs that protect land that has been used and abandoned against being reoccupied too quickly. So long as evidences of former use (such as fences and storage huts) exist, it is forbidden for a stranger to occupy the land. Many tribal groups have no conception of the sale of land; the idea of transferring ownership without a prior and obvious change in use is totally unknown.

The tribal-tenure concept of use-occupancy as the basis of ownership was apparent in American homestead laws, which generally held clearing, cultivation, and improvement of land to be prima facie evidence of the right to title. Whereas in Africa the chief gives his permission for the opening of land to cultivation, in the United States the government permitted the land development. The token payments that were made for homestead land are similar to the beer given to a tribal chief or the "first fruits" offered to a village deity.

In areas strongly influenced by the Hindu *Law of Manu,* the members of a family using the same land for several generations under a use-occupancy pattern of tribal tenure frequently regard the land as being owned by the ancestor who first cleared it for use and look upon themselves as being only caretakers responsible to the ancestral spirit.

The more primitive and more nomadic tribal groups of the tropical rainforest of the Congo Basin, the Amazon Basin, and the hills of southeastern Asia and its adjacent islands generally clear only one plot of land per family. Eventually, if they develop better tools and land becomes more abundant, these tribal farmers (like other tribal farmers before them) may find out by leisurely experimentation (trial and error) that certain soils are better for one crop than for another. As a result of this discovery, the tribal farmers will gradually learn to grow on each soil only those crops which will do well there. Since soil types are scattered, the cultivated plots will also be scattered. The dispersal of fields so typical of small-scale farming in Eurasia may well be the result of such a process as this (Fig. 15.1).

Relation of Tribal Tenure to Division of Labor. In matriarchal societies such as that of the Hopi Indians, it is the woman who receives permission from the clan to use land, although much of the cultivation is done by her husband and her son-in-law. In many other American Indian tribes, women did the cultivating of all the crops except tobacco; because tobacco had great ceremonial importance, the old men of the tribes were charged with its growth and harvest. Likewise, in the Zulu area of southern Africa, tobacco is grown only by the village or kraal elders. Evidently, the sexual division of labor within the tribal farming family is one cause of scattered fields.

Within a tribal family, the allotment of the products of the land and the assignment of work tasks differ considerably from area to area. In southern Africa the Zulu require the men to care for most tasks connected with cattle. In much of central Africa there are co-operative work associations of men; rather than working individually on their own plots, the men work on each other's plots in rotation. Co-operation of this sort among women is much more rare.

Where nomadic tribal groups pass through areas of settled agriculture, a mutually profitable interdependence quite often develops between the nomads and the farmers. In Iran the nomadic tribes follow by custom a certain well-defined migration route, on which each subgroup has the traditional right to use specific areas. Although the passage of the nomads may cause losses to be inflicted upon the crops in the settled areas, the farmers gain the advantages of having a plentiful

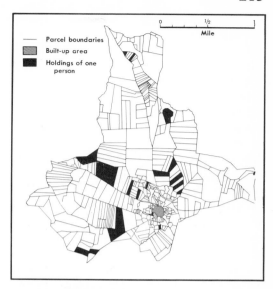

Fig. 15.1. Fragmentation and dispersal of land holdings in an Arab village of Palestine prior to 1948. (Courtesy of E. C. Willatts of the Royal Geographical Society, and the Department of Statistics of the Government of Palestine.)

supply of butter and meat at relatively low prices when the nomads pass through. Similarly, in West Africa the cattle-owning Fulani sell milk to settled farmers while their cattle are grazing on the stubble of harvested millet and other crops and leaving droppings which enrich the soil for the next crop.

Opening of Tribal Lands to Cultivation. In areas where cultivators operate under tribal tenure, a farmer's right to the original use of a piece of land derives from his clearing of the land with his chief's permission. His right to continued use of the land and retention of its harvest, called the *usufruct* of the land, depends upon his membership in the community; that is, he derives security of tenure from his village status rather than from his maintenance of the plot of land. There is in tribal land systems a distinction drawn between the ownership of land by the chief as a result of his sovereignty and the ownership of land by the tribal member as a right of usufruct. In a sense, this distinction is a precedent for our present concept of the difference between the political sovereignty which is derived from actual land area and the right of a nation's citizens to use that land area in whatever way they deem proper.

In most of the tribal-tenure areas of Africa there are two ways of obtaining the right to occupy and use land. One of these ways is dependent upon a man's status as a member of his kinship group. If his kinship group occupies a piece of previously unused land, he has the right—by virtue of his membership in the kin group—to cultivate it. The second way of getting the right to use land devolves largely from the idea of political rights introduced into Africa as a result of European political control. If a chief is politically appointed, a tribal subject of that chief has the right of clearing the land simply because of his chief's position.

In the Nyakusa area of southwestern Tanganyika, villages come into formal existence whenever a new chiefdom is proclaimed. The members of a village locate their house plots according to the directions of the chief, and each man tends to cultivate that part of the land that is found immediately behind his house. Once the village has been established, villagers can extend their cultivation to any land which is vacant—that is, land which is not being cultivated by another villager or lying in fallow for another villager. If, because of death in his family or some other reason, a villager accumulates more land than he can cultivate, the chief may try to persuade him to give some of this land up to someone else. If the cultivator exercises his right of refusing to do so, the headman generally has to accept his refusal.

Improvements in the land are the tribal justification for the right to use the land. The most permanent improvement made in land results from the planting of trees, and it is not surprising that land thus improved rarely changes hands. In the Nyakusa area of Tanganyika it is common for a man's land and the trees which he planted on it to be in-herited by his successors. If the heirs have enough of their own land and are not interested in continuing cultivation of the inherited land, they nevertheless usually keep the more important trees. In some instances, bamboos, because of their value as a building material, may be assigned to the chief. Trees or plants (like the banana) that have a very short growing period generally go with the land. That the ownership of trees may cause a certain amount of friction can be seen in the Sukuma area south of Lake Victoria. Planted trees there remain the property of the planter and his descendants even after they have abandoned the land on which the trees are planted. Later groups that occupy the area are not permitted to cut the trees or to use their products.

In most tribal areas a cultivator is left in undisturbed occupance of the land so long as he remains both socially and politically correct. Once he conforms to the tribal mores, he is able to remain in continued possession of the land; thus his sons can cultivate the plots and hold the rights to grazing, water, and trees and firewood. In many tribal areas, rights established in the past are still valid today. When one man in a tribe temporarily has more land than he can use, it may become necessary for him to let someone else use the land. When the occupier is approached by friends, neighbors, or relatives offering a certain consideration in return for permission to use the land, a type of temporary tenancy arises in the tribal system. This type of tenancy will be mentioned later in the section on tenancy.

In the Shan plateau of Burma each plot of land belongs to the lineage that first cleared it. If the land is cleared a second time and the same lineage is not interested in using it, it may then be utilized by a second lineage either upon the payment of a token rent or simply with a formal act of "borrowing."

In some hoe-culture villages which have tribal mores regulating land use, the natural increase in population may lead to the founding of new settlements in virgin land by people splitting off from existing villages. An older village may thus serve as mother village to several colony villages established within a walking distance of about six or seven miles; these colonies rely upon the mother village for markets, festivals, and political guidance.

Communal Tenure

Although there is relatively little communal land ownership in the United States, it is rather common in the world as a whole, being the dominant form of land tenure in the U.S.S.R. and China and (in varying degrees of strength) in their satellite countries. A form of semicommunal land ownership existed in Europe after the end of the Roman Empire, and communal tenure was practiced in early China and early Japan. The communal ownership of about 75 acres of land on the isolated island of Kudaka in the Ryukyu chain is all that remains of what was once a widespread communal system. The present pattern of tenant tenure in much of the Arab Near East was probably superimposed by force and conquest upon an earlier system of communal ownership. The form of communal ownership now carried on in Israel seems to be a successful adaptation of the older communal system.

Communal ownership of farmed land was the common pattern in the New World before the Spanish conquistadores instituted a system of private land ownership and large estates. In some isolated areas of the high Andes the old communal system has survived to the modern day; in other areas of Spanish America, such as the *ejido* areas of Mexico, the communal system has been revived. The nonagricultural American Indians for the most part did not have any conception of land ownership and only came into contact with the idea of land ownership when a communal system was imposed on them by virtue of their confinement to reservations.

One of the reasons for communal tenure is that it gives each operating or cultivating family an equal amount of land (and thus serves as a type of temporary freehold system). A second reason often cited for communal tenure is that it gives equal income to the operators of land, either because of their actual work or because of their membership in the community. The equal distribution of income among all the members of the community is the ideal of the major communist countries.

Marxist theory postulates that the evils in economic life are the result of private ownership, and it states that these evils will disappear if private ownership of productive facilities, including land, is abolished. Marx proposed collective ownership and operation of land and collective distribution of the profits from land. The first major nation to become communist, the U.S.S.R., delayed collectivization—except for a few experiments—for more than a decade after the revolutionary change of government in 1917. Collectivization was opposed by many farmers, particularly the more wealthy ones, and great starvation in the countryside was the initial result of the attempt to introduce it. The eventual achievement of collectivization probably owes a good deal to the *mir* system, with which the Russian peasant had long been familiar. In common use since the second half of the 18th century, the *mir* system had two aspects: first, the collective use of indivisible plots of land such as forests and meadows (a practice common also in northwestern Europe, particularly in England and Germany); and second, the periodic reallotment of farmland based upon the growth in population and the changes in family structure that had taken place since the previous division of the land. In some areas the division of land was proportional to the number of adult workers of both sexes, and in other places it was proportional only to the number of males in a family.

In the decade after the Russian Revolution the Soviet planners experimented with state farms of extremely large size in order

Fig. 15.2. Worker delivering farm produce on V. I. Lenin collective, Moscow district.

to test the possibilities of large-scale farm management. The relative success of the experimental state farms, or *sovkhozi,* hastened the planners' decision to collectivize the land in 1928, and in a few years all but the most isolated of some 25 million farmsteads were incorporated into some one of the 200,000 new collectives. Because the Russian peasant at that time was most commonly either illiterate or undereducated, as well as unfamiliar with modern technology, the collective farms were serviced by machine tractor stations. All machines for plowing and harvesting were centrally located there and were rented by the collective farms. During 30 years of collectivization the number of collective farms dropped considerably (from about 200,000 to 94,000) and the level of educational and technical training among the collective-farm population increased. Because of the fewer farms and the higher level of training, the machine tractor stations were abolished in 1948, and the machinery formerly rented by the collectives was permanently assigned to them.

The members of each collective farm (Fig. 15.2) work in groups or brigades and receive credit according to the number of work-days accumulated. A day on a Russian collective farm does not constitute a work-day. The more advanced and technical jobs may be worth three or four work-days per day of work, while jobs of tedious hand labor (perhaps done by slow-moving old women) may be worth only one half of a work-day per day of work. When the harvest is in and the profits are known, they are divided in proportion to the accumulated work-days. Dissatisfaction with this system is somewhat mitigated by the farmers' being allowed the use, which amounts almost to private ownership, of an acre or so of land near the collective farm. Because there are long stretches of time on a wheat or rye collective when the farmers are not required to be in the fields, the collective farmer can devote a good part of his time to his private holding. In the late 1940's about 25 per cent of Russian farm production came from privately held plots, although in area these plots accounted for only a tenth of the farmed land. Also, each family on a collective farm is allowed certain livestock—generally a cow, a few pigs, and several chickens. If private production exceeds the needs of the family, the excess products may be sold in "free" markets in the cities; and the income thus gained does not belong to the collective.

During the first three years of communism in China (from 1950 to 1953) there was a gradual elimination of the landed gentry, or landlords, who had controlled a good deal of China's land. Although many of the landholdings of the gentry were less than 20 acres in size, it was decided to eliminate landlords as an economic class in order to satisfy the great demand for their highly productive land (which was, in general, much more highly productive than land in the West). From 1954 to 1956 it was the policy to amalgamate the peasants who had received land from this land reform into agricultural producers' co-operatives. The goal of this policy was to have one third of China's peasant households in these co-operatives (organizations less highly developed than collectives) by 1957. Whether this goal was achieved or not is now immaterial, because in 1958 a policy switch instituted the giant communes —great rural agglomerations of collectives aggregating as many as 100,000 people each. Although the communes achieved some increase in farm productivity, the increase was not nearly as much as had been hoped for. By 1960 there were indications that the drive to have all crops submitted to giant communes was slackening and that each family might be allowed to keep a small plot for vegetables, a pig, and a few chickens. This Chinese pattern of having a small amount of private landownership exist within a communist society resembles the Russian plan.

Land reform in the satellite communist countries has generally followed the pattern of collectivization. However, in many cases collectivization has not been as successful as it was in the U.S.S.R. because local factors have differed somewhat. Opposition to the Russian version of communism has been so strong since the Revolt of 1956 that even three years later barely half of Hungary's area was in collective farms. In Yugoslavia the collectivization drive has slowed down because of the small size of the farms in the valleys bordering the northeastern plain; in addition, governmental pressure for collectivization in Yugoslavia has been somewhat less severe than it was in the U.S.S.R. Poland's postwar experience with collectivization was rather an unhappy one. As a result, after the change in Polish governmental policy in 1956, vast areas once devoted to collectivized farms became small farms held under what was essentially freehold tenure. Apparently, freehold tenure was permitted because the increased production which came from individual farms was for the moment more important than a theoretical communist victory combined with less production. Although collectivization has proceeded in the other satellites, the success of the communist policy is less evident there, primarily because adequate mechanization of the collectives has not yet been achieved.

Other than in the communist countries there is no remnant of communal land tenure in modern Europe. A semicommunal system known as the open-field system was, however, common in Europe in the Middle Ages, spreading over Germany (where it was known as the three-field system) in the 8th and 9th centuries and lasting in England from Anglo-Saxon times to the 19th century. Under this system a village community divided its land into several open fields, which served as grain fields, pasture, and fallow in rotation. Within each cultivated field each landowner farmed a certain number of strips that were divided from each other by grassy ridges. A man's strips of land were both temporary and scattered. They were temporary because, after grain had been grown for two or three years in a field, the entire field was fallowed and then planted to grass; while his former farming area was thus in use, the farmer transferred his operations to another few strips of land in a large field newly plowed for grain. The farmer's fields were scattered because, according to the egalitarian division made by the village, a man was entitled to his share of the better land and had to take his proper portion of the worse land.

On the fields which were devoted to pasture in the course of rotation, a man had the right to graze his cattle in common with everyone else's cattle. The grassy fields of pasture were generally referred to as the village commons. Each villager also had rights in the commonly owned and rather extensive wastelands beyond the arable area. However, when the demand for wool textiles grew in England, the large landowners enclosed much of the former common land for the purpose of grazing privately-owned sheep and rendered the land unavailable for use by the village communities. Since, in addition, the countryside was being rapidly depopulated by the cities' demand for labor to sustain the Industrial Revolution, the open-field, or three-field, system for all practical purposes disappeared in England (except for a small area near Laxton). On the continent of Europe a similar rise of industry and extension of cash and commercial crops had similar effects. Thus, today, the three-field system is almost entirely absent from the continent of Europe.

According to Lewis Morgan, an American anthropologist, "primitive communism" was once the prevalent form of land ownership. The more we learn about the history of early peoples, however, the less we accept this often repeated claim. This claim was not original with Morgan, for Confucius believed that some form of primitive communism existed in China during the prehistoric past. Much of the Confucian system was concerned with trying to achieve a simplicity and order in human affairs like that which was believed to have existed during the ancient time of communistic land ownership.

There evidently was a communal well-field system in ancient China (circa 1200 B.C.). The ideograph for "well" in Chinese resembles the crossed lines American children use in playing tic-tac-toe. When land was divided along similar lines in northern China, it was assumed that each of eight farmers would cultivate his own plot and that the ninth plot, the center of the lines, would be cultivated jointly by the eight farmers. One ninth of the total produce of the entire area was sent to the local lord or to the emperor. As the population grew and the area of arable land increased, reapportionment took place on an egalitarian basis; still the yield due the emperor remained one ninth of the total.

In Japan rice farming was engaged in from about 200 B.C. At first, since the population level was low and the marshy tracts were widely distributed, there apparently was no competition for land; as the population grew, however, and competition for land developed, land was divided according to a system imported from China in the 6th century A.D. An elaboration of the well-field system, this system, the *jō-ri,* was a method of dividing land into squares, with each person alloted so much land within the surveyed area. Apparently, the idea of having a periodic division and redistribution of village land carried over from a somewhat earlier period in Japanese history. Although it is doubtful if any land was redistributed in this way in Japan after the 12th or 13th century, communal ownership of land and periodic redistribution of this sort was followed until 1899 on the Japanese-influenced island of Okinawa. The Japanese displacement of the Okinawan king ended the system, except on the isolated isle of Kudaka, where the system remains to the present day. Kudaka is a fishing village with a very limited amount of agricultural land. The fields lie in various land-quality areas, and each family has a field from three to four feet wide and from 80 to 100 feet long in each of the areas.

In the Middle East there are two kinds of communal land: *matruka,* or "left-over," land and *mashaa,* or "shared," land. *Matruka* land includes roads, paths, and threshing floors held and used in common, as well as uncultivated grazing lands on the edge of the village. The uncultivated lands belong to all the villagers and are not allotted; the common flocks are driven out and grazed wherever they can find grass. On the other hand, the village owns *mashaa* land in common, and each family has rights to a certain number of the shares which are redistributed by the village elders at intervals of from one to five years. Ann Lambton, who has studied intensively the problem of land tenure in Iran, has concluded that "the present form of ownership by large landlords, which is the dominant form of tenure in Persia today, has developed out of or been imposed upon an earlier communal form of settlement with equalized individual rights." In Islamic areas, where the tradition is followed that "the Prophet forbade the sale of water," it is assumed that water is a kind of communal property. The owner of a spring or a well cannot keep flocks of livestock or travelers from using the water, although he can prevent the use of the water for irrigation purposes without his permission. It is also held in these areas that, if a person digs canals to bring water to dead lands, these canals belong to their developer. This example of the tradition of usufruct by development is very close to the practice of the tribal tenure system.

In India the common lands of the village have served in the past a far greater role than they do at present. The pressure of population has become so great that much of the land formerly held in common for fuel or grazing purposes has been turned gradually into cultivated land. The use of the remaining common lands is somewhat restricted by the caste system: the right to use the common lands is based in many cases upon the amount of private land that a person owns, which ownership in turn may be a function of his caste membership.

Before the advent of the Spanish, land tenure in the farming areas of the New World was predominantly communal. In a system both pre-Incan and pre-Aztec, lands were held in common by the *ayllu*, or village community. With the rise of the empire of the Sapa Inca, land ownership became exclusively Incan, but the rhythm of life in the village communities remained the same and the non-Incan villagers continued to cultivate the land in common. The old ways of cultivation also persisted after the founding of the Aztec empire in Mexico.

When the Spanish came to Mexico and Peru, they took possession both of vast areas of *ayllu* land and of the Indians who lived upon it. In the high intermont basins of the Andes, they established large haciendas (which are still in existence) comprised of several *ayllu* each. Many farmers in the more remote or isolated *ayllu* still live in their prehistoric fashion and give a certain percentage of the crop to their distant landlord. Those communities which are closer to the hacienda house are often directed by the landowner, or his agent, and may grow commercial crops in addition to those needed for community subsistence. The hacienda, as a privately-owned estate incorporating several communal *ayllu,* is an instance of the combination of two systems of land tenure. Advocates of land reform in Latin America want to abolish the haciendas and return the profits of the land to the *ayllus*. In 1940 the First International Conference on Indian Life supported the continuance of the *ayllu,* both because they perform a valuable social function and because their large areas are amenable to mechanization.

In Mexico many of the village communities lost land wholesale to the Spanish, who often converted the land from food crops to such cash crops as sugar cane and cotton. Most Mexican land consisted of large estates before the 1910 Revolution, the aim of which was to split up these estates, or *latifundias,* and return the land to the villages. A 1920 law established the principle that the individual farmer in the *ejido,* or communal land, should have an income per day from the land equivalent to twice the average daily wage in the district. Though communal in theory, the *ejido* lands are most often held and cultivated in small areas by individual farmers and their families. However, in a few areas of Mexico the entire *ejido* area is cultivated communally for some cash crop, with the profits from the crop being divided among the cultivators. Although most *ejidos* have not been mechanized, the farmers are not opposed to mechanization since any increase in income from mechanization would be to their advantage. The Mexican government does not tax the communal land of *ejidos.* Moreover, although the plots first allotted to *ejido* farmers were rather small and thus more suitable for subsistence crops than cash crops, the Mexican government has recently adopted a new policy of requiring more acreage per family in newly formed *ejidos.* This increase in acreage will no doubt facilitate both the growing of cash crops and the mechanization of the land.

It is ironical that most migratory Indians of North America, who never had any concrete idea of land ownership, should have been subjected to a communal tenure system by a government devoted to the achievement of freehold tenure for its voting citizens. Indian reservations maintain a form of communal land tenure in areas where land tenure was totally unknown in pre-Columbian days.

Americans often assume *a priori* that systems of communal tenure are inherently less efficient than freehold systems. Although it is true that communal systems tied to traditions and religious rites are often inefficient and unadaptable, the fact that communal systems are not inherently unworkable is illustrated by the success of communal tenure in Israel. The establishment there of collective farms, *kibutsim,* has gradually replaced a subsistence economy with a modern commercial agriculture in which citrus crops are emphasized.

During the early settlement of New England land was often owned and operated on a communal basis by Puritan groups; later, the Shaker sect came to operate communal farms in New England. With the settlement of the more humid parts of the Middle West, numerous religious groups opened communal farming operations. One such group, the Amana colony in Iowa, diversified their operations after 1930 and now also engage in the manufacture of high-quality household appliances.

Within the United States communal tenure is still practiced by choice in the Hutterite farm settlements of North Dakota. The Hutterite sect holds its land in common and farms cash crops so efficiently that the freehold farmers in the neighborhood have forced legislation prohibiting further acquisition of farmland by Hutterite communities.

Freehold Tenure

Freehold tenure, otherwise known as fee-simple tenure, generally implies the right to buy and sell land freely and to cultivate it as one pleases during ownership. Applicable to both subsistence farms and commercial farms, freehold tenure is the preferred and dominant method of land ownership in the English-speaking areas of the world; it also is the preferred and increasingly dominant form of ownership in much of western Europe, Japan, and India. Although freehold tenure has stable historical roots in many areas, as a system it is somewhat less stable than a tenancy system since it has problems of subdivision and fragmentation of land through inheritance that are generally not found in tenancy systems.

It is hard to define freehold tenure rigidly, for many tenant situations approximate freehold tenure in practice and many so-called freehold situations differ little from tenancy. For instance, in the Yoruba area of Nigeria slaves cultivate the land for masters who hold their land under either tribal or freehold tenure. So long as the slaves regularly supply a designated amount of produce, they are left free to farm as they please; and the produce demanded is scarcely more than a government would exact in taxes. On the other hand, in the Midwest section of the United States (especially in the dry-fringe prairie areas) many of the farms are "owned" by farmers who have large mortgages at banks. Thus, in these instances, "freehold" status may be said to exist on slave-cultivated land and "tenant" status may be said to be effective on land held in fee simple.

There is a feeling in Anglo-Saxon areas that freehold tenure is the basis of stable political life. Presumably, the farmer owning his own land need not be dominated by other persons and can, therefore, vote freely and make political decisions of consequence without fear of economic reprisal. There is also a belief that freehold tenure is the most efficient method of operating farms. That freehold tenure often contributes to efficiency is beyond doubt, but (as will be made evident by the material below) efficiency is not always or necessarily the result of freehold tenure. There are conditions under which fee-simple ownership encourages poverty and under which certain types of tenancy status promote more efficient use of the land and the obtaining of greater profits.

Just as in tribal areas the right to permanent usufruct was granted to those who first cleared and tilled the land, so in more civilized areas (urban-based states) there were laws according to which persons who improved land for cultivation or reclaimed land from waste were given rights as permanent tenants which approximated the rights of freehold tenure. In ancient Greece rights were conceded to farmers in order to encourage cultivation. In medieval Japan people who reclaimed land could operate it essentially without taxes for a number of years and claim rights that differed very little from freehold rights. Also, it was long ago established as a principle of Moslem law that "whoever cultivates waste lands thereby acquires the property of them."

A state or political unit will often guarantee occupance of land that amounts in security of tenure to freehold rights. An illustration of such occupance is given by C. K. Meek:

In the Dera-Ghazi-Khan district of the Punjab the person who clears jungle and brings land under cultivation is protected by statute. He cannot be ejected as long as he continues to cultivate; his occupancy right is heritable; he can cut down selfgrown timber for agricultural purposes; he can build houses, though if he vacates his holding he can remove only the materials he has paid for himself; he can sink a certain type of well; and he can sublet his holding temporarily but not permanently.[1]

In medieval Persia, after the Mongol invasions, the state held that people who reclaimed dead land acquired thereby the rights of ownership and sale. On the other hand, even in areas of freehold tenure such as Britain, land may be appropriated by the state if a farmer is not using his holdings wisely; although the farmer maintains ownership of the land, it is operated under state control. Governmental control may serve to diminish the extent of freehold tenure. Under Turkish law, even though a farmer owns the soil and its produce, he does not own the subsoil. In Canada, mineral rights for mines and oil under the surface are vested in the provincial governments, not in the agricultural occupants.

Land Ownership and Prestige. Much land in the world is owned by persons who, though large landholders, do little toward cultivating the land. There is a tendency in the Middle East and much of Latin America for the ownership of land to be the prime base of prestige in political life. Prestige is derived in these areas not from the bank account resulting from profitable management of land but from the number of acres or square miles of land owned, regardless of its quality or degree of cultivation. For a long time, political power in both the Middle

[1] C. K. Meek, *Land Law and Custom in the Colonies* (Oxford University Press, London, 1949), p. 23.

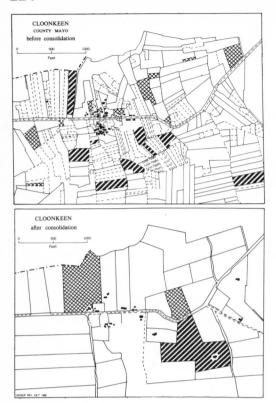

Fig. 15.3. Irish landownership before and after consolidation. (Reproduced by courtesy of the *Geographical Review*, American Geographical Society, New York.)

East and Latin America has been limited mostly to landowners and, although the situation is changing somewhat, land still determines prestige. The historical development of tenancy in Latin America upon large freehold estates will be noted in the section on tenancy systems.

Subsistence Freehold. Subsistence farms in the United States are often referred to as stump farms because many of them are located at the edge of a forest or in a marginal area remote from markets. Most freehold subsistence farms are small because of inheritance practices; the fields (often scattered as a result of farmers' desire to have land in various kinds of soil) are sub-

divided for inheritance purposes and grow smaller generation by generation. In contrast, freehold commercial farms are most often maintained as units rather than as fragments and are likely to grow larger with increased mechanization and additional investment capital. Since about 1920 farms in the United States—particularly those in the Midwest—have had a tendency to become larger; that is, the blocks of land owned by each farmer are growing larger. Often a farmer will buy part of a farm from a retiring or migrating neighbor, who may sell the remaining portion of his farm to a third person, thus making two farms out of land which once was divided into three farms.

Fragmentation and Freehold Tenure. The fragmentation of land under freehold tenure is now common in most areas of subsistence cultivation, including a great deal of western Europe and much of eastern and southern Asia (Fig. 15.3). Subdivision or fragmentation of property was also practiced in early times. Among the American Indians, the Tolowa in California divided river banks into individually owned fishing grounds and possessed individual tracts for the hunting of deer. The Nevada Washo Indians individually owned clumps of pinenut trees and passed them along to their children. Likewise, the saying of the Yoruba in Nigeria that "a tenant should not raise his eyes upward" reflects the practice of property fragmentation. Among the Yoruba, the person who plants a tree generally owns it always, even if he leaves the plot or village. In the village-oriented society of the Yoruba, land plotted, trees planted, and wells dug are the property of the person developing the resource. Where land is regarded as the gift of nature, property rights do not apply to it until there is a capital improvement made on it through the expenditure of labor.

In the Middle East the system which allows one man to own the trees on another man's land may have originated in a very early period, possibly in the period when

Moslem law was first applied. In Islamic areas it is the general rule that a man's widow gets one eighth of his holdings while his children get the remainder, each son receiving two shares for each daughter's one share. Generally, these shares remain undivided and the fruit of any inherited trees continues to be shared according to the original proportions. In such areas as Cyprus, however, there has been excessive subdivision of trees, with the result that plantations of coconut palms are rendered almost valueless because so many heirs own them. When there are too many heirs, no one person has enough trees to take responsibility for maintaining the plantings. Likewise, the substitution of better varieties of palms may be inhibited by the joint ownership of the palms to be replaced, perhaps even of the single palm to be replaced. In some places (Iraq, for instance) feuds are carried on not only by shooting people but by firing bullets into an enemy's tree.

Varieties of Freehold Tenure. Freehold tenure is the dominant form of landholding in Japan. Before the land reform of 1948, small landlords (each with less than 25 acres of cultivated land) represented 90 per cent of the landlord class and controlled 55 per cent of all land. Although the peasants of Japan still do not own all the land they cultivate, the reform of 1948 broadened the ownership base considerably. Since land lying within the boundaries of the house-lot has traditionally not been taxed, over the centuries it has become some of the most intensively used land in Japan. Though they may otherwise be tenant farmers, peasants growing food in their own house-lots are *de facto* freehold persons; thus, Japanese house-lots are comparable in some respects to the private garden plots maintained on collective farms in the U.S.S.R.

Since 1950, as a result of various programs of land reform, the ownership base has been broadened on the island of Formosa. In Okinawa, after the abrogation of the old communal tenure system in 1899, the land came to be owned more by individual farmers than by landlords; as a result, the proportion of freehold area to rented area is extremely high.

In southeastern Asia some of the land is owned in fee simple, but much of it is under some form of tenancy. About 15 per cent of the cultivated land in the most populated parts of Indonesia is taken up by garden crops rather than by the dominant cash crops or rice. As the amount of cropland per person decreases, there is an increase in both the percentage of each holding allotted to gardens and the intensity of cultivation. With regard to these gardens, Karl J. Pelzer has written:

One of the great advantages of garden culture over field culture is that there is always something ready to harvest from the former and therefore something to sell when money for daily household needs becomes scarce. Another advantage is that the garden supplies the family with a great variety of side dishes rich in vitamins; the vegetable proteins of the garden produce are also of high value.[2]

Garden culture, whether under a system of freehold tenure or tenancy, is a dominant pattern in most of southeastern Asia, in Ceylon, and in much of southern India. In Ceylon most of the *chena,* or slash-and-burn land, is either communally or tribally owned; on the *chena* that is privately owned, the constant use of the land, without crop rotation, produces deleterious effects on the soil.

In India there are two major categories of private ownership. So-called perfect ownership entitles holders of land to rights in the village common that are proportional to the size of their private holdings. The second type of ownership does not entitle the landowner to use of the common. There is also the rapidly disappearing type of ownership

[2] Karl J. Pelzer, *Pioneer Settlement in the Asiatic Tropics* (Institute of Pacific Relations, New York, 1945), p. 45.

known as *zamindari* ownership. The zamindars (or landowners) are descendants of persons who, employed by the British in the 18th and early 19th centuries to collect revenue from the tillers of land, came to have proprietory rights over the land they administered. The *zamindari* system is gradually being replaced by *ryotwari* tenure, under which a farmer owns his land in fee simple and pays taxes directly to the state.

Carleton Coon has written of the Khunik villages in Iran, in which the villagers are both owners and cultivators and have a general air of prosperity. These villagers raise saffron as a cash crop and are able to keep a large proportion of their total income. A fifth of their income goes to the tax collector, a tenth to a local mosque, and perhaps another fifth to a family charity in a nearby city.

Two types of freehold ownership are recognized in the Middle East. *Mulk* land is held in absolute freehold ownership. The owner can do with his plot as he wishes; the fact that any improvements he may make remain his own property encourages his exercising foresight and initiative. Much *mulk* land is held only on the basis of tradition, there having been no registration of ownership; in some areas whatever records once existed have been lost. Absolute freehold ownership of land is comparatively rare; even the large tracts of absentee landlords may be held under the more common type of tenure, called *miri*. Although *miri* land theoretically belongs to the state, most farmers on *miri* land are for practical purposes freeholders. Sometimes *miri* land is leased only temporarily, but it is often leased in perpetuity, under qualifying conditions. If *miri* land remains unworked for from three to five years, it reverts to the state; likewise, it reverts to the state if no heirs claim it. *Miri* land can be inherited only in accordance with Moslem law, and the owner cannot leave it to a religious foundation or family charity. In much of Syria and Iraq the most common

form of land tenure is ownership of large estates under *miri* conditions; on these large estates the cultivators are usually sharecroppers.

In Africa most of the outright freehold tenure is found in the Union of South Africa and in some areas of West Africa. In the freehold areas of South Africa most of the work is done by black contracted labor; however, some freehold areas near the larger cities are becoming mechanized. In West Africa the most successful small holders are the Ashanti cacao farmers of Ghana. Among the Ashanti each farmer generally owns from 12 to 20 acres and works them with the aid of his family and migrant labor coming from the Moslem north. In Uganda the British established a freehold tenure system which modified the political and other rights of the chiefs. Also, the rights of peasants on estates were defined and regulated by law. When a subsistence economy was dominant, Uganda women provided most of the labor. With the introduction of cash crops, the men have become active as cultivators of the economic crops, while the women continue to produce the food for subsistence. In parts of East Africa the plantation system is practiced. Given land on which to establish a sisal, coffee, or banana plantation, a European farmer may either hold the land in fee simple or have a lease of sufficient length to justify large-scale investment. Also, the *paysannat* system has recently been developed in parts of Angola. Under this system the Portuguese government gives a tract of land to a skilled and well-to-do farmer, who comes in, develops the tract for cash crops, and stays on the land as overseer and cultivator.

It is almost impossible to generalize about freehold tenure in Europe. Freehold areas abut areas maintaining various tenancy systems. In southern Italy and Sicily the great estates or *latifundi,* extensively rather than intensively cultivated, lie side by side with small plots characterized by intensive cultivation. Northern Portugal is a land of small freeholdings and a high population density; southern Portugal has large estates and a low density of population. In France most of the farmers own the land they operate. In Belgium, Luxembourg, and parts of the Netherlands tenancy is quite common, while landowning farmers predominate in the eastern portion of the Netherlands. In Scandinavia, England, and Ireland, freehold tenure is common, although at the time of the potato famine of 1848 most of Ireland's land consisted of tenant farms. Since the famine, governmental action has transferred land to the farmers, and the economy has changed from one based predominantly on food crops to one based on the raising of cattle for British markets and the keeping of poultry and dairy animals for local cities.

Freehold tenure is becoming somewhat more common in Latin America. For example, immigrants into Brazil from Italy, Germany, and Japan have settled in southern Brazil and have made a commercial success of freehold tenure in a country where small-scale freehold tenure has traditionally been associated with poor subsistence farming.

In the United States the ownership of land is still in flux. From the seven decades of homesteading (1865 to 1934) and the earlier period of governmental sale of trans-Appalachian lands, we have inherited a strong tradition of freehold ownership. Sometimes this system is called ownership in fee simple. In recent decades the accelerating pace of economic life has meant that farm production must increasingly respond to market conditions. For the individual farmer, such response means increasing the size of his holdings, making more intensive investment of capital and horsepower on the land he already has, or moving to an area where market conditions and competition are less strenuous. Any of these responses is likely to involve a mortgage. Both the farmer's mortgage and the urban dweller's house mortgage not only represent an effort toward an ideal of fee-simple ownership but also mirror the high degree of mobility in American life.

Most American farmers desire, of course, to own the land they operate, but in many cases economic competition forces them to be tenants, at least in part. In his study of farming in the spring-wheat belt of the Dakotas and Montana, Walter Kollmorgen has found two important types of nonresident farmers—*sidewalk* farmers (Fig. 15.4) and *suitcase* farmers. In regard to sidewalk farmers (those who reside in town and commute to the farm, rather than living on the farmland which they operate), Kollmorgen states:

Many informants in dryland wheat farming areas relate sidewalk farming to absentee landownership. . . . [In Toole County, Montana] about 41 per cent of the sidewalk farmers are full renters, as against about 27 per cent of the rural farmers. Conversely, rural farmers rate higher in full and part ownership.[3]

In regard to suitcase farmers (farmers who live 30 miles or more from their operations), Kollmorgen says:

Absentee ownership—largely by suitcase farmers themselves—and suitcase farming do seem to be closely related. . . . For the most part suitcase farmers must either buy land or find absentee owners from whom to rent. It is not popular in the County to rent land to suitcase farmers.[4]

Sidewalk farmers and suitcase farmers both generally operate more than one farm, and their holdings are scattered for protection against the vagaries of drought, insect damage, and plant diseases.

[3] W. M. Kollmorgen & G. F. Jenks, "Sidewalk Farming in Toole County, Montana and Traill County, North Dakota," *Annals of the Association of American Geographers*, Vol. 48, p. 220.
[4] W. M. Kollmorgen & G. F. Jenks, "Suitcase Farming in Sully County, South Dakota," *Annals of the Association of American Geographers*, Vol. 48, p. 37.

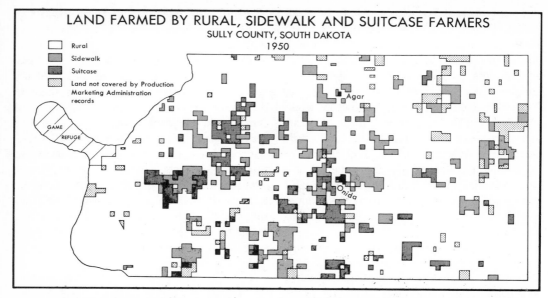

Fig. 15.4. Three kinds of farmers in the Great Plains. Rural farmers live on their own holdings or on rented lands. Sidewalk farmers live in small towns and commute to work on the farms. Suitcase farmers live in another county or state, and visit their farms at infrequent intervals. (Reprinted by permission of the Association of American Geographers.)

Tenant Tenure

When the people who work the land do not own it, they are considered to be tenants. (Much of the land outside the U.S.S.R. and mainland China is cultivated by tenants.) In return for use of the land, a tenant may either pay a cash fee or give his landlord a share of the crop. The origins of tenancy are diverse and involve historical factors, rates of population growth, and matters of preference. Tenancy tends to modify the use of the land in those areas in which it is practiced. In many areas the widespread occurrence of tenancy has given rise to movements for land reform. The following section considers types of tenancy, origins of tenancy systems, and the relation of tenancy systems to land use and land reform.

Types of Tenancy. Cash tenancy is relatively rare in the world as a whole, occurring mostly in advanced countries where commercial agriculture is dominant (the

United States, Canada, Australia, Argentina, and Brazil, for example). Cash tenancy is defined as a system under which a fixed amount of cash is paid to a landowner or a company for the use of land for farming. After the landowner has been paid the fixed amount (which is generally fixed by the landowner in a one-sided way), any profit derived from the land benefits the tenant.

Sharecropping is much more common than cash tenancy. Under this system, if there is a bad year, the crop is often distributed in such a way as to help the tenant through. If the year is good, both landowner and tenant see profit in their share of the crop. The proportion of the crop received by the landlord depends on population density, competition among tenants for available land often permitting the landlord to demand a greater share. The proportion taken by the landlord also depends on the amount of capital which he furnishes. For instance, if he furnishes the seed, fertilizer, and oxen or machinery for plowing, his share is far greater than it would be if the tenant provided them. In most areas where share-tenancy prevails, the amount taken by the landlord is established by the economic law of competition and is regulated by custom.

Carleton Coon reports that in one village near Tehran the yield of the grain is divided into five parts,

. . . one for the owner of the land, one for the water, one for the seed, one for the owner of the oxen, and one for the farmer who has done the work.

The landlord owns the land, and also the water, and usually he is called upon to supply the seed as well, which gives him three fifths of the crop. The oxen are owned by only a few men in the village. . . . Most of the farmers, who own no ox, receive only a fifth of what they produce.[5]

In almost all areas devoted to share-tenancy, there is a very complex system of proportions which depends on whether the tenant or the landlord provides the manure, machinery and implements, chemical fertilizers, aid and advice, threshing machinery, and marketing facilities. Because of this complexity, it is not possible to formulate a hard and fast rule for the division of shares that will be strictly applicable, even to a small area.

Although the cacao areas of Ghana were mentioned previously as being dominated by freehold tenure, a Ghana farmer who owns land which he does not operate often permits someone else to plant a cacao grove on his land. In such a case, one third of the crop goes to the farmer, one third to the landlord, and one third to the hired laborers from the north. If the tenant farmer is able to operate the land without hired labor, he takes two thirds of the crop. In a sharecropping scheme in Nigeria, the company which cleared the land and settled farmers upon it took two thirds of the produce, leaving one third of

the crop for the settlers. Eventually, the fact that each settler cultivated 24 acres and got the income from only eight acres proved a great deterrent to increased effort in the scheme.

Where tenants are not in competition for the land, landowners often find that they must make concessions to them. In some areas tenants acquire a right of priority, especially if they bring estate land into cultivation; the labor they put into the land brings them a sort of semipermanent tenancy, and they have the right of usufruct in the vines, trees, and fruit trees which they plant. In some areas of Iran the tenant may continue to operate the land as long as the roots of the alfalfa he has planted remain in the ground. Iranian landowners often discourage the planting of gardens by their tenants since tenants who have gardens tend to become more prosperous and to develop a more independent attitude. (The Iranian landlord thus has a problem with gardens which is similar to that faced by the government of the U.S.S.R.)

Origins of Tenancy Systems. Tenancy may come about as a result of such factors as invasion, indebtedness, land hunger, and personal preference. Tenancy systems have often originated in a "time of trouble" caused by an invasion or a military clique's assumption of power. Military groups often do not appropriate the land for themselves, preferring to sponsor the consolidation of agriculture under a different and sometimes initially rational system. In the Philippines the Spanish conquerors claimed all land for the Crown but recognized that persons actually working the land had rights of usufruct. Land not in cultivation when the Spanish took over the Philippines was often given to army personnel and politicians, who became extremely wealthy when this land was later brought under cultivation. When the United States assumed control of the Philippines in 1898, it generally confirmed the former Spanish land grants, disregarding any vaguely defined boundaries and relying on established

[5] Carleton S. Coon, *Caravan: The Story of the Middle East,* rev. ed., p. 183.

traditions of control. The problem of land tenure in the Philippines continues to plague each succeeding national administration. The pattern of large landholdings in such Spanish-conquered areas as Middle and South America and the Philippines resembles the pattern established in southern Spain when the *reconquista,* or reconquest of southern Spain from the Moors, was completed in 1492—the year Columbus sailed for the New World. Since small, owner-operated holdings were predominant in both northern Spain and northern Portugal at that time (as they still are), these areas were not open to those desiring vast landholdings. As a result, the soldiers of Queen Isabella who were unsuccessful in gaining estates in southern Spain quickly turned to the New World for land.

Indebtedness to moneylenders has proved to be another reason for tenancy. A succession of two bad harvests may force landowning peasants to become so indebted to a city merchant that he can eventually take over their land by mortgage foreclosure. Much of the rural land in Syria is owned by Christian merchants in the towns; these merchants have never farmed the land which they obtained through moneylending practices that reduced the former owners to the status of tenants. In Burma the rice areas of the lower Irrawaddy were once owned by the Chettyar moneylender caste from Madras; however, when Burma gained its independence in 1948, the government dispossessed the Chettyars and returned the land to the tenants. In Indonesia the Agrarian Decree of 1870, issued by the Dutch, forbade the alienation of land to Europeans and Chinese but made no provision against the alienation of paddy land to the well-to-do Indonesians of the cities who regularly made loans against mortgages on rice land. Because of the high interest rates that these men generally charged, borrowers frequently could not repay the loans and became tenants upon their formerly freehold land.

Because the original zamindars, or tax-collectors, leased out their interests, the *zamindari* system in India gave rise to various levels of tenancy. As the population grew, those who leased from the zamindars leased in turn to others, until a long chain of tenants and rent-receivers was formed. Proprietory rights in eastern Bengal were often held at seven or eight levels! In the process of land reform, the Indian government has reduced the amount of land held by zamindars from 43 per cent to 8 per cent of the arable areas. Various levels of tenancy also exist in southern India, where temples own large landed properties acquired through gifts. The temples lease their land to rich tenants who, in turn, sublease it to cultivators. After he has made a cash payment to the temple in return for a lease of perhaps a dozen years, the first tenant leases or sublets the land annually at a rather large profit from shares in kind.

Tenancy has also originated in land hunger brought about by population increase. Population pressures often result in greater intensity of land use, under which a small area may give the same profit as a larger plot under less intense cultivation. In an area of intensified cultivation, a farmer who owns a certain amount of property may rent out a part of it, particularly if he has a social or ritual obligation to lease land to friends or relatives. In Ceylon tenure systems are quite often arrangements between relatives; in Japan before the 1948 land reform, much of the rented land was held by family members. The social obligation to rent to family members is so strong that many of the colonists on newly reclaimed government land in Ceylon illegally and secretly rent out land to relatives and other persons. Population pressure in the Philippines has resulted in sub-tenancy. An agreement is made between an owner and a tenant, called an *inquilino,* who pays a certain amount of annual rent in kind or in cash. Although the *inquilino* owns the farm tools and animals and finances the farm operations, he often has share-tenants under him to do the actual farming; such share-tenants, called *kasamas,* amount essentially to agricultural laborers rather than tenants.

Still another origin of tenancy is personal preference. Sharecropping is often preferred by rather wealthy tenants in the United States because it permits fluidity of farm operations and mobility of tenants. If a sharecropper's family labor supply decreases, he can operate a smaller farm; if his labor supply increases, he can rent a larger farm. In such areas as northern Spain and northern Italy the sharecropping system works out extremely well. In those areas the landlord is resident, takes an active interest in the manuring of the land and the selection of good seed, and supervises the farming. He also arranges for co-operative buying and marketing and is more intimately involved in the system than is the landlord who leases for money or the owner who comes to the country only at harvest time.

Relations of Tenancy to Land Use. The relation of land-use patterns and emphases to tenure systems is indirect and by no means always clear. In a cash-crop economy there seems to be a tendency for tenant-operated farms to become larger as a result of the economies of scale connected generally with mechanization. In areas of subsistence economy and a growing rural population, fragmented holdings and smaller units of holdings tend to be characteristic of tenant farming. For instance, in the Kikuyu area of East Africa tenants may rent from two or more landowners and thus have fragmented and scattered plots of land. From the tenant's point of view, one drawback to the tenancy system is the fact that a tenant who is leaving the land is not ordinarily compensated for any improvements he may have made on the land; by and large, any improvements become the property of the landowner. In areas where land is held on long-term lease (in Hawaii both urban residences and rural farmhouses are often held on a 55-year lease), all improvements must remain on the land at the termination of the lease.

In areas where many people are competing for tenant tenures, the new tenant may have to pay the landowner a certain premium for the privilege of cultivating the land; land held under such circumstances may be used rather roughly, without practices conducive to soil conservation. On the other hand, in areas where the tenant has the traditional right to pass on his holding to his son, the land is used in a more rational and soil-conserving manner.

One rather significant relationship between environment and land tenure exists in Iran, where it has been noted that the land with the highest average annual rainfall is the land with the greatest percentage of large landed properties.[6] As the rainfall declines, the amount of owner-operated land increases; hence, as the rainfall increases, the rate of tenancy increases.

In Chile many of the large estates employed workers on what amounted to a hereditary basis. These tenants, or *inquilinos,* worked the land of the owner, lived on this land in separate family houses, and were allowed to have garden plots and small fields for themselves. The labor of the tenants was shared, rather than their produce, with each *inquilino* working three days for the landowner and three days for himself.

In a study of tenancy systems in Malaya, L. A. P. Gosling contrasted operations on sharecropped land, owner-cultivated land, and cash-tenancy, or fixed-rent, land. He found that ". . . less than one percent of share-cropped land is planted in fruit crops and vegetables; but more than 7 percent of owner-cultivated land, and more than 13 of fixed-rent land is so utilized."[7] He further noted that ". . . total time spent in weeding the crop—an indication of good farming—

---

[6] From an unpublished engineering report by Khwajeh Nuri, cited in Ann K. S. Lambton, *Landlord and Peasant in Persia,* pp. 269-271.

[7] L. A. Peter Gosling, "The Relationships of Land Rental Systems to Land Use in Malaya," *Papers of the Michigan Academy of Science, Arts, and Letters,* Vol. XLIV, p. 329.

averages only 18 man-hours per crop year on share-rented land, as compared with 23 man-hours on owner-cultivated land, and 37 man-hours on fixed-rent land."[8] Thus, where the fixed-rent system is predominant, the tenant engages in much more intensive cultivation; also, the tenant in the fixed-rent system puts more of his land in those subsistence crops, such as fruit crops and vegetables, which he can sometimes sell in the markets. In addition, Gosling found a significant difference in yields, noting that "yields on owner-cultivated land average 12 percent higher than yields on shared land; yields on fixed-rent land average 23 percent higher than yields on share-rented land."[9]

Tenancy in the United States. Farm tenancy, mostly of the share variety, is quite common in the United States. A summary of farm tenure in the United States indicated that in 1954 tenant operators were about 11 years younger than owners; also, in 1954 full owner-operators had farmed their holdings an average of 17 years, as against only seven years for tenants. These differences show a process rather than a class division, since many tenants eventually save enough money to become owner-operators.

As was indicated in the summary of farm tenure, sharecropping is the most common method of operation in the United States and prevails where staple crops are produced. Cash renting is limited in general to the poor land areas and to areas near cities; share-cash renting is concentrated in the areas of cash grain. There has been an increase in the size of farms operated by both tenants and part-tenants. According to the summary, the "average size of farm has increased by one-third since the beginning of the century. Part-owner farms have increased in average size by 103.4 percent, tenant farms have increased by 40.6 percent, and full-owner farms have *decreased* by 7.3 percent."

Movements for Land Reform. Land reform is of major importance in many of the

overpopulated areas of the world, where the demand for reform has been strengthened by the increasingly short supply of land. Those who want land reform do not necessarily want complete equality; they may want only to achieve greater equality by giving easier access to land, by breaking monopolies of ownership, and by reducing rents. A major program of land reform was carried out in Pakistan in 1959, when between three and a half and seven million acres of farmland were sold to two million landless tenant farmers, the 6000 former landlords to be repaid over a period of 25 years. Whether it is feasible to have widespread freehold tenure on such a small scale will depend upon the ease with which the peasants may buy seed, fertilizer, bullocks, and equipment normally provided by the landlords. In much of the Near East, land ownership has traditionally been dominated by large absentee landlords; where peasant proprietors or small owners exist, they farm only a small portion of the arable area. In much of Iran, for instance, small owners are at present confined largely to mountain regions and less fertile regions. Since freehold plots are often too small to support a family, outside income must be obtained through the women's weaving, the keeping of flocks, or occasional work on roads. Where small-owner villages are found side by side with villages of sharecropping peasants, the former are better cared for, just as the small-owner lands are better cultivated. In areas where crop failures are frequent, the small owner may suffer more than the sharecropping peasant during a bad year.

Doreen Warriner, an experienced observer of the Middle East, has stated that land reform in the modern world represents a turning point comparable in importance to the abolition of feudalism. The demand for and the implementation of land reform are the most insistent themes of our time. It is significant that many of the military regimes established since 1945 in Eurasia, Africa, and Latin America have stressed reform in

[8] Ibid., p. 330.
[9] Ibid.

land tenure. Since many of the systems of land tenure in these areas result from foreign conquest, or are associated with foreign rule, land reform represents one dimension of a growing nationalism and anticolonialism. Political popularity can commonly be gained by the promise of land reform, and few tenants or landless laborers would disagree with the view of Pliny that large estates destroy empires.

Institutional and Corporate Ownership

Unrestricted private ownership of every acre of land in a country would make society unworkable. Since, in every country, certain uses of the land are thought to be important for the community as a whole, ownership is often lodged in a government or a corporation of some sort. Land not privately owned may be owned or operated by various levels of government, by legal corporations, or by religious institutions. Among governmental types of ownership, we can distinguish four; national, state, county, and city ownership.

National Ownership of Land. National ownership of land results most frequently from conquest and less frequently from changes in government. Much of the land in the Middle East and most Latin American land became government property through conquest; in Latin America the land was soon parcelled out by the governments to private individuals. When the United States became independent of Great Britain, land belonging to the Crown was automatically considered to be public domain of the new country. In many British colonies and countries of the Commonwealth, Crown land is the necessary step between tribal or communal ownership on the one hand and private ownership on the other. In New Zealand the Maori voluntarily conceded many of their lands to the Crown in return for a monetary consideration. The assumption in English law that the rights of the freeholder are subordinate to the paramount powers of the Crown is the origin of the doctrine of eminent domain, whereby private land can be taken for public purposes upon the payment of adequate recompense. In Saudi Arabia much of the farmed land is owned by the royal family, which constitutes the government (Fig. 15.5).

The greatest degree of national ownership in the United States is found in the western part of the country, where national parks and national forest lands occupy a large proportion of the area. Federal ownership also applies to canals, many of the new highways, and all of the airspace. In the United States the national government has tended to limit its control of agricultural land, while maintaining and even expanding its control of forest land. Unlike Turkey and Canada, the United States allows freehold owners to hold subsoil mineral rights. Much of the public domain obtained through the Louisiana Purchase was distributed to homesteaders in the period from 1830 to 1890. The homesteaders' settlement of the public domain took place so fast that the government was not able to adjust its requirements on farm size rapidly enough to accommodate the need for larger farms in the less humid lands.

In the disposal of the public domain, one or two sections (a section is one square mile in area) of each township were kept out of private ownership for the purpose of financing schools. (This reserving of a portion of land for the common weal resembles the well-field system of ancient China described previously.) The ultimate origin of freehold land in the public domain is apparent to anyone buying land in the United States, for each deed traces the ownership of the land back either to Indian treaties or to original grants of land by English, French, or Spanish kings.

In such pastoral commercial economies as those found in the United States and Australia, pasture is most often owned and leased out by the government. The Taylor Grazing Act of 1934 codified and regulated United States policy on the use of government-owned pasture. In such pastoral subsistence economies as occur widely in Eurasia and Africa, pasture is most often communally owned.

National ownership of land results when the national government acts as middleman in land-reform transactions. During most processes of land reform, the national government buys the land from landowners and continues to own it until it is distributed to farmers in some manner. The new owners pay the government for the land over a period of time, generally 20 or 25 years, and the government reimburses the former owners for the expropriated land.

Since modern governments sponsor research of various kinds, they may own land for the purpose of agricultural experimentation. Most governments do not hold a great amount of land for this purpose, but the U.S.S.R. has devoted much land to state farms, called *sovkhozi,* which are operated by the national government for experimentation with various kinds of crops, various methods of planting and harvesting, and types of large-farm organization.

State, County, and City Ownership of Land. Political units smaller than the nation often own land in their own right. In the United States counties and states own forests and lands such as gravel pits for the repair of roads and highways. Since 1953 each ocean-bordering state has also had control of its offshore oil deposits. A state may also own such scattered properties as penitentiaries, mental homes, juvenile institutions, recreational areas, and educational institutions.

Although most city land is privately owned, the city as a unit may own the parks, the city-government buildings, and various areas where machinery is maintained for the upkeep of urban facilities and streets. In recent times some cities have purchased recreational areas beyond the city limits; for example, the Denver Mountain Parks area along the Front Range of the Rockies is about a dozen miles west of Denver. In New England certain towns now own property in the countryside for industrial development and recreational use—property which was once owned by a small number of individ-

Fig. 15.5. Livestock on the Khafs Daghra farm, Saudi Arabia.

uals; in a sense, this ownership is a return to a kind of communal tenure.

Corporate Ownership of Land. Ownership of land may be lodged in temporary corporations (such as the privately supported Bhoodan movement in India) and in legal corporations set up for the specific purpose of operating such areas as cemeteries and plantations or particular large-scale agricultural projects. Neither of these types of corporations is governmental in nature.

The Bhoodan movement, or "land-gift" movement, is the brainchild of Vinoba Bhave, a disciple of Gandhi, who travels around persuading landowners to give a portion of their land to be redistributed. By 1956 almost four million acres had been donated, of which about a quarter of a million had been distributed to some 8000 landless families; the remaining land was either nonarable or of such poor quality that no decision had yet been made as to its disposal.

Legal corporations in the United States and Canada may own cemeteries in order that persons belonging to certain organizations may be buried there; a corporation is able to provide a cemetery with "perpetual care."

A company plantation is usually dominated by a single cash crop and is, as a result, sometimes referred to as a farm factory. It is usually located in the tropics, where it has been initiated by a mid-latitude enterprise in response to demand for products not producible (or producible only at great cost) in nontropical areas. Since plantations (both within the tropics and on their fringes) have generally been associated with foreign capital and operation, they have often inspired political opposition. However, when (as in the eastern and western regions of Nigeria) plantations have been established by production-development boards under local governments, political opposition has been quite limited.

Production may involve either a local crop or an introduced crop like rubber in Malaya

or cacao in West Africa. Despite some instances of local regulation, capital and control are essentially foreign; and often the labor supply is foreign as well. (For example, many of the rubber-tappers in Malaya are Tamils imported from southern India.) Less than 1 per cent of the land area of the tropics is devoted to plantation agriculture, but plantations provide most of the tropical cash crops. Company plantations are generally much more extensive than private plantations; companies, for example, own large rubber plantations in Malaya, cacao plantations on the islands off the Guinea coast, and banana plantations in Central America. Such company-owned plantations seldom cause trouble except where they keep land out of cultivation. They may be responsible for certain undesirable social consequences, but they remain productive investments.

The large cotton plantations in the Gezira area of Sudan are unique examples of co-operation between a government, private corporations, and peasant tenants (Fig. 15.6). The government of the Sudan built a dam for the storage of irrigation water and canals for its distribution. Two companies, Kassala Cotton Company, Ltd., and Sudan Plantations Syndicate, Ltd., held concessions to market the crops and gave technical advice and assistance to the cultivators. The cultivators got 40 per cent of the profit from cotton sales, the remainder of the profit being shared by the two companies and the government. When the plantation system was nationalized in 1950 (upon Sudan's attaining its independence), the Sudan government assumed the role of owner and became the middleman in transactions concerning land management and cotton sales. The government has maintained the former provisions against sales of land to merchants, absentee ownership, and fragmentation of holdings.

Land owned and operated by religious institutions is now common in Latin American and Middle Eastern countries and was once common in feudal Japan. In the 12th century the Japanese government supported Buddhist temples directly; later, any land dedicated to temples and developed either by them or by farmers assigned to them was held to be exempt from taxes. Under the impetus offered by this system, land reclamation flourished in areas belonging to the temples, while the revenues of the central government declined and the nation lapsed gradually into feudalism. In areas (like Japan) where expanding population is exerting pressure upon a limited amount of cultivated land, the government often encourages the development of wasteland by giving remission from taxes for a period of years. Frequently, the reclamation of wasteland is done under the direction of a religious institution. Since the remission of taxes amounts to a subsidy that is supported by owners of land subject to taxation, it has been opposed in many areas.

In Islamic areas there is an institution known as *waqf,* wherein a person may dedicate land in perpetuity to a religious foundation or trust. The administrator of a *waqf*

receives 10 per cent of its produce; the remaining 90 per cent goes to fulfill the terms of the trust. Although a person cannot make a *waqf* in favor of himself, he may share in it if he falls within the category of persons for whose benefit it was created. When a *waqf* is dedicated, it becomes subject to a number of state controls; and in modern times it has been the policy of governments to resume national ownership of *waqfs* which have become defunct or misused.

Carleton Coon writes of *waqf* as follows:

As far as villagers are concerned, waqf property may consist of buildings, fields, orchards, individual trees, or public fountains; it is fixed property of any conceivable category. While miri land may not be given to a waqf, its produce can be so dedicated. This second kind of waqf property is called false waqf, as distinguished from true waqf, which is owned outright by the foundation and is inalienable. All waqfs, it will be remembered, do not belong to mosques or churches. Some are dedicated to specific charities, while others provide a secure income to the descendants of the donor and thus serve as

Fig. 15.6. Irrigated cotton fields in the Gezira plain, Sudan. The water is taken from the Blue Nile.

a trust fund. The waqf which maintains a public drinking place, however, is of benefit to everyone.[10]

Who Owns the Land?

In the above consideration of tribal tenure, communal tenure, freehold tenure, tenant tenure, and institutional ownership, one theme has been quite evident: the *social nature of land ownership*. Tenure systems, devised to facilitate the aims of a society, in turn reflect the dominant values of that society. It is interesting that consideration for the "greatest good of the greatest number" is found in most systems of tenure. In tribal tenure, the good of the group is thought most important; in communal tenure, equality of opportunity is a social goal. A basic purpose of plantation ownership by private corporations is the satisfaction of consumer demand; even in freehold tenure the use of the land is ultimately controllable for the public benefit through governmental application of the principle of eminent domain. Perhaps nowhere else than in systems of land tenure is it so apparent that "man is a social animal."

[10] Carleton S. Coon, op. cit., p. 186.

CHAPTER 16

The Search for Useful Minerals

As man gradually explored the face of the earth, he constantly searched for anything which might be of use. At the beginning of the Stone Age, man discovered that stones picked up on the surface could be broken in such a manner as to produce sharp edges with which to cut, scrape, and dig. This discovery was the humble beginning of what has become a long and elaborate search for various kinds of useful minerals. Unlike the widespread soils and natural vegetation, minerals are likely to occur in small pockets, mostly beneath the earth's surface. Since the beginning of industrialism, the search has been highly selective and well organized, making use of the latest scientific discoveries.

Primitive man found a variety of minerals on the surface of the earth, some of which he could use with very little processing. Stones of various hardness could be fashioned into weapons and simple tools; salt was obtainable to season and preserve food. Gold, silver, and copper occurred in the native metallic state; each could be pounded readily into any desired shape, but the fact that none of them could hold an edge very well led early man to seek other metals.

Iron was available to primitive man only in the form of meteorites. Although most meteorites are stony, a few are metallic and are composed largely of iron and nickel, which man soon found to be much harder

materials than gold, copper, and silver. With the aid of fire, man gradually learned to smelt the ores containing metals which did not occur in the native state and thus to bring about great improvements in his tools and weapons (Fig. 16.1). Some of the ores containing copper, tin, lead, and zinc could be reduced to metals very easily; moreover, since many of the ores were mixtures, the development of alloys was by no means difficult.

For many centuries these minerals played an interesting but minor role in human affairs. Some of them, such as gold, silver, and gems, provided man with a means of measuring value and of storing wealth. Some of the other elements, such as copper, lead, iron, and tin, served important functions in the manufacture of simple weapons and tools. It is only in the last century or so, however, that minerals have come into their own as the "vitamins" of industry, without which it would be impossible to carry on modern civilization.

The Useful Minerals

Modern industry depends upon an adequate supply of the right minerals. Every country or region with a well-rounded industrial development must possess or have access to essentially all of the fundamental minerals. These fundamental minerals may

238

be divided into groups according to their qualities and uses (Table 16.1). One group includes iron ore and such fuels as coal, petroleum, and natural gas; another includes the ferroalloys, such as tungsten and manganese; a third, the nonferrous metals, such as nickel, copper, lead, zinc, and tin; a fourth, the light metals, principally aluminum and magnesium; a fifth, the building materials, such as cement, sand and gravel, and stone; and a sixth, the chemical minerals.

Modern industry is based on iron ore and fuel minerals. Most modern industries use great quantities of power machinery, most of which is constructed of iron and steel. Iron, therefore, is the fundamental basic mineral, even though other minerals, such as aluminum, have been substituted to some extent for iron and steel for certain uses. The production of iron and steel calls for a special fuel, coke, most of which is derived from high-grade bituminous coal. Good coking coal is not too abundant. There are large supplies of it in eastern United States, western Europe, U.S.S.R., and China, but many countries are almost completely lacking in it. A very large part of the fuel used in manufacturing is consumed in the conversion of iron ore into pig iron and finally into steel. Petroleum and natural gas play a most important role in transportation and space heating all over the world; they are also basic raw materials for industry, especially for the chemical industries.

The iron alloys, or ferroalloys, are not needed in such quantities as iron ore and fuels; however, with the modern demand for special quality steels, the iron alloys are of critical importance. Such iron alloys as manganese, nickel, tungsten, and vanadium, as well as some nonferrous metals, give steel the special qualities needed for certain purposes; a very hard steel may be needed for some uses and a very tough steel may be needed for others. Since certain alloys also increase the tensile strength of steel, their occurrence is of great strategic importance.

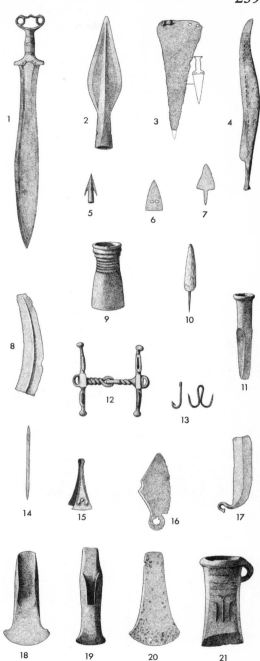

Fig. 16.1. Typical bronze implements (greatly reduced) of the Bronze Age in western Europe. 1-4, blade implements; 5-7, arrowheads; 8, saw; 9, hammer; 10, awl; 11, chisel; 12, bridle bit; 13, fishhooks; 14, needle; 15, tweezers; 16-17, razors; 18-21, axe blades.

TABLE 16.1   Mineral Resources of the World

		IRON	Iron ore
METALS	FERROUS	FERROALLOYS	Manganese Nickel Chromium Molybdenum Tungsten Vanadium
	NONFERROUS	BASE	Copper Tin Mercury Zinc Lead
		LIGHT	Aluminum Magnesium
		PRECIOUS	Gold Silver Platinum
		RARE	Uranium Radium Berylium
NONMETALS	MINERAL FUELS	FLUID	Petroleum Natural Gas
		SOLID	Anthracite coal Bituminous coal Lignite
	OTHER NONMETALS	BUILDING MATERIALS	Sand and Gravel Stone Cement materials Asphalt
		CHEMICAL MATERIALS	Sulfur Salt Lime
		FERTILIZER MATERIALS	Phosphate Rock Potash Nitrates
		CERAMIC MATERIALS	Clay Silica Feldspar Pumice
		REFRACTORIES	Silica Fire Clay
		ABRASIVES	Sandstone Corundum Industrial Diamonds
		INSULATING MATERIALS	Gypsum Magnesia Asbestos Mica
		PIGMENTS AND FILLERS	Ocher Clay Diatomite Barite
		GEMS	Gem Diamond Amethyst Amber

Fig. 16.2. An open-pit copper mine at Chuquicamata, Chile. The terraced levels permit the small railroad to "spiral" out of the pit.

The nonferrous metals include copper, lead, zinc, tin, aluminum, and magnesium. Copper is of great critical importance because of its use as a conductor of electricity (Fig. 16.2). Lead has many uses, including the very significant one in modern times of shielding nuclear devices in order to protect workers from radioactive emanations. Aluminum and magnesium, often called light metals because of their low specific gravity, have been produced in greatly increased amounts in recent years. Aluminum, now produced in large quantities, can, with suitable alloys, take the place of steel. Magnesium, somewhat lighter than aluminum but not quite so stable, is produced in smaller quantities than aluminum from both ores and sea water.

The construction minerals include building stone, sand and gravel, cement, gypsum, lime, asphalt, and asbestos. No one of these materials is especially critical since certain substitutions can be made. Cement can be produced wherever shale and limestone occur, either separately or in combination. Since building minerals are bulky and expensive to transport, it is essential to have sources of sand and gravel, cement, and other materials fairly close to important industrial areas.

The chemical and industrial minerals are often discussed together. Examples of these minerals are the nitrate, phosphate, and potash minerals, all of which are used in the manufacture of fertilizers. Another significant mineral is sulfur, which is used in the manufacture of sulfuric acid. Sulfuric acid is necessary in the processing of mineral fertilizers. The mineral fertilizers make a great contribution to agricultural production in many parts of the world, and they also enter into industrial processes, including the production of chemicals and drugs. The geographical location of these minerals in relation to areas of industrial development is not so important as the location of iron, fuels, and some of the ferroalloys and nonferrous metals.

Mineral Exploration

In order to supply the world's industries with various minerals, a search for new deposits is constantly being made in all areas of the earth. Unlike other resources, minerals are often very scattered, and some deposits are hidden far beneath the surface of the earth. The search for minerals goes on constantly all over the world with the aid of the most modern scientific apparatus. The method of search depends upon the nature of the ore deposits. A few minerals, including common salt, building stone, and sand and gravel, occur in great abundance very near or on the earth's surface. On the other hand, the ores of metallic minerals occur for the most part at some depth, although they may be exposed in part at the surface or there may be surface indications of their existence. The search for minerals is complicated by the fact that mineral deposits must have a certain degree of concentration in order to be workable. For example, iron ore must be at least 35 or 40 per cent iron before it can be profitably mined at the present time. (It would be possible, of course, to extract some iron from almost any part of the earth's crust since iron is a very widespread element and on the average makes up about 5 per cent of the earth's crust.) In some cases lower concentrations can be worked. Copper ores can be worked with a copper content of only 2 or 3 per cent. The concentration of the mineral required for mining depends upon the difficulty of the mining and smelting and on the value of the product. Gold, silver, and platinum can be mined profitably in low concentrations. Iron, aluminum, and manganese must have higher concentrations.

Primitive man explored for minerals by examining the materials that appeared on the surface of the earth. If he found a strange, heavy, black piece of rock, he might throw it into the fire to see what would happen. If the rock proved to be of some value, he might dig in the vicinity, hoping to find other specimens of the same material.

Today, prospecting for minerals is a very complicated process involving many devices. Most familiar of the recently developed techniques is the use of the geiger counter in prospecting for uranium and other radioactive materials. A geiger counter enables a prospector without much training to find indications of these materials. Prospectors may also use the magnetometer, which measures changes in the magnetic force of the earth. Sudden changes indicate a variation in rock material and the possibility of large deposits of some heavy metal, probably iron or some related mineral. Prospecting with a magnetometer can be carried on from an airplane; and thousands of square miles can be covered, at least in a preliminary sort of way, in a few hours. If hopeful indications are found, more detailed investigations can be made on the ground, including test drilling to locate and evaluate the ore body.

In the last century millions of prospectors have roamed over a large part of the earth's surface looking for mineral deposits of various kinds. Some of these prospectors have used fairly good methods and good instruments. Others have gone out with limited knowledge and a great deal of hope and, in many cases, have drilled or dug into the earth's surface without any definite indication of valuable deposits; despite its unreliability, this wildcat method has sometimes been successful.

With out-of-the-way areas being explored more and more carefully by thousands of prospectors dragging geiger counters over remote sections of the earth, the discovery of new deposits is becoming less likely and less easy. Nevertheless, there is indication that a great many mineral deposits remain to be discovered; discoveries have recently added to the reserves of certain minerals which were

Fig. 16.3. A gold dredge at Bonanza Creek, Yukon Territory, Canada. This dredge is equipped to thaw out frozen gravels in order to exploit deposits previously untouched.

considered to be approaching imminent exhaustion.

In the last 150 years there has been new development of mineral deposits in many parts of the world. Favored by large deposits of coal, petroleum, iron ore, copper, lead, zinc, gold, and many other minerals necessary for industry, the United States has made great industrial progress. As some of the deposits have neared exhaustion, new processes of mining and smelting have made it possible to work low-grade deposits economically. For example, newly developed methods of copper smelting and refining have made it possible to use ores that previously were of no commercial value. Concentration of low-grade iron ores through crushing and sorting has made them usable. Improvement of dredges has made it profitable to work gold-bearing gravels with only a few cents of value per cubic yard (Fig. 16.3).

Minerals and Modern Life

Historically it has been true that the nations with the best supplies of minerals and the most skill in their use are likely to be the most powerful nations. In ancient times the use of minerals was chiefly for tools, weapons, household utensils, and the construction of buildings, aqueducts, and roads. Today, when the chief use of minerals is for the production of power-driven machines, the distribution and supply of minerals is even more important. To be sure, minerals of high value per unit weight (such as gold, uranium, and diamonds) can be transported economically all over the world. However, heavy, bulky minerals of low value per unit weight must be mined relatively close to their area of use or must be able to take advantage of cheap methods of transportation.

The distribution of good-quality coal beds

Fig. 16.4. A strip coal mine at Fushun, Manchuria, closely resembles those in eastern Pennsylvania. This is similar to an open-pit metal mine but with fewer levels.

which could be readily mined has played an important part in industrial location. Coal attracts other minerals; iron ore goes to coal to be smelted and, as a result, the great iron and steel centers of the world have grown up in the coal fields: Pittsburgh, Birmingham, the Ruhr, and the Donbas in the U.S.S.R., to mention a few. Other factors were involved, including the location of earlier metal industries based on wood as a fuel. In England, for example, wood charcoal was used in smelting iron ore and in the manufacture of steel long before coal was used for these purposes.

At first, there was much opposition to the mining of coal because it interfered with the sale of wood; nevertheless, the use of coal spread rapidly in England (partly because the forests were almost completely exhausted) until, at the beginning of the 18th century, there were at least 600 ships carrying coal from Newcastle to London and other places to be sold for the modern equivalent of about four dollars per ton. Shortly afterwards, France began to mine coal in some quantity, and many other countries began to show some production. In the 1750's in Samuel Johnson's *Dictionary of the English Language,* both coal and petroleum were mentioned, but a mill was referred to as something driven by wind or water and sometimes turned by hand or animal force. In other words, although coal was used as a heating fuel and perhaps, to some degree, in the smelting of minerals, it was not used as a motive force.

In the United States the use of coal was developed somewhat later than it was in England. Although coal had been noted very early by a Franciscan monk in the vicinity of Peoria, Illinois, there was little or no use of coal in the United States until the 18th century. Wood was used for fuel and, since wood was abundantly available, there was no interest in developing coal as a fuel, even though outcroppings of coal were widely observed. It is probable that some coal was dug in western Pennsylvania by 1760, but at that time there were very few people living there. A few years later, anthracite coal was dug and consumed in small quantities in eastern Pennsylvania (Fig. 16.4). After the American Revolution, coal-mining companies were organized in Pennsylvania and coal was shipped by barge down the Susquehanna River to the towns below. At first the sale of coal was very limited, partly because no satisfactory stoves were available for burning it.

In the late 1700's and early 1800's, the invention and spread of the steam engine as a source of power had little effect upon the use of coal; wood was still too abundant. Actually, coal did not reach its peak of production until the advent of electric power and the generation of electric power from fuel plants. Today, in many countries, petroleum has replaced coal as the chief source of energy. Few coal-burning locomotives are left in the United States and many power plants which formerly used coal have converted to oil.

During the early part of the 19th century, especially during the 1830's, oil wells began to appear in the United States. These first oil wells were tapped accidentally during the process of drilling for water and brine. When oil was first discovered, there was little demand for it. Some oil was used for liniment and some was occasionally used in the crude state for fuel, but the demand was too small to encourage the further extension of well drilling.

A stimulus was given to the production of petroleum by the development of kerosene for lighting purposes, and for many years this development was responsible for the only substantial use of petroleum. The invention and perfection of the internal-combustion engine, however, changed the whole picture: it put a premium on gasoline rather than kerosene and greatly expanded the market for petroleum (Fig. 16.5).

Fig. 16.5. A portion of an oilfield on the northern coast of Peru. The derricks are used in drilling the wells, and the pumps are connected to large motors by the horizontal cables near the ground.

By 1870 coal and petroleum had many small-scale uses, but they were still very primitively developed as sources of power. Railroads were in use, but they burned wood; steamships had been developed, but many of them still used sails for auxiliary power. However, wood was becoming scarce near the cities, and more and more coal mines and oil wells were being opened up; man had, for the first time in history, the means of large-scale power development and industrial enterprises.

Today it would be difficult to overestimate the significance of the mineral fuels. More than half of the power in the United States comes from petroleum; coal is a close second in power production; hydroelectric energy, although increasing in importance, ranks a poor third. Still in an early stage of development, the large-scale use of nuclear energy is dependent on increased mineral production. Many industrial operations require mineral fuels for which there are no substitutes. For instance, although it is possible to supply heat from sources other than coal (such as hydroelectric energy), coal is essential to the smelting of many minerals and is an important source of many chemicals. Likewise, it would be very difficult, though not impossible, to run internal-combustion engines without petroleum products in airplanes and automobiles.

What is the future of the world production of mineral fuels? So far as coal is concerned, there are large reserves which are usable, if not of the highest quality. Anthracite is scarce and high-grade bituminous is not too plentiful, but low-grade bituminous coals are present in enormous quantities and lignite, the lowest form of coal, is also available in large quantities. On the other hand, although the best supplies of petroleum are relatively near exhaustion, new fields are being discovered almost every day. Reserves of petroleum are increasing in spite of the large production. Although we are taking out a larger and larger quantity of petroleum from the earth every year, the estimated supply continues to increase because of the dis-

covery of more liquid fuel. The question of how long this increase will go on has no certain answer, and it is very difficult to make an adequate statement about the future of world production. We have to assume that the present estimates (which indicate an adequate supply for the next 25 years) are reasonably correct and that the demand for petroleum will keep on increasing from year to year. It is significant, of course, that in recent years the production in the United States has not been sufficient to supply the country's own needs. Sometime in the future, the world may very well utilize some form of nuclear energy, instead of petroleum and coal, as its main source of power. It is impossible to determine at the present time just exactly when this change will come and what it will mean.

Many times in the past history of mineral utilization has the discovery of a new use for a mineral revolutionized industry. For example, the whole fabric of energy production has been changed by the discovery made in 1945 that uranium, hitherto considered to be of limited use, was a source of energy a million times more concentrated than any material used before. Of course, the impact of this discovery on world politics and warfare has been fully as important as its impact on energy production—perhaps even more important. It is possible now to provide a long-lasting source of energy within a very small space that in the long run may be cheaper than any other form of energy now in use. Nuclear energy is not an unmixed blessing, however, because its use produces harmful by-products and wastes which are very difficult to dispose of without contaminating air, water, and soil. One current method of disposal involves filtering nuclear waste products and storing them in large iron tanks which are to be buried in the ground. Since these tanks are subject to rust, they eventually free the wastes, allowing them to contaminate the ground water. This method of disposal is also very expensive and results in such a high price for nuclear energy that the older sources of power—such as hydroelectricity and fuel—can easily compete. If

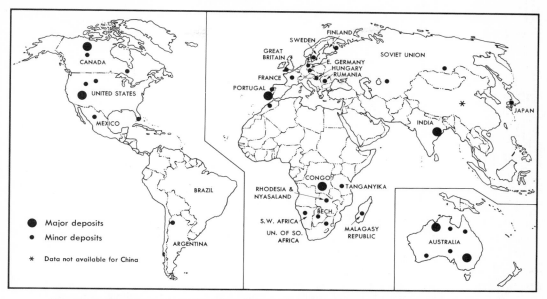

Fig. 16.6. World uranium deposits. (After *Focus*, American Geographical Society.)

and when successful methods of waste disposal are developed at low cost, they will undoubtedly have a very strong effect upon the location of industry and population concentrations. It is possible that disposal may be worked out in connection with underground beds of rock salt. If such should be the case, the great cities of the future in the United States might be located in western New York, southern Michigan, and eastern Kansas.

Uranium is a fairly abundant metal in the earth's crust, but it occurs in such small concentrations that it is somewhat difficult and expensive to process. Discovered in 1789, uranium was considered a rare metal until recent world-wide exploration, on a scale never before known in history, resulted in the uncovering of many sources of uranium. Some of these sources represent very low-grade deposits which cannot be favorably mined at the present time but constitute possible sources for future use. At the present time there are major uranium-mining operations in the Congo, Canada, the United States, Australia, India, Portugal, and the U.S.S.R. (Fig. 16.6). In the Congo and in

Canada (especially in the Sudbury and Great Bear Lake areas) uranium deposits contain from 1 to 4 per cent uranium. Elsewhere, the concentration is much lower, but deposits containing less than 1 per cent have been successfully exploited in South Africa and in the United States.

In the future probably the most important use for uranium and the associated radioactive metals will be in the conversion of nuclear power into electrical energy. This conversion is very important for parts of the earth which do not have good supplies of fuel or favorable conditions for hydroelectricity. However, for most countries the development of nuclear energy or atomic energy is not immediately critical since reserves of coal and petroleum are still fairly large and since hydroelectric energy, once developed, is continuous.

The nuclear-power era which is being ushered in at the present time will have abundant source material in uranium, thorium, and other metals. The efficient use and economic utilization of these nuclear fuels is a problem which is currently being studied. The amount of energy resource in nuclear fuels is much greater than the total amount contained in all the other fuels and sources of energy found in the earth itself. (Solar energy is not included in this comparison.) According to present developments, uranium will probably be the most important nuclear fuel for the near future.

It is evident that the greatest changes in the production and use of minerals in the near future will be in the field of the fuels, including the nuclear fuels. Petroleum, for example, will probably reach a maximum peak of production in the United States between 1965 and 1975 and in the world as a whole perhaps a few years later. Thereafter, because of the increased demand per capita in other countries, it will be increasingly difficult for the United States to import cheap petroleum. The peak of world coal production will probably be around 1975 or 1980. After that, although there are large reserves of coal in the United States and elsewhere, coal will be more expensive to mine and transport to the places where it is used. The rapid development of nuclear energy may modify some of these predictions by taking over some of the uses of petroleum and coal. Many people believe that in a decade or less the use of nuclear energy will be common throughout world industry. However, any consideration of the various sources of energy must be concerned not only with the total energy available from the sources but also with the cost of the energy unit by unit. Thus, although nuclear energy is coming into use rapidly, the cost of its production may be too great for many years to allow it to become a replacement for coal or petroleum.

Strategic Minerals and the Effects of Scarcity

The rank of a mineral in terms of its monetary value does not really express its total significance for modern industry and for the well-being of man. Such minerals as copper, lead, zinc, and iron are used in large quantities, whereas only small amounts of other minerals are needed. For example, germanium is a critical metal in the manufacture of transistors, which have replaced radio tubes in many instruments. Because it is a scarce metal, it is fortunate that only a very small fraction of an ounce of germanium is needed for each transistor. The ferroalloys are of great importance. For instance, varying amounts of manganese, molybdenum, chromium, vanadium, and several other ferroalloys are used in the manufacture of steel and are essential to its quality. The importance of a mineral then is to be judged not only by the total monetary value of the quantity used but also by its scarcity and the significance of its use. A mineral which a country itself cannot supply in quantities sufficient to satisfy demand within the country is usually considered to be a strategic mineral in that country. In the United States minerals considered to be strategic include uranium, tin, various steel alloys, manganese, industrial diamonds, and quartz.

The fact that many of the most useful minerals are relatively scarce in many parts of the world has a profound effect upon the political and industrial life of many nations. Faced with problems related to strategic minerals, the United States has taken two lines of action. In the first place, government subsidies have been directed toward the development of the low-grade deposits of such minerals as chromium. Although chromium is a very important member of the ferroalloy group and chrome steel is a necessity for modern industrial development, the United States has no high-quality or rich chromium deposits of any size and its miners cannot carry on chrome-ore production at the world price. In order to encourage chromium production in the United States, the Federal government undertook a system of purchasing chrome ore from miners at a price well above the world market price. This purchasing program led to the development of many low-grade deposits, as well as some small high-grade deposits, and boosted the production of chromium very substantially; eventu-

Fig. 16.7. Strategic minerals are stockpiled in many parts of the United States. These piles of copper ingots, in the foreground, and aluminum pigs, in the rear, are located near Cincinnati, Ohio.

ally, as a result of this increase in production, the subsidies were discontinued.

The scarcity of strategic minerals has also been dealt with through extensive peacetime purchasing. In times of peace, when the strategic minerals are available on the world market, large quantities of the minerals may be purchased abroad and stockpiled as reserves to be used in case foreign supplies should ever be cut off (Fig. 16.7). Such purchases are feasible in connection with minerals which can be stored without deteriorating through oxidation or contamination.

Every region in the world has its own special problems with relation to mineral resources. In South America, for example, metallic minerals (including iron ore) are fairly abundant, but good coking coal is scarce. Africa has a somewhat similar problem. In western Europe there is a fairly abundant supply of coking coal, as well as de-

posits of high-grade iron ore. The U.S.S.R. has good supplies of both coking coal and iron ore, but it is short on some of the ferroalloys. In India and China there are fair supplies of coking coal and high-quality iron ore. The most densely inhabited countries on the face of the earth, India and China are now going into a period of very rapid industrialization based upon their own mineral resources, plus imports.

One of the effects of scarcity of minerals has been greatly accelerated exploration of most parts of the earth. Another effect has been the necessity for the "have" countries to aid the "have-not" countries with loans and grants to provide for mineral exploration and construction of processing plants. Still another profound effect has been the realization that no country is self-sufficient in all the essential minerals—a fact which has far-reaching political meaning.

Invention is a drama enacted on a crowded stage.
Michael Polyani

CHAPTER 17

Man and Technology: The Role of Invention

Throughout human history and prehistory, man has been fascinated by tools and machines. He has tinkered with, changed, tested, and retested countless thousands of methods of extending his meager physical power. Just as man's inventions have necessarily depended upon the general level of technology, so his use of resources has depended on inventions enabling him to do something new with, or to, his environment.

Early Inventions

Every invention depends upon one or more previous inventions or discovered techniques. H. S. Harrison, an English archaeologist, has pointed out that "the harpoon could have been invented only by a people who already had the spear, and the loom only by those who were familiar with textiles made by hand."[1] Though some curious men in any group are liable to chance upon an invention, the contention that a man would far rather borrow from another man than invent something of his own seems to have been proven by human history. Even as early as the Neolithic period, tribes of varying backgrounds scattered over a wide area used tools and weapons that conformed fairly closely in style. Since such a similarity in the making and using of tools could certainly not have been accidental, it may be assumed that these people were in communication with each other. Although these people certainly

[1] *A History of Technology,* Vol. I, p. 62.

did not have the rapid means of communication now available, ideas were slowly and gradually passed from tribe to tribe until they became rather widespread. Since the body of ideas composing Paleolithic and Neolithic cultures was not vast, it was easily spread and widely adopted. Fishing hooks and lines, lassoes (running nooses), bolos (weighted cords), fishing nets, and spears were all in use very early in prehistory almost everywhere man lived. Most groups were using hand drills by upper Paleolithic times.

Discovery of Rotary Motion. During the Mesolithic period the bow drill was invented, probably being used first for making fire. The

Fig. 17.1. Indonesian pump drill. The flywheel is a stone-filled coconut.

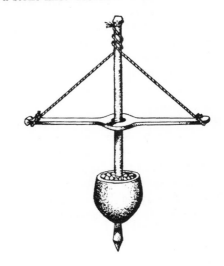

pump drill (Fig. 17.1) was not invented until Roman times. Whereas both these drills involve discontinuous rotary motion, continuous rotary motion was introduced with the invention of the potter's wheel, the first use of which is considered to have been in Ur between 3500 and 3000 B.C. Probable dates for the diffusion of the potter's wheel are shown in Table 17.1.[2] The lathe, the first application of horizontal-axis rotary motion, probably did not come into existence until classical times.

TABLE 17.1

Diffusion of the Potter's Wheel

Sumer	3250 (±250) B.C.
Syria-Palestine	3000 B.C.
Egypt	2750 B.C.
Crete	2000 B.C.
Mainland Greece	1800 B.C.
Southern Italy	750 B.C.
Upper Danube-Upper Rhine	400 B.C.
Southern England	50 B.C.
Scotland	400 A.D.
Americas	1550 A.D.

Wheeled Vehicles. The history of the Old World is intimately bound up with the use of wheeled vehicles. The principle of the wheel was applied to transport probably a short time after its application to the making of pottery. As in the case of the potter's wheel, the first reliable evidence of wheeled transport comes from Sumer, in the Tigris-Euphrates Valley. The first wheeled vehicles were hearses and war chariots, both of which had solid wheels. The spoked wheel (which probably led ultimately to the cogged wheel by extension of the spokes beyond the rim) did not appear until 2000 B.C., when horses were first introduced into the Near East from the north. The dates of the appearance of wheeled vehicles are shown in Table 17.2.[3]

[2] Derived from *A History of Technology*, Vol. I, p. 203.

[3] *A History of Technology*, Vol. I, p. 211.

TABLE 17.2

Appearance of Wheeled Vehicles

(All dates B.C.)

Sumer	3500
Assyria (upper Tigris River)	3000
Indus Valley	2500
Upper Euphrates River	2250
Southern Russia-Crete	2000
Central Anatolia	1800
Egypt-Palestine	1600
Mainland Greece	1500
China	1300
Northern Italy	1000
Southeastern Sweden	1000
Britain	500

Plows, Sickles, and Weaving. Made with a horizontal stock, the plows of the Near East and the Mediterranean area barely disturbed the soil's surface; but they were quite adequate in the light soils of these areas, where conservation of moisture (through dry farming) was of primary concern. Since the fields in these areas were cross-plowed, they were most often square in outline.

Cultivation spread from the Mediterranean area to the heavier clay lands of northwestern Europe as a result of the demand for grain to supply the growing Roman Empire. To cut and farm the sticky sod of northwestern Europe demanded a different sort of plow. From their experimentation in pre-Roman times, the northern Europeans had evolved a keel plow that was effective in sticky soils; when tilted in action by the plowman, it provided a turned sod. By the 11th century the mouldboard plow, which automatically overturns the sod rather than merely disturbing it, had come into use. (Although in common use for centuries, the mouldboard plow was not perfected until Thomas Jefferson designed its optimum shape.) The fields of northwestern Europe became long and narrow as they were plowed by the keel plow and the mouldboard plow. Since cross-plowing was not necessary and since heavy soils were being worked, the farmers did not want to

Fig. 17.2. Model of Egyptian weaving and spinning from the tomb of Nehen Kwetre at Thebes. Period is Middle Kingdom.

loom, which persists to this day (Fig. 17.2). The warp-weighted loom dates from about 2500 B.C., the earliest example being credited to Troy. Weaving and basketry were found in Peru as early as 2000 B.C., and higher weaving techniques appeared there about 800 B.C. The first "modern" weaving pattern, that of twill damask, appeared in China about 1000 B.C. and was diffused very slowly, not reaching the Mediterranean area until about A.D. 50.

Inventions of the Greeks. Pulleys and winches first appeared in Greece between the 6th century and the 4th century B.C. Both were applied in (and probably invented for) navigation and the theater, which used similar devices. It is not surprising that inventions should have arisen in connection with ships and stages, for sailing and the drama were of central importance in Greek life.

The mathematical bent of the Greeks may have led them to invent other machines by analogy. At any rate, the number of devices (Table 17.3)[4] invented by the Greeks between 600 B.C. and 100 B.C. is a tribute to their imagination and skill.

take their plowshares out of the ground frequently. As a result, there developed the typical field pattern of northwestern Europe, the strip-field.

According to present knowledge, the first farming tool was a primitive sickle—made of a bone set with flint teeth—that was used by cave-dwelling farmers near Mount Carmel, Palestine, about 6000 B.C. Except for some technical improvements in shape and the application of its form to metal, this sickle remained the main harvesting tool until the invention of the mechanical reaper in the 1840's.

Weaving and basketry, already well developed, appear in the archaeological record of the Near East about 5000 B.C., having originated perhaps more than 10,000 years ago. The first loom appeared in Egypt about 3000 B.C.; a horizontal ground loom, it was simply pegged out on the ground. By about 1400 B.C. Egypt also had the vertical framed

TABLE 17.3

Greek Inventions, Prior to Our Era

Wood-turning lathe	late 6th century B.C.
Winches	early 5th century B.C.
Pulleys	late 5th century B.C.
Auger (screw)	late 5th century B.C.
Bow drill	late 5th century B.C.
Analysis of lever action	probably 3d century B.C.
Compressed-air weapons; suction pumps; air pumps	attributed to Ctesibius, dates uncertain, but no later than beginning of 1st century B.C.

The Greeks distinguished five basic types of simple machines or devices for the conversion of motion: lever, wedge, winch, pulley, and screw. Hero, a scientist of Alexandria (who died about A.D. 75), later reduced the

---

[4] Derived from *A History of Technology*, Vol. II, pp. 630-636.

five simple machines to the principle of the lever, the principle of the wheel, or a combination of the two.

Further important advances were made during the Late Middle Ages, when reduction gears, cranks, and connecting rods were invented, all allowing conversion of either motion or power. Well known to most college history students are the mechanical inventions and adaptations of Leonardo da Vinci (A.D. 1452-1519). Less well known, but certainly as important for the development of western Europe, are the experiments of the Cistercian monks, who operated flour mills, cloth-shrinking and cleaning machines, and various powered crushers and grinders. Cistercian monasteries were often built near rivers in order to gain water power.

Early Development of Prime Movers

Machines that provide motive power for other machines or tools are called prime movers. In describing the advance of technology, scholars distinguish five stages in the development of prime movers:

I Muscle power, mainly from human effort.
II Increased human and animal power.
III Power from the water mill and later from the windmill.
IV Power from the steam engine and internal-combustion engine.
V Atomic power.

The advance from one stage to another indicates the availability of more concentrated energy. The transition from stage I to stage II has sometimes been slow. For example, in ignorance of animal anatomy, the Romans attached the ox-harness indiscriminately to horses and mules and obtained only four times the work of a man rather than the 15 times as much work gradually made possible after the 12th century by the use of a modern harness, independently evolved but very similar to the Chinese harness.

By far the most important prime movers in the Middle Ages and the Renaissance

period were wind and water mills. The experience gained in stage III, the age of mills, made possible the expanding settlement and the growing urbanization of Europe.

Water-Driven Mills. Water wheels apparently originated during the 1st century B.C. Used by the Greeks to grind grain (a constant task in all households), the first horizontal water wheels were limited to high-speed mountain streams, each wheel serving the needs of only one farmhouse. Although water wheels would not work in the sluggish rivers of Egypt and Mesopotamia, the use of the water wheel spread east to China and west to Ireland during the four centuries after its invention.

Not long after the discovery of the horizontal water mill, a Roman engineer invented a more efficient vertical mill. First using an undershot wheel placed in a stream, the developers of the vertical mill eventually found that the wheel did more work if the water overshot it and pulled it down. Aqueducts, common in areas influenced by Roman civilization, often provided the water necessary for the operation of vertical mills. The introduction of the vertical mill into major urban centers is thought to have been prompted by a shortage of slave and pauper labor.

By applying the principles of the water wheel in reverse, the paddle wheel was developed for moving boats and was first used (around A.D. 370) in propelling warships. When the Goths besieged Rome in A.D. 537, they tried to starve the city by destroying the aqueducts that provided power for its grain mills. To counteract the effects of this destruction, the Romans put a paddle wheel between two boats anchored in the middle of the Tiber River and thus made the power of the flowing river available for the grinding of grain. Floating mills of this type still survive in the Po Valley.

Between the middle of the 10th century and the end of the 12th century, mills relying on water power became common in northwestern Europe. They were basic to the economic revival of the Late Middle Ages and played a large role in the urbanization of northwestern Europe. The following list of uses for water power from A.D. 1050 to 1380 is by no means exhaustive:

Water-lifting wheels	Tanning mills
Wood-turning mills	Iron mills
Cutlery-grinding mills	Hemp mills
Irrigation wheels	Saw mills
Pigment-grinding mills	Malt mills
Stamping mills for crushing rock	Hammer mills
	Oat mills

Windmills. The earliest windmill-type objects were found by Chinese explorers in central Asia about A.D. 400. Consisting of scoops on wind-rotated prayer wheels, these early examples may have inspired the invention of the windmill designed for power purposes. The first working windmill for producing power for work was built by a Persian about A.D. 640; although 300 years later it was still confined chiefly to the Persian plateau, it spread to China in the 12th century.

Windmills with four vertical sails attached to a horizontal shaft played a great part in the settlement and urbanization of northern Europe. In areas far from dependable streams and in swampland, windmills (Fig. 17.3) could be used where water mills could not. First employed for grinding grain, windmills soon came to be used to lift water from poorly drained areas.

The first verified reference to a windmill in northern Europe dates from about A.D. 1180, and by the late 13th century windmills were common there. As the growing settlements in the gradually urbanizing portions of the North European Plain (Flanders to Paris and eastward to Lübeck) demanded fuel, peat bogs were exploited. As the peat bogs were dug, windmills were used (circa 1430) to pump water out of the shallow man-made lakes. Later, about 1600, windmills became common in the polder areas under reclamation by the Dutch.

Reclamation in Europe. The 15th century in northern Europe was a century of advance in the application of known power techniques to new uses, most of which uses had direct geographic significance. Because the growing amount of trade demanded better ports, new ways of dredging shallow existing ports were devised. New methods of draining swamps were instituted, combining the Archimedean screw (a screw encased in a cylinder) and the windmill (Fig. 17.4). Port facilities were improved by the addition of hoisting cranes (which ran on wooden rails) and swivel cranes, both of which offered greater ease of handling. The internal network of canals in Europe for the most part dates from the 15th century and results from lock-gate systems which were much improved during that period. The successful development of various devices for draining and filling water locks permitted many new canals for inland navigation and many new connections between major navigable rivers.

The combination of the Archimedean screw and the windmill that was introduced into the Low Countries in the 16th and 17th centuries was gradually replaced after 1640 by scoop wheels. In draining polders, scoop wheels worked in rows at a series of levels, lifting water from one level to a higher level until the water was pumped out of the polder.

Fig. 17.3. Detail of etching of windmills (by Hollar in 1650) based on painting by Breughel.

The screw-windmill combination, however, continued to be used in the northeastern parts of the Netherlands, where small polders were very common. Of the land reclaimed in the Netherlands between 1540 and 1690, about four fifths of it, or 650 square miles, was not drained by windmills and water lifts; it was reclaimed by man's diking off of the sea (Fig. 17.5) and his efforts in assisting accretion and accelerating sedimentation.

A second area of attempted reclamation in Europe included the Pontine marshes, an area of about 300 square miles to the southwest of Rome. Although reclamation efforts had been attempted, at the beginning of the 16th century the area was still a marsh with a notorious reputation as a malaria center. Between the beginning of the 16th century and the middle of the 17th century, there were four separate attempts to drain the Pontine marshes, each of which failed after the death of its chief engineer. At the beginning of the 18th century, the plans of the last unsuccessful engineer were carried out by his son; but the plans failed, largely because of the opposition of the local inhabitants.

Fig. 17.4. Archimedean screw used for raising irrigation water in modern Egypt.

Fig. 17.5. Closing the gap in a Zuider Zee dike, 1931.

In the Wash area of England some 700,000 acres, or 1100 square miles, of low grassland and marsh began in the 17th century to be regarded as fit for reclamation. Since there was no pressure for increasing the amount of agricultural land, the reclamation was undertaken primarily as a financial venture. In 1630, with the advice of one Dutch engineer and reports by others who had once studied the project, the first drainage of the Wash area was attempted. The project, covering 307,-000 acres, or about 480 square miles, was completed 23 years later in 1653. The area reclaimed was about 70 per cent of the total area reclaimed in Holland in the previous 150 years.

Reclamation of marshes in France followed the successful pattern developed by the Dutch both in their own country and in the Wash of England. Because French reclamation was more politically centralized, the problems of organization and finance were solved speedily. Between 1607 and 1685 the marshes of Poitou, Normandy, Picardy, Languedoc, Provence, and other areas were drained and made into fine agricultural land.

Windmills made available considerably more power than was offered by other prime movers in use at the time. R. J. Forbes has written that ". . . eighteenth-century Dutch marsh-mills . . . needed a wind velocity of 8 to 9 m/sec [18-21 miles per hour] to work efficiently and they produced 10 to 12 hp, or 15 hp at the utmost, in an average wind."[5] Table 17.4 shows the relationship between this amount of power and the power produced by prime movers contemporary with the windmill.[6]

The Industrial Revolution

In the British Isles the years between 1760 and 1830 constituted a period of great ferment in ideas about the control of nature. Science had widened man's concept of the universe, and foreign trade had expanded his

[5] *A History of Technology,* Vol. IV, p. 159.
[6] Ibid.

TABLE 17.4

Horsepower Generated by Various Prime Movers

Man working a pump	0.036
Man turning a crank	0.040-0.078
Man pushing a capstan bar	0.047
Horse turning a gin at a walk	0.367-0.578
Various 18-foot overshot wheels	2 - 5
Post windmill	2 - 8
Turret windmill	6 - 14

view of the world. The cumulative effect of the changes during these years justifies our calling the period the Industrial Revolution. R. J. Forbes, a technological historian, has stated that "four basic technical achievements" constituted the Industrial Revolution. These achievements were the "replacement of tools by machines, the introduction of new prime movers, the mobile prime mover, and the factory as a new form of organization of production."[7]

Steam Engines and Coke. Among the numerous inventions of the Industrial Revolution, most outstanding were the invention of the steam engine (the new prime mover mentioned by Forbes) and the discovery of the usefulness of coke in smelting iron. Between 1765 and 1788 James Watt of Scotland experimented with the principle of the steam engine, adding various refinements from time to time. In 1784 Henry Cort discovered that coke (coal partially burned in a shortage of air) could be substituted for charcoal in the process of smelting iron (Fig. 17.6).

These two inventions had important geographical effects. The use of coke freed forge masters from their dependence on woodlands and permitted dozens of formerly scattered mills to be centralized around the four main coal fields of England. The use of steam as motive power allowed factories to be located away from high-gradient streams and permitted their concentration around the major coal fields. The economies that resulted from the coming together of iron mills and powered factories near the coal fields encouraged a

[7] Ibid., p. 150.

STEAM POWER

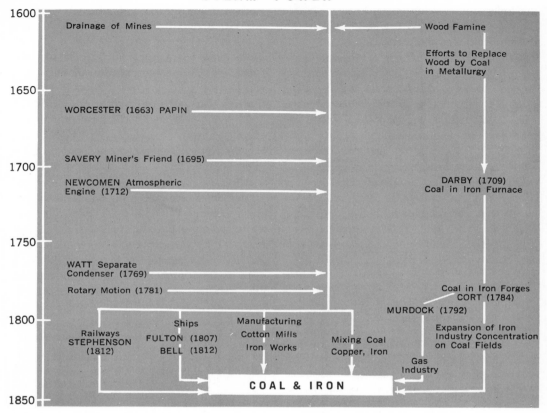

Fig. 17.6. Stages in the development of steam power in England leading to application in the Industrial Revolution.

growing supply of investment capital. Industries of all kinds expanded as profits were reinvested to take further advantage of the economies of centralization and the growing supply of cheap labor from the countryside. The "animating effects of cheap iron" were felt in shipbuilding and in agriculture, in weaving and in engineering. The geographical centralization of industries eventually led to central control or ownership of all the elements of the industrial process: from the mining of ore and coal to the processing of the final product of the mills. The cumulative effects of technology are well illustrated in the Industrial Revolution. Techniques used in one industry were often modified for use

in a different industry; new machines and new processes often resulted from attempts to imitate old machines and processes.

The Industrial Revolution would hardly have succeeded had it not been for progress in the making of machine tools, or machine-making devices. Basic machine-tool types include gear makers, milling machines, planers, boring machines, lathes, and drills. Most of the fundamental thinking about machine tools, including even those used in modern times, was done between 1775 and 1850. The machine-tool industry was first developed by the British, but by 1850 the machine-tool industry in the United States was also advanced. Many machine tools were made possible by the discovery of the cam principle; machines for making metal-boring screws, for planing metal, and for making gears all utilize variants of the cam.

After the introduction of the Siemen's open-hearth process in 1856 and the coming into use of the Bessemer converter the same year, the price of steel dropped precipitously. The development of cheap steel vastly extended the range of machine tools, just as the introduction of cheap iron had previously extended the range of machines in general.

Increase in Living Standards. The growing urbanization caused by the Industrial Revolution was accompanied by better health and a reduced death rate. T. S. Ashton, an English historian, describes these improvements in *The Industrial Revolution 1760-1830:*

Many influences were operating to reduce the incidence of death. The introduction of root crops made it possible to feed more cattle in the winter months, and so to supply fresh meat throughout the year. The substitution of wheat for inferior cereals, and an increased consumption of vegetables, strengthened resistance to disease. Higher standards of personal cleanliness, associated with more soap and cheaper cotton underwear, lessened the dangers of infection. The use of brick in place of timber in the walls, and of slate or stone instead of thatch in the roofs of cottages reduced the number of pests; and the removal of many noxious processes of manufacture from the homes of the workers brought greater domestic comfort. The larger towns were paved, drained, and supplied with running water; knowledge of medicine and surgery developed; hospitals and dispensaries increased; and more attention was paid to such things as the disposal of refuse and the proper burial of the dead.[8]

Technology and Farming. The Industrial Revolution was accompanied by many changes in agriculture. The headlong migration of people to the cities was, of course, due in part to the pull of the cities and the opportunities offered by growing industries;

[8] Thomas S. Ashton, *The Industrial Revolution 1760-1830,* p. 4.

but there was also a push from the villages as new and better methods of farming gradually came into use, making it possible for one man to do the work formerly done by three. New fertilizers were introduced, crop rotations became more complex, and there was a shift from smaller to larger properties through consolidation in most of England.

Between 1760 and 1850 farm implements changed almost completely from homemade, relatively crude, and for the most part wooden hand tools to factory-made, standardized, and for the most part iron and steel-framed implements. The development of farm machinery coincided with the enclosure movement, which resulted in the creation of large farms and estates in England; had the machinery been invented earlier, it would have been useless on the strips that characterized the three-field system (see Chapter 15). Self-sharpening, factory-made plows of cast iron that had been tempered in various improved ways were substituted for locally-made plows. Scythes were replaced by rather intricate machines for harvesting, and the flail disappeared in favor of a prototype of the modern threshing machine. Seed which was formerly broadcast on fields came to be sown in rows by seed drills.

The first reaper successfully adapted to farming was invented by Patrick Bell in 1826 (Fig 17.7). Pushed by a team of horses, this reaper had sickle clips in front and a bar to bend grain over the clips (which features are like those still used on modern combines). This rather cumbersome reaper was not generally adopted, largely because Cyrus McCormick invented the pulled reaper in 1831 (Fig. 17.8). Threshing machinery, using the age-old principle of the flail, had been developed somewhat earlier; one patent dates from 1732, but the first successful threshing machine was built by Andrew Meikle in 1786. All the early threshers were stable machines to which the grain was brought. Many threshers were driven by water power, while others were powered by horses walking around them. Threshing machines caught on very quickly and were widespread over the British Isles within a short time after their introduction.

German agriculture lagged about a century behind that of Britain because German skill and technology were not actively applied to agricultural problems until the unification of Germany in the 1870's. Once a start had been made, however, German farming rapidly became very scientific; it benefited from the knowledge of scientific farming that had been accumulated in Britain during the previous century, as well as from the ability of the German industrial setup to produce the materials and fertilizers needed by a modern agriculture.

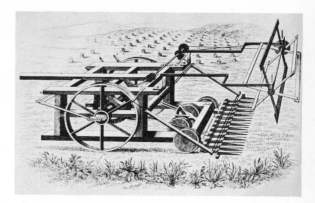

Fig. 17.7. Patrick Bell's pushed reaper, 1826.

As Britain industrialized, it was able to provide machinery for farming to areas which supplied wheat for its growing urban labor force. The interrelation between agricultural advancement in the United States and industrialization in Britain has been well pointed out by Sir Alexander Fleck: "In the 1870's the improvement of the marine steam-engine permitted an increase in the size of transatlantic grain cargoes, and this was decisive in bringing ruin to the British farmer. Conversion to an industrial society was thenceforth inevitable in Britain."[9]

Fig. 17.8. Rear view of the original McCormick reaper of 1831.

The Last Hundred Years

Among the many changes wrought by the increasing pace of technology in the past century, none has had greater effects upon population distribution than those permitting non-nomadic settlement of the world's grasslands. Similarly, no invention has had more radical effects upon modern life than the invention of the internal-combustion engine, which powers our automobiles and most of our trains. Without this engine, living in large cities would not be feasible.

Settlement of Grasslands. Between 1850 and 1900 four major developments permitted a great rise in the population of Europe. In the first place, since industrial production

[9] *A History of Technology,* Vol. V, p. 819.

grew more rapidly than population, the inhabitants of Europe were able to exchange their manufactured goods for food from abroad and for raw materials to maintain their industries. Also, although imported food could not have reached Europe in good condition before 1850, new methods of transportation, the introduction of steel ships, and the use of refrigeration to preserve food in them caused a revolution in food supply. Thirdly, it was possible for Europeans to import large amounts of food after 1850 because there was an enormous increase in the amount of land farmed by Europeans living abroad. Much of this land was in the newly-opened grasslands of Australia, Argentina, and North America, as well as in South Africa and the steppes of southern Siberia, and was for the most part actually farmed by European immigrants and sons of immigrants. In such other areas as Malaya, Ceylon, and West Africa, tropical products were made available by the plantation system. In the intermediate areas or subtropical areas of Egypt and India, vast new irrigation projects permitted the growth of a number of industrial products, especially cotton destined for the markets of western Europe. Finally, there was an increase in the productivity of European agriculture which was the result of better use of the land, increased use of machinery, new fertilizers, and improvements (through selective breeding) in the quality of farm animals and plants.

Mechanization of the North American grasslands proceeded rapidly after 1850. The McCormick reaper was selling at the rate of three per day; the wheat drill was in general use by the end of the decade; iron and steel plows were being sold in 1857 at the rate of 30 per day. However, it was not until a labor shortage was induced by the American Civil War that mechanization became absolutely mandatory in the prairie areas of the United States. In Australia the cultivation of wheat lagged behind that of the United States; because the soil was difficult to work, it was not until the stump-jump plow came into general use that the area devoted to wheat was expanded. In both the Australian grasslands and the American prairies, wheat was grown on the humid fringe, while open-range cattle in great numbers grazed in the semiarid parts. To supply the growing cities with meat, railroads were extended into the semiarid cattle areas.

It was the simultaneous development of iron ships and refrigeration which permitted the great expansion of meat growing in Australia. The iron ship dates back to 1787, when the barge *Trial* was built in England; in 1819 the first all-iron barge was completed, and the building of iron ships flourished from about 1850 to 1880. About 1880

the first steel ships marked the end of iron-ship construction: the last major iron ship, *City of Rome,* was constructed in 1881, while the launching of the warship *Iris* in 1877 is considered to be the beginning of the era of steel ships.

In 1851 the world's first refrigerating machine was set up for an Australian brewing firm. By 1873 refrigeration had been developed enough to allow frozen meat a full six months old to be eaten at an Australian public banquet, and in 1875 a slaughterhouse was constructed alongside ammonia-compression machinery for the freezing of meat. Thomas Mort, who had set up the first works for freezing meat in Sydney in 1861, told an audience in 1875: "Where the food is, the people are not, and where the people are, the food is not. It is, however, within the power of man to adjust these things."[10] Despite their skill and enthusiasm in developing refrigeration, the Australians were handicapped by being so far away from the European markets; with the limitations of the first refrigeration techniques, it was not certain that Australian meat would reach Europe in good condition. The first successful shipment of chilled beef arrived in England from the United States in 1879. Two years prior to that, a successful shipment of frozen mutton had been made from Buenos Aires to France. Australian research in refrigeration eventually yielded results, making it possible for a vessel to arrive in England in 1879 with Australian beef which could not be distinguished from freshly killed English beef. By 1880, when New Zealanders could successfully send frozen lamb and mutton to London, the age of refrigerated ships was considered to have arrived.

Automobiles and Rubber. The invention of the internal-combustion engine dates from about 1860. Between 1858 and 1862 three French inventors—Lenoir (Fig. 17.9), Meugon, and Beauderochas—worked on slow-speed gas engines, most of which had horizontal cylinders. In 1878 Otto, a Ger-

10 Ibid., p. 47.

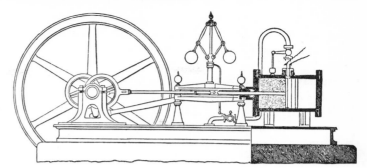

Fig. 17.9. Lenoir gas engine of 1860.

man technician, invented an internal-combustion engine which resembled that of Beauderochas and became very successful. In a few years, more than 35,000 engines of this type had been sold all over the world; like the earlier engines, the Otto engine was a slow-speed engine with horizontal cylinders. The modern automobile can be traced to two devices invented in 1886. Daimler in this year invented a vertical-cylinder, enclosed-crankcase engine with a carburetor. (In testing this engine on a bicycle, he created the prototype of the modern motorcycle.) In the same year Benz, also a German, worked out his idea for an automobile (Fig. 17.10). The Benz automobile and the Daimler engine were combined a few years later into the first feasible automobile, the prototype of all automobiles made after that time.

Eventually, rubber tires were developed for use on automobiles. Rubber had been known since the 18th century, when experiments were made with latex from the Amazon forest. In 1819 an Englishman named Hancock first became interested in rubber, and by 1843 he had discovered a method of vulcanizing latex. His invention was stimulated by pieces of rubber he had obtained from Goodyear, the American inventor, and their patents were taken out within two months of each other in 1843 and 1844.

Hancock developed most of the rubber goods which are used today, including shoes, rubber hose, valves, and rings. In 1888 an Irish inventor named Dunlop used the first air-filled tires on a bicycle for his 10-year-old son, and in 1895 the brothers Michelin used the first pneumatic automobile tires in the trial runs between Paris and Bordeaux. The use of air-filled tires on bicycles was so successful that the demand for rubber rose rapidly.

The rising price of rubber from the Amazon Valley stimulated the India Office of the British government to search for areas in southern Asia where rubber could be grown. In June of 1876 some seeds from rubber trees arrived at Kew Gardens from the Amazon Valley; by August 2000 young rubber plants were on their way to Ceylon, to form the nucleus of the rubber industry in Ceylon and Malaya. The wisdom of this move became apparent when demand for rubber tires

Fig. 17.10. First successful automobile, built by Karl Benz, 1885.

on automobiles skyrocketed some 25 years later, just as the rubber plantations in these areas were about to come into full-scale production.

Modern Prime Movers. The Industrial Revolution had been partly brought about by the invention of the steam engine in the 18th century, and the 19th century saw the invention of three more prime movers: the internal-combustion engine, the water turbine for generating electricity, and the steam turbine. The 20th century has produced still another prime mover—the gas turbine. These inventions have made possible an extremely flexible application of power to a wide variety of uses. For example, the increasing amount of power made available by thermal generation of electricity (through burning coal or petroleum to form steam) has had a great influence upon mining. Besides permitting greater flexibility in ore-recovery operations, the increased availability of power has made possible the processing of ores once considered worthless. Renewed life has come to many mining areas where tailings (waste ore) are reprocessed for low-concentrate ore once thought far beyond recovery.

In addition, the constant supply of power offered by the modern prime movers has permitted a wide diffusion of the mass-production system. The dockyards of Holland and Venice and the artillery schools of Spain and Austria in the early 18th century started the system of mass production; the system was subsequently improved when the idea of having completely interchangeable parts was developed in France by Le Blanc in 1785 and in Eli Whitney's gun factories in 1798. The American Civil War was the first conflict in which standardized factories utilized mass production for military purposes. Replaceable parts for guns were made, and the manufacture of ammunition, canned food, and clothing on an assembly-line basis became common.

Mobility and Man. The increasing mobility of man is intimately related to the development of technology. The discovery

that horses could be ridden and the discovery of the wheel; the invention of the chariot, the solid-wheeled chariot, and the spoked chariot; the building of the Roman roads, the construction of seagoing vessels of large size, the development of canals in the late 18th century, and the subsequent development of railroads; the modern development of cars and various kinds of airplanes: all these mark a progression which has meant a constantly increasing physical mobility for mankind. As people develop the means of getting from one place to another faster or with greater ease, there are necessarily modifications of the cultural landscape; the changing cultural landscape in turn affects the evolution of technology.

The student may find it profitable to attempt to calculate the future geographical effect of the various technological revolutions now under way. The rising standard of living in the major industrial areas of the world, the development of nuclear energy as a dispersable source of energy, the possibility of transforming sea water into fresh water and using it to develop desert areas, the possibility of using sunlight as a direct source of energy by means of a solar converter (Fig. 17.11) or a solar stove (Fig. 17.12), the decentralization of settlement and factories made possible by distilled and natural gas and by new methods of transmitting electricity more than twice as far as was formerly possible: add these together and imagine what changes they might induce in man's mobility and in the present world-wide distribution of population.

Any new source of energy contains within itself the possibility of a relocation of human settlement, particularly if it is a new fuel or a source of energy which can be substituted for a fuel. Nuclear energy is the most spectacular of the modern prime movers, but its use is still hindered by the fact that it must first be converted into steam energy in a process which requires a large supply of water. Other sources of energy which have come into use in the last 80 years are elec-

Fig. 17.11. 1912 Baker electric automobile. Power is gained from the 1961 sun-cell panel at top.

Fig. 17.12. Solar stove developed for use in the fuel-short villages of India.

tricity, industrial gas from coal, natural gas, and various petroleum products.

When iron was first produced, it did not have the effect of localizing industry to any great extent. Iron ore of various degrees of richness was widespread, and charcoal for smelting of iron could be made anywhere in the world that forests were found. However, agglomeration of iron smelters occurred, both in England and elsewhere, when coke was developed as a means of smelting iron and iron ore was consequently attracted to the coal areas. The vast number of dispersed charcoal iron smelters gave way within a few decades in every country to the closely compacted agglomeration of steel mills. As a result of advances in iron technology, it is possible that production will become dispersed again. Since soft iron ore may be treated by oxygenation or some electrical method, the widespread availability of electricity is making possible the dispersal of new steel mills.

Although coal and oil are often found in the same areas, the existence of one in a certain area does not guarantee the existence of the other in that area; in fact, many of the world's major oil fields are not near coal fields. Natural gas, which occurs in oil fields, may be used almost anywhere because it can be conveyed a long distance by pipelines. As a result, it has not as yet caused any significant relocation of industry. With the development of electricity from hydroelectric sources, power has become even more widely available; most hydroelectric dams are located in areas other than those where coal is found, particularly in the Pacific Northwest. In addition, since coal in the future will probably be distilled rather than burned, industrial gas (which can be piped like natural gas) will be abundant in many areas. The geographical proximity of coal and iron will no longer be the main determinant in the location of industry.

Sensing Devices and Automation. In the past century, man has greatly increased his knowledge of the external world by developing or improving a variety of sensing devices which permit him to detect and record what is happening at a distance. The most familiar examples of distance-sensing devices are

263

the telephone, radio, and television; records of what has been sensed by such devices may be kept on magnetic tape for future use and reference.

Of great utility in enabling man to sense and understand his environment are a number of less common devices. Recording barometers permit man to gather information on air pressure that is needed in making weather maps, and barometric devices have been used to record nuclear explosions in the atmosphere. Barometers sent aloft record the air pressure at various altitudes and enable man to make pressure maps of the upper air regions. Recording thermometers aid in the interpretation of pressure information. Seismographs (machines for recording earthquake waves) have permitted precise locating of earthquakes and occasionally have predicted when tsunamis (earthquake-generated sea waves) will arrive; the machines are also useful in studying the composition of the earth's core. Radar performs a function analogous to the detection of earthquakes in connection with disturbances in the atmosphere and beyond. Both radar and seismographs may be used to gather information on nuclear explosions. The navigating of ships and aircraft and the guiding of missiles are now aided by very accurate inertia-guidance devices unknown two decades ago. Telescopes, both visual and radio-beam types, have extended by many times the "visible" universe. The development of the transistor to replace bulky vacuum tubes has permitted the development of lightweight sensing and recording devices for exploration at great heights above the earth. The dangerously radioactive Van Allen belts were found and studied with such devices. Perhaps the most important development of all from the viewpoint of geographers has been the satellite-borne camera. The use of high-resolution film in photo-satellites allows records to be made of the cloud cover over vast areas, which records may be instantly transmitted to ground stations for analysis. The increasing accuracy of weather forecasting based on

such information will permit far more efficient planning of man's activities on the earth.

Paralleling the development of sensing devices used to gather information has been the growth of automation and automatic-control devices. The familiar household thermostat, one of the many automatic-control devices, uses the feedback principle that is common to them all. (Feedback control means that a machine may work only between preset limits, and that there is constant communication between the control sensor and the machine —between the thermostat in our example and the furnace.) Automated factories now exist in many places, and large automated petroleum refineries can now be maintained "on stream" by half a dozen engineers. The problem of technological unemployment caused by automation is grave enough in the United States to have induced legislative action to provide funds to retrain displaced workers for other jobs.

Technology Old and New. Certain techniques and inventions of the modern world parallel those of the ancient world in their effect on man's life. The domestication of grains in the ancient world permitted nucleation of the population. With the domestication of grain, the people of the world were no longer exclusively hunters and gatherers; as agriculturalists, more people could live in less area. The experiments of modern scientists with the growth of algae may presage a similar change in the availability of food.

The rise of cities in the ancient world was largely dependent upon the development of irrigation techniques for the growing of bread grains and rice. Early civilizations were almost by definition irrigation civilizations; the rise of cities depended on the extension of social control, which in turn depended on the control of water. The mobility offered by the invention of the chariot in the ancient world permitted cities to combine into states and states to combine into empires. The high degree of mobility given the modern world by the automobile, the airplane, and other vehicles using internal-combustion engines has had similarly important effects. Finally, the development of the alphabet had an effect upon communications in the ancient world that may be compared to the influence that radio and television have had on the spread of information in the modern world.

All these inventions and techniques involve the extension of human effort. Irrigation in ancient times served to bring formerly unused areas into use, just as the modern irrigation of deserts serves to extend crop area. Likewise, the domestication of grains in the ancient world and the modern experiments with algae both involve an extension of food varieties. Both the chariot of the ancient world and the internal-combustion engine of today involve an extension of physical mobility. And the alphabet, radio, and television all involve an extension of the mobility of ideas.

All these inventions utilize the inherent mobility and adaptability of man. Man can live almost anywhere on earth, can eat almost anything, and is apparently able to use almost any system of communication. The techniques and inventions discussed in this chapter do not represent ways of conquering or subduing nature (although Western man generally views them in this light); rather, they represent discovery of the possibilities inherent in the earth. The adventure of finding and testing these possibilities is not unlike the gradual discovery by a child of his own capabilities.

CHAPTER 18

Cities

As population increases and man discovers new resources and learns to use familiar resources more effectively, hamlets grow into villages, villages blossom into towns, and towns expand or even "explode" into cities. Like the smaller settlements, the city is a central place, but it is much more complicated than the hamlet, the village, or the town. The city should be located on the most favorable site available with a large, productive hinterland, and it should be on navigable water or at the crossroads of trade routes. Of course, some cities manage to grow and survive with none of these advantages. Mecca in Arabia, for example, has no productive hinterland and is on no important trade route. Structure is an important characteristic of the city. Unlike the town or village, the city has clearly differentiated parts with different functions. Whereas commerce and manufacturing are likely to be mingled in the town or village, perhaps in the same building, in the city there is a clearly defined manufacturing district and a distinct central business district (CBD), as well as residence districts and various other "quarters" which have special functions and, in many cases, special forms. Another feature which distinguishes the city from the village and town is its almost complete transformation of nature. In the city the whole natural environment, except for a few parks, is covered up

with streets, houses, and large buildings of all kinds (Fig. 18.1). City dwellers are engaged in secondary activities rather than in the production of primary goods: the city has carpenters rather than loggers, millers and bakers rather than growers of grain, and metalworkers rather than miners.

Emergence of the City

The city emerged from the village and town first of all because of improvements in agriculture. During Neolithic times the changes that occurred in plant cultivation and livestock breeding included the appearance of the hard grains, such as wheat and barley, which could be preserved for many years. The ability to store surplus hard grains made the city independent or partly independent of lean years; and, if the local supply of hard grains was limited, the city could sustain itself on hard grains transported from distant lands. The early Greek cities brought wheat from southern Russia, and Rome depended upon Africa for grain. The development of livestock likewise helped to maintain the city. Live animals could be kept in reserve until the city needed them for food and could also be transported alive over long distances for consumption by the city. The traffic in grains and livestock, in addition to the trade in such nonperishable goods as jewels and silks,

266

Fig. 18.1. A part of the central business district of Chicago, Illinois, showing the Merchandise Mart and the confluence of the north and south branches of the Chicago River. Lake Michigan is to the right.

brought about a chain of commercial development that encouraged the growth of cities in many parts of the world.

Of great importance in the early expansion of the city was the proximity of a considerable area of fertile land where grain and other crops could be grown in abundance to provide a surplus which the city might gather together and transport to distant places in exchange for other goods. Cities like Paris, which was established at the center of the Paris Basin, drew much of their support in the early days from their immediate environs (Fig. 18.2). It was not until the last century that Paris came to depend for its food upon distant places.

Many other cities owe their first urban development pattern to fertile agricultural land, forests, or mineral deposits in the vicinity. Another important factor in the development of cities has been accessibility to trade routes, many cities having grown up at crossroads, sea ports, and river ports.

The unfolding of the modern city has been dependent upon the growth of new sources of energy or power. So long as man had not developed much water power or steam power and was confined to the use of human power and animal power, the city was limited in its function, particularly from the standpoint of manufacturing; also, transportation was necessarily slow, capable of accommodating

Fig. 18.2. Le Bourget Airfield, near Paris, is on a smooth portion of the Paris Basin. In the foreground are hangars, shops, apartment buildings, and residences.

only relatively small burdens. The evolution of the modern city, then, awaited the Industrial Revolution, when the energy from coal, petroleum, and water became of great importance.

Location and Size of Cities

Cities are to be found in all parts of the earth that have even moderately dense population. Most of the large cities, however, are located in regions with both dense population and adequate resources and production. Large cities, arbitrarily defined as metropolitan centers of one million or more people, are to be found in eastern North America, California, central Mexico, southern South America, western Europe, western U.S.S.R., Egypt, India, China, Japan, and Australia. The population, in millions, within the city limits, according to latest available estimates, is given below:

Canada:	Montreal	1.1
United States:	New York	7.8
	Chicago	3.6
	Los Angeles	2.5
	Philadelphia	2.0
	Detroit	1.7
Mexico:	Mexico D. F.	2.7
Brazil:	Rio de Janeiro	2.3
	São Paulo	2.0
Argentina:	Buenos Aires	3.8
Great Britain:	London	8.2
	Birmingham	1.1
	Glasgow	1.1
France:	Paris	2.8
West Germany:	Hamburg	1.8
	Munich	1.1
Belgium:	Brussels	1.0
Spain:	Madrid	2.0
	Barcelona	1.5
Italy:	Roma (Rome)	1.8
	Milano (Milan)	1.3
	Napoli (Naples)	1.1

Austria:	Wien (Vienna)	1.8
Hungary:	Budapest	1.8
Poland:	Warszawa (Warsaw)	1.1
U.S.S.R.:	Moskva (Moscow)	5.0
	Leningrad	2.9
	Kiev	1.1
Turkey:	Istanbul	1.7
Egypt:	Cairo	3.0
	Alexandria	1.4
Pakistan:	Karachi	1.1
	Lahore	1.0
India:	Calcutta	2.8
	Bombay	2.5
Indonesia:	Jakarta	2.1
	Soerabaja (Surabaya)	1.1
China:	Shanghai	7.0
	Peiping	4.1
	Tientsin	3.1
	Canton	1.6
Hongkong:	Victoria	3.0
Japan:	Tokyo	9.6
	Osaka	3.0
	Nagoya	1.5
	Kyoto	1.4
	Yokohama	1.3
	Kobe	1.0
Australia:	Sydney	2.1
	Melbourne	1.8

An interesting theory as to the size of cities in various countries is the "rank-size rule," which states that the population of the largest city in a big country is essentially equal to the population of any other city in that country multiplied by the smaller city's rank. Thus, the population of New York City, 7,800,000 in 1960, should be twice that of Chicago, 3,600,000, and 100 times that of Lansing, Michigan, which had 92,-000 in 1960. It is obvious that this rule works only for large cities and then only approximately. Exceptions include countries with only one large city which, in some cases, accounts for a large percentage of the total population. Mark Jefferson called these primate cities. Copenhagen in Denmark; Vienna, Austria; Mexico D. F., Mexico; Havana, Cuba; Santiago, Chile; and Oslo, Norway are examples.

The Hinterland

Important to every city is the tributary area or hinterland, the area for which the city is a focus (Fig. 18.3). This is both the area served by the city and the area upon which the city is dependent. The city gathers the products of the tributary area and prepares them for either local use or export to other regions. The city also imports products from other regions and distributes them to the hinterland. The area of a city's hinterland depends on a number of factors, in-

Fig. 18.3. Map of hinterlands showing two phases of the hinterland of Joplin, Missouri. The inner line marks the immediate hinterland, the outer hinterland is marked by a line indicating the circulation of newspapers. (Adapted from *The Geography of Economic Activity* by Richard S. Thoman. Copyright 1962. McGraw-Hill Book Co., Inc. Used by permission.)

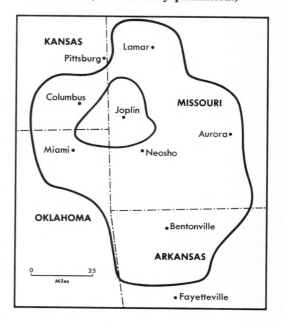

cluding the size and character of the city, the nature of the goods produced, and the efficiency of the transportation system. If one factor is taken separately, it is possible to apply the central place theory.

Central place theory, and that portion of economic geography which considers the relations between primary agricultural production and its marketing, started with the contributions of Johann Heinrich von Thünen (1783-1850). Von Thünen assumed a single market town in the center of a uniformly fertile and arable plain, accessible equally from all directions. He stated that the prices of farm goods in the market and the cost of taking the goods to the market would determine rather regularly how near to, or far from, the market these goods would be produced: in other words, the extent of the town's hinterland.

For the purpose of studying systematically the ways in which goods production and land use vary by distance from the market, we may rephrase von Thünen's verbal model: "Because market price equals the cost of production plus the cost of transport plus the profit to producer, land use will vary systematically with distance of the producing unit from the market point." Symbolically this reads: $M=P+T+G$, where M is market price, P is production cost, T is transport cost, and G is gain, or profit.

The easiest situation to deal with in logic or laboratory is one in which all possible complicating factors have been eliminated. After understanding how a model works under conditions of restraint or limitation, we can progressively approach reality by relaxing the theoretical restraints. For our present purpose, the basic restraints on the von Thünen model may be assumed as follows:

(a) a single selling point, the *market;*
(b) a single good produced on each production unit;
(c) equal level of fertility everywhere;
(d) equal land transport facilities everywhere;

(e) no political regulation of the economic factors in the model;
(f) a constant market price for a given good;
(g) no upper limit on the amount of arable land;
(h) one political unit.

Since most cities have multiple functions, it is not easy to define the hinterland quantitatively. Within the hinterland of large cities, there are smaller cities, towns, and villages which take on some urban functions common to the larger city. Generally, these are retail and service functions needed rather frequently by people, for which they are not willing to travel often to a large city far away. The drawing of hinterland boundaries becomes complicated, but it has pattern if we think of a hierarchy of central places. The goods and services not frequently in demand by large numbers of people (such as heart surgery, opera, foreign consulates) are found in only the large cities, while more frequently needed goods (furniture and automobiles, for example) are found in smaller towns. Villages may exist only to supply daily necessities such as bread, tobacco, and gasoline. With these limitations in mind, a map of the hinterland of a city may be made on the basis of the city's chief function, such as wholesale trade. Some difficulty would be encountered since the areas served would obviously be different for such different products as hardware, groceries, drugs, gasoline, and meat. A map may also be made on the basis of the city's retail trade, after interviews or some other means have been used to determine where people trade. The retail areas of two cities may be found approximately by measuring the highway traffic between the cities and marking the boundary between the hinterlands at the point of least traffic. Still another method of determining the hinterland of a city lies in the measurement of newspaper circulation; this method is based on the assumption that the people who are most interested in the commerce or other functions of a city will subscribe to the papers of that city. Other methods are based on the charting of power sources and water supplies. Although each of these methods may yield slightly different results, there is usually a certain amount of similarity in their findings. The fact that the boundaries of the hinterland of a city are difficult to define does not lessen the influence of the hinterland on the characteristics and functions of the city.

The Major Characteristics of Cities

The cities of the world are so different that they must be roughly classified before their characteristics can be properly discussed. Harris classified cities as follows (Fig. 18.4):

1. Retail centers.
2. Manufacturing cities.
3. Wholesale centers.
4. Transportation centers.
5. Mining towns.
6. University towns.
7. Resort and retirement towns.
8. Diversified cities.

This system of classification is obviously based upon major function, since nearly all large cities have some element of most of the classifications mentioned. Thus, a manufacturing city also has important retail-wholesale functions, as well as functions characteristic of transportation centers.

Very important qualities of a city are its site and its situation. The site is the actual location of the city, the ground upon which the city is constructed; the situation is its general location with respect to the surroundings. Thus, the site of New York City is Manhattan Island and adjacent parts of the mainland and Long Island, while the situation of New York City is in northeastern United States at the mouth of the Hudson River. The site usually has great influence on the form of a city; the situation of a city and the characteristics of its trade area or hinterland often have much influence on its functions.

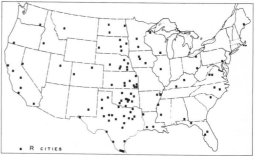

Fig. 18.4. Classification of cities. In the M' cities manufacturing is dominant. In the M cities manufacturing is important but not dominant. In the R cities retail trade is dominant, and the D cities are diversified. (Reproduced by courtesy of the *Geographical Review*, American Geographical Society, New York.)

In addition to the functions of a city indicated in Harris's classification, there are other functions performed by the city, particularly secondary functions that have to do with the support of the city itself. Although a city may be primarily engaged in trade, wholesale and retail, for the benefit of the

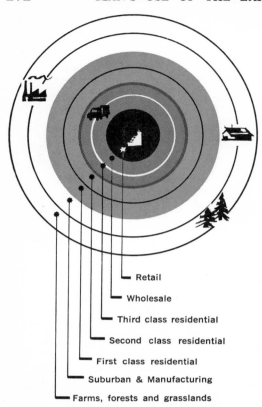

Retail

Wholesale

Third class residential

Second class residential

First class residential

Suburban & Manufacturing

Farms, forests and grasslands

Fig. 18.5. Diagram of an ideal city. The shape of most cities is influenced by the site, by lines of transportation, and by other factors.

light manufacturing, are not so easy to recognize since many of them are carried on in the upper stories of buildings which house retail stores on the street level.

The central business district of the city is clearly distinguishable by its banks, wholesale and retail stores, and hotels. The wholesale section is usually distinct from the retail, at least in part, being represented by large warehouses and a congestion of heavy transportation, including railroads, trucks, and occasionally water-borne carriers. Cities also have such clearly defined transportation centers as railroad stations, railroad yards, truck terminals, bus stations, and airports.

An important feature of every city is the residential district, where the people live who carry on the work of the city. Although residential districts are characteristically peripheral, there are some that are well within the heart of the city. Usually, residential districts are pushed out into the rural areas as the city grows, and their former area is occupied by retail, manufacturing, or wholesale establishments.

Although the functional parts of the city (the manufacturing, retail, wholesale, and residential districts) can usually be recognized by their structures, confusion may arise in areas of rapid growth. In cities where the rate of growth has been rapid, it is common to find houses which were obviously constructed for residential purposes being used for retail trade or light manufacturing.

Based primarily upon the arrangement of streets and avenues, the pattern of a city's functional parts gives the city a distinct character. Since the arrangement of streets was established by the lines of transportation that were set, in many cases, when the city was only a village or town (Fig. 18.6), the pattern of the city is very difficult to change. Where change has been attempted by city planners, there has been great expense and great difficulty from the political point of view. Because the original lines of travel were adapted to the site, the pattern of the

surrounding area, it still has to take care of the people living in the city; this secondary function of the city is quite important in terms of the number of people employed.

Typically, there is differentiation and specialization in the city. In other words, different parts of the city do different things (Fig. 18.5). It is easy to recognize the manufacturing district of the city, especially when it is composed of the more obvious forms of manufacturing. Heavy manufacturing carried on in steel mills, large automobile or airplane factories, and machine shops is clearly indicated by the form of the structures and by the activity that is going on. Other kinds of manufacturing, especially various types of

a   b

Fig. 18.6. Street patterns: (a) the street patterns of Amsterdam, the Netherlands, are in reality canal patterns, one series radiating from the original nucleus of the city and the other series arranged in crude arcs; many of the canals have been replaced by streets; (b) view of Pittsburgh, Pennsylvania, looking east; the city lies on the point of land between the Monongahela River, on the right, and the Allegheny River, on the left; the major streets are parallel to the rivers; (c) Capetown, Union of South Africa, is located at the foot of Table Mountain on Table Bay; the street patterns reflect the configuration of the shoreline; the extent of the city is limited by the steep slopes of Table Mountain.

c

city is often the result of site characteristics. If a city develops in a smooth, uniform plain where land transport is not restricted in any direction by the topography of the area, it should develop in a star-shaped pattern (Fig. 18.7). The main lines of communication should radiate in various directions from the original center of the city, and the city should tend to grow out the farthest along these main lines of transportation. The fact is, however, that no city has developed in such an ideal site, there usually being some restriction which makes it easier to build in one direction than in another. Cities have often developed in a modified star-shaped pattern as a result of having been established along a lake, river, or ocean. Such a location tends to give a somewhat semicircular pattern to the city, with streets radiating out in every direction except the direction of the water body. Since hills, streams, swamps, and other features of the site tend to restrict and modify the city's pattern of growth, a careful analysis of the site is necessary to any historical study of the city's development.

Fig. 18.7. Chicago and vicinity, showing the radial character of the main lines of communication. Chicago is located on the western side of the southern end of Lake Michigan, rather than at the extreme southern tip of the Lake.

Planned Cities

City planning is taking an increasingly important part in the development of cities. Because most modern cities were allowed to evolve without any planning or discipline, their different parts tend to interfere with each other in the execution of certain functions. The main goal of city planning is to make cities more pleasant places in which to live by planning each function so that it interferes as little as possible with the others.

A major effort of city planning has been directed toward the improvement of residential districts (Fig. 18.8). In modern cities, residential districts often are located close to industries that have considerable nuisance value; furthermore, as the retail districts and other central districts of the city grow outward, they tend to absorb and interfere with the residential districts. Planners are using

several methods to effect the improvement of residential districts. One method, called urban redevelopment, provides for the clearing of slums and the construction of new residences, usually at government expense. Although urban redevelopment is a very expensive means of improving the city, it is necessary in areas where slum conditions are so bad that they reduce the efficiency of the city.

Another form of city planning directed toward residential districts is the development of neighborhoods, usually on the margins of a city, where land can be obtained without interfering with the functioning of the city. Neighborhoods, as conceived by city planners, are distinct units, usually about one quarter to one half of a square mile in area. Surrounded by through streets which divert the main traffic away from it, the neighborhood often has dead-end streets to reduce or eliminate through traffic. Each neighborhood has a school with an area suitable for playgrounds, shops for local shopping, and a number of other facilities. The architecture and arrangement of the

Fig 18.8. Engravings: plans of ideal cities of the 16th and 17th centuries. Photos: modern planned cities; upper, Greenbelt, Maryland; lower, Harlow, England. Planning is reflected in the geometric arrangement of streets, in the uniform height and character of the buildings, and in provision for forest and park areas.

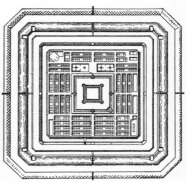

houses are carefully planned to make the neighborhood as pleasant as possible without making too great a sacrifice of space.

Another important concern of city planners is circulation. The congestion near the center of large cities is so great that the movement of people and goods is very slow and difficult. Congestion is particularly noticeable in cities with narrow downtown streets; although fairly satisfactory when the cities were small, these streets later became very inadequate from the standpoint of moving traffic. The circulation problem can be attacked in several ways. Subways may be constructed under the ground; new streets known as freeways may be built to allow traffic to move very rapidly. As a method of solving the circulation problem, the construction of freeways is very expensive, largely because it involves the acquisition of property which is being used for other purposes and carries a very high price per square foot.

In order to apply planning to the development of industrial, retail, and wholesale districts, as well as residential districts, most cities use the practice of zoning certain areas for specific purposes. Thus, an area may be zoned for single-family residences, apartment houses, retail business, light manufacturing, heavy manufacturing, or some other use. It is difficult to enforce most zoning ordinances because of the pressure exerted by individuals to use zoned land for prohibited purposes, particularly profitable ones. Thus, an area that is zoned for single-family residences may be diverted to apartment houses if the owner of the land is successful in bringing about an exception to the zoning law.

Cities are like organisms: they grow in size and change in quality and function; they grow old and sometimes die. Though they may not continue to expand, they usually keep changing. Sometimes the centrifugal forces which tend to throw the city outward overbalance the centripetal forces which tend to bring it in toward the center. As a result, there may be decentralization of industry and business, despite the strong pull of centralizing factors.

It is apparent that from nature's great geological lottery a few nations were given access to peerless energy and machine resources. This is probably the most important single fact in the geography of modern times.

J. Russell Smith

CHAPTER **19**

Manufacturing

Although not all manufacturing is in cities, all cities have some manufacturing, and it is, by and large, an urban function. Originally, manufacturing meant making things by hand (a process that is now called handicraft) with the aid of a few tools but no external power. As machines and tools were developed and new forms of energy were made available, the process of manufacturing was greatly complicated. It became diversified and subdivided on a piecework basis, and specialists were trained to do different parts of the manufacturing process. Nowadays, manufacturing is a highly diversified and complicated operation, the production of each item involving many people, many different kinds of raw materials, usually some kind of machinery, and much transportation.

Location and Location Factors

Manufacturing is widely distributed, but most of it is concentrated in a few districts in which cities are engaged in manufacturing on a large scale and perform very special functions. The most extensive areas of manufacturing include northwestern Europe and northeastern United States (with the adjacent parts of Canada), but other countries and other continents have smaller areas of manufacturing and all large cities have a considerable quantity of it. The distribution of

manufacturing can be measured in various ways. The way which involves determining the number of people engaged in manufacturing is easily applied because there is material available which indicates the number of people engaged in various occupations. Of course, the number of people engaged in a certain manufacturing process does not always indicate the relative importance of that process. In a flour mill, for example, most of the operations are automatic and require the services of only a few inspectors, adjusters, and maintenance people. Another method of determining the distribution of manufacturing is to measure the value added to products by the manufacturing process; the resulting value definition of distribution has a great many disadvantages as well as advantages. Still other methods of determining distribution are used, but these two are the most important and the most commonly used (Fig. 19.1).

Geographers are most concerned with the location and distribution of manufacturing and the study of related geographic qualities. Location factors are factors which tend to encourage the location of industries in certain cities or certain areas. The most important factors which influence the distribution of manufacturing are raw materials, power, labor, transportation, and the market for the finished product. The importance of each of

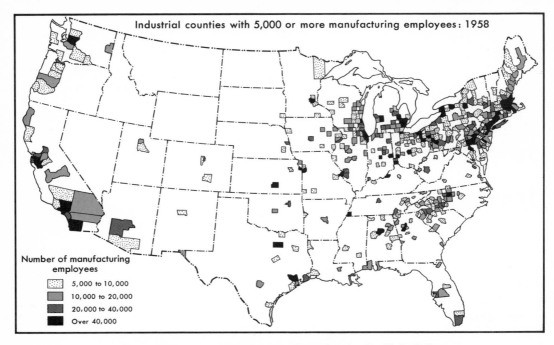

Fig. 19.1. Persons engaged in manufacturing in the United States.

these varies with different industries and from time to time.

Raw Materials. The relative importance of the raw-material factor depends upon the weight and bulk of the raw material. Thus, in the manufacture of cement, the raw-material factor is very important; the factory must be located close to the supply of shale and limestone from which the cement is made. At the other extreme, a watch factory need not be particularly concerned with the location of its sources of raw materials because the small quantities of metals and other materials needed in the manufacture of a watch can be easily transported thousands of miles, if necessary, with little cost. The raw materials for industry come from all sorts of primary production: from agriculture, mining, fishing, and lumbering, to name a few. Obviously, the significance of the raw-material factor in the location of a city will depend partly upon the nature of the materials—whether or not they are

perishable, whether or not they can be readily shipped in bulk—and upon the form of transportation available.

Labor Supply. Another important location factor is the labor supply needed in the manufacturing process. Unlike some other factors, labor can migrate to areas where factories are constructed. Thus, if a factory is constructed in a rural location in order to take advantage of low land costs or low taxes, it is likely either that workers will migrate to the factory on a daily commuting basis from nearby cities or that residences will be constructed in the vicinity of the factory to accommodate the laborers.

On the other hand, industries requiring highly skilled labor may be located in areas already populated by skilled laborers. This practice tends to concentrate certain industries, such as high-quality textile industries and automobile industries, in a few localities; this concentration leads in turn to the development of specialized factories that produce only a certain part of a product—an automobile speedometer, for example.

Transportation. The transportation factor involves such other factors as raw materials, labor, and market. Transportation is less of a problem for light industries than for heavy industries, since light industries may be located on highways with truck service and do not require rail service. Heavy industries, on the other hand, not only must have railroad connections but must often have water connections as well. Transportation systems are constantly changing as highways are improved and extended, as rail transportation is improved, and, particularly, as air transportation lowers its rates on a per ton per mile basis. Many industries depend upon airlines for at least a part of their transportation, and isolated industries find air transport especially valuable in getting parts or materials in a hurry.

Power. The power factor is increasing its role in industries that are accustomed to use large quantities of energy. Power is derived mainly from coal, petroleum, and hydroelectric energy, but there are other sources providing smaller amounts. Since power can be transported efficiently for some distance by high-voltage transmission lines and power-producing coal can be carried on railroads and trucks, it is possible for power to be brought to some factories, making it unnecessary for them to locate in areas where power is already available. The industries that require large amounts of power, however, are likely to locate close to the power source. Thus, the refining of aluminum, which needs large quantities of hydroelectric energy, is likely to be located near water power. In North America most of the aluminum-refining industries are in the Pacific Northwest, taking advantage of the abundant power there, or in eastern Canada, which also has an abundance of power. The fact that both of these regions are somewhat remote from large manufacturing areas and markets for aluminum products is of little concern to these industries.

Market. The market factor is extremely complicated. Since any given weight of finished products is likely to be more valuable than the same weight of raw materials, finished products are more easily transported. Transportation thus serves to decrease the effect of the market factor on the location of industry. However, the location of the market is rather an important factor in the marketing of such heavy commodities as crude steel, many kinds of wood products, and cheap food products like grains. As a commodity becomes more valuable per unit of weight, the market factor becomes more negligible. Thus, California can market citrus fruits in New York City in competition with Florida fruits, even though Florida is much nearer to the market. Of course, the location of the market is especially significant in relation to perishable commodities, including some vegetables and fruits and fresh milk.

Other Factors. The tax structure, which varies from city to city, from state to state, and from country to country, is likely to have an influence upon the location of certain industries. Some countries and areas have a very lenient tax structure and will, in fact, grant tax immunity to industries for 10 years or more after they establish themselves. Some areas have high income taxes, some none at all. Not surprisingly, taxes are one of the things considered very carefully before a new factory or a branch of a factory is located in an area.

Such a factor as climate is of some significance in the location of industries, but climate is perhaps less important than it was in previous years since air conditioning now makes it possible to produce and keep uniform the kind of climate most favorable for manufacturing processes. For many years, because cotton thread tends to break very easily under dry conditions, the cotton-textile industry was located only in regions with a normally high relative humidity. As a result, the Manchester area of England and the New England and southern Piedmont areas of the United States became centers of textile manufacturing. Since air conditioning involves additional cost, such humid regions still have a slight advantage.

Within the continental United States, location factors may make a crucial difference in the cost of producing a manufactured article which must be sold in competition with domestic and foreign articles of the same kind. Since each location factor is related to other location factors, it can be evaluated successfully only after all the location factors have been considered. Today there is a very intense study of location factors being carried on by experts.

An Example. Because Puerto Rico has had a tremendous industrial expansion in the last 10 years, it is instructive to examine the area in terms of its location factors. Puerto Rico used to be regarded as being far from continental United States, but it is now only three hours by air from Miami, Florida. The island has over 3000 square miles of territory and a population of two and a half million, a substantial labor force. Puerto Rico has most of the rights and privileges of a state of the United States, except that it has no voting representation in Congress and no Federal taxation. The lack of Federal taxation has been of great importance in the location of industries on the island. Though Puerto Rico obviously has some disadvantages in its supply of raw materials and transportation, the qualities which have attracted a great many industries in recent years are a large labor supply with a low average wage and a tax structure which serves as an incentive for industry. Of the labor force, which is drawn from the two and a half million people of Puerto Rico, about 40 per cent is rather young, between 20 and 35 years of age. Such a proportion of young workers is related to the fact that half of the population of the island is under 14 years of age; it is very different from the proportion of young workers in continental United States. Puerto Rico has a reservoir of unemployed labor which consists of from 70,000 to 120,000 workers, the larger number of unemployed occurring during the slack season when agriculture uses the fewest workers. In 1954 the average hourly wage of industrial workers in Puerto Rico was slightly more than $.52, as compared to $1.81 on the United States mainland. Though not all of the labor force in Puerto Rico is skilled, in most cases the required skills can be taught to the workers in a comparatively short time.

One of the Puerto Rican tax incentives to industry lies in the fact that corporate income is tax exempt for 10 years after the start of a factory. Municipal license fees for factories are likewise suspended for the first 10 years of operation. For residents of Puerto Rico, personal income from dividends is exempt from taxes for the first seven years after earning starts. (One has to establish local citizenship to take advantage of this particular tax structure.) Real and personal property is tax-exempt for from five to 10 years, depending upon the size of the investment involved. To be eligible for this tax exemption, a firm must be engaged in producing a commodity which was not in commercial production in Puerto Rico prior to January 2, 1947. Conditions in Puerto Rico especially favor light manufacturing. For example, a manufacturer of a popular fountain pen began operations in Puerto Rico in October, 1952, employing 80 workers. All the parts were made in Puerto Rico and then flown to California to be assembled. In spite of this transportation cost, the firm made a very good net profit and proceeded to expand production.

Manufacturing Regions

The world-wide distribution of manufacturing depends upon a series of complicated and interrelated factors. These factors are constantly changing, and countries which a few years ago were doing very little manufacturing are now embarking upon vigorous campaigns to increase the amount and variety of their manufactured goods. One useful index of the importance of manufacturing in a particular area is the percentage of the total population engaged in it. An even more significant figure, perhaps, is the percentage of the actively producing population which is engaged in manufacturing.

Small countries which have a limited amount of agricultural, mineral, and other forms of primary production are often busily engaged in manufacturing in order to be able to exchange manufactured goods for raw materials. It is for this reason that a large proportion of the active population of Switzerland, Austria, Germany, and Czechoslovakia is employed in manufacturing, both light and heavy. In Austria a very large percentage of the population engages in manufacturing in the city of Vienna. On the other hand, in many countries there is only a very small proportion of the population occupied in manufacturing. Thailand, for example, has only about 2 per cent of its people so employed. Such a percentage means, of course, that most manufactured goods are imported, but it also means that the people of the country do not consume large quantities of manufactured goods.

In the world today there are four major manufacturing regions which supply a very large proportion of the world's factory products. One region is in eastern North America and includes parts of the United States and Canada. Another, located in northwestern Europe, runs from southern Great Britain across northern France into Germany and Czechoslovakia and includes Switzerland on the south and the Netherlands on the north. The third region lies in the U.S.S.R. and includes the area around Moscow, the Donbas region of southern U.S.S.R., and a number of somewhat more scattered areas in the Ural Mountains and Asiatic U.S.S.R. The fourth region includes eastern China and Japan.

These four major regions have certain favorable location factors in common. For example, all have access to high-quality coal. Iron ore is either found within each region or readily available by water transportation. All the regions have access to petroleum, although the European area is in itself deficient in the resource. Water power is available in all the regions and plays an important role in each. Except for some of the areas of the U.S.S.R., all of the manufacturing districts are fairly close to the sea.

The variety of goods manufactured in these regions runs to many thousands of items. All the regions emphasize food processing—milling, baking, canning, freezing, and drying—and the manufacture of textiles and clothing. The tendency is for more and more food and clothing to be processed in factories and less to be processed in homes. All regions have iron and steel industries, petroleum refineries, and metal-manufacturing plants for such diverse products as ships, automobiles, radios, and tools. Chemical industries produce fertilizers, drugs, and plastics; glass, cement, leather, and wood industries make up most of the remaining manufacture. The relative importance of these products varies widely, depending in part on location factors and in part on such other factors as local customs, average income, and purchasing power.

The relative importance of the different regions and countries is commonly expressed either in terms of the number of persons employed in manufacturing or in terms of the value added by manufacturing. The following table lists the total labor force for selected countries and the percentage engaged in manufacturing. These data are approximate since the census methods vary somewhat from country to country. (Figures in parentheses indicate additional percentage of people engaged in handicraft.)

Country	Total Labor Force (in millions)	Percentage in Manufacturing
Canada	5	26
United States	60	27
Brazil	17	6 (5)
Great Britain	23	37
Western Europe	180	24
Soviet Union	101	13
India	101	2 (8)
China	195	2 (5)
Japan	39	18

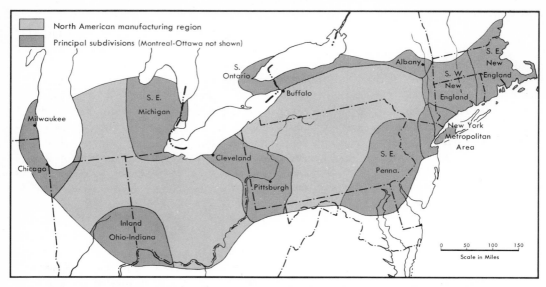

Fig. 19.2. North American manufacturing region. (Adapted from a map by Richard Hartshorne in *Economic Geography* **by Samuel Newton Dicken. Copyright 1955, by D. C. Heath and Company. Used by permission of D. C. Heath and Company.)**

The North American Manufacturing Region. The North American manufacturing region is, in many ways, the most diverse and highly developed of the four regions. It is especially noted for its large-scale development of machinery and such advanced techniques as the assembly line and very fine division of labor in manufacturing processes. The North American region takes advantage of its position on the North Atlantic, which is the most important ocean from the standpoint of traffic. This region also has the advantage of water transportation in the Great Lakes and the St. Lawrence Seaway and on rivers. Numerous and well situated, the harbors along the Atlantic afford the manufacturers of the region access to the hinterland. In the broadest sense, the hinterland of the region may be considered as including all of Canada, all of the United States, and, to a very large extent, all of Latin America.

Internally, the North American manufacturing region is highly diversified and specialized. For example, heavy industry is con-

centrated in or near the coal fields or on navigable waterways; cotton textiles are in southern New England and the southern Piedmont; automobiles and farm machinery are in the Chicago-Detroit district. The following subdivisions are generally recognized (Fig. 19.2):

1. Southeastern New England, textiles and shoes.
2. Southwestern New England, hardware, tools, and small arms.
3. Metropolitan New York, clothing, printing, and refining.
4. Southeastern Pennsylvania, steel, shipbuilding, wool, and synthetic fibers.
5. Albany-Buffalo, clothing, glass, and electrical goods.
6. Southern Ontario, steel, automobiles, meat packing, and flour milling.
7. Montreal-Ottawa, aluminum refining, paper, and sugar refining.
8. Pittsburgh-Cleveland, steel, glass, ceramics, and rubber.
9. Southeastern Michigan, automobiles, farm machinery, furniture, and hardware.

10. Ohio-Indiana-Inland, machine tools, electrical goods, soap and shoes.

11. Chicago-Milwaukee, steel, milling, agricultural machinery, and printing.

Additional outlying districts include the southern Piedmont, cotton textiles; the St. Louis district, shoes, bauxite processing, meat packing, and steel; Los Angeles, airplanes, petroleum refining, and clothing; San Francisco, oil and sugar refining and printing; Portland, wood and food processing; Seattle-Vancouver, airplanes, wood industries, and food processing.

The Western European Manufacturing Region. The European manufacturing region includes parts of England, France, the Netherlands, Belgium, Germany, Czechoslovakia, and Switzerland and is closely connected with a few outlying areas in Italy, Spain, and Scandinavia. This region depends heavily upon coal, especially in England, northern France, and Germany. All of the region is close to the sea and also benefits from excellent water transportation provided by rivers and canals. The products of the region are marketed in many countries with high

density of population and large demand for industrial goods. The European region is the oldest and, in many ways, the most skilled in manufacturing, although it is only recently that it has developed the assembly-line technique which is so characteristic of the North American manufacturing region. The European region has the special advantage of a very large pool of skilled labor. As a result, it not only exports manufactured products in large quantities but also actually exports large numbers of skilled laborers to other regions.

The European manufacturing region, like that of North America, is specialized by districts (Fig. 19.3) and extends from the central lowland of Scotland to northern Italy and western Poland. Since parts of 10 countries are involved, tariffs and trade agreements play an important role. In recent years, the tendency has been to relax trade barriers gradually, beginning with the Benelux (Belgium-Netherlands-Luxembourg) agreements and spreading to adjacent countries. This tendency is leading to increased specialization. One of the strongest remaining barriers is between East and West Germany or, more broadly, between western Europe and the Soviet zone. The most striking recent change has been the rapid recovery of West Germany's industries which were destroyed or disorganized during World War II.

The chief subregions are as follows:

1. Scottish Lowlands and northeastern Ireland, steel, shipbuilding, and textiles.

2. Northeastern England, shipbuilding, steel, lead refining, and glass.

3. Yorkshire, steel, machine tools, and woolen goods.

4. Lancashire, cotton textiles.

5. The Midlands, steel, automobiles, hardware, and synthetic fibers.

6. Southern Wales, metal and petroleum refining.

7. London, printing, chemicals, clothing, and instruments.

8. France-Belgium, clothing, textiles, and metals.

Fig. 19.3. Manufacturing regions of western Europe. (Adapted from *Economic Geography* by Samuel Newton Dicken. Copyright 1955, by D. C. Heath and Company. Used by permission of D. C. Heath and Company.)

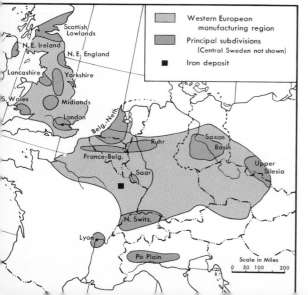

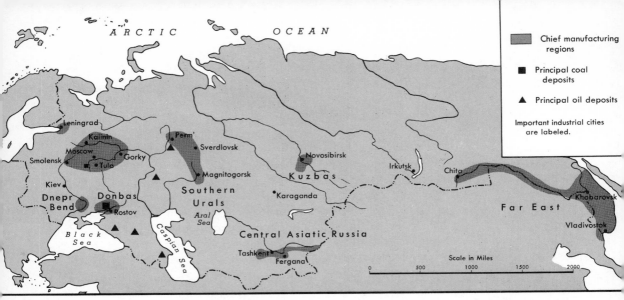

Fig. 19.4. Manufacturing regions of the Soviet Union. (Adapted from *Economic Geography* by Samuel Newton Dicken. Copyright 1955, by D. C. Heath and Company. Used by permission of D. C. Heath and Company.)

9. Belgium-Netherlands, sugar refining, textiles, rubber goods, and fertilizers.

10. Ruhr, heavy industry, iron and steel, locomotives, textiles, cutlery, and chemicals.

11. The Saar, iron and steel.

12. Saxon Basin, chemicals, optical goods, and printing.

13. Upper Silesia, steel, woolen goods, and linen.

14. Northern Switzerland, watches, instruments, textiles, and small machines.

15. Central Sweden, paper, pulp, wood products, textiles, and high-grade steel.

16. Lyon, silk, cotton textiles, and leather goods.

17. Po Plain, textiles, including cotton, silk, and rayon, and automobiles.

The Manufacturing Region of the Soviet Union. The U.S.S.R. manufacturing region extends from Leningrad eastward through the Urals into parts of Asiatic U.S.S.R. and southward to the Black Sea. Although recent statistics and information on Russian manufacturing are not available for the most part, its general character is well known in the Western world. Russian manufacturing has been intensified in recent years on the basis of techniques obtained from western Europe and North America, in part through the advice of many technical experts from these regions. Though the Russian manufacturing system has been patterned on that of western Europe and North America, it has been modified by the Russian way of life. For example, the Russian manufacturing system has put greater emphasis upon war materials of all kinds, certain transportation facilities, and agricultural machinery, and it has placed less emphasis upon what are generally referred to as consumer goods.

The manufacturing districts of the Soviet Union are scattered throughout the breadth of the country from Leningrad and the Donbas on the west to Vladivostok on the east. Although the rules for the location of industries apply in part to the various districts, it should be noted that the central government has established many of the new industrial districts by decree, partly for strategic reasons and partly to stimulate the growth of the less-developed parts of the nation. The districts in the west, however, (shown in Figure 19.4) were of some importance in the time of the czars. Because of strict government regulation, the districts (listed below) are highly specialized.

1. Leningrad, metal refining, wood processing, paper, matches, and cotton textiles.

284

2. Moscow, textiles, farm machinery, ceramics, light metal goods, and rubber.

3. Donbas, iron and steel, heavy machinery, sugar refining, chemicals, locomotives, and ships.

4. Dnepr Bend, steel, sugar refining, flour milling, and chemicals.

5. Southern Urals, metals, chemicals, paper, and textiles.

The Manufacturing Regions of Japan and Eastern China. In Japan, and to a limited extent in eastern China, manufacturing is growing rapidly in importance. The Japanese industrial belt is well developed and well known to the outside world, whereas little specific information is available for the Chinese region.

The main Japanese manufacturing region is located in the southern and western portions of the country, extending from the vicinity of Tokyo westward for 800 miles to the west side of the island of Kyushu. It is a highly urbanized zone with a variety of industries on the west end where

most of the good coal is located and the iron and steel industry is well developed. The distribution of the other industries depends on location and transportation. Especially noteworthy is the complementary relationship between Osaka and Kobe, and between Tokyo and Yokohama. Kobe is the deepwater port for Osaka and has heavy industries, while Osaka is a much larger city with many textile mills and light metal manufacturing; clothing factories are mostly in the outlying towns. Tokyo and Yokohama have much the same relationship and similar industries, although Tokyo is more a commercial than a manufacturing city. Nagoya has no deep-water port and is limited to the lighter industries—textiles, chemicals, machine tools, and ceramics.

Japan's industries recovered rapidly after World War II and compete successfully, in spite of tariff walls, for the world market in textiles, optical goods, electrical goods, and wood products (Fig. 19.5). Many of the raw materials used by Japanese industries must

Fig. 19.5. This paper mill at Yoshiwara, at the foot of Mt. Fuji, is much like the paper mills of the western world.

Fig. 19.6. The steel mill at Volta Redonda, Brazil, is located on the plateau to the west of Rio de Janeiro. The local region supplies neither iron ore nor coal, but is convenient to lines of transportation. This mill is large enough to supply most of the present-day needs for the entire continent of South America.

be imported from afar, and the finished products are sold in distant lands. For instance, Japan purchases logs in Washington and Oregon and turns them into plywood, some of which is sold in Washington and Oregon to the dismay of the United States competition.

China has a great potential for industrial development, but only about 2 per cent of the labor force is engaged in manufacturing. The resources of coal, iron ore, and other minerals are adequate and the domestic market is crying for more industrial products, but the growth of manufacturing is very slow. Most of China is still in the handicraft stage; some iron ore is still smelted in small backyard furnaces.

Prior to 1937 most of the industry of China was concentrated in a few large cities on, or near, the coast: Mukden, Manchuria (heavy industry), Tientsin, Shanghai, Nan-

king, and Canton. With the beginning of the Japanese occupation much of the industrial equipment was moved inland, some as far west as Chungking. After China was liberated, industries were restored to the coastal cities, but they also continued to operate inland. In recent years great emphasis has been placed on the increase of producers' goods: tools and agricultural machinery.

Other Manufacturing Regions. Outside the four major regions, manufacturing is of great local importance in a number of places. Particularly in Brazil, Australia, and India great strides have been made in recent years in converting from handicraft to modern manufacturing. Undoubtedly the greatest stimulus to the development of modern manufacturing (Fig. 19.6) in these and other countries was the shortage of goods which developed throughout the world as a result of World War II. Countries which had depended upon western Europe or North America for their manufactured goods found themselves cut off from these goods. In some cases consumer goods were no longer manufactured; in other cases transportation was not available. The scarcities which developed in many fields stimulated many countries to begin manufacturing on their own or, more accurately, to expand their manufacturing systems to cover a greater variety and a greater quantity of goods.

The general tendency in the world today is toward a wider distribution of manufacturing. This distribution has been made possible by improved transportation and by the technical and material aid given to countries which were previously very low on the manufacturing scale. The migration of skilled peoples, particularly from western Europe, has helped the progress of manufacturing in such countries as Australia and Brazil. Another factor of great importance in the spread of manufacturing is the spirit of nationalism: many countries consider the development of domestic manufacturing to be the means by which they can become independent of the great manufacturing countries of North America, western Europe, and the U.S.S.R.

Transportation is geared inextricably to the
working of the entire economy.
W. S. and E. S. Woytinsky

CHAPTER **20**

Roads, Rails, and Runways

Circulation, the movement and exchange of people, goods, and ideas, is the combined circulatory and nervous system of the world. All over the world, people are on the move —on foot and in carts (Fig. 20.1), wagons, automobiles, airplanes, trains, boats, and ships. Goods are likewise on the move in all kinds of conveyances on all sorts of routes and roads. As people come into contact with other people, migrate, and exchange goods, they also exchange ideas concerning inventions, language, political organization, and many other aspects of civilization.

The effect of communication is far-reaching and continuous. In general, communication makes people more alike. Nowadays, as people are exposed to ideas from many lands, they tend to adopt some of the ideas of other people, language barriers break down, and ways of life are modified. Conversely, communication also serves to intensify differences between regions: the exchange of goods may enable one region to specialize in a certain kind of production and thus become different from the adjoining region. In the early days, two agricultural regions fairly close to each other might be growing the same crops and producing the same staple foods, textiles, and clothing. With the establishment of transportation between these regions, however, each would be able to specialize to a certain degree in some products and to give up the production of other things. Thus, one region might spe-

cialize in wheat while another specialized in flax, the one producing a staple food and the other producing a staple fiber. Of course, there are many barriers to transportation which tend to limit its effect: transportation costs, tariffs, and embargoes, for example.

The first roads used by man were animal tracks. The trails of grazing and browsing animals might be long, straight, or crooked, but they usually followed the easiest route across the terrain, whether it be forest, brush, or grassland. At first, man moved along these trails as he hunted the animals, but later the animal trails became permanent man trails which eventually became modern roads. Many of our early roads were so obviously animal trails that they were sometimes referred to as cow paths. In Africa elephant paths provide easy routes through forests which otherwise would be very difficult to traverse. Antelope tracks serve as trails in other areas, and in the middle part of North America buffalo trails were used by the early travelers and hunters. Even small animals can, by continuous use, make a trail large enough for a man to travel. Man used the early trails and roads to get his prime needs —food, water, and fuel. The earliest roads probably led from such primitive shelters as caves to streams or shores where water and fish could be obtained and into woods and prairies where game could be hunted.

In modern times the very diverse media of transportation have brought great changes in man's relationship to the natural environment. Man's concept of a mountain range changes when a new road or a new kind of transportation is involved. The kind of transportation which is best suited to a region is gradually developed and becomes predominant there. All over the world millions of people are engaged in transportation. People and goods are moved by many kinds of carriers: there are still human porters carrying goods in parts of Africa and Asia; there are goods being moved by wheelbarrow, cart, automobile, truck, jeep, pipeline, and various kinds of pack animals.

Transportation employs one fifth of the world's man power and energy. In primitive societies the methods of moving people and goods are laborious, with the result that goods do not move very far and the volume of goods transported is small; muscle power, human and animal, is the chief moving force. In an industrial country about one person out of five is engaged directly in transportation or in the servicing and selling of goods that are used in transportation. Consider, for example, the large number of people engaged in servicing and operating automobiles, trucks, trains, and airplanes. Large amounts of mechanical energy, derived largely from coal and petroleum, are also used in transportation.

Variety of Carriers

The people, goods, and ideas of the world are transported from place to place by a variety of carriers. Though each type of carrier can be evaluated in terms of the cost of transporting one ton for one mile (Table 20.1), every carrier has qualities which cannot be shown by a ton-mile evaluation. The ocean liner, for example, can carry goods to the land, but no farther; the truck can carry goods to particular localities, from door to door, while the railroad can deliver only to a station; human carriers and pack animals can penetrate areas that do not have roads or even adequate trails. Thus, a comparison

Fig. 20.1. Both the wheels and the body of this Costa Rican oxcart are decorated with various colors and patterns.

TABLE 20.1

Cost Per Ton Mile of Various Carriers (in cents)

	1940	1960
Pack Animals	10.0 to 100.0	50.0 to 200.0
Railroads	0.7 to 5.0	1.5
Motor Trucks	2.0 to 8.0	6.5
Pipelines	0.3	0.3+
Tankers	0.1 to 0.5	0.3
Airplanes	15.0 to 30.0	18.0 to 20.0

All figures are approximate.

of carriers that is based solely on ton-mile costs is not entirely valid.

A century and a half ago, the muscle power of human porters and pack animals, the force of wind-driven sails, and the downstream flow of water were the principal sources of power for transportation. Although these sources of power are still in use, a number of new sources have been tapped, making possible railroads and ocean freighters powered by steam and oil, motor trucks and automobiles with internal-combustion engines, and airplanes, the latest forms of which are jet-powered.

Limited in range and speed, human porters today can transport goods for about one dollar per ton-mile; the cost for pack animals in most parts of the world is about the same. Two horses and a wagon, formerly a very important mode of transport, can move

289

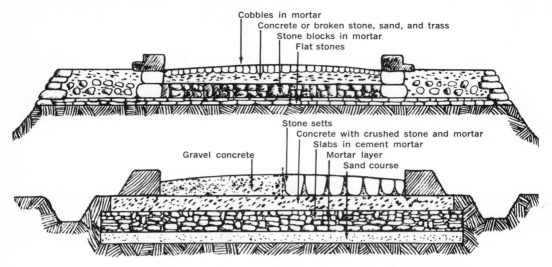

Cobbles in mortar
Concrete or broken stone, sand, and trass
Stone blocks in mortar
Flat stones

Stone setts
Concrete with crushed stone and mortar
Slabs in cement mortar
Mortar layer
Sand course

Gravel concrete

Fig. 20.2. Cross-sections of two Roman roads; the actual road bed in each case was from six to eight meters in width.

goods at a cost of from 10 to 25 cents per ton-mile.

The motor truck, some form of which is now used in most parts of the world, can transport goods at a cost of about 10 cents per ton-mile. The main advantage of the truck lies in its ability to travel over all roads and reach remote localities. It can carry its load from an original source, like a wheat field, to a processing point, like a flour mill; it can carry coal from a mine to its place of consumption.

Railroads, which have played such an important part in world transport in the last century, can move goods at a cost of from one to five cents per ton-mile. Naturally, the cost will vary with the nature of the material carried; coal, oil, wheat, and other bulk goods can be carried more cheaply than packaged goods, which have to have special handling.

The ocean freighter can carry goods more cheaply per ton-mile than any other form of transportation, the cost running from two tenths of one cent to about one cent per ton-mile. Whenever long hauls are possible and speed is not a factor, the ocean freighter is a preferred means of transportation.

Today, the airplane carries people and goods of all kinds to remote localities and offers the advantages of speed and long range. The cost per ton-mile varies widely, but it averages about 25 cents for air freight.

The pipeline is only useful in transporting gases and fluids, such as oil and gasoline, but it can carry these materials very efficiently and at low cost. The cost of pipeline transportation is slightly higher than that of transportation by tanker if the hauls are comparatively long.

Since transportation needs vary from place to place and from time to time, as a result of the widely varying conditions in the different parts of the world, each of these forms of transportation is particularly applicable in some instances. Because space is not available here to discuss in detail all of these carriers, special attention will be given to roads, railroads, and airways and, in a subsequent chapter, to a discussion of ocean transportation. It should be noted that the various kinds of carriers are rivals for the transportation dollar, but it is also important to note that the various kinds of carriers complement each other and are necessary to one another's functioning. For example, rail-

Fig. 20.3. An old Roman stone bridge on the Gard River in southern France.

Early Roads

ways leave freight at coastal terminals for further shipment by ocean freighters, and vice versa.

Until transportation by wheeled vehicles became common, there were almost no roads with prepared surfaces. In the forested areas of northwestern Europe, some areas of soft ground had trackways of brushwood, or of timber. Some of the Bronze Age lake villages in Switzerland had corduroy streets. Processional roads of limited length, with gypsum slabs over burnt brick, are known from the Near East as early as the third millenium B.C. The first road systems built for wheeled chariots and carts were in the Assyrian Empire of the 7th century B.C. A short, paved road built about 2000 B.C. was found in Crete, at the Palace of Knossos. In other places in the eastern Mediterranean and the Near East, similar short stretches have also been found. In China, laws were evolved prescribing a uniform size for carts, laws prohibiting reckless driving, and regulations for traffic at congested crossings.

The first great Roman highway, the 162 mile-long Appian Way, was begun in 312 B.C. It was at first merely graveled, but two decades later paving was added. Two typical Roman roads are shown in Figure 20.2 in cross-section. The cost of transporting goods on these roads was great, and it is estimated that the value of a load would double in the first 100 miles. From about 500 B.C., special messengers on horseback could travel 90 miles per day on roads and leveled tracks. This speed was average until after the early 1800's. A century after the starting of the Appian Way, the Flaminian Way, linking Rome with the Po Valley, was built. Thereafter, these were continuously added to, and new roads built. The Roman Empire was the gift of its roads (Fig. 20.3), just as Egypt was said to be the gift of the Nile. Only after A.D. 200 did the pace of road building in the Empire slacken.

The first roads of any length were developed in order to make widely available some of the valuable goods which could be obtained in only a few localities. Such valuable goods included amber, lapis lazuli, tin, and silk. Amber, a fossilized gum excreted by coniferous trees, was produced in ancient times on the shores of the Baltic Sea. From the Baltic Sea the amber, which was considered to be a precious stone, was transported across Europe to the Mediterranean along roads which are indicated today by the occurrence of small pieces of amber in areas where it was not produced. The earliest amber road led from the vicinity of Danzig (Gdansk) on the Baltic southward through what is now Poland and Austria to the Adriatic Sea in the vicinity of Trieste. Later, other amber roads were developed which ran south from Denmark by way of the Elbe River to Czechoslovakia and reached the Adriatic in the vicinity of Venice. These roads, together with their several branches or alternate routes, were the first roads to be used in Europe. The trade in amber, which was known in the Mediterranean in the time of Homer, began about 2000 B.C. and continued, with some interruptions, for 20 centuries.

The roads across Asia in the early days were limited by terrain and climate to two routes. One of these routes began just to the south of the Black Sea, continued eastward to the south of the Caspian Sea, and ran through Turkestan and on into central Asia. This is essentially the route followed by Marco Polo many centuries after the first roads were built. A more southerly route led through Turkey, Mesopotamia, and Persia and provided for the transportation of silk and a few other very valuable goods.

As early as 3000 B.C., lapis lazuli was a very important trade item upon which routes were based. (This semiprecious gem has been found along the early routes which led across Afghanistan, Persia, and Arabia.) Blue in color and very scarce, lapis lazuli was used both as a gem and as a pigment and was especially valued by the Persians and people in neighboring countries.

In western Europe a number of the early roads were developed by the traffic in tin. Tin was in great demand in the Mediterranean, particularly in the Roman Empire, where it was used as an alloy with copper to form bronze. Perhaps the first movement of tin was from Cornwall, a source of tin in southwestern England, by boat to the Baltic

and thence overland to the Mediterranean along the amber road. The later tin routes which were developed across France and Italy to the Mediterranean required that the tin be ferried across the English Channel from the vicinity of Dover to one of the French ports, usually Boulogne, and carried overland to Marseilles on the Mediterranean by pack horses. So that it could be easily packed on horses, the tin was cast into large ingots, shaped, and notched; an average load consisted of two ingots weighing 130 pounds each. Although such commodities as amber, lapis lazuli, silk, and tin were also carried by sea, the land traffic had the effect of establishing through routes in regions which had previously had only local roads.

The first great continental system of well-built roads was constructed by the Romans. This system, originating in Rome, extended as far as Scotland to the northwest and beyond Jerusalem to the east. The longest road in the system was nearly 4000 miles long, and the total length of the Roman road system at its maximum development was more than 50,000 miles. The quality of the roads varied widely from place to place; some sections were paved, either with slabs or cobbles, and some were not. Although the Roman roads are sometimes characterized as solely military, the fact is that they were usually constructed after a country had been conquered in order to maintain traffic for administrative purposes and to allow the movement of peoples and goods. Soldiers and common people moved along the roads by foot at the rate of about 20 miles per day; the rate of movement for the post and officials on horseback was about 40 to 50 miles, a day. Chariots, or stages, were used for special purposes and Caesar, by using a series of chariots, once traveled 100 miles in a day. Using three relays of chariots, the emperor Tiberius once sped from Germany to Lyons in France at the rate of 200 miles a day. (There was no improvement on Tiberius's speed for long-distance travel until the introduction of railways.)

One of the most remarkable of the ancient roads was the road built by the Incas of Peru. Stretching from Quito, Ecuador, into central Chile, this road was about 20 feet wide and paved by blocks, even though the Incas had no vehicular traffic. Used by foot travelers and pack animals (such as the llama), the road climbed mountain ranges 14,000 or 15,000 feet high by easy grades and switchbacks; it crossed canyons thousands of feet deep, bridged roaring torrents, and, in some places, reached into the desert. Humboldt described the road as having a deep understructure and being paved with hewn blocks of black porphyry. According to Humboldt, none of the Roman roads in Italy, southern France, or Spain was more imposing than this road of the Incas.

Road Materials

The main features of a road are its grade, its curves, and, above all, its materials of construction. For thousands of years man has attempted to place a surface material on his roads and trails that will make them easily traveled in all weather conditions. Since early man used whatever material was close at hand, the first material to be used was soil, which was followed by broken rock of various kinds, including gravel usually obtained from stream beds or glacial outwash. Many kinds of crushed rock, including limestone and basalt, are used in the construction of modern roads. Of the many kinds, some of which are much better than others for road construction, limestone is particularly good because the limestone dust produced by wear forms a cementing material. The famous pikes of a century ago were constructed mostly of limestone and served their purpose very well. As they hardened, they became fairly smooth, all-year roadways which provided very satisfactorily for the slow-speed wheel traffic of wagons and buggies. Eventually, the introduction of high-speed automotive traffic rendered these roads inadequate.

Roads are also commonly surfaced with blocks of various kinds, including bricks, cobblestones, and wood. Some cobblestone roads have endured for centuries, but cobblestones do not usually make a smooth road. Wood blocks have been used in many cases, but they are subject to expansion and contraction with changing moisture conditions. (Usually, wood blocks are impregnated with asphalt, creosote, or some other material to make them last longer.) Bricks have been used for roadways, particularly in eastern United States, with fair success.

In modern times most roads are constructed of concrete, and asphalt, or a combination of the two. Both of these materials can be applied in even layers of uniform character to produce roads which endure well under ordinary conditions. Concrete is more expensive and a little more difficult to apply than asphalt, but some modern roads have been successfully built of a mixture of asphalt and concrete. In constructing an asphalt road, it is necessary to provide a thick base of stone, gravel, or other material and also to provide for subsurface drainage. Although many other road materials (including rubber, cottonseed, and iron or steel plates) have been used experimentally in small quantities, they have been proven too expensive for general use despite their advantages.

The culmination of modern road construction lies in the modern freeways and toll roads, with their multiple lanes, limited accesses, and elaborate clover-leaf intersections and exchanges. These roads, constructed with easy curves and gentle grades, enable traffic to move at high speed through congested areas. Freeways serve to channel an even greater percentage of the passenger traffic into private automobiles.

Car, Bus, and Truck

The motor car, bus, and motor truck revolutionized the use of roads all over the world by providing more rapid transport for passengers and freight. A motor car carrying five or six people at a cost of roughly five cents a mile can compete very successfully with railroads and airlines on a cost basis. Although the airline is more rapid, the lower cost of the motor car, plus its added convenience, makes it the largest carrier of passengers in many parts of the world.

In the carrying of freight, the motor truck has many advantages over other means of transportation. For one thing, it can carry small units efficiently. Also, it has reasonable speed and lower rates for short haul door-to-door transportation; neither the airlines nor the railroads can handle door-to-door traffic. In addition, the schedules of trucks are more flexible; their services are always available since they are on the highways day and night. For many types of freight, truck transportation means less packing and less damage in transit. On the other hand, there are some drawbacks to truck transportation: for example, trucking charges are relatively high and by no means uniform; many truckers have only limited liability; and there is a great deal of irregularity in the scheduling and regulation of truck traffic. For very long hauls of large bulk shipments, rail transportation is cheaper. A combination of rail and truck transportation, called "piggy-back," in which the trailer portions of larger trucks are loaded on flat cars, is widely used. This method combines the low rail rate for long distances with the flexibility of trucks for door-to-door delivery.

Railways

Nearly every country today depends more or less upon railroads to transport heavy goods over relatively long land distances. In the United States railroad construction began in the early part of the 19th century. At the beginning of the 19th century the chief Atlantic ports—Boston, New York City, Philadelphia, Baltimore, Wilmington, Charleston, and Savannah—were all about the same size, and a contemporary observer might have hesitated to say which of these cities

would ultimately be the largest. Many people thought that Philadelphia might become the largest because at the time it was somewhat larger than any of the others. Before the construction of railroads there had been a widespread interest in canal construction; therefore, others thought that New York might become the largest since the success of the Erie Canal had given it an advantage over the other cities and caused it to spurt ahead in population growth. Not all the canals were as successful as the Erie. The Chesapeake and Ohio Canal, for example, which was planned to connect the Potomac River with the Ohio River, was not successful, never having been entirely established as a water route (a short rail connection was necessary over the crest of the Appalachian Mountains).

Once rail construction was undertaken, it proceeded very rapidly and involved most of the Atlantic port cities. The Pennsylvania Railroad was completed from Philadelphia to Harrisburg in 1852; the Boston and Albany was completed in 1841, shortly before the Boston and Maine. The big problem in rail construction in the United States, as in many other parts of the world, lay in mountain barriers. Once the Appalachian barrier was crossed and the interior lowland was opened, railroad expansion was very rapid indeed.

Today the railroads of the United States reach all parts of the country, the densest network being in the eastern half (Fig. 20.4). The New England group of railroads serves the northeastern part of the country and carries large quantities of Canadian wheat from the St. Lawrence Seaway to such ports as Boston and Portland, Maine. The Trunk Lines connect New York City and Chicago and carry large quantities of freight, including grain and coal, as well as passengers, mail, and express. Of the Trunk Lines that cross the Appalachians, the New York Central has the easiest route—up the Hudson River, across the Mohawk Valley to the Lake Ontario Plain, and thence close to the Great

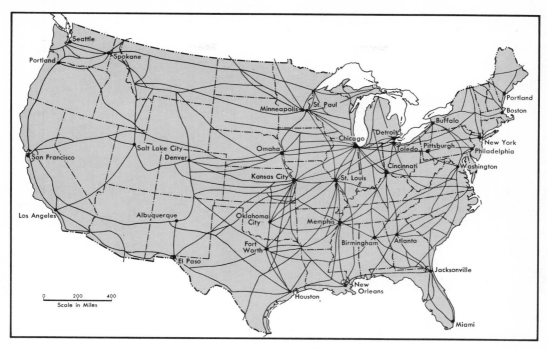

Fig. 20.4. Railways of the United States.

Lakes all the way to Chicago. The Coal Roads, another group of railroads, are designed primarily to get the coal out of the Appalachian coal fields.

The Granger Lines connect the upper Midwest area, including Chicago, and the northwestern part of the United States; these lines include the Northern Pacific Railway and the Milwaukee Road. The Southern Roads generally run north and south, connecting Chicago to the Gulf ports of Houston, New Orleans, and Mobile; the Illinois Central Railroad and the Southern Railway are examples of these roads. The Southwestern Roads connect Chicago with what might be called the Old Southwest, mainly Texas and New Mexico; an example of these is the Missouri-Kansas-Texas Line.

Finally, there are the Transcontinental Lines, which mostly connect Chicago with the ports on the Pacific. (Obviously, the Granger Lines could be classified as transcontinental in this sense.) Only one of the

Transcontinental Lines, the Southern Pacific, does not come into Chicago. Whereas the Southern Pacific is a truly transcontinental line, in that it reaches from Pacific Coast ports to Gulf ports (specifically New Orleans), the other Transcontinental Lines reach only to Chicago and connect there with the Trunk Lines to the Atlantic; the Union Pacific Railroad and the Santa Fe are examples of these transcontinental lines, which feature de luxe passenger service to the Pacific Coast.

Railroad maps show the density of the railroad network in the different parts of the country. The very open network of railways west of the 100th meridian is related in part to the low traffic density and in part to the barriers of mountains and the equally important barriers of dry, unproductive areas in which little or no traffic is to be picked up. In the eastern half of the country, which has a generally close network of railways, there are some areas with few railroads; examples of such areas are the hilly or mountainous

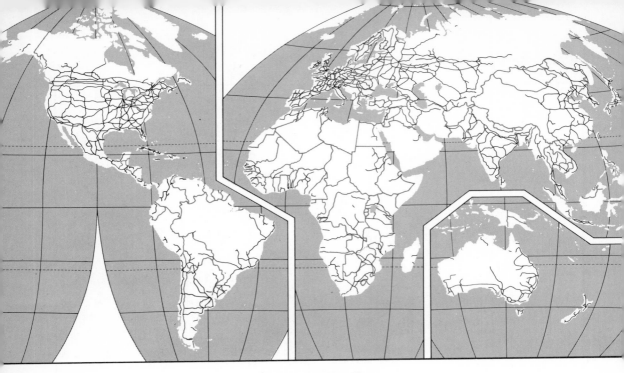

Fig. 20.5. World railways.

sections of the Ozarks and the Appalachians and somewhat remote districts like northern Maine and northern Minnesota.

The Canadian railroads, concentrated in the southern portions of Canada, are closely connected with those of the United States. Two Transcontinental Lines, the Canadian Pacific Railway and the Canadian National, connect the ports on the St. Lawrence Gulf with the west at Vancouver and Prince Rupert in British Columbia. In Mexico the rail network is very open. Railroads serve as connections with the United States and carry a fair share of the Mexican freight, but Mexico depends much more than many countries upon truck transportation.

In South America railroad building was started very late and has not reached a high stage of development in most parts of the continent. Only in small parts of southeastern Brazil, eastern Argentina, and Middle Chile is there an adequate railroad net. It has been said that South America jumped from the age of human and pack-animal transportation into the age of air transport without going through the railroad stage of development. This is at least partially true, but at the present time some additional railroad lines are being constructed in South America, notably those connecting southern Brazil with Bolivia, northern Argentina, and Chile.

Only the southern and northwestern parts of Africa have fairly adequate rail connections. Some rail connections have been established between especially productive areas in the interior, such as the Katanga copper district, and the coast. It is possible to cross Africa by rail from east to west but not from north to south.

In western Europe, particularly Germany, France, Great Britain, Switzerland, and the Low Countries, a very close network of railways exists. Since rail transportation came to western Europe after the cities were well established and a very elaborate system of roads and canals was already in use, the railroads followed the already established lines of communication. It should be noted that a European railroad station is likely to be found on the periphery of a city rather than in the center (unlike many American railroad stations). The railroads of Europe face serious difficulties of terrain. Even in the Paris Basin, which is considered to be a fairly level region, it has been necessary to construct some tunnels in order to make easier grades. In general, tunnels are more numerous in Europe than in other parts of the world; many European tunnels, such as the spiral tunnel in the Swiss Alps, have been built not to go through mountains but to make gentler grades over them.

The rail network of the U.S.S.R. is generally open, but it plays a very important part in the economy of that country. In recent years the Russians probably have built more new rail lines than any other country. They have especially concentrated on the routes in central Asiatic U.S.S.R. and on the extension and improvement of the Trans-Siberian Railway; they have also given attention to the Turk-Sib Railway, which connects the Caspian Sea with the Trans-Siberian Railway by way of south-central Asiatic U.S.S.R. Many parts of the Soviet Union, particularly northern Siberia, have no railroads at all and depend mainly upon air transportation.

Among the Asian countries, only India and Japan have fairly elaborate railroad networks. In India, particularly, railroads play an important part in transportation. Because the source of coal in India is mostly in the east near Calcutta, railroad trains must haul a burdensome amount of coal as they leave the Calcutta area, in order to assure their return to the source of supply. In Japan narrow-gauge railways are used because of the hilly and mountainous terrain, the sharp curves, and the steep grades. The railroads played an all-important part in carrying the goods of Japan until truck transportation was widely developed (Fig. 20.5).

Airways

This is not merely the Air Age, it is the Jet Age. Throughout the world airplanes have taken over a good share of the world's transportation. The airplane has, first of all, a great advantage in speed. Even the slowest airplane in current use is likely to be faster than any other type of carrier, and the fastest commercial planes now approach the speed of the earth's rotation (while military and experimental planes, of course, far exceed this speed). Another advantage of the airplane is its ability to travel in direct routes; unless detoured by local and temporary severe weather conditions, planes can fly great-circle routes for long flights and take the shortest routes over mountains, deserts, and water barriers.

In many places the airplane has competed so successfully with other carriers that they have been eliminated entirely. For example, airlines from the Pacific Northwest to Alaska now carry all the passengers, mail, and express; the regular passenger ships formerly in service have disappeared completely, and only tankers, freighters, and the cruise ships with summer tourists make the voyage. In Hawaii planes have long since taken over most of the passenger traffic from the mainland and have taken over all the interisland traffic formerly carried by coastwise steamers and motor ships. One can now travel from Oahu to the Island of Hawaii by plane in an hour, whereas the trip formerly required an overnight voyage which might be very rough. That the competition of planes is not limited to areas of water transportation or to areas without rail and inland transportation is illustrated by the fact that planes have largely replaced the boats on the Magdalena River in Colombia which, in conjunction with short-line railroads, carried passengers and freight from Barranquilla on the northern coast to the capital at Bogotá. Airplanes can function in places where there are no roads or other carrier routes and can even operate without specially prepared airfields or airports.

The airplane is versatile partly because it can be constructed in various sizes and outfitted with various kinds of equipment. In Canada and Alaska the float plane (Fig. 20.6), equipped with skis in the winter, ef-

Fig. 20.6. Small floatplanes like this are used extensively in Alaska and Canada and in other regions with lakes.

fectively provides transportation in the vast northern areas. At Anchorage, Alaska, two small lakes form the airport for hundreds of float planes, many of them privately owned. Since Anchorage has limited contact with its hinterland by rail and road, the planes, served by the numerous lakes which can accommodate float planes in summer and ski-equipped planes in winter, go a long way toward solving the transportation problem. The planes are inactive only during the period between the freezing and thawing of the lakes when neither floats nor skis can be used. There are planes larger than float planes also being used in the area; unlike float planes, these planes require established air routes with airfields, beacons, and other adjuncts to navigation. Weather reports are, of course, of great importance to all types of planes.

The principal airways of the world are concentrated in North America and western Europe and are interconnected by many transatlantic lines. The main world route might be described as originating in New York City and connecting western Europe, southern Europe, India, southeastern Asia, and Australia (Fig. 20.7). The fairly heavy traffic on the air route is carried by a number of airlines from various countries. The transoceanic airlines carry a volume of tourist traffic that is far greater than that carried by passenger ships.

In North America the principal air routes run east and west, much like the main railroad routes (Fig. 20.5). Some less important air routes run north and south, and a number of lines have routes going both east and west and north and south. Air traffic is heaviest in the northeastern part of the United States and the adjacent parts of Canada—areas of intensive industrial development. The major cities are all connected by a number of airlines; such cities as New York City, Chicago, San Francisco, and Los Angeles both initiate much traffic and handle connecting air traffic. At Chicago one passenger plane takes off almost every minute from one or the other of the two major airports. New York City with its several airports has an even greater density of flights. Some cities, however, do not function in any large measure as exchange points; not many passengers en route to other cities actually deplane in such cities as Philadelphia, San Antonio, Albuquerque, El Paso, Reno, and Spokane.

In South America the principal air routes are peripheral to the continent. One route from the eastern coast of North America leads almost due south to strike the western coast of South America. Other routes lead down the eastern coast of South America and cut directly across the Amazon River without following the line of the coast in great detail. Although short connecting routes lead into the interior at many points, there is not a dense network of airlines in South America.

Western Europe has the world's heaviest concentration of airlines, and cities like London, Paris, and Berlin have very heavy air traffic. From these cities the traffic radiates in all directions: across the Atlantic, down the western coast of Africa and thence to southern South America, eastward into eastern Europe, and southeastward into Asia. Even though many of the flights in western Europe are short, the plane competes very

successfully with rail and highway transportation. Ground traffic is congested and slow, especially where bodies of water or high mountains are encountered.

In Africa the principal routes are along the western coast and north and south along the Nile into the Cape region (the old Cape to Cairo route on which a rail line was planned but not completed). Since Africa has very few railroads and highways in the interior, planes are often used for short, local trips. It is much easier, quicker, and cheaper to fly from the western coast to the Katanga copper area than to travel there by boat and rail.

In the U.S.S.R. the airplane has been very important to the remote sections of the country. Although the percentage of traffic devoted to passengers has not reached that of other countries, the plane carries much of the passenger, mail, and light express traffic in central Asiatic U.S.S.R. and Siberia. Countries like Japan, India, and Australia, remote from the industrial areas of Europe and North America, are well served by airlines. Japan and southeastern Asia are reached by airlines across the Pacific, one main airline flying via Hawaii and another traveling the shorter, great-circle route via Alaska and the Aleutian Islands.

Altogether, the growth of air transportation during the last 40 years has been phenomenal; and continued growth is evidenced by the development of larger planes with greater payload efficiency and the increasing amounts of freight and express (as well as more passengers and mail) being handled by the airlines. A part of the growth of airlines has been the result of various government subsidies, especially mail subsidies. It has been common governmental practice to pay airlines sums of money for carrying the mail which are far in excess of the postage received. It is considered good practice in many countries to encourage commercial airlines, as part of the national defense program, to increase the number of planes and to improve the airports and other facilities.

Fig. 20.7. World air routes.

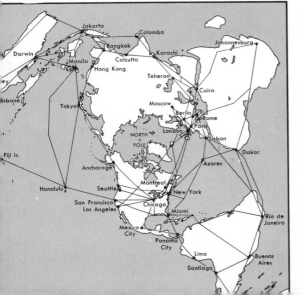

Formerly, only high-priority materials and goods could be carried efficiently by airlines, but it is apparent that more and more commodities will be transported by air as the carrying efficiency of planes increases. Already coffee, livestock, and many other commodities are being carried by planes where other carriers are not readily available or where, because of the nature of the roads or railroads, the ground traffic is very heavy. The development of world airways has made profound changes in the economy of some parts of the world. It has, for example, made it possible to transport oil-drilling equipment and other pieces of heavy machinery, as well as the men and supplies to implement them, into out-of-the-way places. Huge gold dredges weighing hundreds of tons have been dismantled and flown into remote districts.

Other Carriers

In addition to roads, railways, airlines, and ocean carriers, which carry a large part of the world's traffic, such other carriers as inland waterways, pipelines, and power lines have a share in the total transportation picture. Pipelines carry oil and natural gas from the producing fields to the markets or to ports where tanker service is available. The distribution of natural gas is almost completely dependent upon pipelines, whereas oil can also be transported by tanker, rail, and truck. Pipelines also carry water to cities and areas of irrigation. The use of power lines to transmit energy for hundreds of miles has had a profound effect on industry, serving in many cases to decentralize it. Paralleling the expansion of transportation, the easier transmission of ideas by means of the printed word, telephone, telegraph, radio, television, and the spoken words of millions of world travelers brings all parts of the inhabited earth closely together; no one part of the world can now be independent of the others. This interdependence is a new phenomenon, the effects of which are just beginning to become apparent. It is obvious that, in the years to come, the communication complex will play an even more important role than it has in the past.

CHAPTER **21**

Land Use and Conservation

In previous chapters frequent references have been made to the effects of man's occupation of the earth; in this chapter some of the problems of conservation are discussed with reference to specific types of land use, such as forestry, mining, and agriculture. It is often assumed that the problems of conservation are most pressing in regions of dense population and highly developed machine technology, but this is obviously an oversimplification. In some areas of dense population most of the problems of conservation have been solved, for the time being at least, while in some sparsely peopled areas the resources are being rapidly exhausted. In any broad view of conservation and land use, one is impressed with three aspects: the variety of resources in different parts of the earth; the diversification of peoples, customs, and land use; and the present rapid intensification of land use as population increases and machine technology spreads.

If one considers the variety of resources, on the one hand, and the various types of land use, on the other, there is the temptation to infer a simple correlation between them. It would simplify the problems of defining land-use types, for example, if they could be correlated with climate, soil, natural vegetation, and mineral deposits. To be sure, a rough correlation can be made between agricultural types and climate (Fig. 21.1). It is possible to speak of the "wheat climate," the "corn climate," and the "coffee climate"

and to devise climatic definitions to fit the major distribution of these crops. But it must be noted that wheat grows better in the corn climate than it does in the wheat climate and that all three crops grow fairly well in a variety of climates. Land use certainly depends on physical resources, but it also depends on the character of the people and the stage of their development.

As life becomes more diverse and intense, the attitude of man toward the resources of the earth—toward conservation—changes, sometimes very abruptly. In the early days of the hunting-gathering-fishing peoples the idea of conservation, of saving resources, had not emerged. They collected what they could, usually fruits and nuts. If nature was kind, there was an abundance of everything; if disaster struck—drought, flood, or fire— the people probably blamed it on the "spirits." The attitude of the modern American pioneers was scarcely better, and the effect was much worse. They put the ax and fire to forests to clear land. In eastern North America, oak trees which would be worth $1000 each today were cut and burned to clear fields for corn and tobacco. These pioneers could not foresee, with a whole continent before them to exploit, that in a few generations all the good land would be occupied and most of the hardwood forests destroyed. The pioneers worked hard and were proud of the acreage they had cleared and cultivated.

In some parts of the world the attitude of

301

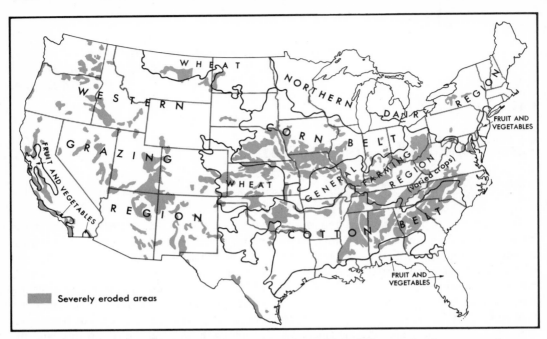

Fig. 21.1. The major agricultural regions of the United States, showing areas of severe erosion. The most severe erosion has occurred in the southern part of the Corn Belt, in the southern Appalachians, and in the eastern part of the Cotton Belt.

these pioneers still prevails, but many peoples have developed a different point of view. Thomas Jefferson and his contemporaries in the Virginia piedmont learned to plant trees, to terrace the hill slopes, to cultivate carefully, and to improve the soil by the use of fertilizers and manures. Not far away, however, other farmers were cultivating with little thought for the future, leading to soil erosion and loss of fertility to the point of uselessness.

The intensification of life involves more people, with increasing desires, more tools, more trade, more communication, and a greater transfer of goods and ideas. The basic needs of man—air, food, and water—are almost forgotten in the demand for the perquisites of modern civilization. The demand for such things as elaborate houses, automobiles, airplanes, and (of late) space vehicles has greatly intensified the production and ex-

ploitation of the earth. Strangely enough, the intensification plus improved circulation is tending to decrease the diversification in man's activities. Machine farming with its large tractors, plows, and harvesters, once limited to very large farms, has been adapted to smaller ones. Even the rice farmers in Japan now use rototillers and, as a result, rice farming has become more commercial; the farmer must now sell some rice to pay for the rototillers, fuel, and repairs. War has accelerated this intensification and has led to more uniformity in production methods. During World War II the United States shipped tractors to England and the Soviet Union in order to make up for their loss of man power in military service. In each case the shipments contributed to a permanent change-over from horse-drawn farm implements to power cultivators.

For the purposes of this chapter most of

the land use of the earth may be generalized under a comparatively few types:

NONAGRICULTURAL

HUNTING-GATHERING-FISHING
NOMADIC HERDING AND COMMERCIAL GRAZING
FOREST PRODUCTION
MINING
MANUFACTURING (discussed in Chapter 19)

AGRICULTURAL

HOE CULTURE
PLOW CULTURE
   Rice Farming
   Mediterranean Agriculture
   Small-Grain and Livestock Farming
   Dairying
   Corn-Belt Farming
   Wheat-Belt Farming
   Plantations

Hunting-Gathering-Fishing

The hunting, gathering, and fishing economy, once widespread over many parts of the earth, is now confined, for the most part, to the fringes of the Arctic Ocean in northern North America and northern Eurasia. To be sure, many other people practice some hunting, gathering, and fishing along with agriculture as a means of subsistence, but in the arctic regions agriculture is impossible and the people must depend entirely upon hunting, gathering, and fishing. This is mainly a subsistence form of land use and the natives, whether they are Eskimos, Lapps, Tungus, or Yakuts, must use a great deal of skill and invention in order to live in the very harsh, difficult climate. The reindeer, a browsing animal, enables some of these peoples to live a partially pastoral life, in contrast to the pure hunters, gatherers, and fishers. All the arctic peoples depend upon wild animals to a considerable extent for their food, clothing, and shelter since vegetation is very scarce and very limited in variety. The hunters tend to congregate near the sea so as to hunt the sea animals—the seal, walrus, and whale—and to have access

to sea fish. Hunting and gathering on the land is less extensive in North America than it is in northern Eurasia.

In North America the hunting, gathering, and fishing region is occupied mostly by the Eskimo people, who range from Alaska to Labrador and Greenland (see Figure 11.1); some Eskimo also are found in northeastern Siberia. Throughout this vast area the total population is not much more than 25,000. The Eskimo tend to concentrate in a few districts, particularly where trading posts are established; one of the principal effects of the contact of white people with the Eskimo was the development of the fur trade and markets for the furs taken by the Eskimo.

In northern Eurasia the zone of the hunting-gathering people who depend on the reindeer extends from Norway to northeastern Siberia. Several tribes are usually recognized here, including (in order from west to east) the Lapps, Samoyed, Ostyak, Tungus, Yukagir, and Chukchi, numbering altogether about 30,000. Unlike the Eskimo, most of these tribes tend to avoid the coast, which is foggy and unpleasant. They use skin tents made from the hides of reindeer or other animals; they gather some berries and roots, and their migrations carry them to the southern end of the tundra, where some wood is available. The Eurasian zone includes nomadic herding along with hunting and gathering; some of the tribes are almost entirely dependent upon reindeer for their livelihood. The use of the reindeer varies from place to place. The Lapps in the west use their tame reindeer as temperate-belt farmers use their cattle—for meat, hides, and milk. Farther east the half-wild reindeer roam in herds over much of the region; the natives hunt these animals for meat but do not milk them. The migration of the nomadic peoples of eastern Siberia depends upon the movement of these herds.

In the hunting-fishing-gathering and pastoral regions bordering the arctic, the changes brought about by man are comparatively slight even after centuries of occupation.

Some over-browsing has undoubtedly occurred, and the numbers of native animals have been reduced. However, the population is so sparse and the area so vast that man-made changes are scarcely noticed. The population has been kept small by the hazards of the area—cold, starvation, and disease. Diseases introduced by the white man have been especially devastating. These regions are definitely on the fringe of human occupation and up to the present have had very little population pressure on them.

Nomadic Herding and Commercial Grazing

Over much of the earth's surface there is too little rain for cultivation of any kind except where special local water supplies are available for oases. These arid lands, if occupied at all, are mostly used for pastoral purposes and may be classified either as areas for nomadic herding, which is a wandering, subsistence type of land use, or as commercial grazing areas, representing the commercial ranch type.

Nomadic herding areas extend from northwestern Africa, eastward through Arabia, Turkey, and southeastern European Russia, all the way to the Gobi country of Mongolia and western China, an area four times as large as the United States. The occupation of the land is very uneven; many parts are completely unpopulated, mostly because there is no pasture or water for the herds and flocks. The total number of people involved in the practice of nomadic herding is much greater than the number found in the primitive hunting areas previously described. Altogether, perhaps a million or more nomads, including Berbers, Arabs, Turks, Kurds, Jews, Afghans, Khirgiz, and Mongolians, inhabit this area. Within the broad region described, many millions of people live in the oases. In lower Egypt alone, which can be described as one huge oasis, more than 25 million people reside. The oases scattered throughout the nomadic herding regions have an important effect upon the life

of the nomadic peoples: they provide them with many products which they otherwise would not have, such as grain, dates, tools, and guns. The nomadic peoples in turn supply the oases with meat, leather, and cheese.

Although the character of the peoples and their nomadic life varies somewhat from place to place, their mode of living is generally similar throughout this vast region. They are forced to migrate from time to time in order to find forage and water for their livestock. In many cases this is a seasonal migration, called *transhumance*: a migration up the slopes in summer to the greener pastures and down to the lower elevations in winter. But in other areas the migration is much more irregular, and the nomads do not migrate unless the local supply of grass gives out. Most of the nomadic groups have a variety of livestock—horses, cattle, sheep, and goats, for example. However, in some places a single animal may have a very dominant position—the camel in Arabia, the horse in Mongolia, and the yak in Tibet. (The Tibetans do not migrate, normally.) In recent years the impact of neighboring industrialized peoples has had a great effect upon the life of the nomads. In Algeria and southern U.S.S.R., for example, the nomads have more or less been forced to settle down and become agriculturalists because their best grazing lands have been taken over by other peoples for agriculture.

The occupation of the arid and semiarid lands by nomadic peoples has brought about some significant changes in the natural vegetation. The population tends to expand to the limit of the food supply. In times of excessive drought the native grasses and other forage plants are so reduced as to change the whole aspect of the land. When rains again occur, the original native grasses may be replaced by less desirable species. Once the pastures are badly damaged, the nomads tend to migrate to other regions and, in time, the damaged pastures are at least partially restored.

Commercial grazing, in contrast to nomadic herding, is a fairly recent develop-

Fig. 21.2. Cattle on a ranch in the California Coast Range north of San Francisco.

ment. The chief regions are western United States, northern Mexico, and parts of Venezuela, Brazil, Argentina, South Africa, New Zealand, and Australia. Large areas of semi-arid land, though too dry even for dry farming, provide a large quantity of forage for livestock which can be marketed, in one form or another, in the great industrial regions far from the grazing lands.

The characteristic feature of commercial grazing is an established ranch or headquarters, where the livestock can be winter-fed, branded, and prepared for the market. Some of the ranch lands are fenced, some are not; in any case, many hundreds or even thousands of acres of land are necessary for one ranch because, in the lands too dry for agriculture, the carrying capacity of the grasslands is so small that from 15 to 75 acres of pasture are needed for one cow (the usual unit of measurement). In a few places, as in southwestern Texas, the goat is of considerable importance, but cattle, for beef and hides, and sheep, for mutton and wool, are the dominant animals in the areas

of commercial grazing. In western United States the principal sheep areas tend to be concentrated near the mountains, which provide summer grazing for the animals, or near irrigated lands, which supply winter feed. Range sheep production, as contrasted to the sheep production on humid farms, has declined in recent years. In the more remote areas of commercial grazing, such as southern Argentina, the principal product is wool, since it can be exported at a profit even under difficult transportation conditions. More and more, the important areas of commercial grazing are establishing freezing plants so that the meat, mostly beef and mutton, may be shipped in a frozen state and thus bring a higher price in the world market.

Commercial grazing (Fig. 21.2) with its permanent location puts even greater pressure on the land than nomadic herding. In western United States some areas have been so heavily over-grazed that native grasses have been replaced by sage brush, a plant which has little value for forage. Once the native grasses are damaged, it is very difficult to restore them. Only in the few humid areas of commercial grazing, such as New Zealand and the Argentine Pampa, is it feasible to reseed the pastures.

Forest Production

Forest production in the world today may be divided into tropical and temperate types. The tropical forests, located mostly in central South America, equatorial Africa, and Indonesia, have a great many kinds of trees, mostly hardwood. Their very variety makes it difficult to harvest them, since any one wood, such as mahogany, is represented only by scattered trees throughout a large area. More and more attention is being given to the tropical forests, however; in addition to cabinet woods and hardwoods of various kinds, the tropical forests supply such products as chicle, wild rubber, palm oil, quinine, and Brazil nuts. It is to be noted that the cultivation of some of the tree crops, notably rubber, quinine, and palm oil, was preceded by the gathering of wild varieties of these crops from the tropical forests.

Little attention has been given to conservation of tropical forests, perhaps because the exploitation is usually on a small scale and regrowth is rapid. A few species, however, such as teak and some varieties of mahogany are becoming scarce.

In the forests of the temperate and cold climates, both hardwoods and softwoods are exploited. The hardwoods, especially oak, maple, birch, poplar, gum, walnut, and cherry, occur mostly in a belt that has now become largely agricultural; and these hardwoods are now limited to comparatively small areas in the agricultural zones. To the north of the agricultural zones are the principal stands of softwoods—pine, fir, cedar, and spruce. These supply most of the lumber and paper used today; the largest producers are Canada, the United States, the U.S.S.R., and the northern European countries.

The northern zones, in which forest production is dominant, are also utilized in other ways. Many places have mineral deposits of considerable value; in some favorable locations agriculture is possible, especially where there is a good local market for agricultural products, perhaps adjacent to a large lumber or paper mill.

In the last half century, great attention has been given to conservation of the forests in various countries, after the complete destruction of large areas of forest land, particularly by clear-cutting operations. In Norway, Sweden, and parts of Finland the coniferous forest has been largely cut-over, and the logging industry is now carefully regulated, whether on private or state-owned lands. The excellent pine forests of Michigan and Minnesota have been almost completely destroyed and in such a manner that they cannot grow back without expensive replanting. To a lesser extent, this destruction has occurred in other areas. It is obvious that the forested areas must be carefully managed if they are to continue to produce wood for lumber, pulp, paper, synthetic fibers, and various other uses (Fig. 21.3). A new approach in many places today is the tree farm, in which a large tract of timber is carefully managed, usually by a private company. Precautions are taken to prevent fires and to protect the seeds from rodents, the young seedlings from animals, and the trees from diseases. Logging of small areas is carefully supervised so as to permit rapid reseeding, preferably by natural means, from the nearby remaining stands. Usually, a tree farm includes many thousands of acres of forest land, and the company which owns it often controls many tree farms in the vicinity. The efforts needed to preserve the forest lead to costs for log production which are higher than those associated with the old method of ruthless, complete cutting of large areas. Companies with these increased costs are faced with competition from other forested lands, such as those of Japan or the U.S.S.R., where labor costs are much lower.

Fig. 21.3. Old and new methods of logging: above, felling a tree with long-handled axes and an extra long crosscut saw, on the Olympic Peninsula of Washington; right, the chain saw makes it easier to fell a tree; this view is near Wooster, Ohio.

Mining

Mining is very widely distributed in various parts of the world, and there is a great variety in minerals. Mining is often referred to as the "robber economy," since every bit of mineral mined means that much less remaining for future generations. Some minerals are quite abundant (such as salt and building stone); others are moderately abundant in some specific localities (coal and iron, for example); still other minerals are scarce or expensive to move, and if they are badly needed in industry in a particular country, they are considered to be strategic minerals (such as nickel, platinum, and chromium in the United States).

The strategic minerals present some special problems in conservation. Is it better for a country to subsidize its mining industry and produce some of the strategic minerals at high cost, or is it better to import these minerals and stockpile them for future use? Another type of problem is the effect of mining on other forms of production. Placer mining (with dredges) and strip mining often destroy the soils and leave once fertile areas totally unfit for agriculture or grazing. Also, the fumes from copper smelters usually located near the mines often destroy all vegetation within a radius of several miles.

Hoe Culture

Two broad phases in the development of agriculture are commonly recognized: hoe culture and plow culture. Man has used a variety of implements in the practice of hoe culture, not only digging sticks and the crude stone hoe but later the iron hoe, crude spades, and many hand implements. Obviously, plow culture is a more advanced and intensive type of agriculture than hoe culture, since the plow, whether drawn by human, animal, or mechanical power, is a much more efficient machine in cultivating the soil.

At the time America was discovered, all of the agricultural practices of the New World could be described as hoe culture. The natives in various places were cultivating a variety of plants, using sticks and crude hoes and supplementing their crops by hunting, fishing, and gathering. Perhaps the principal area in North America where scattered cultivation occurred at this time was to the south of the Great Lakes and to the east of the Mississippi River; some of the tribes, such as the Iroquois in New York State, depended on agriculture to a considerable extent for their subsistence.

In hoe culture new land is cleared from time to time so as to maintain yield and

307

Fig. 21.4. The use of the hoe in this small garden in Malaya is similar to that of the primitive hoe culture areas.

fertility (Fig. 21.4). It is common practice to girdle the trees by cutting through the bark or to burn the forest, following which crops are sown between the standing tree trunks. It is characteristic of hoe culture that fertilizer is not used.

Hoe culture is practiced today on the fringes of plow culture, especially where steepness of slope or character of the soil makes plow culture unfeasible, as in tropical America, Africa, and southeastern Asia. Various crops are grown for food and fiber, including maize, bananas, manioc, yams, squash, and beans. The native term applied to this form of cultivation is usually "shifting patch" cultivation (*conuco* in tropical America, *milpa* in Mexico, and *ladang* in Malaya). It is typical of hoe culture that, in addition to hand-implement cultivation, there is usually a periodic shifting of the patches, allowing a natural rotation to renew the nutrients in the soil. In some places the occupation is made more permanent by the construction of terraces on steep hillsides. The hoe-culture settlements are scattered, usually clearings in the forest. Occasionally some of the towns or villages are large, but

the usual settlement probably contains not more than 200 or 300 people. Over the centuries hoe culture has resulted in some soil erosion in the most hazardous places and, undoubtedly, great changes have been made in the natural vegetation, but the changes are very slight compared to those brought about by plow culture.

Plow Culture

The beginning of plow culture, a much more advanced form of cultivation than hoe culture, depended upon a combination of circumstances, particularly the invention of the plow and the domestication of herd animals large enough to pull a plow. Also associated with this beginning was the development of metallurgy to the point where a metallic plowshare could be invented. To be sure, wooden plows without metal are still used in isolated cases. The earliest plow culture probably originated in China, India, and southwestern Asia and was associated with the cultivation of the small grains, particularly wheat, barley, and the millets. The peoples who cultivated these plants probably had sheep, goats, asses, horses, and cattle, but only the larger animals were suitable for pulling the plow.

There is a great deal of physical diversity in the plow-culture areas; plow culture exists in a great variety of climate and terrain, from the irrigated oases around the fringes of the Sahara to the cool lands of northwestern Europe and the tropical lands of southeastern Asia. The plow-culture peoples have a much greater variety of crops available for cultivation than the hoe-culture peoples. And, with the possibility of much more thorough and larger-scale cultivation, some of the crops have become very important: for example, grains in the western part of the plow-culture area, notably in the Mediterranean region and northwestern Europe. The part that livestock plays in plow culture, aside from the mere drawing of the plow, varies with the nature of the people and also with the climate under which the crops and the livestock are grown. The following types of plow culture are based mainly on differences in crops and livestock, their uses, and the methods of production.

Rice Farming. In southeastern Asia, including south China and India, rice farming is one of the most dominant forms of plow culture. This region is particularly suited to rice in that the summers are warm and rainy and, in many places, the winters are dry and mild. Rice requires a long growing season with warm weather and abundant rain; it profits by a drier season near harvest time so that it may ripen and also be dried and preserved after harvesting. Rice is cultivated in two ways: it may be grown by broadcast seeding, particularly on hillsides after the land has been plowed and otherwise prepared; but the most important form of rice cultivation is by planting in small enclosures or paddies.

In the regions of heavy rainfall it is only necessary to build up a small ridge to enclose the paddy—the rains flood the paddy from time to time and, by a little manipulation, the paddy can be drained. This method of alternate drainage and flooding yields the greatest returns; also, the rice fields can be used for other crops, such as wheat, barley, and millet, during the mild winter season. Rice farming is a very intensive form of agriculture in which a large amount of labor is expended upon a small plot of land. Associated with rice farming is the cultivation of other crops—small grains, vegetables, spices, and many kinds of tree and bush crops (tea, for example)—on the adjacent hillsides.

In the areas of lighter rainfall, irrigation is necessary to get the maximum yield of rice. This can often be done by diverting a stream and leading it onto the paddies, or by digging shallow wells in the alluvial soils of the great river flood plains, such as the Ganges or the lower Yangtze.

A number of animals, including horses and oxen, are used for draft purposes in the areas of rice farming, but the most successful draft animal for the rice paddies is the carabao (water buffalo). This animal likes the muddy, wet rice paddy and is able to pull a plow through it to better advantage than other animals. However, as noted above, the rototiller is displacing the draft animals in some rice regions (see Figure 12.6).

At its best, rice farming is probably the most stable and conservative form of agriculture; for 40 centuries or more, Chinese farmers have cultivated the same paddies with no indication of declining yields. These farmers, as Paul Sears once said, "cultivate their paddies with the same loving care which a Dutch housewife bestows on her window box." All of this intensive use of the land results in a very close organization and cooperation among the people, in order to use the water and the land most efficiently. It results also in large concentrations of population in the flood plains of the great rivers. The dense population in the rice-farming regions allows only a small plot of land for each family; all, therefore, take care that no erosion shall occur, that no fertility shall be lost. Sewage and green-manure crops are used for fertilizer; plowing, transplanting, weeding, watering, and harvesting are given meticulous attention. To be sure, floods and drought often result in crop failure and severe famine, but production is soon restored. The secret of the long, successful cultivation in the rice paddies is the enormous amount of labor applied to small plots of land. In the Tonkin Delta 80 man-days of labor are required for one acre of paddy, and the production is about 2000 pounds of rice. With modern machine methods, one acre would require only a few man-days, but what would become of the surplus population? Indeed, the paddy rice regions may have been successful in conservation practices only because the population has been reduced from time to time by famine and emigration.

Mediterranean Agriculture. On the shores of the Mediterranean Sea and in similar areas in California, Chile, and South Africa, the summers are long and very dry, the winters mild and rainy and yet colder than in the rice lands. Certainly this climate is not especially suited to rice: rice can be grown, of course, in the dry summer with the addition of enormous amounts of irrigation water, but it will not grow well in winter when the rains are most abundant. On the other hand, wheat and barley thrive in the mild winters, growing slowly through these long rainy periods and taking advantage of most of the rain that falls. Consequently, the combination of crops grown in these areas, to be sure, is very different from the crops grown in the rice-farming regions. Great emphasis is placed upon the growing of winter grains with the addition of crops which can be grown in the summer, either with or without irrigation. In the latter category is the olive tree, which is characteristic of Mediterranean agriculture; with few exceptions, it grows only in the Mediterranean lands. It requires long, hot, dry summers, deriving moisture by means of long roots which reach down into the ground water. The olive makes up in many ways for the scarcity of animal products, taking the place of meat, milk, and cheese in the diet of the people, particularly in certain areas of the Old World. Olive oil is readily preserved and, therefore, can be carried over from one season to another. Conditions for livestock are not favorable. Forage is scarce and limited in quality; although the brushy areas of the Mediterranean region furnish forage for goats and asses, cattle and horses cannot thrive on it.

Other crops are the citrus fruits—orange, lemon, and citron—and the grape. Some of the citrus fruits mature principally in the winter and form a welcome supplement to the winter grains. The grape occupies a very special place because of its wine-making qualities (Fig. 21.5). Some believe that the scarcity of good drinking water in parts of the Mediterranean lands stimulated the development of wine making; others believe that at first the juice of the grapes was merely stored for a while and the natural fermenting processes initiated the grape-wine development.

Mediterranean agriculture has had contributions from a variety of places. Some of the contributions (citrus fruits, for example) came from the rice-growing regions of southeastern Asia. As time went on, there were contributions in the form of livestock from the nomadic peoples who lived on the fringe of the Mediterranean lands. In more recent times (after the Age of Discovery), a number of crops came from the New World, including maize, potatoes, cotton, and tomatoes; few of the New World crops have been successful on a large scale, however.

Like rice culture, Mediterranean agriculture involves a large amount of labor applied to small plots of land—a kind of garden culture. Cultivation is intensified by several devices, among which are multiple cropping (two or more crops on the same field), intercultivation (alternate rows of different crops), and two-story cropping (in which grapes, for example, are grown on a supporting framework several feet above the ground while vegetables grow underneath). Terracing with rock walls makes it possible to use steep hill slopes and, as long as the farms are small and labor is abundant, there is little or no erosion problem since the rains are usually light and gentle. But serious erosion has occurred on the hill slopes as a result of deforestation and fires. This is especially true on the Adriatic coast of Yugoslavia, where all the soil has been removed over large areas, exposing bare rock.

Mediterranean agriculture, which was largely for local subsistence in the initial stages of development, has become highly commercial in many regions, notably in California. Machine methods are now applied, and the crops are highly specialized. In most cases the principle of careful cultivation has continued, thanks perhaps to the

Fig. 21.5. Grape harvest near Tours, France. Note the large castle-like stone house which suggests a large landholding.

migration of many thousands of people from the original Mediterranean lands to the newer districts in California, Australia, and South Africa.

If the light rainfall minimizes soil erosion, it accentuates the water problem. For many cities in the Mediterranean lands, it is necessary to bring water from long distances. Ground water is rarely sufficient, and many wells have been pumped to the point of exhaustion. In some areas near the sea, the lowering of the ground water has resulted in invasion of salt water into the wells. Cheap methods of purifying sea water will be a great boon to these districts.

Small-Grain and Livestock Farming. North of the Mediterranean lands in Europe, people are faced with a different environment and have developed a more general type of farming, in which the field cultivation of grains and forage crops and the raising of livestock play the dominant role. This type of agriculture reaches from northern Spain through France, the Low Countries, Germany, and Poland to western U.S.S.R. Only small areas of this type are to be found outside of Europe, notably in New Zealand and the Great Lakes region of North America. The winters are colder and, perhaps, of greater consequence to land use than they are in the Mediterranean lands; since the summers are much cooler, some of the crops of the Mediterranean lands cannot be grown. The olive cannot be grown since it does not thrive in the rainy summers of central and northern Europe and since it is susceptible to heavy frost in any period of the year. The citrus fruits are even more restricted in their distribution than the olive. The grape is successfully cultivated in the southern part of central Europe, as far north as Paris and southern Germany.

Fig. 21.6. Harvesting oats in the Gudbrandsdal Valley in southern Norway. This type of small mowing machine is still used where the fields are small. Tractor-drawn machines are used on large fields.

But the small grains—wheat, barley, rye, and oats (Fig. 21.6)—thrive in the moist climates of central and northern Europe to even better advantage than in the Mediterranean lands. Pastures are better, and hay is readily produced as feed for the livestock that are used as draft animals, for meat, and for dairy products. Forage crops are diversified as a result of the introduction of potatoes, sugar beets, mangels, and maize from the New World. The most important of these is the white potato, which is used for food, for livestock feed, and for the manufacture of starch and alcohol. Four countries—France, Germany, Poland, and U.S.S.R.—are the greatest producers and consumers of potatoes. The introduction of

the sugar beet was also important since Europe has no other satisfactory means of producing sugar. The only previous production of sugar was from honey and this only in small quantities. The growing of sugar beets makes it possible to produce quantities of sugar at low cost, rivaling the production of cane sugar in the tropical lands. Another important root crop is the mangel, which grows well and is used mostly for livestock feed. Since a good part of this area is too far to the north to produce good wine grapes, there is emphasis upon barley and hops for beer and other malt beverages. One crop that cannot be successfully introduced as a grain into northwestern Europe is maize (corn) since the growing season is too short and the high temperatures necessary to produce a good crop are lacking; maize can be grown for fodder only.

The small-grain and livestock type of farming, evolving slowly over the centuries, represents the best traditions in conservation. As population increases, the pressure on the land leads to improved methods of cultivation and to the reclamation of salt marshes and inland fresh-water swamps (Fig. 21.7). By the application of mineral fertilizers and green-manure crops, and by long cultivation, the quality of soils has been improved. Most of the region lies in the great lowland plain of western and central Europe, but fairly steep hill slopes are also common. Areas of steep slopes or low fertility are used for forestry and grazing. Even the severe damages resulting from modern warfare, which

much of this region has experienced, are carefully repaired in the intervals of peace.

Dairying. In the cool summer lands to the north of the small-grain and livestock regions, in similar climates in the Great Lakes region and the Pacific Northwest of North America, and in parts of New Zealand and Australia, milk production is dominant. Crops and meat animals are usually of minor importance. Much of the farming land is devoted to hay and pasture, and since cultivation of row crops is minor, soil erosion is not usually a serious problem. Dairying on a large scale depends on location near centers of population, which assures a market for the milk, butter, and cheese. In parts of northwestern Europe, notably in the Netherlands, marsh land, some of it below sea level, has been reclaimed and is used for dairy farming.

Fig. 21.7. Polders drained by windmills in the Netherlands. Most windmills have been replaced by diesel-powered pumps.

This land presents special problems in conservation, in drainage, diking, and reclaiming of salt marshes. In recent years the increase in the use of vegetable oils—cottonseed oil, peanut oil, and corn oil—as substitutes for dairy products has had an adverse effect on dairying. Faced with the loss of some of his market, the dairy farmer turns to the production of meat animals or to cash crops (such as potatoes) for which the climate and soil are suited.

Corn-Belt Farming. The corn-belt type of agriculture is similar to the small-grain and livestock type except that corn (or maize) is the dominant crop and the small grains and other crops play secondary roles. The principal area is in eastern United States, extending from Nebraska to Pennsylvania, from the Great Lakes to the Ohio River. Other corn-belt regions are to be found in southern Brazil, Argentina, the Po Plain of Italy, and the basins of Hungary and Romania. The ideal corn climate has hot summers, including hot nights, and moderately heavy rainfall. A dry period before and during harvest time is an advantage. Corn is an excellent fattening feed for livestock and is used in a variety of forms for human food. The combination of corn, small grains, hay, and pasture makes possible the large-scale production of beef, pork, lamb, and poultry. Most of the billions of bushels of corn produced are fed to livestock on the farm; only a small part enters world commerce.

The growth of the corn belts, the American one especially, was rapid and resulted in serious damage to the land in some areas. Much of the land was prairie before cultivation, but, in addition, large acreages of forest were cleared to make way for corn. In this hasty occupation of the land, even gentle slopes were eroded and fertility lost. Corn is a row crop and, unlike the small grains, leaves the land nearly bare at harvest, subject to gullying or sheet wash. As a result, much of the land is poorer today than at the time of settlement. Many

corn-belt farmers do not think of themselves as permanent occupants of a certain farm. A large proportion are tenant farmers who expect to move on in a few years. In most cases, however, erosion damage is not irreparable; careful conservation practices are halting excessive erosion and restoring a measure of fertility to the damaged lands. Many of the smoother areas have suffered little, and some have had their fertility increased by careful methods of cultivation. The United States Corn Belt is probably the richest agricultural region in the world, in spite of the fact that some parts of it have been misused.

Wheat-Belt Farming. As agriculturalists moved into the drier lands, an unusual specialization developed. Because it became necessary to leave behind many of the crops which grew well in the humid lands (hay, corn, and many other crops cannot be grown in the drier lands without irrigation, which is not generally available), the result has been a specialized wheat belt in which livestock, forage crops, and all the grains except one or two are not present. The great wheat farms with their use of heavy machinery have become an essential part of the agricultural system of the United States (Fig. 21.8), Canada, Australia, and Argentina. Many of these farms do not even have a house. The owner lives in town and simply attends to his acreage at the planting and harvesting seasons. Many farms have no livestock at all, although there is some grazing land available in the vicinity; on some farms it is the custom to graze animals on the stubble of the grain fields.

The extensive machine cultivation of the semiarid wheat farms greatly accelerates wind erosion and dust storms. Especially on the lighter soils, the pulverizing effect of the disc harrows and other cultivators causes severe losses of soil in times of severe drought and high winds. A single storm may remove all of the topsoil from many thousands of acres. And once the native grasses have been plowed under, it is very difficult to

Fig. 21.8. Harvesting wheat with a combine near Great Falls, Montana. Note that the wheat has been drilled (seeded) in rows. Strip cropping is shown at upper left.

re-establish them. Attempts to reduce wind erosion by the planting of shelter belts of trees have met with little success; rainfall is not sufficient for the growth of trees. In spite of government controls, there has been an increase in the acreage of wheat in marginal lands which should never have been cultivated. The average wheat farmer does not consider himself a permanent resident of the wheat belt; rather, he expects to make quick profits for a few years and retire to pleasanter climes. Wheat farming of this sort is sometimes referred to as "soil mining," since nothing is returned to the soil.

Some aspects of wheat-farm conservation are unique. Wind erosion commonly leaves the land smooth, with little evidence of erosion that is apparent to the casual observer. Dust storms from wheat farms reach cities, sometimes hundreds of miles away, to the distress of the city people and lead to demands for conservation measures by government agencies. The most effective low-cost method of reducing erosion in the wheat lands is strip cropping, with long, narrow strips of wheat alternating with untilled strips.

Plantations. Some of the European agriculturalists who settled in the New World moved into tropical and subtropical lands where a whole new vista of crop possibilities opened up before them; at the same time certain conditions, such as the prevalence of plant diseases, made difficult the pursuance of their customary agricultural practices. The outstanding agricultural type developed in the tropical and subtropical areas is the plantation. The plantation provides the means of producing large quantities of cash crops which, with few exceptions, cannot be produced in a temperate climate. These crops include sugar cane, rubber, spices, coffee, cacao, and bananas. The plantation

Fig. 21.9. Banana plantation in Costa Rica. The plantation is served by railroad and highway. At several points irrigation by spraying is in progress.

depends upon cheap land (which can often be acquired for the asking), cheap labor (much of which in the early days was slave labor), and some commercial crop which is in demand in areas of dense population in the temperate belt; coffee is a good example. For special crops certain conditions of soil, drainage, and climate are desirable. The plantation, then, is an adaptation of European agricultural practices to an entirely new situation (Fig. 21.9).

The plantations are so varied in different parts of the tropical and subtropical climates that an assessment of their effect on the land is particularly difficult. In the United States Cotton Belt, which was once a plantation region, the system based on one cash crop has resulted in the most severe soil erosion in the country. Cotton cultivation, like corn farming, leaves the soil nearly bare after harvest, and the heavy rains attack even gentle slopes unless protective measures, such as terracing and strip cropping, are adopted. Nor does the

substitution of the tenant "sharecropper" system for the plantation system improve matters. On the other hand, the large, well-managed plantation with its staff of experts provides a basis of permanent production and land conservation. A sugar plantation in Louisiana or Puerto Rico, a coffee plantation in São Paulo, Brazil, or a rubber plantation in Malaya usually has too much invested in improvements to permit soil erosion or depletion of fertility. Great care, then, is taken in the selection of the site, in clearing and cultivating the land. Not all plantations are successful, but few fail nowadays for the lack of conservation measures.

From this brief study of land use and the conservation problems associated with it, a few general statements can be made which the reader may wish to consider and debate:

1. The land use of a particular region is limited by the natural resources of the region, but it also depends on the character and back-

ground of the people who live there. The corn-belt farmer and the coffee planter alike owe a debt to their European antecedents.

2. The land-use regions with the best conservation practices are those which have developed slowly so that plans could be made and methods could be devised to protect and conserve the resources.

3. Land-use types which apply a large amount of labor to a small area of land are likely to be more stable than those in which heavy machinery is used.

4. Good conservation practice usually accompanies a permanent rather than a transient occupation of the land.

5. The production must provide a margin of profit large enough so that time and money are available for conservation.

6. Although some types of land use are associated with special problems in conservation, such as dust storms in the wheat belts, in the long run it is the character of the people and the society and economy in which they live which determines the wise use or the misuse of the land.

7. It is hoped that sufficient examples of conservation and land-use types have been described to suggest that the problems of conservation are, to a large extent, unique for every land-use type and for every region.

Part V

TOWARD ONE WORLD

CHAPTER 22

Men and the Sea

The seas around us are full of meaning for the people who live near their shores, and not without significance for those who live far inland. The seas furnish a variety of food, and they provide highways on which ships carry many of the heavy commodities that move from country to country. The seas also temper climate, making winters milder and summers cooler near their shores. The very size of the seas, which cover nearly three fourths of the area of the earth's surface with depths of up to six miles, implies their importance. Long struggles, patient work, and invention, accompanied by many lost lives, have given man a partial control of the seas; but those who know the seas respect their power.

To the early Greeks the sea was the Mediterranean, which they called "our sea" or "nurse of heroes." Odysseus, the hero of the early Greeks, traveled over most of the Mediterranean and returned to Greece; many potential heroes attempting the same exploit never returned. The Greeks first thought of the sea as an endless river of water running around the outer rim of the continents, beyond which lay the home of the gods. As their knowledge grew, the Greeks developed the idea of the sphericity of the earth, but they still thought of the ocean as a single body of water bordering all of the land, a concept which the Romans adopted (Fig. 22.1). The Greeks developed the concept of climate and thought that the ocean probably boiled at the Equator and

that the land north of the Arctic Circle was too cold for any life to exist.

The Greeks reasoned about the ocean, but the Phoenicians, great traders and navigators, learned about it through practical experience. Although some doubt has been cast on the legend that the Phoenicians circumnavigated Africa, there is no doubt that as early as 1500 B.C. the Phoenicians were sailing along the eastern coast of Africa, which they reached by way of the Red Sea. Their expeditions were obviously intended to bring back valuable trade goods to the eastern

Fig. 22.1. Ancient Roman map showing universal ocean. (Adapted from *General Cartography* by Erwin Raisz. Copyright 1948 McGraw-Hill Book Co., Inc. Used by permission.)

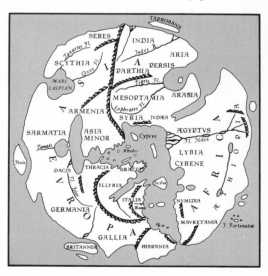

end of the Mediterranean. On one expedition, the details of which are on record, five ships set out and brought back myrrh, ebony, gold, ivory, cinnamon, incense, eye cosmetic, monkeys, apes, dogs, and various skins, as well as a number of slaves. The Phoenicians were also active along the western end of the Mediterranean, and some legends indicate that they sailed into the Atlantic and probably into the Bay of Biscay and the North Sea.

In later years the voyages of the Phoenicians stimulated the Arabs and the Portuguese to continue explorations down the coast of Africa and eventually around it. Altogether, the desire for trade in the rare products that would bring great prices in the markets of the Mediterranean led to a very considerable knowledge of the Mediterranean and the margins of the Atlantic and Indian oceans. Later, the same desire for trade led Magellan, Columbus, and their contemporaries to travel much farther and eventually to circumnavigate the globe.

Meanwhile, scientific curiosity concerning the oceans led to many expeditions, the purpose of which was not to trade but to find out more about the seas. One of the earliest voyages of marine exploration was made by Pytheas, a Greek of Massilia (Marseilles), about 300 B.C. Though very little of the record of this voyage remains, it is known that its object was to find out how far land extended, to discover where the Arctic Circle was located, and to see the land of the midnight sun. Pytheas presumably had some sort of astronomical instruments by which he could determine latitude. In the last part of the 9th century A.D., Ottar, a Norwegian, sailed northward along the coast of Norway, around North Cape, and into the White Sea. Although his narrative indicates that his principal purpose was exploration, he mentioned the possibility of obtaining walrus tusks which, he said, contained much valuable bone. There is not very much known about the explorations of the Vikings in the northern Atlantic, but it is known that as

early as the 3rd century there was a good deal of traffic between the seas of northwestern Europe and the Mediterranean. Doubtless the Vikings extended their voyages as they improved their ships. Nevertheless, despite various improvements, northern sailors worked under great handicaps until the time of Columbus because they had no compass and no means of finding their position at sea (although the Greeks, of course, had had instruments centuries before). Also, since their ships were equipped with square sails, they did not find it feasible to tack against the wind.

Eventually, new instruments, the magnetic compass, the sextant, and the chronometer, enabled man to find his way over the oceans; improved ships made the voyages safer and more profitable. The evolution of the modern ship was a long, slow process and improvements are still being made. Some of the earliest boats were made in Egypt of papyrus bundles, similar to the reed boats used today on Lake Titicaca, Bolivia. These were suitable for paddling, but not for rowing or sailing. The prophet, Isaiah, referred to vessels of bulrushes on the waters of the sea (about 740 B.C.). The first Egyptian boats of wood had no keels, and were simply copies of earlier reed boats. Ships of Homeric times (Late Bronze Age) had well-developed keels, and the distinction between sail-driven merchant ships and oar and sail-driven warships was definite. By the middle of the third century B.C., the warships had developed into two major types, heavy galleons, the father of our modern battleship, and light galleys, prototype of our destroyers. The larger galleons had two, three, and sometimes four decks of oars. On modern ships, the only survival of oar-using warships is the round porthole. The early ships were quite seaworthy, and Hanno, the Carthagenian, coasted down the western side of Africa before 500 B.C. His claim to have entirely sailed around Africa is not accepted by all geographers.

The improvement of sailing ships and sailing techniques was a great step forward; it enabled the merchant ships to carry large cargoes with comparatively small crews. From the time of Homer to the middle of the 19th century, the sailing ships were supreme; even today a few are still in use for short voyages along the coasts of southeastern Asia, as freight ships in the South Seas, and as pleasure craft on all the oceans. Early in the 19th century ships made of iron and powered by steam began to replace the sailing vessels, since they were more durable and dependable, and less subject to unfavorable weather. Later steel replaced iron as the principal ship-building material and special types of ships were designed for varying conditions and cargoes. The oil tanker provides low-cost transportation for the most important fuel; the ocean-going barge is used widely in coastwise transport for heavy, bulky commodities, such as coal and lumber; the large, deluxe passenger liners compete with the airplane for trans-oceanic travel; special types of river boats and barges are used on the inland waterways. Of late atomic-powered ships are coming into use, making it possible to carry large pay loads many thousands of miles without refueling.

In modern times man has, to a limited extent at least, conquered the seas. With abundant power, nuclear and otherwise, and with many ingenious craft, he moves above, on, and below the surface of the ocean with comparative ease. Special devices enable him to penetrate the greatest depths. Icebreakers make it possible to approach shores usually blocked most of the year by ice, and an atomic submarine can move with little difficulty under the ice floes of the North Polar region. Even so, man is just beginning to understand, appreciate, and utilize the ocean. Optimists look forward to the day when plankton (upon which many large sea animals subsist) will be used for human food, when sea water will supply most of our minerals, and when the tides will furnish abundant power. The potential of the ocean is as vast as its surface, as unplumbed as its great deeps, and limited only by the desire and in-

genuity of man. In the brief discussion below only three broad aspects of the seas will be discussed: the tides, the effect on climate, and the wealth of the seas.

The Global Air Conditioner

Most people know that the Gulf Stream has a strong effect upon the climate of northwestern Europe, but this may be the extent of their knowledge concerning the effect of the sea on the climate of the land. Generally, the Gulf Stream is given too much credit and the sea not enough; even without the warming effect of the Gulf Stream, the sea can moderate the winter climate of the adjacent land areas. The Gulf Stream is a river flowing on top of the heavier, saltier waters of the Atlantic Ocean. As the Gulf Stream moves along the coast of eastern North America, it does not markedly affect the climate of the adjacent lands to the west; the climate of these lands is mainly determined by the westerly offshore winds blowing over them. The Gulf Stream (Fig. 22.2) is always a warm-water current, but its temperature, as well as its course, varies somewhat from year to year. Brooks, a British climatologist, compared the North Atlantic to a great bathtub with a hot tap, the Gulf Stream, and two cold taps, the cold currents along eastern Greenland and the Labrador Current. Nature adjusts each of these taps from time to time, determining the temperature of the bath and affecting the weather in western Europe. Although the weather in western Europe is somewhat affected by the temperature of the North Atlantic, it is more largely conditioned by the air masses that move across the North Atlantic. Thus, the proposal made many years ago by an American Anglophobe that the United States dam up the Straits of Florida and in this way cut off the Gulf Stream and freeze England was not only uncivilized but unscientific: no dam could essentially divert the Gulf Stream; but even if it could, England would not freeze.

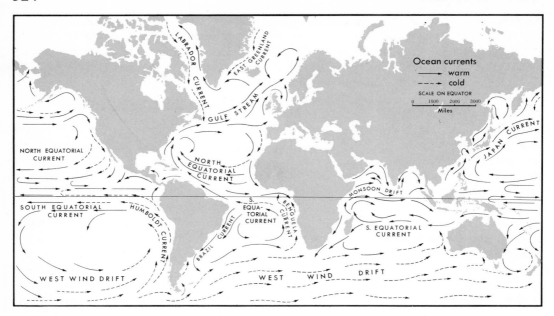

Fig. 22.2. World ocean currents.

The oceans stabilize the temperatures of the earth by absorbing and storing solar energy and transferring it to the land from time to time. Although ocean waters absorb tremendous quantities of heat from the sun, they do not become hot because of their great volume; likewise, they can lose much heat and not become cold. The heat stored in the oceans is transmitted to the land by a complex combination of ocean currents and air masses. At the contact between the ocean surface and the overlying air masses, there is continuous interaction of great importance to the climates of the earth. The air warms or cools the ocean water, depending upon the contrast between the two, but, more importantly, the ocean water acts to warm or cool the air. It takes 3000 times as much heat to warm a given volume of water as it does to change the temperature of an equal volume of air by the same amount. In other words, one cubic meter of water cooling through one degree centigrade will raise the temperature of 3000 cubic meters of air by the same amount. Thus, though an ocean seems to maintain a fairly even temperature, it has the

effect of lowering the temperature of the warmest season and raising the temperature of the coldest season on the adjacent lands.

The effect of cold currents on adjacent lands is even more clearly marked than that of warm currents. The Humboldt Current, which moves northward along the coast of Chile, and the Benguela Current, which runs along the western coast of South Africa, combine with winds blowing from the sea over cold land to produce a climate which is almost rainless but likely to be quite foggy. Though this climate is very stable most of the year, there are important results when the temperature of the currents changes temporarily. When, for instance, the cold water of the cold currents is replaced temporarily by warm water, there are often very severe storms (with very heavy rains and high winds) on the coast of Peru and the Namib Desert of Southwest Africa. Ocean storms, to be sure, do not depend entirely upon the changes in currents. They occur frequently on western coasts in the middle latitudes. For many centuries the Bay of Biscay has been noted for its storms and its hazards to navigation and fishing, as have the western coast of North America and many other coastal areas in similar latitudes.

The Tides

The tides constitute another feature of the sea which is of profound importance to man. The difference between high and low tide is only a few inches in some places and nearly 100 feet in others. Man has learned to adapt himself to tidal changes in many ways and has benefited from the fact that the tides in most parts of the world are accurately forecast. The United States Coast and Geodetic Survey has an electronic computer which will automatically give the time and height of the tide on any future date at any place in the world where records have been kept.

Forecasting, however, is of limited use in the case of so-called tidal waves, or tsunamis, which are associated with earthquakes. Although such sea waves (traveling several hundred miles an hour) can be forecast a few hours in advance if sufficient seismographic records of the earthquakes are available, it is difficult to warn all people living near the shore. The tsunamis rise high on the land with a tremendous volume of water and force enough to wreck ports and shipping. Most of the people in the world live at very low altitudes, many of them only a few feet above sea level, and are, therefore, exposed to tidal waves and high tides, some of which are generated by hurricanes.

The Wealth of the Seas

The ocean has long been a source of food, minerals, vitamins, and other materials which man can glean from its shallow margins and its greater depths. With the exception of some shallow margins which have been reserved as oyster beds or special fishing grounds, most seas are available to anyone who wishes to exploit them (see Chapter 25).

Primitive man hunted for food in the seas at low tide, gathering the relatively immobile sea animals and plants—clams, mussels, oysters, abalones, sea snails, and a great variety of other edible materials. The great shell heaps, acres in extent and many feet in thickness, that have been found on the shores in many parts of the world attest to the long-continued use of clams, mussels, oysters and abalone as food by primitive peoples. As time went on, people began to move out over the seas and harvest a greater variety of sea food, including the large mammals—the whale (Fig. 22.3), walrus, and seal—and many fishes—herring, cod, mackerel, tuna, shark, salmon, bream, sole, sardine—as well as many miscellaneous foods such as octopus, squid, and seaweed.

Most of the fish and other types of sea food come from the shallow margins of the sea—the continental shelf with depths down to 600 feet. Here the environment is most favorable for the growth of plankton, the small organisms which supply the basic food for many forms of marine life. The continental shelf is most extensive near the coasts of northwestern Europe, eastern and southeastern Asia, and eastern North America. The dense population of these regions creates a demand for sea food so great, however, that fishing is increasing in the more distant banks of the Arctic Ocean and off the coasts of South America, Africa, and Australia. The largest producers and consumers of fish are Japan, the United States, China, the U.S.S.R., the United Kingdom, Norway, and Canada. Of these, only Norway has a large surplus for export. The total catch for all countries is worth more than one billion dollars.

The production and consumption of fish depend on a number of variable factors, which include wide expanses of the continental shelf adjacent to areas of dense population and suitable harbors for the fishing fleets. A smooth bottom is favorable since otherwise the bottom nets and trawls become snagged; in tropical waters coral reefs often prevent the use of large-scale fishing methods. One of the most favorable locations is the contact of two ocean currents,

Fig. 22.3. Whaling operations near Valparaiso, Chile. This small whaling vessel tows the captured whale to the port of Quintay for processing.

one warm and the other cold; the mixing of these waters is likely to correspond with a concentration of fish. The contact of the Gulf Stream with the Labrador Current in the North Atlantic and the meeting of the Japan Current with the Kamchatka Current in the North Pacific are good examples. Another significant factor which affects the consumption of fish is the eating habits of people; the Japanese consume a great variety of marine foods, including octopus, squid, shark, and seaweed, as well as the more common varieties of fish and shellfish. Religious beliefs also contribute to fish consumption, in southern Europe for example. Perhaps because of the relative abundance of land-produced food in many parts of the world, man has yet to realize the full potential of the sea as a source of food. In Argen-

tina, for example, beef used to be so cheap that it was not feasible to market the fish which existed in quantities on the shallow ocean shelf of the nearby coast; it was only when the price of beef rose that more fish was eaten.

Off the coast of New England and eastern Canada from Cape Cod to Newfoundland, the continental shelf is wide and comparatively shallow; and the numerous banks, such as Grand, Georges, Sable, and St. Pierre, are heavily fished for cod, herring, rosefish, and others. The bottom is smooth, and the mingling of the warm and cool currents accompanied by fog is a favorable factor for fishing but not for shipping. The irregular shoreline affords numerous harbors and the large urban centers nearby provide a large market for the fish. The fast, modern fishing boats

Fig. 22.4. Salmon fishing off the northern coast of British Columbia near Ocean Falls. The salmon are taken to nearby canneries.

are refrigerated so that the catch can be processed on board and marketed fresh. These waters are also fished by Europeans; France has bases on the islands of St. Pierre and Miquelon.

The continental shelf off the coast of northwestern Europe, including the North Sea and the Baltic, is fished heavily by the people of the United Kingdom, Germany, France, the Netherlands, Norway, Sweden, the U.S.S.R., Denmark, Belgium, and Spain. Fishermen from these countries also visit the waters off Iceland and Spitzbergen. Cod, herring, and mackerel are the most common varieties but quantities of plaice, sardines, salmon, hake, lobsters, and oysters are also taken (Fig. 22.4). The herring fishermen use gill nets which are floated on the surface. The herring are small but welcomed in the diet of western Europeans because of their high-fat content. The cod, bottom feeders, are taken mostly in trawls dragged along the bottom; the best cod fishing is along the northern coast of Norway. Although much of the catch of northwestern Europe is marketed fresh, quantities of herring are smoked and pickled, and much of the sardine catch is canned.

In Japan where beef production is very small, fish plays a more important role in feeding the people than in any other large country of the world. The Japanese consume about 75 pounds of fish per capita per year and the tonnage of the catch is at least twice

Fig. 22.5. Salt pans near Cádiz, Spain. The long, dry summers are favorable for the extraction of salt from sea water.

that of the United States, the nearest rival. A part of the Japanese catch is exported, either canned, dried, or frozen, including tuna, crab, and shrimp. A large proportion of the sea food is similar to that of other lands—herring, cod, mackerel, salmon, tuna, crab, shrimp, sardines, and flounder. Shellfish are important and, as a by-product of the oyster industry, so is the culture pearl. But the Japanese fisheries, as a whole, are characterized by the great variety of species taken and by the different methods of fishing and preserving the catch. Inshore fishing accounts for most of the herring, sardines, mackerel, bream, yellowtail, tuna, and flounder; in deeper waters Japanese fishing ships formerly ranged from Bering Strait to Antarctica and from Ceylon to Hawaii, taking large quantities of salmon and crab and processing them in huge floating canneries. After World War II Japanese fishing was for a time restricted to the waters immediately adjacent to Japan.

In recent years fishing has increased on both the west and east coasts of South America, especially near Peru and Argentina; it has also increased around Tasmania, off the northwestern coast of Australia, in New Zealand waters, and on the west coast of Africa. The increasing awareness of the wealth of the sea has led to increased restrictions: Iceland now forbids foreign fishing ships in her nearshore waters; Peru has proclaimed a 100-mile limit and bars foreign ships from the great wealth of the nearby Humboldt Current; and the U.S.S.R. guards the waters off eastern Siberia. Meanwhile, many countries have scientific "search" vessels looking for new fishing grounds and seeking other sources of marine wealth.

Minerals, as well as food, are obtained from the sea. Common salt, the most important of these minerals, was the first to be exploited. Early man found that he could obtain salt by evaporating sea water in pools and shallow lagoons. Nowadays, much of the salt produced in the world is either evaporated from sea water or obtained from lagoons which have accumulated salt for thousands of years. Blown by sea breezes, some of the salt from the sea may find its way back to the land. These small particles of salt serve as nuclei for raindrops and thus have a very important effect upon precipitation. In England as many as 25 pounds of salt per acre per year are blown in on sea breezes; Sambhar Salt Lake in northern India receives yearly about 3000 tons of salt which have been carried in by the hot monsoon of summer from the sea 400 miles away.

The most favorable places for obtaining salt are the shallow margins of the sea where, in natural basins, sea water can be cut off and evaporated with the help of high winds, sunshine, and low rainfall (Fig. 22.5). Such a place is the Rann of Cutch, an area the size of New Jersey on the western coast of India. Here the winds of the southwest monsoon carry water inland to cover the plain. Then later, as summer winds blow from the opposite direction, salt crust forms (sometimes to a thickness of several feet) in the pools which have been left all over the area. Similarly, there is a large bay on the eastern side of the Caspian Sea that is almost completely cut off from the main body of water. When the narrow passage connecting the bay and the sea is closed and the sea water (of high salt content) remaining in the bay is allowed to evaporate, salt deposits form and the salt

Fig. 22.6. Oil wells in shallow Lake Maracaibo, Venezuela. Oil from this area is transported by pipeline and shallow-draft tankers.

is collected. Then, after the salt has been collected, additional sea water is admitted to the bay.

In recent years the margins of the seas have yielded great quantities of petroleum. Oil-bearing sands are found underneath the shallow surface of the sea, particularly in the Gulf of Mexico, along the coast of California, and in the margins of the Gulf of Maracaibo in Venezuela (Fig. 22.6). Much planning and invention were required before man could drill wells and maintain pumps in the sea, but the large sea-going rigs which are now transported from place to place represent at least a partial solution of many of the problems involved. The discovery of oil in the sea and the techniques which have been developed to exploit it have added enormously to the world's potential supply of petroleum. Oil production, which seemed to be declining some years ago, now appears to be sufficient for the foreseeable future, perhaps for the next century. The discovery of offshore oil has raised many questions about the various ownership claims of federal governments, state governments, and private organizations.

Man has extracted successfully (though not necessarily commercially) at least 50 different minerals from sea water, including calcium sulfate, potassium sulfate, bromine, vanadium, gold, and magnesium.

Trade results in broadening the sustenance area
for an individual or a group.
Richard Elwood Dodge

CHAPTER 23

World Trade

Almost as strong as man's urge to travel to distant and unknown places has been his desire to possess the products of other lands. The exchange of his own produce for the produce of others may bring him a better version of some tool or device he already has, or an entirely different commodity not available to him because of the climate or the resource endowment of his locality.

Our modern world is heavily involved in the exchange of commodities, and we often regard this situation as a new one. It is true that the volume of trade between countries is now the largest in history. However, what we call world trade has strong roots in the past; there was, for instance, early trade between China and the civilizations of southwestern Asia and the Mediterranean.

Early Trade Between China and the West

Trade in the ancient world (3000-500 B.C.) involved mainly the eastern Mediterranean and the adjacent Fertile Crescent. The Egyptians, the Phoenicians, the Sumerians, and later the Hittites all traded with each other in relatively limited area—within a radius of 500 miles from Damascus.

It was not until after the establishment of the Han Empire (circa 200 B.C.) that China began to be directly interested in the West. The envoy Chang Ch'ien is credited with the introduction of the grapevine and alfalfa into China about 125 B.C. He also gave impetus to the silk trade; as a result of his explorations, the first "through" silk caravans traveled between China and Persia in 106 B.C. —eight years after his death. Introduced from Persia via central Asia along the old silk road sometime between the 3rd and 7th centuries of our era were chives, the cucumber, figs, sesame, pomegranates, and walnuts.

Almost simultaneous with the development of overland trade between China and the West was the growth of trade between India and the West, particularly Greece. Pepper and lac began to be used by the Greeks and were brought in by vessels coasting along within sight of the shores of southern Arabia and Baluchistan. Sometime between 85 B.C. and 15 B.C. it was discovered that the seasonal winds (monsoons, from the Arabian *mausim,* meaning "season") could be used to sail directly between the Straits of Bab El Mandeb and the ports of southern India. Ships from the West—"Roman in name but actually Graeco-Egyptian"—became dominant on these routes from about A.D. 50. For about 200 years they reached progressively farther east: coins of the time of Antonius Pius (A.D. 150) have been found in Indochina. However, by the 2nd century A.D., Indian ships began to compete with those from the West and gradually replaced them in handling the southeast Asian trade.

Only gradually did Chinese ships tentatively reach out toward the West. They

Fig. 23.1. The port of Portland, Oregon. Docks, railroad yards, and warehouses are found together along the Willamette River.

reached Penang (Malaya) about A.D. 350 and Ceylon about A.D. 400 and a few decades later were calling at Aden and the head of the Persian Gulf. As late as A.D. 850 Sīrāf on the Persian Gulf was referred to by an Arab merchant-historian as the terminus of Chinese shipping, which was already declining. By this time Arab ships were calling at ports on the south China coast, and Arabs were maintaining "factories" at Canton and Hangchow. Arabs dominated the Pacific maritime trade from the 9th century through the 12th century, when they were eclipsed by the Chinese. There was a short-lived period of Chinese trade expansion in the 15th century under the Ming dynasty. Chinese ships then reached as far as East Africa and were thick in the ports of Ceylon and Malabar.

The persistence of the maritime trade route between China and the West may be explained in part by the cheaper mode of transport offered by the sea. However, the maritime route also allowed the traders to eliminate the middlemen—the small empires in central Asia—who were overly enriching themselves on the land trade. A similar desire to avoid middlemen led in the 15th century to the discovery of a sea route to the Indies.

The Generation of Trade

Trade may arise whenever one area has a surplus of goods or services that are wanted by the inhabitants of another area. The second area may pay for these by complementary goods and services. Trade may also occur when a nation exports nonsurplus items in order to obtain a trade item which is of paramount importance to it. For instance, China after 1950 often exported food products to the U.S.S.R. in exchange for needed industrial equipment.

Surpluses are generated by differences in the physical environment and the human environment. If an area has good soils, moderate relief, and an equable climate, it probably will have an agricultural surplus. Geological events of the past determine the nature of an area's mineral surplus. Since the differences in the physical environment are less readily changed than those of the human environment, trade ultimately rests primarily on differences in resources. Of course, the factors in the human environment still have a certain degree of importance. Differences in technical abilities and the economic momentum of a "head start" in industry are forces making for areal differences in surpluses.

World trade involves the exchange of surplus goods and services between countries. Portland, Oregon (Fig. 23.1), is a port city which is important in world trade. Ships come partially empty up the long Columbia River estuary and dock along the banks of its tributary, the Willamette. Here at Portland they unload the cargoes, which for the most part are manufactured goods. Much bulky raw material (lumber, wheat) is loaded, as are such processed goods as aluminum ingots, plywood, light machinery, and canned fish.

Most of Portland's exports are only slightly processed primary materials: wood from the Douglas-fir forests west of the Cascades, wheat from the dry-farming areas east of the mountains, and aluminum refined by electricity near dams located where the Columbia River divides the Cascades. In exporting raw materials and importing finished products, Portland is typical of ports located outside the Japan-Northwest Europe-Northeast United States area.

The Roles of Physical and Human Environments

Trade within a climatic zone depends less upon differences of physical environment than upon geographical division of labor. This division is due to differences in population density, historical background, and level of technology. Since climatic zones tend to parallel or be subparallel to the Equator, we may say that trade moving within a climatic zone or production region tends to be based primarily on differences in human environment. Conversely, trade moving between climatic zones tends to be based more firmly upon differences in physical environment.

A good example of trade within a climatic zone is the rice trade in Asia. Heavily populated China, Japan, and India are large rice producers, but they consume all of their production. The more sparsely populated countries of southeastern Asia produce a surplus of rice, which moves outward to the more densely populated areas. Burma sells to India and Ceylon, Thailand to Java and Japan, and Vietnam to Malaya and Java. Thus, within the area in which rice can be grown, surpluses in one place and need in other places give rise to foreign trade.

Trade generated by differences in physical environment is illustrated by the exchange of commodities between tropical and mid-latitude areas. For instance, cacao, bananas, and palm oil from West Africa are exchanged for canned beef and cotton textiles.

Tropical agricultural products are supplied to the mid-latitude countries from three sources. Most simply, wild products are collected by people who wander through forests and grasslands. Chicle was gathered in Middle America until the 1950's, and during World War II some rubber was gathered in this way in the Amazon Basin. A second source of supply is the plantation developed and controlled generally by outside capital. The rubber plantations of Malaya have for years supplied a large part of the world's natural rubber. Bananas from Middle America and coffee from Brazil are typical plantation products. A third source, less but increasingly important, is the farm of the small peasant-owner of the tropics. The cacao farmer of Ghana and the small rubber farmer of Malaya are examples of peasant-owners. About one third of Malaya's rubber now comes from small acreages owned locally. All the cacao of Ghana—constituting one third of the world's production—derives from small farms in the Ashanti hills.

In much of southeastern Asia and much of Africa, large plantations operated by Europeans were long the rule, and such plantations are still dominant in world trade. In much of the development of African tropical crops, however, co-operative societies care for production and marketing. The cacao board in Ghana and the coffee board of the Chagga tribes near Mount Kilimanjaro are good examples. Marketing boards attempt to even out prices paid to farmers from year to year so that they are less violently affected by annual price changes. Price fluctuations are especially typical with regard to plantation products. The marketing boards—a postwar phenomenon—are most highly developed in the Commonwealth areas of West Africa:[1]

[1] F. J. Pedler, *Economic Geography of West Africa*, p. 196.

Name of Board	Date of Formation
The Gold Coast Cocoa Marketing Board	1947
The Nigerian Cocoa Marketing Board	1947
The Nigerian Groundnut Marketing Board	1949
The Nigerian Cotton Marketing Board	1949
The Gambia Oilseeds Marketing Board	1949
The Sierra Leone Produce Marketing Board	1949
The Gold Coast Agricultural Produce Marketing Board	1949
The Nigerian Oil Palm Produce Marketing Board	1950

The former French areas of West Africa are without marketing boards and are thus subject both to the effects of price changes and to the exactions of a series of middlemen.

Trade which flows between mid-latitude continents is based to a smaller extent upon natural differences (for most mid-latitude lands have similar endowments) than upon differences in the human environment. Much of the bulk of the transatlantic trade, for instance, consists of wheat from the sparsely populated prairies of Canada. The grasslands of Europe are more densely populated and do not produce the surplus of wheat which they once did. Europe, however, cannot rely solely upon Canadian wheat. The sparsely populated grasslands of the Southern Hemisphere, particularly those of Argentina and Australia, provide further sources of wheat and flour. In the same way, the Manchurian grassland once provided overcrowded Japan with wheat and soybeans.

In general, we may say that sparsely populated countries export food and that densely populated countries either are self-sufficient or import food. Also, old established nations tend to import raw materials, while newer nations tend to export raw materials. Examples of these tendencies follow. Ghana, a young and sparsely populated country, exports bauxite, manganese, and cacao. Japan,

an old and densely populated country, imports iron ore and coal, as well as about one fourth of her food requirements. Indonesia, a new but densely populated (in the core area of Java and southern Sumatra) country, exports petroleum and industrial crops, such as tobacco and kapok, but imports foods, especially rice. Canada, a relatively old but sparsely populated land, imports bauxite and iron ore but exports wheat.

It is difficult to find examples of old but sparsely populated countries, for most of the sparsely populated areas have been late in becoming separate political entities in the national sense.

Agriculture and World Trade

Since farming is the most widely spread of the major occupations, it is not surprising that products of farm, ranch, and plantation should bulk large in world trade. The agricultural situation is not a stagnant one, however, for agricultural products face notorious rises and falls in prices, which may over a period of time effect major changes in the productive landscape.

Fluctuation in the prices paid for agricultural products may result from changes in technology or from changing production conditions. The development of a plastic base for chewing gum in the mid-1950's reduced the market for chicle almost to zero. Synthetic rubber production has caused great concern in the areas growing natural rubber. That the growing of natural rubber has not disappeared is due to its superiority as a product in certain vital uses, as well as the continuing cost of the synthetic product. It is interesting to note that Brazil—the parent country of the rubber tree—has set up a butadiene plant to produce its own synthetic rubber. A plant may be built within six or eight months, while rubber trees require 10 or 15 years of growth to begin yielding and take 25 years of growth before the optimum yield is forthcoming. In Brazil the time factor is obviously the overriding concern.

Climatic and labor advantages may sometimes tend to promote activation of tropical economies. For instance, olive cultivation in many Mediterranean areas is declining due to competition from the increasing production of inexpensive vegetable oils in the labor-abundant tropical areas. The oil marketing boards in West Africa, by their wise buying and selling policies, are in good part responsible for this situation.

Dependence on World Trade

Japan is an interesting example of a nation dependent on world trade. Until the late 19th century, Japan was self-sufficient in food and almost without foreign trade. Now about one fourth of her food must be imported. To pay for imports, dollars and sterling must be earned abroad through exports. Being poorly endowed with natural resources, Japan depends upon a well-trained and abundant supply of labor, which processes imported raw materials, and exports finished products of lesser bulk but higher value. The value-added-by-manufacture earns the foreign exchange used to pay the food bill.

The decade of the 1940's marked a change in Japan's foreign-trade policy. In the 1920's and 1930's, markets abroad were flooded with vast amounts of poor-quality but amazingly cheap merchandise. This kind of merchandise could be produced because Japan's laborers were rather poorly paid. In the 1950's a new policy became evident. Relatively little cheap merchandise is now sold abroad, and in its place there are goods of higher quality. Locomotives for Thailand's railroads and buses for the roads of Argentina are examples of the new trend. Labor is better paid in postwar Japan, and no longer can a cheap-labor economy prevail. The quality of Japanese goods has had to improve as Japan has felt the effects of market flooding and the competition of cheap goods from mainland China.

England has even a greater degree of dependence on overseas trade than does Japan. Only 40 per cent of England's food

is locally supplied. However, her marketing problem is less acute than is Japan's, for she has political ties, which result in economic benefits, with the Commonwealth nations. Japan—without an empire now—must rely on a market created by the good will resulting from high-quality, relatively low-cost goods.

Trade Dominance

Western Europe and Anglo-America together generate two fifths of the world's international trade, by value. Figures for 1959 allot 20 per cent of this trade value to the former area and 22 per cent to the latter. The leading trading nations in western Europe are the United Kingdom, West Germany, and France. The United States and Canada alone constitute the Anglo-American unit.

Canada's major export item is paper, and her predominant import is machinery. The leading export item of the United States is vehicles, while more money is spent on the import of coffee than upon any other product. Only a quarter (27 per cent) of her trade is with her neighbor Canada, though two thirds (67 per cent) of Canada's trade is with the United States.

Within the western European area the imports and exports of the leading nations follow somewhat different patterns. The exports of the United Kingdom are highly diverse and can only be characterized as miscellaneous. Her imports list is headed by meat products. Only 15 per cent of her total trade value is with neighbors. Machinery accounts for more than 25 per cent of the value of West Germany's exports. Her leading import by value is grains, predominantly wheat from Canada. About two fifths (38 per cent) of her trade is with neighbors. France's leading export is steel, which finds markets in the rest of Europe, in Algeria, and in the African areas allied to France politically. Her leading import is crude oil, mainly from the Middle East. She does only a quarter (26 per cent) of her trade

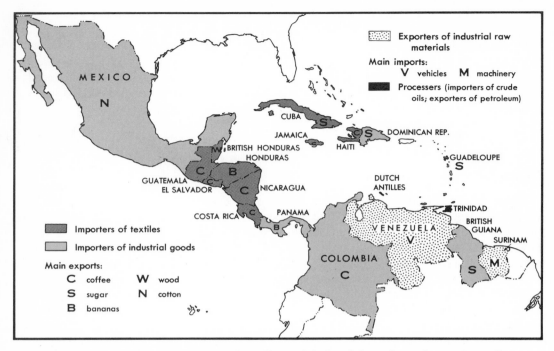

Fig. 23.2. Caribbean importers of textiles and industrial goods, and exporters of raw materials.

with neighbors. It is interesting to note that, in the three nations here considered, the proportion of trade with neighbors increases as access to ocean traffic (insularity) decreases (Table 23.1).

TABLE 23.1

	United Kingdom	France	West Germany
Percentage of trade with neighbors	15%	26%	38%
Square miles of national area per mile of coastline	150	205	316

Around the Caribbean clusters a group of countries that have a high degree of involvement in world trade yet are for the most part economically underdeveloped. The English geographer Brian Berry calls these the "poor trading" countries. The leading import of 10 of these countries (Fig. 23.2) is textiles. Five of the 10 rely on coffee exports, three on sugar, one on bananas, and one on wood exports. It may be said of these 10 nations that they trade slightly processed vegetable raw materials for processed vegetable materials, predominantly cotton products.

Somewhat less far down on the "poor trading" scale are those five nations which trade agricultural products for industrial goods. Vehicles are imported in exchange for cotton by Mexico, for sugar by British Guiana, and for coffee by Colombia. The Dominican Republic exchanges its sugar for steel, while Panama exchanges bananas for a variety of items, more than half of which by value is machinery.

The remaining countries on the Caribbean export industrial raw materials and form a functional cluster of sorts. Venezuela exports crude oil, which accounts for more than half of her value of exports, and in return imports vehicles. Trinidad and the Netherlands Antilles both import crude oil from their neighbor Venezuela and export refined petroleum. Surinam exchanges bauxite for machinery.

Exports

We may categorize nations by the nature and dominance of their exports. Some nations depend heavily on the export of one or more minerals for foreign exchange. Similarly, other nations rely upon the export of one or more agricultural products. Finally, many nations rely for foreign exchange upon the export of both mineral and agricultural products.

Areas Exporting Minerals. Nations relying upon the export of one major mineral are relatively few. Four nations export petroleum. Venezuela provides 30 per cent of the world's petroleum; Saudi Arabia, 17 per cent; Kuwait, 16 per cent; and Iran, 14 per cent. Of these, only Iran processes a considerable amount before export. British Guiana and Surinam each supply 14 per cent of the world's bauxite ore for making aluminum. Bolivia is almost solely dependent upon its tin export to the United States for its foreign exchange and the maintenance of its internal economy.

Those nations relying upon the export of two or more minerals may be said to be somewhat less dependent upon fluctuations in the world market. Seldom will demand for more than one mineral change for the worse at any one time. Only three nations are in this category. Peru produces about 17 per cent of the world's vanadium and 7 per cent of its silver, but its exports of copper and petroleum are relatively insignificant in world trade. Chile produces 19 per cent of the world's copper, most of its natural nitrate, and a considerable amount of iron ore. (The steel mills at Sparrow's Point, Maryland, were constructed specifically for the processing of Chilean iron ore.) Before being partitioned, Korea produced 31 per cent of the world's graphite and 10 per cent of its tungsten.

Areas Exporting Agricultural Products. Nations which rely heavily upon the export of agricultural products are fairly numerous. Those with one-crop exports are eight in number. Coffee is exported by Colombia, with 16 per cent of the world's production, and by Ethiopia, with 5 per cent. Cotton is the main export of both Egypt and Sudan. The former produces one half of the world's total of long-staple cotton, and three quarters of her export value is accounted for by cotton. Sudan produces extra-long-staple cotton and exports it all. Burma exports rice, mainly to her neighbors India and Ceylon. Pakistan is a heavy exporter of jute and produces about 90 per cent of the world's total. Honduras depends largely upon exports of bananas and is the leading producer of this fruit. Ireland exports cattle, predominantly to Great Britain.

Three nations rely heavily upon exports of varied agricultural products. New Zealand relies upon butter for 30 per cent of its export trade, upon cheese for an additional 13 per cent. Three quarters of the wool cut of New Zealand is exported, and meat exports are considerable. Seventeen of every twenty pounds of butter produced in New Zealand are exported, mainly to Great Britain. Another Southern Hemisphere nation, Argentina, has great agricultural exports. Between 60 and 80 per cent of its hard flint corn is exported, mainly to northwestern Europe. Argentine wheat is harvested in November and December and hits the northwest European market when local supplies are low.

Areas Having Major Multiple Exports. Most of the major product-exporting nations rely upon *both* agricultural and mineral exports. In general, they have correspondingly less economic fluctuation than the one-product-exporting nations.

In the Americas, Brazil, Colombia, Cuba, and Canada have multiple major exports.

Brazil exports most of its 6 per cent of world production of manganese and its 45 per cent of world coffee production. Iron ore also leaves the country in considerable quantities. Colombia relies heavily on coffee exports, and most of her platinum and allied-metals production, amounting to 7 per cent of world production, finds markets abroad. Pre-revolutionary Cuba produced over three fifths of all sugar cane that entered world trade. In addition, she produced for export 11 per cent of the world's chromite and 4 per cent of its manganese. Canada exports wheat and nickel; of the latter, it produces 13 per cent of the world's supply. Recently, Canada has started to export great amounts of natural gas to the United States.

Eight nations in Asia rely upon multiple resources for their export trade. Turkey produces 10 per cent of the world's chromite, most of which it exports, and its tobaccos are world famous. Its neighbor Iraq exports petroleum and is the world's leading supplier of dates, which come from the vast groves just north of the marshes

along the head of the Persian Gulf. India exports cotton, predominantly to Great Britain, through the port of Bombay, which was built by the cotton trade. India's major mineral exports include sheet mica (78 per cent of world production) and manganese (13 per cent of world production). Its neighbor Ceylon produces for export 8 per cent of the world's graphite, as well as considerable quantities of tea and copra.

From within the area of southeastern Asia are derived vast quantities of varied exports. Malaya produces for export a third of the world's tin and about 25 per cent of its natural rubber. More varied are the exports of Indonesia, with 17 per cent of the world's tin production, 5 per cent of its bauxite mined, 20 per cent of its rubber, and important quantities of tobacco. To the north, Thailand produces 7 per cent of the world's tin and exports major quantities of rice and teakwood. Eastward, the Philippines are the world's largest producer of coconut products (copra and coconut oil), and one fourth of all its arable land is planted to coconuts. Iron ore from Mindanao and sugar from most of the islands bulk large in Philippine exports.

Three African nations have important mixed exports. Ghana produces for export more than 10 per cent of the world's manganese, while the Union of South Africa produces less than 7 per cent of the amount mined over the earth. Ghana produces a tenth of the world's diamonds, while South Africa's share, though fluctuating considerably owing to sales by the Congo and Sierra Leone, is higher. About 32 per cent of the world's cacao derives from Ghana, and aluminum-ingot exports will become large when the Ajena Dam on the Volta River is finished. About a third of the world's gold is mined in South Africa, and much is exported to the United States. Wine and lobster tails complete the list of South Africa's major exports. Nigeria produces for export 5 per cent of the world's tin (from the Jos Plateau area) and major amounts of palm oil and peanuts.

Fig. 23.3. African importers of textiles and miscellaneous items.

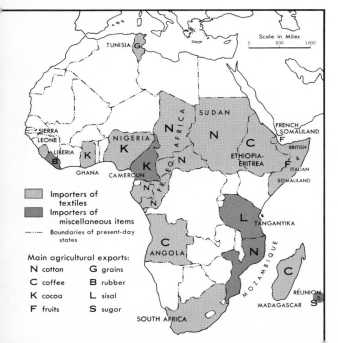

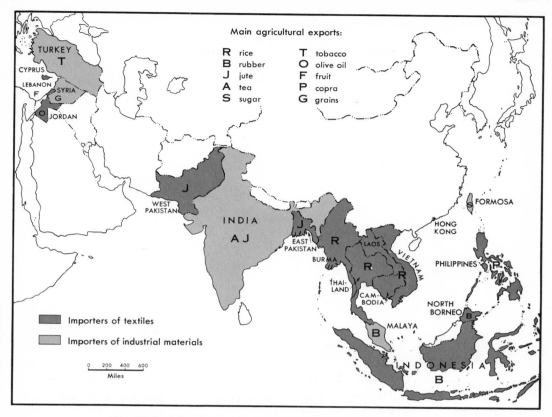

Fig. 23.4. Asian importers of textiles and industrial materials.

Imports

Textiles constitute the major import item of 12 African and 11 Asian nations, as well as of Australia and New Zealand. Only one European nation, Denmark, and one nation in South America, Paraguay, count textiles as their leading import item.

In return for textiles, nine African nations (Fig. 23.3) export vegetable foods or raw materials: cotton, coffee, cacao, fruit, and grains. Two others export animals or animal products, and one exports iron ore. Vehicle imports are paid for by the export of wine from Algeria and coffee from former French areas of West Africa. Egypt and Kenya-Uganda pay for their petroleum imports with cotton and coffee respectively. Five other African nations have imports in the miscellaneous category and pay for them with

agricultural products. One with miscellaneous imports, the Rhodesias-Nyasaland, returns copper as a leading export. Libya, Mauritius, and Morocco are outstanding in the respect that both their major import and major export items are agricultural in nature. Libya exchanges hides for needed grains and Mauritius exchanges sugar for needed grains, while Morocco exchanges its grain surplus for imports of sugar. The industrial backwardness of Africa is illustrated by the fact that 23 of the 26 nations or trading units have an agricultural product as their main export item; only three of the nations export metals (copper and iron ore).

Nine of the 11 Asian nations or trading units (Fig. 23.4) which import textiles export agricultural products as the leading items of export value. Items of export in-

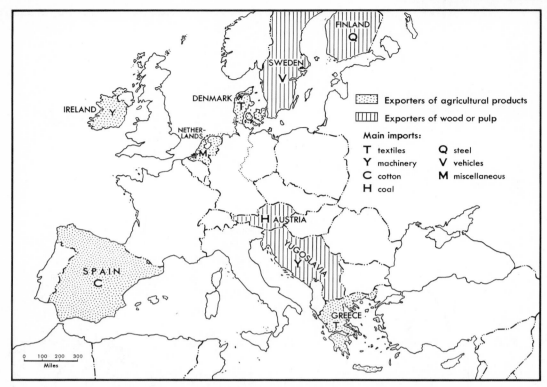

Fig. 23.5. European exporters of agricultural, wood or pulp products, and European importers of manufactured products.

clude rice for three areas, rubber for two, and copra, jute, fruit, and olive oil for one nation each. Hong Kong imports cheap textiles for its growing refugee population and exports high-quality textiles to Europe and Anglo-America. Cyprus pays for its textile imports with copper exports.

Five Asian nations import predominately raw or processed industrial materials and export agricultural produce. Taiwan exchanges its sugar for chemicals; India, its tea and jute for petroleum; Malaya, rubber from its plantations for crude oil; Syria, grains for needed petroleum; and Turkey, its famous tobacco for machines. Two nations of Asia are agricultural in both leading export and leading import items: Ceylon exchanges tea from the Kandy highlands for rice from Burma and the Coromandel coast

of India, and Israel sells fruit to buy grain. Iraq exports crude oil to buy vehicles, while Iran's crude-oil exports pay for sugar. Agricultural products are the leading export items in 16 of the 23 Asian nations or trading units.

When we consider Europe, we notice that the pattern of trade is not what we are often led to expect. That is to say, not all European nations export manufactured goods in exchange for food. Only the United Kingdom and West Germany follow this "traditional" pattern. Portugal and Italy export textiles, but their leading imports are not foods. Five nations of Europe (Fig. 23.5) have agricultural products as the leading export items, and a sixth, Iceland, exports fish. Four export wood or pulp in return for industrial raw materials or manufactures.

Steel is exchanged by France for crude oil and by Belgium-Luxembourg for wool. Malta exchanges minerals for grains, and Switzerland exchanges clocks for miscellaneous imports.

Economic Blocs and Development Areas

Nations with similar political interests often organize themselves into blocs in which currencies are freely convertible and in which considerable agreement on economic policy exists. We speak of Canada and the United States, together with their territories and possessions, as the "dollar area." The French Union is the "franc area," the British Commonwealth (minus Canada) is the "sterling area," and so forth. Occasionally, nations unite in agreements for specific purposes. The European Coal and Steel Community, formed in 1952, and the Common Market and Free Trade Zone areas in Europe, both formed in 1959, are examples.

After World War II, concern for the poverty of much of the world prompted two major development programs, the Point Four program and the Colombo Plan, as well as several minor ones. The Point Four program, now called AID, is supported by the United States government and is concerned with specific industrial, public-health, and agricultural projects. The Colombo Plan, supported in the main by Canada and the United States, applies particularly to areas in, or formerly affiliated with, the British Commonwealth. Within the framework of the United Nations, several aid organizations working toward similar goals include the World Bank and FAO—the Food and Agricultural Organization, with headquarters in Rome. Aid is most frequently given in the form of trade items.

Backwardness, Textiles, and Foodstuffs. Textile industries are generally the first industries to appear when a country industrializes. This has been the case in the industrial revolutions in Europe, the United States, and Japan. If a nation is a major importer of textiles, it may be considered "industrially backward." A map of those countries of the world (Fig. 23.6) for which textiles are the major import item by value is thus indicative, to some degree, of areas of industrial backwardness.

Agricultural exports bulk large in the foreign trade of nonindustrial areas; and as a nation industrializes, its proportion of exports which are agricultural in origin tends to decrease. As a result, a map of those nations whose leading export is derived from agriculture, animal husbandry, or fishing is also indicative of areas of industrial backwardness. Note that many of the textile-importing nations in Figure 23.6 also are nations which export agricultural products in quantity.

Another indication of economic straits, if not precisely of "backwardness," is an unfavorable trade balance. A dozen countries in 1959 imported by value more than twice as much as they exported. The noncommunist portions of Korea and Vietnam received much of their imports as foreign aid, some of which consisted of military supplies. The reason for Panama's import imbalance is not clear, but that of Kenya may be related to its march toward independence. The remaining eight countries, which are either in or bordering the Mediterranean Sea, have chronic problems of trade imbalance.

The Common Market. Experience gained after 1947 through the Marshall Plan for European recovery resulted in the formation in 1952 of the European Coal and Steel Community, whose members were France, West Germany, Italy, Belgium, the Netherlands, and Luxembourg (the latter three are often called Benelux). By this arrangement the steel and coal resources of France and Germany were pooled under a supranational board. The plan worked well, and between the years 1953 and 1960 steel production doubled.

The early success of the European Coal

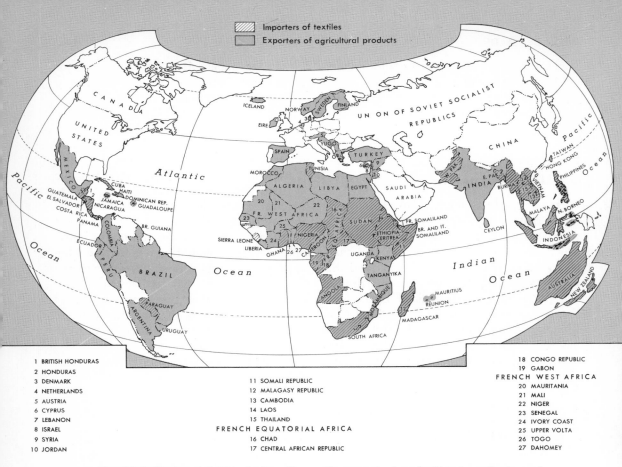

Fig. 23.6. Nations which rely heavily on the export of agricultural products, and world textile-importing nations.

1 BRITISH HONDURAS
2 HONDURAS
3 DENMARK
4 NETHERLANDS
5 AUSTRIA
6 CYPRUS
7 LEBANON
8 ISRAEL
9 SYRIA
10 JORDAN

11 SOMALI REPUBLIC
12 MALAGASY REPUBLIC
13 CAMBODIA
14 LAOS
15 THAILAND
FRENCH EQUATORIAL AFRICA
16 CHAD
17 CENTRAL AFRICAN REPUBLIC

18 CONGO REPUBLIC
19 GABON
FRENCH WEST AFRICA
20 MAURITANIA
21 MALI
22 NIGER
23 SENEGAL
24 IVORY COAST
25 UPPER VOLTA
26 TOGO
27 DAHOMEY

and Steel Community convinced the member nations that a broader organization might be feasible. In 1957 the Common Market of Europe was formed, composed of the same "inner six" countries. Its performance pleased its members and created enough competition that Great Britain in late 1961 petitioned for full membership. Britain's Prime Minister stated, "The plain fact is that the formation and development of the Community has created, economically and politically, a situation to which we are compelled to react." Inasmuch as Britain was a member of the "outer seven" group called the European Free Trade Association, it is likely that Common Market membership will eventually be sought by others of the "seven," particularly by the Scandinavian nations. In late 1961 Israel and Turkey petitioned for provisional membership in the Common Market.

As a unit, the Common Market is now the leading importer of goods in the world and stands in second place in the export of manufactured goods. The member nations also cooperate in encouraging internal trade through tariff reductions and standardization of processing. Evidence of the Common Market's influence is the growth of at least 250 private merchandising and trade associations bearing "European" or "Common Market" names.

The Soviet Bloc. Foreign trade between communist and noncommunist countries tends to be determined less by economic factors of supply and demand than by political factors. Exports to the noncommunist world from Soviet-bloc countries in 1959 amounted to about 2.5 per cent of world trade. Economic benefits of such trade are subordinate to political benefits. Two examples illustrate this. The U.S.S.R. in 1958 sold abroad more than 17,000 tons of tin at a low price. Possibly the Soviet area had an excess of tin, but it is generally thought that the market was flooded in order to embarrass financially the newly independent Republic of Malaya. Also in 1958 the mainland Chinese and private businessmen in Japan negotiated a trade agreement. The agreement was never put into effect, however, because the Chinese were not permitted to fly their flag over their Tokyo headquarters. The communists, not formally recognized by Japan's government, considered the propaganda value of the flag more important than the economic benefits of renewed trade.

The Soviet version of the Common Market is the Council of Mutual Economic Assistance, known in the West as COMECON. Though formed in 1949 as Stalin's answer to the Marshall Plan, it became defunct and was not revitalized until the summer of 1958. The Council's function is to forestall competition among parallel lines of industry within the satellite economies. Thus, it has decreed, for instance, that East Germany (which produces one half of the machines imported by the U.S.S.R. and holds sixth place among industrial manufacturers) is to make trucks weighing less than four tons and that Czechoslovakia is to make heavier trucks. Standardization of parts is also an aim of the Council; plans have been made, for example, to standardize machine tools for ball-bearing factories. Soviet economists refer to such planning as "international division of labor," a phrase deriving from the

Fig. 23.7. Rival trade groups in Europe.

writings of the English economist of capitalist thought, Adam Smith.

General specialties have been determined by the Council—East Germany: chemicals, building materials, precision and light machinery, sugar refineries; Czechoslovakia: heavy machinery (from the famous Skoda works); Poland: transport machinery and coal-mining equipment; Rumania: cellulose, oil-drilling and oil-refining machinery; Hungary: aluminum; and the U.S.S.R.: oil equipment and sugar refineries.

It is interesting to note that in the communist realm, political coercion preceded economic co-operation, whereas in the Common Market area economic co-operation is laying the foundation for gradual increments of political unity. The architect of the Common Market, Jean Monnet of France, has never made a secret of his hope for eventual political unity. The three competing economic federations in Europe—the Common Market, the European Free Trade Association, and COMECON—are shown in Fig. 23.7.

343

Transportation is a true measure of space relations.
Edward Ullman

CHAPTER 24

Trade Routes and Centers

Man produces foods and excavates minerals for his immediate use. However, surpluses of foods and minerals generally enter into trade, for one area may desire to have what another area produces and will be able to pay for its desires with a product of its own. Trade between unlike areas comes about over trade routes, along which are found trade centers.

Trade Centers

Types of Centers. Before the time of bridges, trade routes on land sought shallow crossings, or fords. If a river was generally wide, crossings were sought at narrow points and ferries were installed. Both ford cities and ferry cities eventually get bridges, which become economically feasible to build because of demand for their use. The existence of bridges in turn tends to focus trade routes. The city with the earliest bridges not surprisingly tends to grow faster than other towns along a river.

Many cities develop where a cargo or wagon load of goods must be broken into parts, or where it must change modes of transportation—that is, where the handling of goods must be done frequently and at the same place. A permanent settlement of persons is needed to handle the break in bulk. A city that has grown by doing this service is called a break-in-bulk city. All ports naturally are break-in-bulk cities; if goods are stored in large quantities in a

port city, or for a period of time there, the city may be called an entrepôt. Break-in-bulk cities also tend to grow where trade routes cross rivers. If a river is navigable, it becomes a route in itself and gives added importance to a growing city.

Along seacoasts, many rivers are navigable for a considerable distance upstream. Head-of-navigation cities are a type of break-in-bulk city since transfer from river steamers and barges to land transport occurs there. Of particular note is the string of head-of-navigation cities which grew up along the Fall Line in colonial America. The Fall Line is where the streams flowing over the hard crystalline rock of the Piedmont end in falls upon coming to the softer sedimentary rocks of the coastal plain. The Fall Line cities include Philadelphia, Baltimore, Washington, D.C., Richmond, Raleigh, Columbia, and Augusta.

A valley-mouth town may originate where a valley route enters a plain, and river-delta towns are epitomized by Alexandria, Egypt. A railhead, the terminus of a railroad, is another example of a break-in-bulk city. When produce from the surrounding countryside is brought by truck or wagon to a railhead, a small city springs up.

An interesting example of a break-in-bulk city which depends upon a change in mode of transport is Tatsienlu in western China. The town lies at an elevation of 7600 feet, above which loaded horses find it difficult to climb. The elevation is the lowest that

344

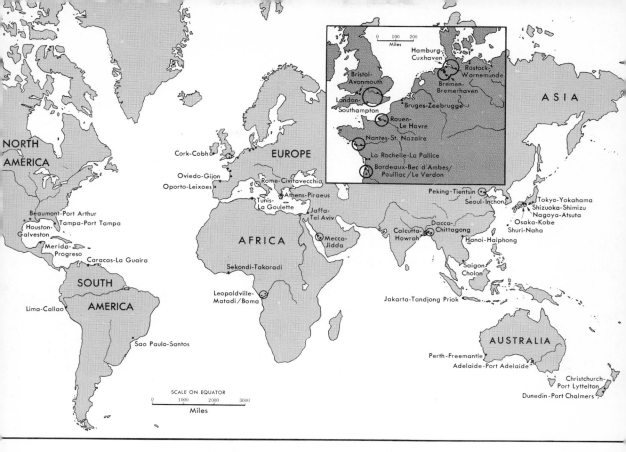

Fig. 24.1. Port-outport trade centers.

Tibetan yaks can reach without becoming ill. Hence, the Tibet-bound trade in brick tea and household utensils is shifted to yaks at Tatsienlu. Yak hides and tails (used for Santa Claus whiskers prior to 1950) are loaded on horses for the return trip to lower elevations.

Ports and Outports. It often happens that a populous center some miles from the sea will become a focus for water-borne trade. A port will then develop to serve as an outport for the existing city. A classical combination is Athens and its outport Piraeus. It may happen that an existing port handling shallow-draft ships will develop a need for a deeper harbor. Another area nearby which has an adequate harbor may become the outport for the existing but inadequate port. For example, Osaka—once a major entrepôt of trade—depends upon Kobe, which

was developed for handling Osaka's deep-draft modern shipping.

The world distribution of ports and outports is shown in Figure 24.1. Most of these cluster in northwestern Europe and eastern Asia. In both areas urban growth preceded commercial revolution, which demanded access to ocean routes through outports. F. W. Morgan, in *Ports and Harbours,* has noted that in the Western world ". . . an outport tendency . . . is almost entirely associated with the estuaries of north-west Europe."

Rarely does a single port become the center of a trade empire, though perhaps Venice was such a port from A.D. 1200 to 1600, just as London was from 1500 to 1900. Most often, trade activity is carried on in several ports in a developed area. The trade of the Phoenicians, which reached to Gibraltar and north to Britain, centered on

345

Fig. 24.2. Hanseatic League towns and their trade routes.

several ports in the Levant. Similarly, the Baltic Sea was once the center of a thriving trade combine, the Hanseatic League.

After the formation of the Hanseatic League in 1256, the Baltic Sea became a major focus of trade. Seaports, chief among which was Lübeck, were the first members of the League, but river ports soon were admitted to membership. Most cities on or at the mouths of rivers draining into the Baltic (Fig. 24.2) were Hansa trade centers. The end of the 14th century saw the height of the League's influence, but it was another century before its power over commerce was broken.

Trade Routes

Roads. In the era before large-scale transportation by railroads and ocean-going liners, roads and canals were the chief routes for trade. The roads of Britain in the early part of the Industrial Revolution were poor in construction and suffered from competition from canals. In the United States, canals were somewhat late in coming into popular favor, and a series of turnpikes was established in the years between 1794 and 1910. In 1794 the Philadelphia and Lancaster Turnpike was begun by a company authorized by the Pennsylvania Legislature to build

the road. Other turnpikes were subsequently built, and soon private turnpikes were found in most of the seaboard areas. However, since their service was inadequate, Congress in 1806 authorized the National Pike, which ran from Cumberland, Maryland, to Wheeling, West Virginia, by 1818. Westward emigration was vastly aided by the National Pike, and for this reason it was gradually extended, reaching Vandalia, Illinois, in 1852.

Most of the turnpikes were covered with about 15 inches of pounded stones or gravel. By and large, the turnpikes in the United States were inadequate to the demands of traffic and were hard to maintain. Toward the last decades of the Industrial Revolution in Britain (1815 and after), the road builder McAdam began to build roads which did not require the heavy, stone, hand-laid foundation inherited in principle from the Romans. According to McAdam, if a road was protected from water under its surface and from infiltration of water from above, a series of broken and compacted layers would form an adequate roadway. In his words:

That it is the native soil which really supports the weight of traffic; that while it is preserved in a dry state, it will carry any weight without sinking and that it does in fact carry the road and carriages also; that this native soil must be previously made quite dry and a covering impenetrable to rain must then be placed over it in that dry state; that the thickness of the road should only be regulated by the quantity of material necessary to form such impervious covering and never by any reference to its own power of carrying weight.

As no artificial road can be made so good as the natural soil in a *dry state,* it is necessary to preserve this state. The first operation should be the reverse of digging a trench. The road should not be sunk below, but raised above, the adjacent ground; that there be a sufficient fall to take off the water, so that it should be some inches below the level of the ground upon which the road is, either by making the drains to lower ground or, if that be not practicable from the nature of the country, then the soil

346

upon which the road is to be laid, must be raised some inches above the level of the water.

Having secured the soil from *under* water, the road-maker is next to secure it from rain water, by a solid road, of clean, dry stone, or flint, so selected, prepared and laid, as to be impervious to water; and this cannot be effected, unless the greatest care be taken, that no earth, clay, chalk, or other matter, that will hold water, be mixed with the broken stone; which must be so laid, as to unite by its own angles into a firm, compact, impenetrable body.

The thickness of such a road is immaterial; as to its strength for carrying weight, this object is obtained by a dry surface, over which the road is to be placed as a covering, to preserve it in that state: experience having shewn, that if water passes through the road and fills the native soil, the road, whatever its thickness, loses its support and goes to pieces.[1]

While McAdam was getting his ideas accepted in Britain, the turnpikes in the United States began to suffer from competition from canals. The canal boom in the United States lasted from 1810 to 1840. After 1840 the canal traffic came to be dominated by a growing network of railroads. The railway boom lasted from about 1840 to 1890, during which time road building languished and vehicles which used roads made little speed and often broke down from the roughness of the terrain. It was only in the 1890's that some of the eastern states passed laws for state aid to road building. This was in response to the growing demand for highway use by steam-driven cars and later by internal-combustion automobiles. Road materials gradually improved. William Hobson took out a patent in England in 1827 for a concrete road which was to be built by methods invented by the Romans, but the extension of the principle of concrete roads did not come about until after the invention of Portland cement in the 1850's. A second method of building roads required the use of asphalt. The use of asphalt in England languished until 1869, when a part of a London street

[1] *A History of Technology,* Vol. IV, pp. 532-534.

was paved with the material; the success of this paving insured a rapid spread of asphalt in England.

Rivers and River-Fed Canals. Any navigable river may become a trade route if it connects areas of unlike resources. The most famous example is the water route followed by the Scandinavian tribes when they found that the Dnepr River provided access to the Black Sea and to trade with Constantinople. From the middle of the 9th century to the middle of the 13th century the rivers between the Baltic and the Black Sea were used to take to Byzantium the slaves, furs, and honey of the north and to return with manufactured objects, art works, and weapons.

Canals are most often dug to join navigable water bodies that are close to each other. Seldom are canals for navigation dug over long distances of land, but frequently they parallel rivers, or use river water. It is worth while to look in some detail at the history of canal development in Europe.

The construction of canal locks to overcome differences in water level had well advanced by 1400. The first canal to have locks overcoming differences between level of water and level of land was built in Germany in the closing years of the 14th century, between Lauenburg on the River Elbe and Lübeck on the River Trave. The next lock canal of importance was in northwestern Italy, in the area of Lombardy. This canal had originally been designed for irrigation, but about 1270 it was enlarged and used by boats. The canal ended in a basin near the western wall of Milan. In the 1380's plans were afoot for building a new cathedral at Milan, and improvements in the canal were made. The first pound lock (a double-gate arrangement for changing water level) in Italy was constructed in this canal in 1438, and the second lock was added a few years later. These works set the stage for a new era of canal building.

Canal building in Italy benefited, as did so many other fields in mechanical arts and practical technology, from the work of Leonardo da Vinci. About 1492 he began to make plans for the construction of six new locks on the Milan Canal. These were completed in 1497. After 1503 Leonardo made plans for a canal to lead from Florence to the River Arno, but this work had to be abandoned because of its technical complexity. By 1595 complete proposals for aqueducts, bridges, locks, and so forth for the canal between Pavia and Milan were completed. The work was started, but it was abandoned when Meda, the engineer, died.

The first important lock canal outside of Italy was the Brussels Canal, constructed in the decade 1550 to 1560. This ran from Brussels about 20 miles east to the town of Boom on the Rupel River and cut in half the distance that boats had previously traveled. Flanders became a center of canal building, and a 44-mile canal dating from about 1622 linked Bruges with Dunkirk. An extension was made to Ostend in 1666, and a tide lock was constructed there three years later.

In England the era of canal building corresponded almost exactly to the period of the Industrial Revolution, 1760 to 1830. Its geographic effects were quite marked. It reduced the fear of local shortages of fuel and food. It brought new agriculture into existence by bringing formerly unused areas closer to market, and it quickened economic life in the older but more removed farm areas. It also lessened the cost of transporting such bulky materials as building timber and building stone, clay for potteries, and iron ore and coal for the new steel mills.

In France two *summit-level* canals were built in the 17th century. (A summit-level canal crosses the low point of a watershed between two river systems, and the highest portion of the canal derives water not from rivers alongside but from an aqueduct.) The Briare Canal led from the River Loire northward in a gentle arc to the town of Montargis on the River Loing, which flows north to the River Seine. Construction began in 1604 and for the next 30 years proceeded intermittently; in 1642 the canal was ready for

traffic. After its opening in the middle of the 17th century, canal operations became very profitable, and the annual trade was about 200,000 tons. Still in operation, the canal carries annual traffic that is not far short of one and a half million tons. The second summit-level French canal was the Orleans Canal. Built between 1682 and 1692 to supplement the Briare Canal on the south, this canal had a length of 46 miles.

Farther to the south, work was begun on the Canal du Midi in the winter of 1666 to 1667, and two years later more than 8000 men were working on it. Aqueducts carried the canal over the River Cesse. The length of the canal from Toulouse to its end (east of Carcassonne) was 150 miles, with 100 locks intervening. Modeled after the older Briare Canal, the Canal du Midi with its many improvements became the prototype for later great canal-building projects in the rest of Europe.

The third summit-level canal in continental Europe, 15 miles in length, was opened in 1669 in Germany. This was the Friedrich Wilhelm Canal from the Spree River on the west to the Oder River on the east. The canal system in northwest Germany was extended between 1743 and 1746, when a link was made between the Elbe River and the Havel River via Lake Plaue. In Sweden the canal link between Stockholm and Göteborg had been completed in 1610. Traffic was attracted to the canals in such quantity that in the last decade of the 17th century a Dutch engineer, de Moll, was called in to improvise improvements.

The first summit-level canal in Britain was built in the period 1737 to 1745 and led from Newry to Lake Neagh in northern Ireland. Its purpose was to bring coal from the mines near Newry. Until the beginning of the Industrial Revolution (about 1760), most of the internal navigation in England was via canalized rivers, supplemented over short stretches by dug canals. This system, added to by the new canals built after 1760, has been called the arteries of the Industrial Revolution.

Fig. 24.3. Inland waterways of northern Europe and the U.S.S.R.

Canals joining rivers are quite common in northern Europe (Fig. 24.3), where the northward-trending rivers are joined by an east-west canal system.

There are many canals which run parallel to rivers and utilize their water but have separate channels. The Erie Canal, opened in 1825, used for the most part the water of the Mohawk River. Though as the New York Barge Canal it presently carries little freight, it has become important for water supply. The St. Lawrence Seaway canals parallel the river of the same name, and canals in Europe parallel the rivers Rhône and Rhine. In the United States, lagoons behind sand bars are joined to form the Intra-coastal Waterway (Fig. 24.4). The Gulf portion is very important in the transport of oil by tanker, and the Atlantic portion is used mainly by pleasure craft.

The early canals of Ohio and the modern canal system of the U.S.S.R. are examples of canals across portages. Moscow has been called by Russians "the port of the five seas"

since the completion of the Don-Volga Canal in 1952.

The Grand Canal in China, from Peiping to Shanghai, is a rare example of a long overland canal devoted mainly to transport. It was finished in the early years of the 7th century, but it represented, in part, canals that dated back 15 centuries. It was used intermittently until about 50 years ago. The communist government of China in 1954 announced plans to refurbish the route. The utility of the Grand Canal is shown by its other popular name, the Grain Transport River. Stretching about 1200 miles from north to south, it connected the main economic areas of historic China. About 150 miles of the Grand Canal are not operative near the Yellow River and are being rebuilt. The southern end connects with the Shanghai delta area, which has nearly 150,000 miles of locally used canals.

In Russia Peter the Great abandoned his attempt to have the Volga and the Don joined by a canal at the point where they

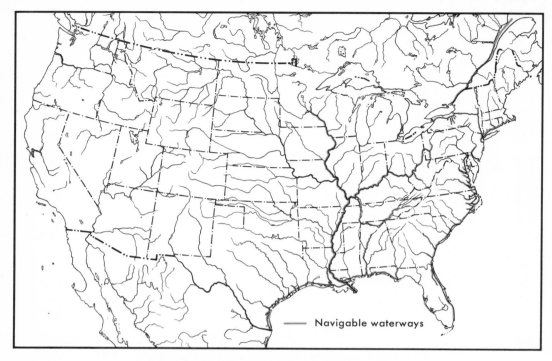

Fig. 24.4. Inland waterways of the United States.

come within 48 miles of each other. (It was not until 1952 that such a canal was built.) However, he had a canal dug joining the Neva River at St. Petersburg with the Volga by way of Lake Ladoga. The draft of this canal was only 18 inches, but by 1760 more than 3000 boats of about 80 tons each were using it annually. A much more direct link between the Neva and the Volga was made in 1808 when the Tikhvine Canal was constructed. Another canal, the Mariinsk, was opened in 1811 and joined the two rivers via Lake Onega. This canal was designed for boats of more than 160 tons. In 1805 the Black Sea was joined to the Gulf of Riga via a canal between the Dvina and the Berezina rivers. By the middle of the 19th century, Russia was hauling barges over more than 50,000 miles of navigable waterways. The U.S.S.R. at present is well provided with canals linking most of the rivers of European Russia.

The canalization of rivers proceeded rapidly in 19th-century Europe. The Danube was worked upon from 1849 to the end of the century, at which time it had almost 2000 miles of navigable waterways. The Danube was supplemented by a number of canals. The Franz Canal was opened in 1802 and provided a link between the Danube and the Tisza. The famous rapids at the Iron Gates, downstream from Hungary, continued to be a problem (although they had once been bypassed by the Romans with a canal a mile and a half long).

For many decades after 1850, navigation of both the Rhône and the Rhine rivers was difficult because of the winding channels and the speed of the current in some sections. In 1840 the Canal de Miribel was constructed south of Lyon. Only in the last decade or so of the 19th century was barge traffic upstream made reasonably easy on the Rhône. The Rhine upstream from Strasbourg began to be canalized after 1840. However, technical problems of silting downstream and of scouring upstream long hindered adequate barge navigation. By far the greatest amount of canal building just before, during, and after the Industrial Revolution up to the rise of the railroads was in the area of France, Belgium, and the Netherlands.

In 1793 the Canal du Centre was built connecting the Loire River with the Saône. This canal completed the first inland route from the Mediterranean Sea to the English Channel. The canal connecting the Rhine and the Rhône rivers was completed in 1834 and provided the second link between the Mediterranean and the North Sea. In the decade between 1818 and 1828 three major canals were built connecting various coal fields, and in 1828 the Sambre River was

canalized. For many decades the Dutch strongly opposed the building of canals and the canalization of rivers in Belgium because of their fear that they would lose the trade flowing into the Dutch ports on the North Sea. Grounds for these fears, of course, existed, but the general geographical position of the entire North Sea area was so favorable that all ports grew and canalization of rivers in one area eventually redounded to the benefit of other ports located nearby. The Dutch in 1825 constructed a 50-mile-long canal bypassing the Zuyder Zee seacoast. The canal was 18 feet deep and 40 yards across, and it represented a masterpiece of canal building across very soft land.

The opening of the Sault Ste. Marie Canal in 1855, with enlargements in 1895, 1896, and 1919, permitted the iron ore of the Me-

Fig. 24.5. Flow of Great Lakes-overseas direct traffic. (Courtesy of Harold M. Mayer, *The Port of Chicago and the St. Lawrence Seaway*, University of Chicago Press, 1957.)

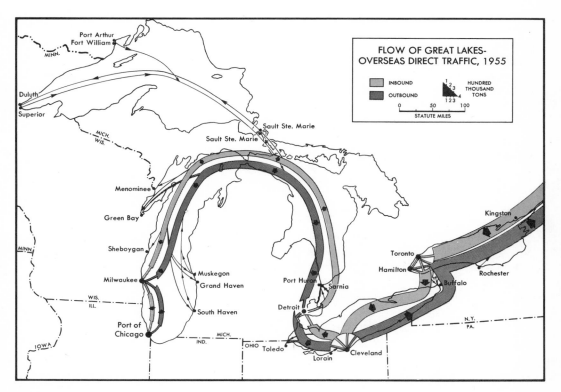

sabi Range to be transported cheaply and in great quantities to the ports of the southern Great Lakes. Chicago and Gary came into being, and steel mills occurred in an almost continuous band from Detroit through Toledo to the eastern end of Lake Erie, where coal was available cheaply from the Allegheny and Kanawha plateaus to the south and southeast. This was an extension of the American manufacturing belt. The marketing of steel from the manufacturing belt was hindered because the steel had to pass by rail or via the New York State Barge Canal or the old Erie Canal to New York City. It was obvious that access to the sea could be had more cheaply if the St. Lawrence River between Lake Ontario and Montreal could be canalized by the bypassing of rapids. The history of the development of the St. Lawrence Seaway, finally opened to deep-draft ocean traffic in 1959, started in 1821. At that time the Lachine Rapids were bypassed by a five-foot-deep canal, which was deepened within two decades to nine feet. Four other major rapids were bypassed by canals at about the same time, and between 1834 and 1847 the Cornwall Canal and the three shorter Williamsburg canals were completed. The route could then be used by ships of

moderate draft as far as Lake Ontario. The old Welland Canal was constructed between 1824 and 1829 to bypass the falls at Niagara and thus join lakes Ontario and Erie. The amount of trade passing through the St. Lawrence route before the opening of the deeper seaway was considerable (Fig. 24.5), and has grown rapidly since 1955.

Irrigation canals generally do not carry freight since most of them are in dry areas having adequate road or rail systems. An example of an irrigation canal in North America is the All-American Canal in California, which parallels the Toda-Mexicana Canal across the border. The distributary canals of the Punjab area of West Pakistan and northwest India are non-freight-carrying canals devoted exclusively to irrigation.

Ocean Routes and Nodes. In this modern age (which is variously called the Air Age, the Atomic Age, the Space Age) many people consider the sea to be somewhat outmoded as a highway. Nevertheless, the traffic in heavy goods between the countries of the world still utilizes the sea to a great extent. Most of the oil, coal, ore, lumber, and grain that is transported moves across the various oceans in modern, efficient freighters, barges, and tankers and thus takes advantage of the

Fig. 24.6. Ocean transport routes.

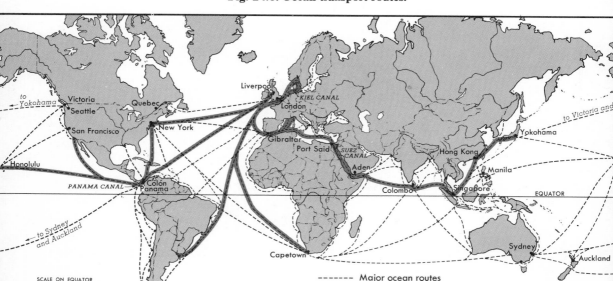

lowest possible costs. This use of the sea continues despite the expansion of air transportation to accommodate people, mail, machinery, and many kinds of articles with selling prices high enough to defray the high cost of air transportation (see Chapter 20).

The great sea routes are not essentially different today from what they were in the days of sail. These routes were developed along the lines that most readily connected the various places in the world which had different commodities to trade. Since some areas have now (as they had then) a surplus of raw, heavy, cheap commodities, exchanges are made between these areas and those that have a surplus of relatively high-cost manufactured goods. Because of the tendency to ship goods at the lowest possible cost where speed is not a factor, the ocean routes continue to handle greater and greater quantities of materials.

Eurasia and North America extend northwards into the polar ocean so far that commercial navigation for long was impossible. Even though the Soviet Union now utilizes the "north sea (Arctic Ocean) route," it is kept open for only two months of the summer, and at great expense. As far as ocean transport is concerned, Eurasia and North America form a northern island, to the south of which all ocean traffic must pass.

Transportation on the sea is much cheaper than on the land, for obvious reasons. No permanent path must be maintained. There is the advantage that ships carry tonnage far exceeding that of any train. Finally, the route is level: no mountains or plateaus must be crossed. In spite of the relative cheapness of sea transport, man still seeks to make the route as short as possible. Fig. 24.6 shows that ocean trade routes follow the shortest possible paths between the major production areas. The ocean routes have been somewhat modified in modern times by the construction of short sea-to-sea connections, especially at Suez and Panama, and by the recent navigational improvements in inland waters, such as the St. Lawrence Seaway. Modifica-

tions have been made in order to provide water routes for cargo as far inland as possible and thus reduce the cost of transportation. Unlike freight, whose means of transportation is governed largely by costs, passengers and mail tend to use air or land transportation as much as possible. A freight cargo bound for London, for example, would go via the Thames Estuary, but passengers and mail would leave the ship at Southampton and complete the journey by rail, thus saving several hours. Some of the other improvements affecting ocean transportation involve the construction of artificial harbors, such as the excellent and spacious harbor of Los Angeles.

The various modifications made in ocean routes during the last century have not profoundly affected the general character of ocean transportation. Grain still moves from eastern Canada and the United States to northwestern Europe by freighter, while it moves in increasing quantities from the western coast of North America to Japan, India, and Pakistan. Iron ore still moves from northern Chile to the steel mills on tidewater in eastern North America. Coal, which normally is not shipped long distances now that oil is widely used to power ships, is still barged in great quantities over water from the North Sea, through the English Channel, and along the western coast of Europe into the Mediterranean, as it is shipped from the "have" countries, particularly Germany, to the "have-not" countries in southern Europe.

The traffic in oil follows the discovery of new fields and the changes in consumption habits in different parts of the world. To counteract Europe's oil deficiency, tankers move in from North and South America and southeastern Asia with both petroleum and refined products. Oil is shipped from the South American areas to the United States for refining and transshipment. Of all the methods of transporting oil, the ocean-going tanker is the cheapest, on a cost basis. The tanker not only has no rival in ocean crossings; it also competes successfully in coastal shipping. Many years ago large pipelines were constructed from the Texas oil fields to the vicinity of New York City. Although these pipelines were used to full capacity during World War II because of the enemy submarines which menaced the tankers, the tankers resumed their dominance at the close of the war and the pipelines were abandoned or converted to other uses.

So far as trade between northern hemisphere points is concerned, four major nodes of ocean traffic, or concentrations of trade routes, are important: Suez, Panama, Singapore, and the English Channel.

The Suez node is of vital importance to Europe, for oil from Iran and the Persian Gulf sheikdoms passes through Suez on its way to markets in western Europe. The vital importance of this node is indicated by the history of attempts to provide a Red Sea-Mediterranean link. The first canal connecting the Nile and the Red Sea was constructed about 2000 B.C. and remained in use for a thousand years. After that other canals were dug and used, but political changes did not permit continuous use and each canal eventually silted up. The present link was opened to traffic in 1869 and has repeatedly been widened and deepened for larger vessels. Even now, dredges must be always on hand to remove the wind-blown sand which tends to fill the channel.

The opening of the Suez route had a tonic effect on the growth of Asian ports by bringing them, in practice, twice as close to Europe as before. The effect on the Asian countries was to change their focus of trade from an internal or centripetal bias to an external or centrifugal orientation. Almost all of the major port cities of Asia had their founding or period of important growth after 1870. These cities include Karachi in Pakistan; Bombay, Madras, and Calcutta in India; Rangoon in Burma; Singapore in Malaya; Saigon in Vietnam; Hong Kong, Canton, and Shanghai on the China coast; and Yokohama and Kobe in Japan. The greatest of these as a commercial center and entrepôt was Singapore.

Singapore was not just the natural topographic focus of routes in southeastern Asia; it also lay in the center of developing resources of natural rubber, tobacco, tin, and petroleum. At the time of writing, Singapore was seeking a federal status with Malaya.

The Panama route was opened to traffic in 1914 and had the effect of reducing the overland-rail freight rates through competition and of encouraging the rapid growth of cities on the West Coast. Los Angeles, being the southernmost large city there, particularly benefited.

Much of the English Channel traffic finds its way to one of the great sea-to-sea connections of the world, the Kiel Canal, joining the Baltic with the North Sea via the Elbe River. Very early the Vikings used this route and portaged their ships across a watershed 10 miles wide. By the year A.D. 1400 the small-craft canal was in use from Lübeck to the Elbe River. The forerunner of the present link was the Eider Canal, cut in 1784 to join Kiel with the Eider Lakes and then the River Eider leading into the North Sea. The canal was 10 feet deep. The year following its opening to local traffic it was opened to all nations' ships and was used for more than 100 years. The present Kiel Canal was opened in 1895 to supplement the Eider Canal because of the greatly increased size of modern ships. At present the Kiel Canal is one of the world's busiest waterways.

Through these four focuses of traffic, and through ones of lesser importance, moves about a fifth of the world's ocean freight on unscheduled cargo ships called "tramps." These medium-sized ships carry predominantly such bulk cargoes as mineral ores, coal, grain (wheat, corn, and rice), sugar, fertilizers, and lumber. Routes of "tramp" steamers may vary with the season, and a ship that carries Norwegian lumber part of the year may carry peanuts from West Africa in the non-lumber months. Tramp steamers are often registered for tax purposes under the flags of Panama or Liberia, but may be owned by citizens of any one of the large maritime-oriented nations.

A nation may be said to consist of its territory,
its people, and its laws.　　**Abraham Lincoln**

CHAPTER 25

Men and Nations

In past eras the population of the world was thinly spread over its surface. Centers of population were recognized and named, but little attention was paid to the precise ownership and status of poor and outlying areas. Wandering peoples were seldom conscious of the centers of power. Villages may have had occasionally to share a portion of their produce with military or priestly authorities in the larger towns, but neither hunter nor nomad, village dweller or town citizen, was aware of the precise physical and legal limits of governmental power which are constantly apparent to people of today's world. More and more our complex political organization has forced us to appear to act as small boys do when they draw a line on the ground and tell others not to "step over it." These mainly arbitrary but necessary lines are the political boundaries around which much tension gathers.

As centers of higher agricultural productivity became organized as centers of power, the persons so united thought of themselves as a unique folk, or organized nation. Because the first countries (delimited sovereign political areas) were generally composed of only one ethnic and linguistic group, we have become accustomed to using the words *nation* and *country* interchangeably. (Sometimes nation is used in a more restricted sense, as when we speak of "the Sioux nation.") Here we shall use the term *country* to refer to the physical area inhabited by a group of people, and to its physical uniqueness. The terms *nation* and *national* are used when referring to the people inhabiting the

political area, and to their political uniqueness.

Growth of Political Communities

As citizens, we view political organization on several levels. Those levels which affect us most often in our daily life are the city and state governments. The national or country-wide level impinges on us when we pay income taxes or serve in the armed forces. The national level is known through the reading of newspapers, but its influence is seldom directly felt unless one travels to a foreign country. We take these governments for granted, seldom realizing that they have evolved in relatively consistent ways.

The Growth of Nations. Scholars have noticed that there seem to be certain uniformities of national growth. That is, most nations go through certain rather well-defined stages of development. Let us use the eastern-seaboard origins of the United States as an example of the process.

When the first white people arrived from Europe, they had to be content in the first few years to grow enough food to support themselves. Gradually, as population increased, some settlements started trading with other settlements, and the exchange of goods stimulated the organization of the settlers into associations for trade and into political activity designed both to stimulate further trade and to regulate the growing society. What had begun as "colonies" on paper became colonial settlements in fact. Each settlement was organized around a major town, and Boston, New York, Philadelphia, Baltimore, and other seaboard centers became cities of importance. Roads were built to connect these cities, supplementing the sea routes between them. By the early 1700's industry began to be so important in the northeast that the British parliament passed a series of restrictive laws that were designed to prevent export of machines and technicians to America. From about the year 1740, analysis of newspaper contents shows that the colonists more and more thought of themselves as "Americans" and of the colonies as "America." Thus, awareness of being somehow separate and distinct preceded actual independence.

Karl Deutsch, an American political scientist, has recognized eight "uniformities" of growth, and the pattern of American growth conforms to them. Deutsch recognizes first the shift from subsistence agriculture to exchange economies. Next, there is a social mobilization of rural people in core areas of more intensive exchange and denser settlement. The growth of towns follows. Then, important towns are linked in basic communication grids, and trade routes result. The fifth step is the concentration of capital and skills, with a resulting buoyant effect on the economy. Following this is a growth of the "concept of interest," and the resulting unification of groups marked by similar language and communications habits. The seventh step is the acceptance of national symbols and the awakening of ethnic awareness. The final step seems to consist of attempts at political compulsion, resulting sometimes in the subordination of other peoples.

It is apparent from this analysis that some countries that are independent are not nations in the true sense. Liberia, for instance, survives through its small size, its isolation, and, until recently, its poverty. Again, it is obvious that some nations as defined by these uniformities are not independent countries. The Hausa, Yoruba, and Ibo areas of Nigeria are all nations by the Deutsch definition. It remains to be seen whether their newly gained independence as a federal state will be successful.

If we accept the above uniformities as a sort of guide to the maturity of a country, it is rewarding to examine various countries to see in what ways they may *not* conform to type. Pakistan is not culturally united, though it has a common religion that is its main reason for being. Punjabis in the west speak a different tongue than that used by the Bengalis in the east, and much strife has resulted from east-west bitterness in Pakistan. Similar situations exist in many countries where cultural unity has not followed political unity.

Let us apply the uniformities developed by Deutsch to the growth of Russia. The Kievan state of early Russian history (circa 880-1170) was not a true nation in any sense, but a trading state ruled by descendants of alien Swedish invaders and adventurers. The breakup of the Kievan state saw the Slavs that were its population base scatter in three directions: northeast, west, and southwest. It was around the migrants to the northeast that the Russian state arose. The duchy of Muscovy started to become powerful as the subsistence farming of the cleared forest areas became an exchange economy. The core area of denser population around the growing cities of Ryazan, Moscow, and Tula resulted in a rise of social mobility. The grid of communication between these cities was furnished by the many low-gradient streams flowing peripherally from the Valdai Hills area. Capital was concentrated in Moscow, where all the tribute for the Tatars was sent and reduced in amount before being transmitted to the Khans of the steppe.

Trade within the upper watersheds of the rivers aided the unification of the Slavic people resident there, and constant opposition to the Tatars helped promote ethnic awareness. The fall of Byzantium to the Turks in 1453 suddenly made Moscow the greatest center of Greek Orthodoxy and the spiritual heir of the Eastern church. The designation of Moscow as the "third Rome," the adoption of the double-eagle standard of the

Byzantine emperors, and the assumption of the title of Czar, or Caesar, by the Russian rulers all sharpened the Russian sense of distinctiveness and were symbols around which the Russians organized a strong state. Political compulsion was a natural concomitant to the expansion outward in all directions from the national core around the Valdai Hills.

Students should apply the uniformities of national growth to the history of other nations in order to gain a feeling for the geographic basis of nations. The growth of an exchange economy, the growth of towns in a core area, and the development of a communications grid—all these are basic concerns of the human geographer. Skill in applying these uniformities to actual situations, past and present, will result in much greater understanding of the background of current events.

Colonies and Economic Penetration. One aspect of political compulsion, the last of the uniformities of national growth, is the gaining of colonies. Justification for the control of colonies has often revolved around their ability to supply raw materials to the factories of the mother country. Also, the colonies have often been considered as buyers of finished products shipped from the mother country. In almost every instance of colony creation in the 18th and 19th centuries, justification was found in the theory that "trade follows the flag." Mercantilism was the economic philosophy justifying the acquisition of raw-materials-supplying, goods-consuming colonies.

National policy makers have often acted as if they believed the dictum of the geopolitician Otto Maull that economic penetration may be considered a perfect substitute for areal domination. Colonialism may exist in the form of economic exploitation even where colonies do not formally exist. Several European nations and Japan practiced economic penetration of China in the "Chinese melon" period (circa 1898-1938). Between wars, from 1918 to 1938, Germany practiced a policy of economic penetration of

Fig. 25.1. German minority areas prior to 1945. (Samuel Van Valkenburg, *Elements of Political Geography.* © **1939. Prentice-Hall, Inc.)**

central Europe. A map of German-speaking minorities (Fig. 25.1) in central Europe prior to 1945 illustrates the extent of Germany's "drive toward the east." Almost all Germans in these minority areas were forcibly returned to Germany after 1945.

An excellent illustration of Maull's dictum is found in the history of the North American fur trade. As the European fur buyers pushed westward, the Indians adjacent to buyers, from whom they bought the furs, tended to bring more distant areas under their tribal control. The nearer tribes were intent upon being the first of the profit-taking middlemen.

In the period following the great discoveries of the 16th century, European nations established many trading stations along the coasts of Africa and Asia. Economic penetration by way of trade from these "factories" was often followed, sometimes accidentally, by political penetration. The British East India Company, for example, felt obliged to aid in local wars the rulers of the areas in which its trading stations lay. The areas thus conquered became British India, and the less attractive and more inaccessible areas became the Princely States.

Fig. 25.2. The Indian subcontinent before independence of India and Pakistan. (Kingsley Davis, *The Population of India and Pakistan*, Princeton University Press, 1951.)

A map of preindependence India (Fig. 25.2) graphically illustrates the hodgepodge result.

Africa until the 1880's was still the "dark continent" as far as European knowledge of its interior was concerned. However, its coastal areas had been occupied and fought over by European powers from the days of

Fig. 25.3. European claims on Africa's coast prior to the Berlin Conference of 1884.

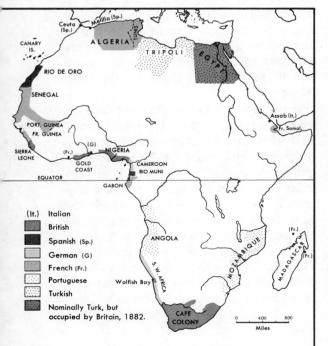

coastal discovery (Fig. 25.3). In 1884 a conference on the division of colonies in Africa met in Berlin. Many of the straight-line boundaries in Africa today were drawn or delimited on such conference tables and only later demarcated on the ground. That such boundaries often arbitrarily cut through tribal areas was of little immediate concern to the powers.

Disappearance of Colonies. All over the world colonies in the traditional sense of the word are disappearing. Colonies, including territories and mandates, may disappear in two ways. They may be absorbed politically into the mother country, or they may become independent. This latter process has seemed the more spectacular, with 44 colonies and mandate areas having become independent since 1944. The general policy of mother countries seems to have been to grant independence to populous areas and to absorb politically the relatively nonpopulous areas. The first pattern is in line with Deutsch's uniformities of national growth. The reasons for the second pattern are less obvious. Possible reasons include the stigma connected with colonialism, the desire for better control of areas abroad, and strategic considerations.

The stigma of colonialism is only recent, but it is nonetheless strong. The older generation in the West feels guilty about owning colonies, and the younger generation feels ashamed. Political assimilation eases the conscience of the older people and changes the official role of the younger citizens, even though no real change may have been effected. Strategic considerations behind political assimilation may include the feeling that attack on a portion of a country is less likely than attack on a colony. Better control may follow the making of "natives" into "citizens" of the mother country. Better control includes uniformity of laws and thus makes administration more efficient.

Political absorption has accounted for about one third as many areal changes as has the gaining of independence, but it has affected far fewer people (Table 25.1).

TABLE 25.1

	Area in Square Miles	Population
Colonies Absorbed	3,243,289	15,048,651
New Nations	10,336,951	852,925,204

Since 1944, the changes tabulated in Table 25.2 have occurred.

TABLE 25.2

Areas Absorbed into Already Existing Political Units

Name	Area in Square Miles	Population
Tibet	470,000	1,273,969
Greenland	839,800	26,192
Newfoundland-Labrador	152,734	431,890
Angola	481,350	4,392,000
Mozambique	302,250	6,234,000
Tannu Tuva	64,000	65,000
Southwest Africa	317,725	539,000
Portuguese India (Goa)	1,301	637,591
Portuguese Timor	7,330	442,378
Portuguese Guinea	13,948	510,777
Alaska	586,400	72,524
Hawaii	6,451	423,330
TOTAL	3,243,289	15,048,651

An agreement of May 23, 1951, placed the defense and foreign affairs of Tibet in the hands of the Chinese but left the Tibetans autonomous in their internal affairs. The Panchen Lama and the Dalai Lama, spiritual and temporal rulers respectively, were appointed members of the Chinese Consultative Conference. Revolt in 1959 and the voluntary exile of the Dalai Lama left the autonomy of Tibet in doubt.

Greenland, much of which is icecap, was a non-self-governing territory of Denmark until June 5, 1953. The constitution of that date made Greenland an integral part of Denmark politically, with the same measure of self-government as the mother country. Newfoundland was made a Dominion in 1917, but by 1934 the financial situation caused a government-by-commission to be set up. In December, 1948, the union with Canada was effected, and Newfoundland is now a province of that country.

Tannu Tuva, a small country in the mountains west of Lake Baykal, was incorporated into the Russian portion of the U.S.S.R. in 1944. It had once been Chinese as a part of Outer Mongolia and in 1921 had proclaimed itself independent. Angola and Mozambique are overseas provinces of Portugal itself. By a law promulgated on June 11, 1951, all Portuguese colonies were changed into overseas territories. (Portuguese Timor had as early as 1926 been made a province of Portugal, thus setting the precedent.) Southwest Africa was assigned by the League of Nations in 1920 as a mandate to the Union of South Africa. In 1949 the Union unilaterally announced that the area was no longer a mandate or a trust territory, and that 10 representatives from Southwest Africa were sitting in the Union legislature. This unilateral change has been opposed in the United Nations.

The New Nations. World War II marks a milestone in the independence of nations. After this time, many of the areas that had become subject to European rule since the Age of Discovery began to gain their independence. The new nations are tabulated in Table 25.3. Much of Britain's empire in Asia became independent but maintained strong trade relations with the Commonwealth. The Netherlands relinquished Indonesia slowly and under considerable pressure. France permitted her larger Asian possessions to become separate nations not long after the war's end. The present division of Vietnam into northern (communist) and southern (free) parts is regarded by both governments as temporary. A decade later, France's African colonies, with one exception, voted for political ties with the French Union and proclaimed their independence within the Union. Some of these former colonies have since moved toward greater independence in a formal sense, while keeping trade and cultural ties.

TABLE 25.3   **Nations Formed Since 1944**

Name	Year of Independence	Area in Square Miles	Latest Population Figure
Lebanon	1944	4,015	1,650,000
Syria	1944	72,234	4,420,000
Jordan	1946	36,715	1,527,000
India	1947	1,266,210	420,000,000
Pakistan	1947	364,737	87,000,000
Burma	1948	261,789	20,255,000
Ceylon	1948	25,332	9,388,000
Israel	1948	7,992	2,054,434
Korea (South)	1948	37,415	24,994,117
Indonesia	1949	575,450	89,600,000
Laos	1949	88,780	1,690,000
Libya	1951	685,000	1,091,830
Cambodia	1954	66,590	4,845,000
Vietnam (predivision)	1954	120,910	26,100,000
Morocco	1956	171,305	10,330,000
Sudan	1956	967,500	11,390,000
Tunisia	1956	48,194	3,830,000
Ghana	1957	91,843	6,690,730
Malaya	1957	50,690	6,278,763
Central African Republic	1958	241,700	1,177,000
Chad	1958	495,368	2,600,000
Congo Republic	1958	134,750	795,000
Cyprus	1958	3,572	549,000
Gabon	1958	102,317	420,709
Guinea	1958	95,000	2,800,000
Ivory Coast	1958	127,500	3,100,000
West Indies	1958	16,155	3,128,000
Mauritania	1959	470,000	624,000
Cameroun	1960	166,800	3,187,000
Congo	1960	905,380	13,658,185
Dahomey	1960	43,630	1,725,000
Malagasy Republic	1960	227,900	5,191,085
Niger	1960	458,875	2,555,000
Nigeria	1960	339,169	33,043,000
Senegal	1960	78,000	2,550,000
Somalia	1960	178,000	1,330,000
Soudan (Mali)	1960	464,752	4,300,000
Togo	1960	21,850	1,161,314
Upper Volta	1960	105,811	3,531,571
Kenya	1961	224,960	6,351,000
Ruanda and Burundi	1961	20,916	4,700,000
Sierra Leone	1961	27,925	2,260,000
Tanganyika	1961	363,000	8,788,466
Algeria	1962	80,920	10,265,000
TOTAL		10,336,951	852,925,204

Political Federations. Unions of two or more political areas into a larger unit or federation often occur on the world political stage. When the basis for federation is strong enough, the union will function well. If the factors which initially gave rise to the union lose their urgency, a federation may weaken, malfunction, and eventually break up. Once started, a federation by its very nature—equal status among the federated units—is amenable to expansion by the addition of new units.

The United States is one of the best examples of a growing federation. From the original 13 colonies of 1776, it has grown to 50 states by accretion of territories on the equality principle. The federating nature of the United States is so well known abroad that occasionally a group will circulate petitions for the inclusion of an area within the United States. (This happened in parts of Japan in late 1945.)

Federation as a political rather than an economic device is most common in areas sharing in the tradition of English law. Australia is a very successful federation of six states. The Union of South Africa is a federation of four basic units, and Canada is a federation of 10 provinces. Even in India, the reorganization of political units in 1956 produced a federation of 15 states (Fig. 25.4) based on language dominance.

Nigeria's independence has been predicated upon successful federation of the Ibo, Yoruba, and Hausa areas. British planning in Africa produced in 1953 a "federation" of the two Rhodesias and Nyasaland. The union has consistently shown signs of weakness which threaten to split it before successful economic development can weld it together. Racial laws and the treatment of Africans and the descendants of immigrant Indians differ in Northern and Southern Rhodesia. Nyasaland—strongly tribal, over-populated, and without major industries—opposes union with the Rhodesias. In early 1959 and intermittently thereafter, Nyasaland has actively rebelled against the federation.

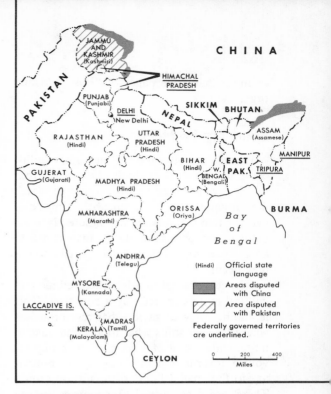

Fig. 25.4. States of the Indian Union, based on language.

Another area with strong British influence decided to federate in 1956. The British Caribbean Federation was the result of the union of Jamaica, Trinidad, and numerous islands in the Lesser Antilles. Provision was made for British Honduras and British Guiana to join the federation at a later date. The federation was dissolved in 1962.

The 1957 union of Syria and Egypt in the United Arab Republic, later joined by Iraq (1963), may have owed as much to absorption of western European ideas as to Arab nationalism. The instrument of the federation of Ghana and Guinea in 1958 acknowledged a precedent in these words: "Inspired by the example of the thirteen American colonies. . . ."

As often proposed, East African federation would unite Kenya, Uganda, and Tanganyika. Much local opposition springing from many sources has prevented completion of the plan. However, there is an informal economic unity to the area, as instanced by the listing in the Nairobi telephone book

361

of more than four pages of "East African" organizations.

Boundary Problems

Boundaries of countries and other political units serve to delimit the areas from which revenue may be drawn and to which the national laws are applicable. Thus, it is evident that boundaries are inherently legal entities and only secondarily may come to have local significance in the areas where they occur.

Disputes are apt to arise where ethnic and cultural groups are split by a boundary. This is another way of saying that tension arises where the law splits what mores and custom unite. Unfair as it may seem to the group involved, it is rarely possible to adjust a boundary to the spatial limits of a cultural group. There are just over 100 countries in the United Nations, while there are well over 1000 distinct linguistic and cultural groups

on earth. The challenge to become a truly multinational group faces the people of most countries today, and the way in which they meet this challenge is a measure of their maturity.

Zones of the International Frontier. Areas of shifting political boundaries, or areas of tension where boundary shifts may well occur in the future, may be called in a political sense the international frontier (Fig. 25.5). The conformation of the frontier is relatively simple. Within the U.S.S.R. and within the Western Hemisphere, relative inactivity is found. But on the borders of the U.S.S.R., in central Europe, in the Mediterranean, in central Africa, and along the eastern shores of Asia and its adjacent islands, there are tensions requiring international attention. In these areas are found most of the world's treaties (both of defense and of demilitarization), its mandates and trust territories, areas ruled jointly (condominiums), and other special tension-easing devices. H. Duncan

Fig. 25.5. The international frontier. Some of the pre-World War I zones have been in existence for centuries, e.g. the line down the Adriatic marks the split in both the Roman Empire and the Catholic Church, and today, between western Europe and the area of Communist-Slav dominion. Other of the zones, such as the Anglo-French condominium in the New Hebrides, are now inactive. (Adapted from the *Geographical Review*, American Geographical Society, New York.)

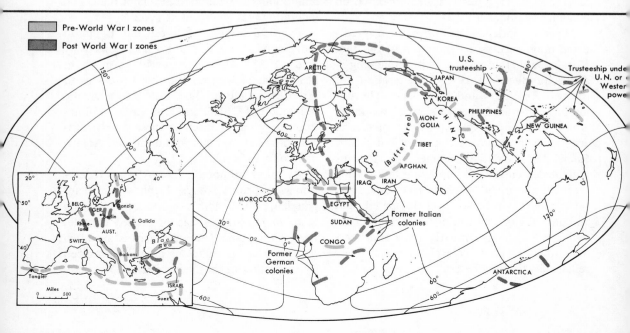

Hall, the international-law expert who first studied the international frontier as a unit, terms the frontier zone a "political rift-valley system" in which tension and constant small adjustments are to be expected.

Shatter Belts and Minority Areas. A close look at the linguistic, religious, and national-origin map of eastern Europe (Fig. 25.6) reveals that it is a jumble of peoples with quite varying backgrounds. Geographers call such an area a *shatter belt*. The origin of this shatter belt is, of course, historical, the result of intense competition among different groups for possession of the fertile agricultural land of the North European Plain and the Danube Valley. This area has lain athwart the eastward press of Teutonic peoples, the northwestward press of Slavs, and the westward press of nomadic peoples from the steppes.

A second shatter belt, one of lesser significance in world politics, lies at the other end of Eurasia. The ethnic and linguistic minority areas of southern China, the Tibetan borderland, and the mainland southeast Asian area have resulted from the centuries-long expansion of the Han Chinese and various Indian peoples. Before the 6th century B.C., the Yangtze river valley was sparsely inhabited by peoples speaking Tai languages. Gradually, they were displaced southwards, and the most southerly of these now form the ruling class in the country called Thailand. Minority areas in China under the communist government, as under the Manchu rulers and the later Nationalists, have a somewhat separate, even legally autonomous, existence.

Minority areas embedded in larger areas controlled by some sort of majority are called *enclaves*. We may note these on many maps. Indian reservations in the United States (Fig. 25.7) constitute a type of enclave which was formed when a primitive people was overwhelmed and pushed aside in the expansion of settlement of the New World. A similar situation is represented in maps of the ethnic areas of mainland China (Fig. 25.8) and the U.S.S.R. (Fig. 25.9).

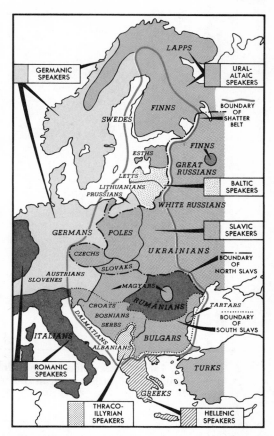

Fig. 25.6. The *shatter belt* of eastern Europe. (Richard Russell and Fred Kniffen, *Culture Worlds*, The Macmillan Co.)

The Russian distribution assumed its present form when the Slavs from central Europe pushed eastward along the line joining the southern edge of the forest and the northern border of the steppe. The Finnic peoples of the forest were pushed northeastward, and most of the Turkic inhabitants of the steppe were pushed southeastward. Bogdan Zaborski, a Canadian political geographer who described the above process, also related how a similar process took place earlier in history when the Teutons advanced southward and then southeastward from the Denmark area: they moved along the line of contact between the Celts in the west and the Slavs in the east. From such instances we might draw the inference that the expansion of

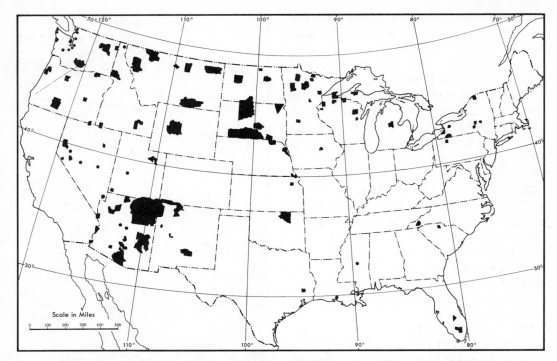

Fig. 25.7. Indian reservations in the United States. (After Sol Tax's map of the distribution of the North American Indians.)

a group on land is easiest along the contact line between two different ethnic or linguistic groups, and hardest when the expansion of a group is aimed at the spatial division of one homogeneous group. This "rule" is not without example in the modern period. Contrast the ease of Japan's entry into Manchuria, where she was essentially driving a wedge between Chinese and Manchus, with the opposition she encountered when trying to enter a wedge into ethnically unified China to the south.

Another sort of minority area has resulted from the expansion of European culture during and after the Age of Discovery: political enclaves in the east and south of Asia. British-leased Hong Kong and Portuguese Macao on the coast of south China are all that remain in eastern Asia. In southeastern Asia the island of Singapore—now in transition to federation with Malaya—was the last remaining example of a Western urban en-

clave, though the Portuguese control two parts of the island of Timor in Indonesia. But in southern Asia examples are more numerous. France once held Pondichéry and Karikul and in 1948 lost the enclave of Chandernagore to India by plebiscite. Pondichéry is perhaps an atypical example of an enclave, for it was divided into eight main divisions and represented a considerable problem for the government of India in the prevention of smuggling, especially the smuggling of diamonds. On the western coast of India, Portugal until 1962 held Goa, Diu, and Damao. These areas had been incorporated into Portugal in 1951 as overseas territories, thus losing their former status as colonies. The Pakistan government in August of 1958 assumed control of Gwadar, an enclave controlled by the sultan of Oman on the Arabian peninsula. All these enclaves were remnants of the trading period that followed the Age of Discovery, and it is

likely that the rest of them will eventually
disappear as nationalist feeling grows in Asia.

Noncoastal enclaves of European culture
are more rare, but they are found in East
Africa in areas that are high enough to be
considered as healthy for European labor.
The Rhodesias, Tanganyika, and Kenya have
seen some white settlement, often on very
fertile land not used previously for agriculture. In other African areas such as Uganda,
Nigeria, Ghana, and Sierra Leone, white settlement has been discouraged both officially
and by the local climate or diseases. The
Mau Mau revolt in Kenya had as part of its
origin resentment against the location of European farms.

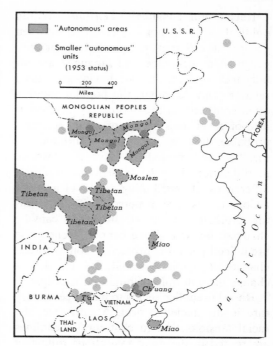

**Figs. 25.8 and 25.9. Ethnic enclaves in China.
(Herold J. Wiens, *China's March Toward the
Tropics*, Shoe String Press, 1954.) Distribution
of ethnic groups in the U.S.S.R., 1939. (*Oxford
Regional Economic Atlas of the U.S.S.R. and
Europe*, 1956).**

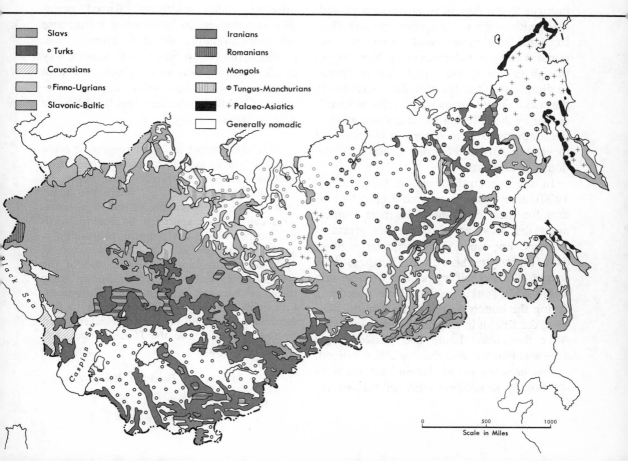

Racial and Linguistic Tensions. Within political units tensions often arise between groups of different race, religion, or language. Although race and language are totally independent, the one having no causal relation with the other, the popular mind is often confused on this score. The actual nature of racial tension is not clear. It seems probable, however, that many attitudes of the "racially" prejudiced have their source in differences in level of living or cultural differences. By attributing dislike of a man's actions to his race, a person shifts his basis for prejudice. Cultural attributes can be changed, but one's race cannot. Hence, the prejudiced person is protected from a forced change in opinion should the hated one change the cultural attribute that is despised.

Racial prejudice seems to have been rather rare in the ancient world. At any rate, the racial tensions that reach today's headlines are rooted in the great migrations following the Age of Discovery. Negroes forcibly brought to the Americas as slaves were saddled with stigma even after gaining their freedom. This status-based social prejudice remains in varying degrees in the New World, though in certain areas prejudice is tending to disappear. That the prejudice is rooted in the social environment rather than in race is shown by the differing treatment accorded in the southern states to American Negroes and to visiting African Negroes of equal educational attainments.

In the mercantilist period (circa 1750-1900) many nations wanted tropical products for their economies. In most tropical areas the local people were not tractable workers, nor were they particularly abundant. Hence, workers from elsewhere were sought. The French introduced Chinese into Tahiti and Tonkinese into New Caledonia during the cotton boom of the 1860's; likewise, the British introduced Indians into Fiji. After the cotton boom had passed, sugar cane was planted, and the workers remained. The growing world demand for sugar in the rapidly developing cities of Europe re-quired imported labor for the cane fields. The boom in India's population after 1850 made labor available for export. At a later date rubber plantations also required imported labor. Hence, there was for several decades a steady migration of Indian labor to areas that were tropical, British-controlled, and accessible by cheap sea transportation. The British West Indies, Fiji, Malaya, Burma, and the eastern coast of Africa from Zanzibar to the Cape thus became areas of Indian contract labor. In all these areas the original contracts have long since expired, and many Indians have saved their money and entered local commerce. Though an Indian's position as middleman may be profitable, it is not enviable since he is subject to "racial" prejudice from both the local people and Europeans.

In much of southern and eastern Africa the Northern European, most often an English citizen, desires to settle and farm. The high plateaus are healthful and bracing, and middle-latitude crops thrive. "Racial" prejudice also thrives. In neighboring Portuguese territories prejudice based on color is less, provided the Negro adopts a European way of life. Philip Mason, in *An Essay on Racial Tension,* sets up these rules for the occurrence of stabilizing devices, that is, of laws to prevent racial mixing:

We should expect to find tension most acute and the stabilizing device most rigid in a temperate climate, where Europeans settle and work for daily wages, . . . where the dominant people are Northern rather than Mediterranean in their approach; as among North Europeans, where the political philosophy is not liberal and democratic. There is a typical cycle of relationships now completed in the case of Europeans and Asians, in an early stage as between Africans and Europeans. From this analysis, we should expect to find the device most rigid in South Africa, followed by the Rhodesias and the United States, followed by Kenya.[1]

[1] Philip Mason, *An Essay on Racial Tension,* p. 141.

Chinese are a focus of tensions in many of the countries of southeastern Asia. For centuries, merchants from China have been settling in ports of the mainland and adjacent islands. In Malaya coolies were brought in as contract labor for the tin mines. In the newly independent Republic of Malaya they form about 45 per cent of the population. In neighboring Indonesia the Chinese are predominantly small merchants. Indonesia and the communist government of China agreed in 1954 that Chinese residents in Indonesia could no longer hold dual cititizenship. On the mainland of China non-Chinese minorities often resist being Sinified by the true, or Han, Chinese. It seems that the 1958 revolts in northwestern China and the 1959 revolt in Tibet were probably more anti-Han than anticommunist.

Linguistic tensions are more widespread and generally less potentially explosive than those connected with race. No modern nation, with the possible exception of Iceland, is without linguistic minorities. Cultural differences are both marked and maintained by minority languages.

After 1918 the principle of self-determination of nations in Europe proved to be linguistically based in great part. Justice was not fully done to all linguistic groups, and economic units were often split to favor a linguistic unity. Modern political opinion holds that the creation of separate nations on a linguistic basis has not been efficient. It remains to be seen whether the reorganization of Indian states into 15 linguistic units will prove a unifying or a divisive influence.

Where interest groups are relatively equal or are sectionally distinct, a nation may have two major languages. Pakistan uses Urdu in the west and Bengali in the east as official languages. Canada uses English and French for the same purpose. Within the United States only one state, New Mexico, is officially bilingual. In Spain the use of Castilian as the only official language continues despite the fact that probably more people

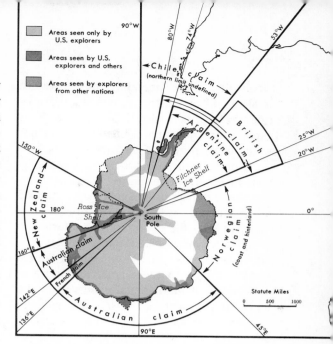

Fig. 25.10. National claims to Antarctica. (Adapted from map in *Operation Deepfreeze,* © 1957 by George J. Dufek, by permission of Harcourt, Brace, and World, Inc.)

speak Catalan, the language used in the Barcelona area.

Sector Problems in Polar Areas. A generally accepted rule of international behavior states that nations may lay claim to unoccupied lands or unused areas *only* by effective occupation of the areas. Effective occupation usually refers to a permanent or semipermanent settlement in the area claimed. This rule has interesting consequences in the polar areas, for it conflicts with claims based upon the nearness of particular areas to claiming countries.

In Antarctica, claims are made both by countries near the continent—Chile, Argentina, and New Zealand—and by those who base their claims upon exploration—Norway, Britain, and France. The United States has not made any formal claim to Antarctica and recognizes no other nation's claim to portions of that icy land. However, the United States reserves the right to claim at some later date those portions surveyed by its citizens, both privately and with government support. It can be seen from Figure 25.10 that British claims overlap some of the pie-wedge areas

367

claimed by Chile, Argentina, and Norway. It is also evident that prior to early 1956, or prior to the International Geophysical Year explorations, potential United States claims would overlap most of the other claims.

At present, the Antarctic is not usable by man in the economic sense of mineral exploitation, though its minerals may be tapped in the future. Antarctica's usefulness now lies mainly in the opportunity it affords for studying the effect of the southern polar area on the world's weather. Ironically, if the ice that covers the southern polar area were to melt, some of the national claims might be rendered impotent. Scientists have recently found that about two thirds of the area is below sea level. Though adjustment for reduced pressure might allow some portions to rise, the gain would probably not be significant.

A possible future use of Antarctica might be as a site for the launching of space missiles. The International Geophysical Year scientists have found that the two bands of deadly radiation that surround the earth have "holes" in them above the two magnetic poles. Hence, Antarctica and northern Canada may prove to be the only feasible launching sites for spaceships carrying men. The strategic value of the as yet unoccupied southern area is thus emphasized.

In the Arctic Ocean national claims extend in time as far back as 1926. In April of that year the U.S.S.R. declared:

> At the time of the present decision, all the land and islands already discovered, or that will be discovered in the future, which are not recognized by the Soviet government as belonging to any other nation, are declared to be the territory of the U.S.S.R. This decision applies only to lands and islands located in the Arctic Ocean north of the Soviet coast as far as the Pole.

> Clarification of this decision included the statement that ice islands were also included as "territory." At the time, it seemed visionary so to claim floating ice, but the use of

such islands by the United States military and by International Geophysical Year scientists has shown their utility.

The main portions of the Arctic Ocean are claimed, naturally enough, by the two countries that border most of that water body, Canada and the U.S.S.R. The United States recognizes neither claim and maintains that the ocean constitutes "high seas." It emphasized this position in the autumn of 1958, when its atomic-powered submarine *Nautilus* sailed under the polar ice pack from Bering Strait to a point north of Iceland.

The Soviets have tried to bolster their claim to the sea sector north of the U.S.S.R. by opening the Arctic Ocean to navigation. Their claim to possession is supported by their utilization of most of the eastern-longitude half of the Arctic Ocean as internal waters of the U.S.S.R. Since 1932, when the northern passage was first traversed in a single season, navigation has increased year by year. With the aid of airplanes, icebreakers, and radio weather stations, ships may now in good seasons sail both directions in a single summer. The most difficult portion is the 600-mile stretch west of Bering Strait, which lacks warm water brought from the south. From the mouth of the Lena River westward, the sea in summer is relatively free of ice for the few weeks devoted to navigation.

Water-Use Problems

The seas are indivisible, and the water of the earth cannot have posted and labeled boundaries. Yet the states of political man come to the sea, and he has increasingly been unwilling to let his sovereignty stop at the water's edge. The stage is thus set for conflict and negotiation concerning the seaward and riverine limits of political areas.

Rivers quite as often as mountain ranges serve as boundaries between countries. If the river is small, disputes may arise over taking water for irrigation and urban use. Should the river be large, tension may arise over navigation and hydroelectric development. Again arises the challenge to seek a peaceful and fair settlement.

Maritime Boundary Limits. For most of human history, people did not bother to define in any rigorous way the seaward limits of their territory. But with the growth of seapower and the increasing possibility that an enemy might approach by sea, offshore limits were devised.

Most countries have used a 3-mile limit since the middle of the 18th century (1744), when an eminent Dutch jurist stated the well-known cannon-shot rule that "land power ends at the limit of arms." Most shore batteries of that day could fire cannon balls for a distance of only three nautical miles, and it was rarely possible to distinguish a small ship from a sea-level shore battery much more than three miles away. Hence, the technologically small limit of arms range and the curvature of the earth combined to make the 3-mile limit seem "natural."

Today the 3-mile limit has not the rational basis it once had. Radar and aerial photography has made it possible for ships and planes to "see" far into a country's borders, while observing the traditional 3-mile limit. The U.S.S.R. has abandoned the 3-mile limit at sea for a 12-mile limit, and has at various times called for 25-mile or even 40-mile limits for aircraft. An international conference meeting in 1958, and another in 1960, could come to no agreement on territorial limits.

Most of the Scandinavian countries have a traditional 4-mile limit. Many of the Mediterranean countries have a 6-mile limit, while Communist China claims 12 miles. In 1958 Iceland extended her claims to fishing rights from the traditional 4-mile limit to 12 miles (Fig. 25.11) and attempted to prohibit the British from fishing within the new seaward limits. Territorial seaward limits of various countries of the world are as follows:

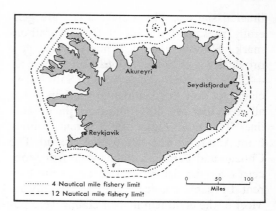

.... 4 Nautical mile fishery limit
------- 12 Nautical mile fishery limit

Fig. 25.11. Iceland's twelve-mile limit. (After *Focus,* **American Geographical Society.)**

3-Mile Limit	British Commonwealth, Denmark, the Netherlands, Belgium, France, Portugal, Poland; Turkey, Bahrein, Muscat, Pakistan, India, Ceylon, Burma, Malaya, Indonesia, Philippines, Thailand, Cambodia, Vietnam (south), Korea, Japan; all of Africa except the Rio de Oro and the former Italian colonies; Canada, United States; all Central and South American countries except Mexico, Colombia, Guatemala, Honduras, Uruguay, and Haiti.
4-Mile Limit	Norway, Sweden, Finland.
5-Mile Limit	Uruguay.
6-Mile Limit	Spain, Italy, Yugoslavia, Greece; Syria, Saudi Arabia, Lebanon, Iran; Rio de Oro; Haiti.
9-Mile Limit	Mexico.
12-Mile Limit	U.S.S.R.; Colombia, Guatemala; China, Iceland.
No data	Albania, Yemen, Iraq, Oman.

The expansion of fishing in an effort to feed the world's growing population and the finding of oil in the relatively shallow sea bed of many areas have led several nations to lay claim to the exploitation rights to continental shelves. These shelf areas are generally presumed to end at the 100-fathom mark. However, as yet international law provides no clear definition. Four countries —Chile, Peru, Honduras, and El Salvador— claim not only the continental-shelf areas but all areas in a belt 200 miles from their coastline. The cold Humboldt Current coming from Antarctica is a rich fishing ground. The Chilean and Peruvian claims stem from concern over the fishing carried on in the current by such nautical nations as Norway. Most of the continental-shelf claims were put forward after President Truman had proclaimed United States sovereignty over the Gulf of Mexico shelf areas bordering the southern states. Claimant countries, as of 1951, for continental-shelf areas seaward of their traditional boundaries were the following:

United States, Mexico, Argentina, Panama, Chile, Peru, Iceland, Bahamas and Jamaica, Saudi Arabia, Bahrein and other Persian Gulf small states, Philippines, Guatemala, Honduras, Pakistan, El Salvador, British Honduras, Nicaragua, Brazil, Falkland Islands.

River-Water Problems. Many of the world's political tensions arise from problems related to the use and disposition of river waters. In humid areas of the world, navigation rights and claims assume importance, while in dry areas irrigation claims and arrangements are a major political issue.

In Asia, Africa, and South America navigable portions of rivers are seldom international boundaries. Hence, the tension arising from navigation problems is minimal. The navigable portions of the Ganges lie within India; those of the Irrawaddy, within Burma; the Menam Chao Phraya, within Thailand; the Si and the Yangtze, within China. The Sungari lies within Manchuria, and the possible tensions that might arise along the Amur water boundary between the U.S.S.R. and China are lessened by the fact that the area is sparsely populated, river traffic is not used to the maximum possible, and the com-

munist governments would rarely permit tension to occur.

In Europe, however, where parts of navigable rivers are often used as international boundaries, where a river may flow from one country, between two others, and later into the territory of a fourth, disputes arise frequently. In particular, the Rhine and the Danube have given rise to much international litigation.

In the desert and semidesert areas of the world, where rivers rising in humid, usually mountainous areas flow across low, potentially arable dry areas, conflict over water use is at a maximum. The United States and Mexico through the years have settled their water problems in a unique way. Mexican tributaries which have many dams for irrigation water bring about four fifths of the Rio Grande water to the boundary area. There are no United States tributaries below the Pecos, but United States lands use far more irrigation water than the fifth that flows from the north. In return for this use by the United States, Mexico is allotted some water from the Colorado River, which has no tributaries within Mexico.

The Nile River in the northeastern portion of Africa has two main branches, the White and the Blue. Summer rains cause the Blue Nile, which rises in Lake Tana in Ethiopia, to flood from September to November. These floods are the ones upon which Egypt for centuries has depended for basin irrigation. The White Nile rises in Lake Victoria, whose coastline is shared by Uganda, Kenya, and Tanganyika. Because of the great storage capacity of the lake—a difference of only three feet in the level of Lake Victoria represents the annual total acre-feet of water flowing into Egypt—the flow of the White Nile is quite regular the year round. The newly introduced perennial irrigation system now used in Egypt depends in large measure on the water from the White Nile. In passing through the Sudd swamps, about half of the White Nile's water is evaporated and lost to irrigation uses downstream. The proposed Jonglei cutoff would allow the Sudd to be bypassed and the extra water to be used by both Egypt and the Sudan.

The Nile Waters Agreement of 1929 states that, within defined periods, the Sudan will not manipulate Nile water to change the timing or the amount of water arriving in Egypt. To date, the Sudan has lived up to the agreement by taking, in late summer and autumn, only the excess water that otherwise would run unused into the Mediterranean. The water is stored in the Sennar Dam on the Blue Nile, 160 miles south of Khartoum. It is used during the winter to irrigate cotton in the Gezira, or "island," between the Blue and White Niles. The Gezira farmers are the most prosperous indigenous farmers in Africa and form the core of the Sudan nation. It is obvious that increasing need for the waters of the Nile system will eventually cause tension between users in the Sudan area and those in the floodplain and delta downstream. Conflict may be averted, however, by implementation of the plans for "century storage" in Lake Victoria. The Owen Falls Dam, completed in 1954, is the first step toward maximal utilization of the waters of the White Nile.

Varying degrees of dependence upon river water are illustrated by a comparison of the Columbia Basin, in northwestern United States, and Egypt. The political units through which the Columbia River flows—British Columbia, Washington, Oregon—have a population of about five million. Egypt has a population of more than 26 million and depends almost exclusively on Nile water, whose flow, as it enters Egypt, is barely one third of the amount that the Columbia annually pours into the Pacific Ocean.

In the Jordan-Israel area, irrigation water is in extremely short supply, and the waters of the Jordan River and its tributary, the Yarmuk, are the focus of political conflict. In southern Asia the Kashmir dispute between India and Pakistan chiefly involves water-use claims. (Some religious factors are also involved.) The rivers which water West

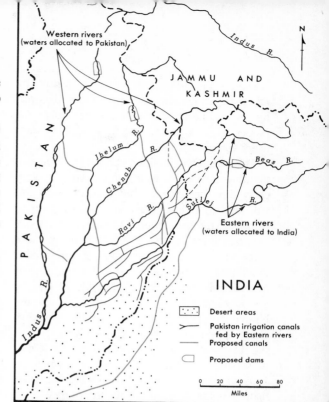

Fig. 25.12. The Indus waters settlement plan. In addition to the division of the river waters, the plan provides for financial aid to Pakistan from India and the World Bank in order to build the new canals and dams necessary to irrigate the areas formerly watered by the eastern rivers. (Courtesy of *Pakistan Affairs*, Embassy of Pakistan, Washington, D.C.)

Pakistan rise either in Tibet or in Kashmir. However, the Sutlej and the Ravi rivers flow through northwestern India, and the former is being diverted by dams to provide irrigation water for the Indian Punjab area. The Indus waters dispute was amicably settled in September, 1960, and a settlement plan (Fig. 25.12) was agreed upon for integrated use of the waters.

Two concepts of river-water use are involved in most disputes. The humid-region concept stresses unrestricted flow so that navigation may continue unhindered. The arid-region concept stresses the rights of the first users of the water, in point of time, regardless of their position along the stream. Occasionally, both concepts are completely interwoven in international disputes. For instance, Columbia River water is desired by its upstream Canadian users for hydropower, by its middle-reach United States users for power and irrigation, and by its downstream users for navigation.

Disputes Over Fishing Areas. Problems of defining territorial waters have from a very early time been connected with fishing (and still tend to be), but disputes with regard to fishing rights extend beyond territorial waters. Since about 1950 Japan and the Republic of Korea have had disputes over the limits of Japanese fishing in the Sea of Japan and the Straits of Tsushima. During the Korean War, a line was drawn by the United Nations Command to prevent smuggling. When the emergency that gave rise to the line had passed, the government of Korea maintained the line as one beyond which no Japanese fishing was to be allowed. Japanese fishing boats cross the line often since their government does not recognize its validity. Almost as often, the boats are seized and the crews temporarily interned.

Japan is the world's leading fishing nation, and it is not surprising that a great proportion of the international disputes over fishing concern her. Before World War II Japan operated extensive floating factories to preserve salmon and king crab caught in waters of the North Pacific. Fur seals were also taken in large numbers by Japanese hunters. Disputes with the U.S.S.R. since 1945 have been frequently resolved in Japan's disfavor, and Soviet ships often capture Japanese fishing smacks within sight of the shores of Hokkaido. Currently, negotiations are being carried on between Japan and the United States and Canada with regard to the conservation of Alaskan salmon. The United States is attaching metal clips to the fins of salmon in Alaskan coastal waters. Japan, in return, claims that it is odd that fish 500 miles out in the open sea should carry these emblems of "United States citizenship."

Norwegian and English disputes with Chile and Peru over fishing in the Humboldt Current; American-British disputes over the ex-ploitation of the North Atlantic fisheries; Icelandic-British disputes over fishing within 12 miles of the shores of Iceland—these and many more such disputes emphasize the inescapable fact that fishing is becoming progressively more efficient and that the implements used in catching fish are more and more destructive to this natural resource. Once again we come up against a problem intensified by the increase in the world's population.

Radioactive Fallout. Problems of nuclear testing constitute another area of world concern. The advent of atomic-bomb and hydrogen-bomb testing has raised questions of the "right" of a nation to use areas under its control for testing purposes. Both the U.S.S.R. and the United States have conducted large-scale tests of nuclear weapons. The United States has used the deserts of southern Nevada and islands in the Trust Territory of Micronesia. The U.S.S.R. has used desert areas in central Asia and may have developed testing areas in the Siberian Arctic. All nuclear tests produce radioactive particles which settle eventually to earth. This fallout affects primarily the test area, but upper-air currents may carry radioactive dust to other political areas. Diplomatic complaints follow. Japan is particularly aware of fallout since Russian tests produce dust that is carried to Japan by the prevailing westerlies and United States tests in Micronesia produce dust that comes north with the monsoon winds. International negotiations to control nuclear weapons have been held intermittently since the mid-1950's.

Strategy: Nations in Interaction

A country exists in space, but its inhabitants exist in an environment created in part by natural forces and in part by the process of history. If nature has been miserly, or history adverse, the people will seek outside their boundaries some adjustment of their lot. Thus are created the motivations behind political alliances and blocs of countries united for some specific common purpose.

Strategic Concepts Involving Eurasia. One of the themes of Eurasian history has been the conflict between the peoples of the steppe and the peoples of the humid lands. Nomads of the Eurasian grasslands stretching between Hungary and the northern Gobi have repeatedly attacked farming areas on the more humid margins of the steppe. No topographical barriers of importance restricted the movements of the nomads, who were free to strike without warning in any direction.

It was Mackinder, an English geographer, who in 1904 formulated a statement of strategy centering on the domain of the steppe dwellers. This center he termed the *Heartland* of the *World-Island* of Eurasia-Africa. His statement ran:

Who rules eastern Europe controls the Heartland;
Who rules the Heartland controls the World-Island;
Who rules the World-Island controls the World.

Mackinder's later statements (1914 and 1943) involved an *inner crescent* of countries on the world island and an *outer crescent* composed of the Western Hemisphere countries and Australia. He revised his heartland-dominance theory to permit the containment of a heartland power by adequate sea-power control of the inner crescent. This corresponded admirably with Britain's position through colonies, mandates, and alliances.

It is not surprising that a British citizen should evolve such a theory. Britain had long been commercially dominant on the seas, and sea routes had to follow the perimeter of Africa and Eurasia. To the north, the Arctic Ocean remained unnavigable until 1932 because of lack of knowledge and the relatively low level of marine technology. In the days of steam power on ships, commercial nations sought political control of coaling stations along commercial routes. The seaward extensions of Eurasia were the most logical points to place fuel stations, for all

sea traffic centered on, or had to pass near to, these promontories, or *south points*. Many of these south points—Gibraltar, Cyprus, Cape of Good Hope, Suez, Aden, Colombo (in Ceylon), Singapore, Hong Kong—became British, and some remain in Britain's control today.

N. J. Spykman, a younger American contemporary of Mackinder, reformulated Mackinder's later thought around statements involving the inner crescent, which he called the *rimland* (Fig. 25.13). Spykman's formulation reads:

Who controls the rimland rules Eurasia;
Who rules Eurasia controls the destinies of the world.

It is interesting to examine recent history in the light of these formulations. Hitler's pact with the U.S.S.R. in 1939 "neutralized" eastern Europe, and his invasion of the U.S.S.R. two years later was made with a view to gaining control of the heartland. The geopolitician Haushofer, who admired Mackinder's strategic formula, is said to have had a strong influence upon Hitler.

Some American historians and geographers have accepted a theory of history which states that for centuries Russia's expansion has been for the dominant purpose of securing ice-free ports. Both czarist and communist governments have indeed tried to gain concessions in warm-water ports, but to read Russian history solely in terms of an "urge to the sea" is to accept too simple an explanation for a complex past.

Elements of the rimland-control strategy can be seen in the Truman containment policy announced vis-à-vis Greece and Turkey in 1948 and later extended to other rimland nations. American airbases have been built along parts of the rimland, to the embarrassment of the communists. Rimland alliances of the United States include the North Atlantic Treaty Organization, the fluctuating Baghdad Pact, and mutual-security treaties with Japan, Formosa, and

Korea. The Organization of American States and the Southeast Asian Treaty Organization are backstop alliances with countries in the outer crescent.

In the period since 1945, the U.S.S.R. has expanded its influence outward and now has a number of countries as satellites. The people's republics of Korea (north), China, Vietnam (north), and Mongolia in Asia have not been major sources of revolt against the communist system. With the European satellites of the U.S.S.R. a different situation exists. Yugoslavia defected, though it still calls itself a communist state. Hungary revolted unsuccessfully in 1956. Riots in East Germany and Poland temporarily brought a lessening of control, particularly in Poland. Reasons for greater tension in the European satellites may include their longer tradition of representative government, their historically close trade ties with the West, and the existence of organized religions with a tradition of protest.

Spheres of Influence. For strategic reasons, countries from time to time claim various *spheres of influence*. When a country claims a sphere of influence, it is understood that other large nations should not interfere with political affairs in the area so claimed. From the standpoint of United States citizens, the most famous of these claims is the Monroe Doctrine. In 1823 President Monroe declared that the United States would look with disfavor upon attempts of European powers to interfere with political freedoms in the Western Hemisphere. From its inception to near the turn of the century, the doctrine was effective in large part due to the noninterference of, and even positive protection by, the British navy. After 1900 the United States developed naval power sufficient to implement the policy by itself.

Britain long maintained that southern Asia was her sphere of influence. When imperial Russia made a counterclaim of influence in Persia, a compromise was negotiated. Rus-

Fig. 25.13. Heartland and Rimland. (Adapted from maps by J. McA. Smiley in *The Geography of the Peace* by Nicholas John Spykman, copyright 1944, by Harcourt, Brace, and World, Inc. and reproduced with the publisher's permission.)

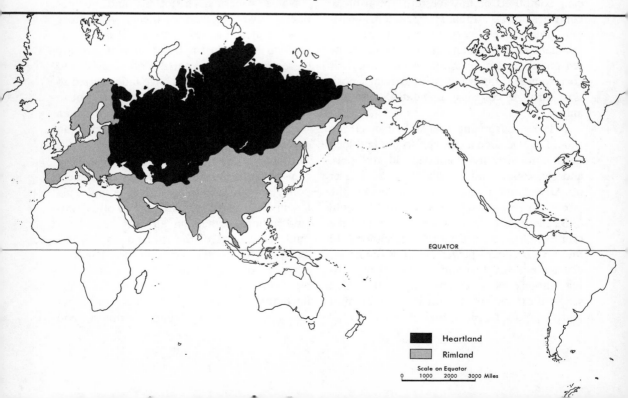

EQUATOR

Heartland

Rimland

Scale on Equator
0   1000   2000   3000 Miles

sia's interests were to be paramount in the north of the country, while British interests were to dominate in the southern portion. This division of the country lasted into the World War II period, when motor vehicles and arms were supplied to the U.S.S.R. through Persia (Iran).

As the Turkish empire gradually dissolved, Britain came to claim the Arabic Near East as her sphere of influence. Political control of Egypt and the Sudan, a mandate over Iraq and Palestine, as well as advisory staffs in Jordan and Saudi Arabia— these were Britain's share of the empire of the Turks.

The decline of British influence in the southwest Asian area has led to American concern with this portion of the rim of Eurasia. An echo of the Monroe Doctrine, the Eisenhower Doctrine was devised in 1956 to encourage maintenance of the independence of the small nations of the Levant. The sending of marines into Lebanon in 1958 was the first test of the new doctrine's effectiveness.

In the late 1930's Japan proclaimed an area of dominance in the borderlands of Asia. Her rimland sphere of influence was named the Greater East Asian Co-Prosperity Sphere. It was to include the Japanese Empire (Japan, Korea, South Sakhalin, the Kuriles, the Ryukyus, Formosa, and the mandate of Micronesia) together with many adjacent areas. To become economically associated in this plan were Thailand, parts of French Indochina, and much of China itself. In claiming parts of China, Japan was expanding her earlier claim of 1921 to a portion of the "Chinese melon." After the Boxer Rebellion of 1898, several nations had claimed economic spheres of influence in China (Fig. 25.14). Since most of these

Fig. 25.14. The "Chinese Melon." (From: *A History of the Far East in Modern Times*, 6th edition, by Harold M. Vinacke. Copyright, © 1950, 1959, by Appleton-Century-Crofts, Inc. Adapted by permission of Appleton-Century-Crofts.)

claims stretched from the coastal, Western-dominated cities, the resultant pattern of claims resembled slices of a melon. Most of China's early railroads were built by foreign interests. The French-built railroad from Kunming ran southeast to the seacoast at Haiphong in French Indochina and dominated the French area of influence without connecting to any other railway within China.

After World War II the U.S.S.R. considered the area from Finland to Greece— the shatter belt of eastern Europe—to lie within her sphere of influence. Finland has maintained a precarious independence with an industrial plant strongly oriented to trade with Russia. Greece fought a civil war to rid herself of communist influence. One by one the countries between Finland and Greece became satellites of the U.S.S.R. Most of these satellites are members of the Warsaw Pact, a communist version of and response to the North Atlantic Treaty Organization of the Western powers.

Treaty Blocs. In an effort to strengthen western Europe against the threat of communist expansion, NATO was formed in 1949. Its European members (Fig. 25.15) are allied with the United States, which sup-

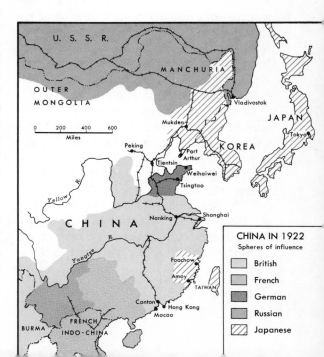

U. S. S. R.

MANCHURIA

OUTER MONGOLIA

Vladivostok

JAPAN

0   200   400   600
Miles

Mukden

Tokyo

Peking

KOREA

Port Arthur

Tientsin

Weihaiwei

Tsingtao

Yellow R.

Shanghai

C H I N A

Nanking

Yangtze R.

Foochow

Amoy

TAIWAN

Canton   Hong Kong
Macao

BURMA   FRENCH INDO-CHINA

CHINA IN 1922
Spheres of influence

☐ British
☐ French
■ German
■ Russian
▨ Japanese

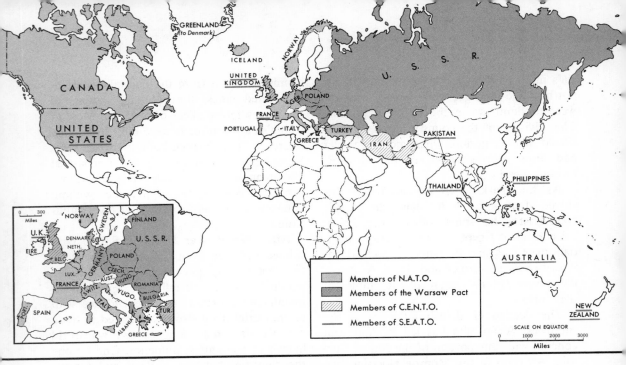

Fig. 25.15. Main treaty blocs of the world.

plies a good proportion of the arms used by NATO forces. As a counterbalance to NATO, the communist nations of eastern Europe, except for Yugoslavia, united in 1951 to form the Warsaw Pact. The suppression of the 1956 Hungarian rebellion was carried out under Warsaw Pact agreements.

In 1954 efforts by Britain and the United States to halt communist influence in southwestern Asia resulted in the formation of the Baghdad Pact. Though Iraq has withdrawn from the organization and the regime in Baghdad is now opposed to its aims, the name of the pact has remained. Its present Asian members are shown in Figure 25.15.

In an effort to strengthen the rimland nations of southeastern Asia, the United States sponsored the Southeast Asian Treaty Organization, or SEATO. Though formed to combat communism, the organization retains a strong anti-Japanese flavor. Australia and the Philippines have been unable to forget their wartime experiences and regard SEATO as a bulwark against Japanese expansion as much as against communist aggression.

Buffer Nations. Small countries lying between two larger countries, or between two spheres of influence, are called buffer nations. They may be independent because their neighbors do not want any direct contact with each other, or because the buffer nations have some resource that both large nations want but do not dare to seize.

Examples of buffer nations are many. A classic example is Afghanistan, which long served as a buffer between the British Empire in south Asia and the Russian Empire in central Asia. It now serves as a buffer between the U.S.S.R. and India-Pakistan. The Wakhan strip of eastern Afghanistan, which prevents Russian and Indian territory from having a common boundary, was deliberately created by the understanding of 1873 and the demarcation agreement of 1887 between Britain and Russia. In the present programs of aid to Afghanistan, American aid is developing the southern portion of that country, while Russian aid is being given the north.

Belgium and Luxembourg long served as buffer states between France and Germany.

376

Fig. 25.16. Roman walls in Great Britain.

In 1867 Luxembourg was demilitarized, but Belgium remained unaffected by the agreement. In both world wars the neutrality and buffer function of Belgium were ignored by

Fig. 25.17. North American radar warning systems. The last of the Texas Towers was dismantled early in 1963.

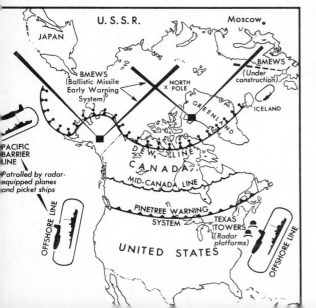

the Germans, and its value as a buffer for France failed.

Thailand served for about a century (circa 1850-1950) as a buffer area between the expanding interests of Britain in the western part and France in the eastern part of the Indochinese peninsula. Perhaps the best example of a buffer state is Switzerland, which for much of the 19th century separated Italian interests from German in the north-south axis, and French from Austrian in the east-west axis.

In the Western Hemisphere, Uruguay and Paraguay are buffer states between Portuguese-speaking Brazil and Spanish-speaking Argentina. The fact that an Indian language, Guarani, rather than Spanish is the popular tongue of Paraguay reinforces the buffer function of that country.

Neutrality Blocs. As the political world increasingly shows a division of the great powers into a communist group and a pro-West group, "uncommitted" nations frequently try to pursue a middle path. As yet, no strong neutral bloc has developed, and no one nation has assumed leadership of the neutral, or non-treaty-bound, nations. Egypt, India, and Yugoslavia seem to be contending for the "more-neutral-than-thou" title. Various conferences of African and Asian nations and colonies have been held (Bandung, 1954; Cairo, 1958) for the purpose of welding these areas into a neutral Afro-Asian bloc. Success has been limited, and the conferences have served in the main as verbal outlets for anticolonial passions.

The Shifting Nature of Strategy. Through the ages, strategic theories have been divided into defensive and offensive. By nature, most of the defensive strategies have involved immobility. Walls of various sorts are the most common expression of defense. Most of the early cities of Europe, the Near East, China, and India were encircled by one or more high walls with guarded gates. The Great Wall of China was consolidated in 256 B.C. from a series of earlier walls built to keep nomads from raiding the grain fields of Cathay. Roman walls were numerous, and still standing in England are the Wall of Hadrian and the Antonine Wall (Fig. 25.16). Lines of forts have commonly been built where physical walls might be too costly. Early examples of such lines are the Roman *limes* along the Rhine and the Tula Frontier Line built in 16th-century Russia for the defense of early Muscovy against nomad attacks. A more modern example is the ill-fated Maginot Line in the northeast of France, which was outflanked by German armies in 1940. Fort lines involve both defense and offense; generally, retaliatory forces are in reserve behind the lines or within the forts.

Radar fences and other early-warning systems for the detection of aircraft and missiles are used by both the United States and the U.S.S.R. In the northern sector of North America are the Distant Early Warning Line (the DEW Line), the Mid-Canada Line, and along the United States-Canada border the Pinetree Warning System (Fig. 25.17). Off both coasts of the United States are floating radar systems designed to give alarm in those sectors.

Strategies of offense in the modern world involve mobility, speed, and secrecy. Mobility for United States forces is achieved by the Strategic Air Command's "in-air" policy; a fully-armed minimal striking force is kept flying so that it may strike more quickly when alerted. Speed of attack is being achieved with the development of intercontinental ballistic missiles. Secrecy of attack has become possible with the development first of snorkel submarines and later of atom-powered submarines which can stay below surface for months on end.

Throughout history, men have devised adequate defenses against any offensive weapon. Whether *adequate* defenses can be devised against supersonic thermonuclear missiles and deep-lurking submarines remains to be seen. The fate of modern urban civilization, and perhaps of mankind itself, depends upon this hope.

CHAPTER 26

The Spread of Ideas

In discussing the spread of ideas, it is useful to distinguish between the circulation of ideas within an area and the diffusion of ideas between areas. When an idea is accepted by a number of people who are far enough from its originator to lack face-to-face contact, the idea is considered to have spread. Once it has spread, any one of three things may happen to it: it may be further developed, it may be soon rejected, or it may be adopted in increasingly attenuated form by successively distant groups of people.

Circulation of Ideas Within an Area

To the present day, people have tended to depend on the few inventors and thinkers in the various nations of the world for the bulk of their ideas. Most inventions revolve around a few basic ideas. The few basic ideas in weapons, crops, and government probably traveled rather slowly over the face of the earth, since men were relatively few in the early period and their different languages impeded communication. Also, they would not pass along any ideas which gave them a technological superiority in warfare.

Although warfare was a reason for hoarding ideas, it was also a means of spreading them. Of the many captives taken in various battles, some were of a higher technological stage than their captors. When Greeks, for example, were captured by Scythians or other peoples, they often drew from their higher civilization and became teachers of the people who captured them. When people of a lower cultural level were made prisoners, quite often they escaped and took back to their own people what they had learned or partially learned during captivity. Such a spread of ideas did not depend upon a common language. The captives generally would have absorbed or learned the language of their captors, and when they went back to their former communities they could, of course, communicate in their native or first-learned tongue. Thus, technology could be diffused without direct language similarity. This is probably what happened during much of human history.

Diffusion of Ideas by Trade

Before A.D. 1500 the wider the spread of any one idea, the older the idea. This relationship was grounded in the fact that there was then relatively little possibility of rapid and sustained exchange. Possibly some rapid exchange was effected by the horse-riding nomads of the steppes of Eurasia, but quick and intermittent contacts allowed for relatively little diffusion of ideas. Ideas and traits are best transmitted by settled peoples who are trading with each other; even though the rate of diffusion is slower, the number of ideas exchanged is probably larger.

One example of the spread of ideas involved the Mediterranean shore of Africa and the states across the Sahara, just inland from the Guinea coast. When Europeans first became acquainted with the tribes of

West Africa, they noted that many of their practices were rather familiar, having a somewhat European cast to them. The peoples of West Africa had a political organization very close to that of the peoples on the Mediterranean shore to the north. Many of the symbols that were used in West Africa, and even some of the costumes worn there, were typical of certain periods in Mediterranean history. Even today, people in northern Nigeria near Kano dress for festivals in costumes that were apparently copied from the dress worn by the Crusaders in the Middle Ages. Also apparently received from the north were the *cire perdue* (waste-wax) method of casting brass and bronze, narrow and broad looms for weaving cotton, and the use of arches and vaults in building. Some ideas were first introduced from the north when pagan Berbers invaded the area. Others came in when Arabs and Islamized Berbers came south across the Sahara and, through trade and occasional force, brought their religion and social concepts to the people living in the grassland and forest fringe south of the desert.

Further Development of an Idea

If a new idea is acceptable to a group, if it fills a need or solves a problem, and if it finds a place in the group's system of ideas, it will probably be developed further. We might consider the hypothetical development of the use of the digging stick in vegetative agriculture. The first group that used a digging stick probably accepted it because it was an improvement over having to scrape earth with bare hands, or because it served the purpose better than just any stick or limb picked up off the forest floor. As more people began to cover plant slips with earth and the problem arose of how to do it with less effort, the digging stick fulfilled the need and solved the problem.

How the digging stick fitted in with the group's system of ideas is not known, but it may have been developed through analogy with the bamboo spear. Sharpening a digging stick was like sharpening a bamboo spear. Moreover, it was a frequent practice to burn the point of a spear to increase its strength, and a spear maker may have thought of thus adding usefulness to a digging stick. Finally, the toe notch which was cut in a digging stick for added power is analogous to the notch in a spear into which a throwing stick was fitted.

Development of an idea by a group necessitates constant communication within the group. As the various reactions to a new idea act to change and improve it, the original idea becomes the nucleus of a cluster of attitudes which form what might be termed a *culture trait*. (The use of cars for individual transportation in the United States is a culture trait.) Constant familiarity with the idea and the use of it in social intercourse almost imperceptibly but definitely "fix" it within a societal environment. As time passes, variations of the basic idea arise and are similarly elaborated, and the eventual "bundle" of similar ideas becomes a *culture complex* (All ways in which cars in the United States are used constitute a culture complex.) An area in which a particular culture complex plays a vital role in society may be termed a *culture area*. The culture area may be small in size, like the culture area of the snow igloo, or it may be large, like the culture area of the idea of writing.

General Examples of Diffusion

For several reasons ideas were exchanged at a much greater rate after A.D. 1500. Western incursions were made into Asia, with the result that factories and trading stations were set up on the shores of India, China, and the peninsulas and islands of southeastern Asia. The exchange of ideas was not one-way, for many of the ideas of the Far East and of India were brought back to the West. India, for instance, had ideas to offer about the weaving of cotton; calico was produced in the port of Calicut on the Malabar Coast, and the technique of making muslins could be learned in the Bengal area.

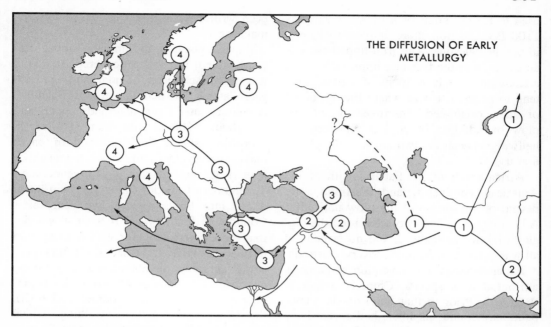

THE DIFFUSION OF EARLY
METALLURGY

Fig. 26.1. Spread of metal technology from central Asia to Europe in four stages. (Charles Singer, E. J. Holmyard, and A. R. Hall, A *History of Technology*, Volume I, Oxford University Press, 1954.)

From China came the Confucian system of thought, which played a great part in the period of the Enlightenment in France because Voltaire was an avid student of Confucian modes of thought and expression, as well as of Chinese philosophies in general.

Iron Smelting. The technique of smelting iron was discovered more than 5500 years ago, but the first soft iron was of little use for weapons or tools. The world's first use of harder iron was in Asia Minor about 3500 years ago. At first, most of the tools made of iron were imitations of familiar bronze tools. However, when it was found that tempering and hardening were possible when the carbon content of the molten iron was increased, many improvements were made. The true Iron Age began about 1200 B.C. Use of iron had spread eastward into India by 1100 B.C. (Fig. 26.1) and westward into Italy by about 1000 B.C. Somewhat prior to 700 B.C. the Chinese began to use iron, and people in both northern Europe and central

Africa were quite familiar with it two centuries later.

Rome was the first empire which came to power relying almost exclusively upon iron weapons. Since the Roman product, though abundant, was inferior to Indian and Persian iron, the Romans imported from them higher-quality iron goods for special purposes. The tendency for new techniques to arise in areas of original invention is well illustrated by the Indian invention of both iron smelting and improved iron weapons.

The Plow. Considerably older than iron smelting is use of the plow. The diffusion of the plow followed much the same pattern as the later diffusion of iron. About 55 centuries ago the plow was used in Sumeria (now Iraq), and 5000 years ago Egyptians made pictures of plows in use. By 2000 B.C. the plow was used in France, and by about 1500 B.C. it had been introduced into India. In both southern Sweden and northern China people made use of the plow by 600 B.C.

Though copper and bronze had never been

used to tip the point of a plow, as early as 1100 B.C. an iron shoe, or plow-sock, was in use in Palestine. The iron-tipped plow is an example of the fact that improvements in a technique, or elaborations of a basic idea, tend to occur first near where the technique or idea originated. Improvement of the plow by addition of an iron tip occurred halfway between the two areas of the plow's first use.

Africa south of the Sahara, both of the American continents, and Australia were devoid of knowledge of the plow until after A.D. 1500. The first two areas used the digging stick for agriculture, and no farming at all was carried on in prediscovery Australia.

Paper Making. The invention of paper is attributed to a specific Chinese artisan in A.D. 105. Prior to that date, oracle bones, palm leaves, and silk fibers had successively been used in China. In the Mediterranean area, papyrus (the pressed pith of a swamp plant) and parchment from sheep or goat skin were used. Even earlier, wet clay had been written upon and then baked for permanence.

Paper appeared in Sinkiang about 150 years after it was first discovered. In 751 it was manufactured in Samarkand, and 40 years later it was manufactured in Baghdad. A century later Egyptians made paper, and by about 1100 it was manufactured in Morocco. Islamic Spain learned of paper making about 1150, and France, her neighbor and rival, was making it 40 years later. Techniques of making paper were not introduced into England until two years after Columbus's first voyage. It is small wonder that the Chinese emperor Ch'ien Lung said to George III's ambassador, "China possesses all things in abundance, and we do not want your products." From the beginning of the Han dynasty (about 200 B.C.), the Chinese invented many things which eventually diffused to Europe. Most Chinese techniques did not reach Europe until after the beginning of the 13th century, as the following table shows:

TABLE 26.1

Transmission of Chinese Techniques to Europe[1]

Invention or Discovery	China: First Precise Date	Europe: First Precise Date	Approximate Time Lag in Centuries
Rotary fan for ventilation	180	1556	12
Wheelbarrow	231	c. 1200	9-10
Wagon mill, grinding while traveling	340	1580	12
Kite	c. 400 B.C.	1589	12
Deep drilling	1st century	1126	11
Iron casting	2nd century B.C.	13th century	10-12
Iron chain suspension bridges	580	1741	10-13
Water-tight compartments in ships	5th century	1790	12
Gunpowder	c. 850	13th century	4
Floating magnet	1020	1190	4
Knowledge of magnetic declination	1030	c. 1450	4
Printing with wood or metal blocks	740	c. 1400	6
Printing with movable metal type	1392 (Korea)	c. 1440	1

[1] Derived from *A History of Technology*, Vol. II, pp. 770-771.

Fig. 26.2. Remains of the grid pattern in the sewer-served Indus valley city of Mohenjo-Daro.

The Urban Grid Pattern. One of the earliest examples of diffusion of ideas for which we have written records occurred when the soldiers of Alexander the Great invaded northern India. In the eastern part of the Ganges Valley the armies came upon the town of Pataliputra (on the site of the present city of Patna). Its streets were formed in a grid pattern which had derived in unbroken tradition from the first known urban grids (Fig. 26.2) at Mohenjo-Daro in the Indus Basin. Most Greek cities were not built on a regular pattern but were constructed with the streets conforming both in width and in direction to the form of the land. Only a few cities, such as Piraeus (the port of Athens), had a grid pattern; the idea for this limited use of the grid pattern had probably been received from Asia Minor, which in turn had long been in trade contact with northern India.

Impressed by the wide application of the grid pattern, the Greek soldiers took descriptions of it back to Greece. As a result, the Greek colonies that were subsequently formed in northern Africa and Anatolia used the grid pattern rather than an irregular pattern in planning their street systems. The grid was found to be quite efficient, and it was later adopted for many new Roman towns around both shores of the Mediterranean.

Many of the Roman towns of Spain were planned on a grid system. When a church was later built in one of these towns, it was placed on the central plaza. From the central plaza the streets went out in a grid pattern, but in many of the Spanish cities the grid form disappeared after a few blocks. More completely grid in form were the Spanish cities developed in Central and South America. In the third decade after the Spanish came to the New World, they started building towns on a grid pattern, using the central-plaza idea from Spain and details of grids from France and Italy. All of the streets were both wide and straight— wide to avoid attack from adjacent buildings and straight to avoid ambush from around corners.

A grid pattern for cities was also used in China, and there is a strong possibility that the Chinese pattern was influenced by the Indian example. An interesting corollary to the urban grid system is the use of the urban block unit as the rural unit of surveying. In Japan, which copied its planned cities from T'ang China, the urban *jo* and *cho* units were used without change for cadastral maps of farmed areas. In Italy the Roman block and the *jugerium* (rural land measure) were of the same size. However, in the American Middle West and other areas where township and range survey is used, the rural survey preceded the platting of towns in many cases, and the town grid was often determined by the section lines. In many of these cities there are 12 blocks to the section, or mile.

Cars and Railroads. The adoption of the private automobile has brought about widespread changes in modern life. Although detailed information on adopters has rarely been kept, such information is available for one area of southern Sweden. Maps of the spread of automobile ownership there reveal that the first owners were fairly scattered and that new owners appeared gradually near original adopters. The importance of word-of-mouth communication is obvious. It might be stated as a general rule that a person will adopt a less costly innovation much sooner than a more costly one but will in either case rely heavily upon a neighbor's advice.

The diffusion of a permanent new form of technology is mappable, even when adoption is by large commercial or political entities. A map of the spread of railroads in Europe (Fig. 26.3) shows how the building of railroads started in England in 1826, "jumped" a decade later to several capital areas on the Continent, and spread thereafter fairly consistently from centers of political power.

Religious Art. The spreading of ideas is, of course, not limited to everyday matters. Diffusion occurs also in a field such as religious art. For example, during the 500 years after the life of Buddha, no representations of him appeared in the art of the Ganges plains area, where he had lived and taught, since it was not the custom of local artists to portray the body of a religious figure. Sculptures portraying the Buddha first appeared in Gandhara, a Greek-influenced kingdom in the plains west of Kashmir. The first statues of Buddha closely resembled those of Apollo. As Buddhism spread to

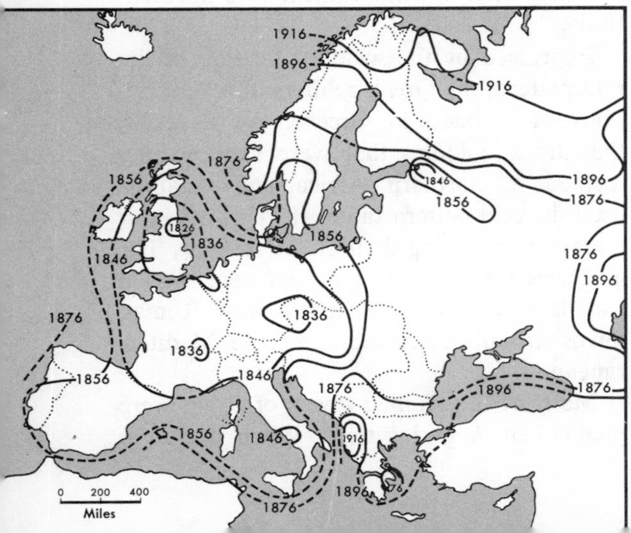

Fig. 26.3. Spread of railroads in Europe. (From Sven Godlund, "Ein Innovationsverlauf . . . ," *Lund Studies in Geography*, Ser. B, No. 6.)

Ceylon, southeastern Asia, and China, the Gandharan style of Buddhist art spread with it. Though the details of execution gradually changed, art historians can still point out the Greek influences in Buddhist art: the bended arm, the wavy or curly hair, the fall of the robe, and the half-smile.

The Spread of Cultivated Plants

The origins of cultivated plants were discussed in Chapter 12. Their spread seems to have occurred in four main periods. The first period was that remote time after domestication had been accomplished, perhaps about 20,000 years ago. The second major period was during the trade interactions and wars of the great empires of southern Asia, from about 1500 to 500 B.C. The third, and certainly the most important, period of plant diffusion included the two centuries after the discovery of the New World. The fourth period is our own time, when plant scientists roam the world looking for new or hardier varieties. This fourth period started when the world's great grasslands began coming under the steel plow after 1850.

Scholars believe that seed agriculture started with rice, which once probably grew as a weed in the taro paddies of southeastern Asia. By constantly being uprooted and tossed aside, rice became hardier and was gradually raised for its grain. The use of rice spread then to the west, into areas where it was hard to raise rice irrigated artificially. Once a seed plant was developed, the idea of using seeds rather than parts of the living plant was incorporated into the experimentation pattern. Seed agriculture apparently developed rapidly once this basic idea was formulated.

In the western India-southwestern Asia hearth of seed agriculture, the crops that were developed were all of the millet variety or the wheat-barley variety. There may have been some stimulus diffusion in this area. It is possible, for example, that some people may have noticed a resemblance between a

kind of millet that was being imported and grown and a similar plant growing wild nearby; seeing the similarity, they may have experimented with the wild plant and developed a different sort of millet.

Cotton may have first been grown in northeastern Africa, but at a very early period (2500-1500 B.C.) it was cultivated in the Indus Valley. (Both the Greek and Babylonian names for cotton indicate an Indian origin.) Cotton first entered the Mediterranean area in Egypt, where it appeared during the 5th century B.C. About the same time Indian rice appeared in Syria and northern Africa. The first rice grown in Europe was planted in A.D. 1468, a mere two dozen years before Columbus sailed westward from Spain.

Arabs introduced spinach into Europe, having gotten it from Persia. They also introduced sugar cane into Egypt in A.D. 641. Sugar cane had been important in India before the invasion of the Macedonian Alexander. Its successful cultivation in Egypt encouraged the Arabs to introduce it farther west, and it was first grown in Spain in A.D. 755.

A major part of the reciprocation between the various areas of the world was concerned with the introduction of new plants. Some Old World crops were not widely spread within Eurasia even by A.D. 1500. Sugar cane, for example, had been grown in southern China for several centuries before it was introduced into Okinawa in 1623. Its success there led to its introduction into southern Kyushu, where it was kept as a virtual monopoly by the feudal Satsuma family. In 1725 the shogun Yoshimune, in an effort to halt the importation of foreign sugar and the consequent loss of coins from Japan, obtained slips of sugar cane from the Ryukyu Islands. Sugar cane came to be grown successfully in several provinces of the Inland Sea area. The first black (unrefined) sugar was sent to Osaka in 1794, and four years later the first white sugar appeared in the Osaka market. With the opening of Japan to foreign trade after 1860, the commercial growing of sugar declined; only a few Japanese farmers still grow it, mainly for children to chew on.

The soybean, originally domesticated in northern China, was introduced into Europe by a Dutch botanist named Kaempfer. After traveling in Japan, Kaempfer brought home in 1712 some seeds of the soybean and of the *azuki* (which since has come to be known as the Irish bean). Since 1854 the soybean has been used in the United States as a forage crop, and since the middle 1920's it has been used as a food for man. Since 1945 it has become a major industrial crop which is valuable for its oil and oil cake and for its potentialities as a raw material in the manufacture of plastics.

The Spanish introduced wheat into Mexico in 1529. In 1602 it was sown in New England by an English explorer named Gosnold and was planted in Virginia in 1611. The Spanish brought it to California in 1769 with the first missions. Wheat was first grown in Minnesota in 1845, and Oregon's Willamette Valley farms supplied the California '49ers with wheat. Many of the varieties of wheat now dominant in the wheat belts of the United States and Canada were imported after the Civil War, particularly from Hungary and Russia.

Rice first appeared in North America in 1647 and flourished from 1694, when seed brought from Madagascar was planted in South Carolina. After the Civil War, rice became important in Louisiana, Texas, and Arkansas. Only since 1903 has rice been grown in the central valley of California, now one of the major producers in the United States.

Sorghums from the Old World appeared in the United States in two stages. The sweet sorghums came in during the decade prior to the Civil War: black-amber sorghums, originally Chinese, were imported from France in 1853; sumac and orange sorghums were brought from Natal in southern Africa in 1857 and planted in the Carolinas and Georgia. The grain sorghums appeared in the United States after the Civil War. Durra was introduced in 1874; kafir, two years later; milo, between 1880 and 1885. The kaoliangs were introduced in the period from 1898 to 1910. Broomcorn, grown for centuries in Italy and Hungary, had been introduced into the United States as early as 1797.

The sweet potato was domesticated in northwestern South America and, before A.D. 1500, diffused into eastern Polynesia, most probably along the route of the *Kontiki* voyage. However, it did not spread into western Polynesia, and the first introduction of the sweet potato into Asia was in the Philippines sometime after 1570, when it was brought on one of the Manila galleons from Acapulco, Mexico. In the 1590's it was introduced into southern China, where it became famous for forestalling a famine when the rice crop failed. It was introduced into Okinawa in 1606 and into the Satsuma area of southern Kyushu about 1670. From there it gradually spread over the warmer parts of Japan and aided materially in permitting Japan's population to increase from 17 million in 1600 to 30 million in 1730.

The various names of the sweet potato in eastern Asia well illustrate the fact that the diffusion of a technique or plant may be traced by nomenclature. In most of Japan the sweet potato is called the Satsuma potato. In Satsuma it is referred to as the Ryukyu potato, and in the Okinawa area it is named the Chinese potato. In southern China it is called the barbarian potato because it was introduced by Westerners. In the Philippines it goes by one of its Amerind names, *camote*.

The white potato, domesticated in the high Andes, was introduced into Europe by the Spanish soon after 1580. By 1700 it had spread all over Europe and the British Isles. In the United States it is known as the Irish potato because it was introduced into New England by the Irish in 1719. Its notoriety in the potato famines of the 1840's in Ireland served to reinforce its identification with

Ireland. The spread of the white potato from Germany into Russia is indicated in the Russian use of the word *Kartoffel*.

The manioc tuber, native to the selva of the Amazon Basin, was first introduced abroad into tropical Africa. Possibly as early as 1530, certainly before 1590, it had been introduced into the kingdom of the Congo, from which the Portuguese obtained most of their slaves. By 1640 it had spread eastward and up the river to the Bushongo area. From the Congo Basin it spread north and south until today all nondesert areas grow some manioc. The Portuguese did not teach the Africans the South American way of preparing the manioc tubers by squeezing out the poisonous juice. After an indefinite period of trial and error, the Africans developed a method of safely preparing the tubers by soaking them for five days in flowing water. Because of the totally different ways of preparing the roots for use, it is not surprising that the processed forms of manioc in Africa differ considerably from the tapioca forms of the Amazon. Manioc is now widely grown in southern and eastern Asia, where it was probably introduced by the Portuguese in the 16th and 17th centuries.

The most fully documented spread of a plant is that of tobacco. Two varieties of tobacco were originally dominant in the Americas, and several other varieties were found locally. *Nicotiana rustica* was indigenous to what is now eastern United States and Canada; the less hardy *Nicotiana tabacum,* which now furnishes most of the world's tobacco, was grown along the southern fringe of the Caribbean Sea. Habits of smoking tend to reflect original contacts. The Indians of eastern North America taught the English to smoke pipes, and over most of northern Europe pipe smoking has long been dominant. In the Mediterranean countries cigar and cigarette smoking long reflected the mode of tobacco use in Cuba and the West Indies.

Tobacco was cultivated and smoked in England from 1573, but its popular adoption dates from 1586, when the first Virginia colonists returned. Within 25 years tobacco was sold in England as widely as it is today. The attribution of medicinal properties to tobacco may have helped to spread its use. Thomas Hearne wrote in 1721:

I have been told that in the last great plague at London none that kept tobaconist's shops had the plague. It is certain, that smoking it was looked upon as a most excellent preservative, in so much, that even children were obliged to smoak. And I remember, that I heard formerly Tom Rogers, who was yeoman beadle, say, that when he was that year, when the plague raged, a schoolboy at Eaton, all the boys at that school were obliged to smoak in the school every morning, and that he was never whipped so much in his life as he was one morning for not smoking.

Snuff was introduced into the French court and into Italy in 1561, and smoking soon followed. English medical students at Leiden taught the Dutch how to smoke in 1590, and by 1650 peasants all over Germany were smoking. A Russian edict of 1634 prohibiting the use of tobacco slowed its adoption there, but by 1700 Peter the Great had decided to permit tobacco for the sake of gaining revenue. The English introduced tobacco into Turkey prior to 1600, but the sultan quickly prohibited it, giving as his reason the fires which broke out when people fell asleep with pipes lit. After 1655 the prohibition was relaxed.

Tobacco spread very quickly to the parts of Africa and Asia that were touched by European ships. A report of 1607 described tobacco cultivation in Sierra Leone, and Hollanders introduced it to the Cape area in 1652. An English captain, Richard Cocks, noted in his diary in 1615 that tobacco had been introduced into Japan scarcely 10 years before. In the early 1600's tobacco was carried from the Philippines (Luzon) to the Fukien coast of China, where it was at first used as a medicine against colds, malaria, and cholera. India received tobacco from

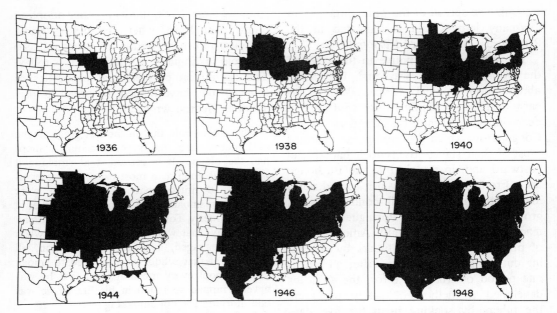

Fig. 26.4. Spread of hybrid corn in the United States. (Reprinted from *Science* by permission.)

the Portuguese about 1605, and Persia, Ceylon, and Java got it very soon thereafter. The Chinese introduced tobacco into the interior of Asia, just as the English had introduced it into Europe. By about 1700, when the European methods of using tobacco clashed with the Chinese methods in the Amur-Baykal area, virtually the entire human race had come to know and use this narcotic.

The Spread of Commercial Cotton. Diffusion comes about rapidly when the demand for a product is high and when information is available. An excellent example of this is the expansion of world cotton acreage in the 1860's. The export of cotton from the Confederate States fell off almost entirely as a result of the Union sea blockade. Mills in England and on the Continent were forced either to look for a new supply or to close down. They did the former. Farmers began to grow cotton in widely separated parts of the world in order to supply the textile mills of industrial Europe.

Egypt, India, and northeastern Brazil began to fill the demand for cheaper fibers,

while Fiji and Tahiti grew the more expensive and longer-stapled "sea island" cotton. The peak of production was reached in most of these areas between 1871 and 1872. After the Civil War the American South gradually regained its markets, and only the large producers with British connections—Egypt and India—survived. In Brazil cotton workers drifted westward by the thousands into the selva to take part in the wild rubber boom, and Fiji and Tahiti turned to the growing of sugar cane.

In modern times the diffusion of new crops is less important, perhaps, than the spread of new crop varieties, or new ways of changing crops to fit production needs. The hybridizing of corn, "an invention of a new method of innovating," was first experimented with in the United States in 1918. Starting from Iowa and northern Illinois in the early 1930's, the planting of hybrid corn diffused over much of the Middle West (Fig. 26.4) in a decade, and in the following decade it was adopted in most parts of the South.

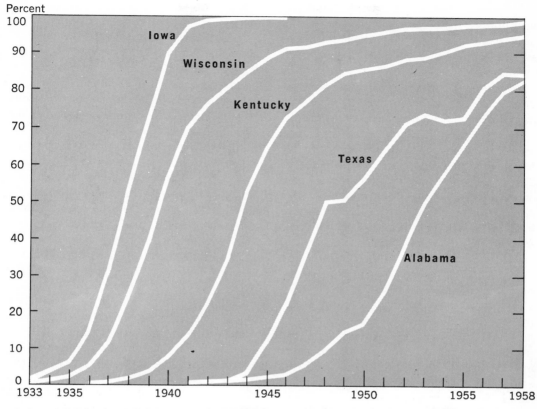

Fig. 26.5. Logistic growth curve for adoption of an innovation: percentage of all corn acreage planted to hybrid seed.

Many studies of innovation have shown that the adoption of an innovation follows a logistic growth curve (Fig. 26.5). The first acceptance is rather slow, but it picks up speed as many people accept the idea or practice. After about eight of each possible 10 accepting persons have adopted the innovation, the acceptance curve flattens out again.

Rejection of Ideas

If an idea somehow does not "fit" technologically within a pattern of life that has already evolved, it may be rejected. New Guinea peoples with a Stone Age material culture cannot adopt airplanes because they

are not able to maintain or repair them. Eskimo, though they are used to seeing "bush pilots" fly airplanes and though they occasionally ride in airplanes themselves, cannot maintain airplanes at their level of technology. These are instances in which a group *cannot* adopt an innovation.

An idea may be rejected if it is detrimental to the values of a culture. The large-scale adoption of celibacy by any group would doom it to extinction. No known group has ever adopted celibacy, though this idea has been advocated for various reasons, usually religious, for many centuries. Within the automobile-conscious United States, one group has rejected the automobile. The Old Order Amish of

Pennsylvania and Ohio consider that the adoption of motor-powered vehicles would destroy the pace of living which they consider all-important. Here is a case in which an innovation seems to threaten the ideals of a group. The group, though it may possess the knowledge of how to cope with the innovation, *will not* accept it.

The adoption of an idea or innovation may prove unfeasible if it is not possible for environmental reasons to maintain it. Thus, the idea of milking cattle is not found in most parts of the tropical rainforest of Africa. The rainforest is the area which is most infested by the disease-carrying tsetse fly, which transmits sleeping sickness to cattle.

Rejection of an idea may not be immediate. It sometimes involves a trial-and-error process on the part of a group; sometime in the distant past, for instance, a group may have tried to raise milk cattle along the savanna margins of Africa. Although there may be acceptance of an idea for itself (the enthusiasm of New Guineans for airplane travel, for example), rejection may result from the inability to continue once the original stimulus has been withdrawn. Finally, an idea may be attractive to some of the people of a group but be rejected by the elite as a threat to values. Thus, rejection has been the fate of Mendelian genetics in the U.S.S.R.; the theory of random selection and mutation does not conform to Marxist doctrines about inheritance of acquired characteristics.

Attenuated Diffusion of Ideas

Adoption of an idea in attenuated form involves acceptance of the idea without the ability to evolve it further, or lack of effort in importing the idea in full strength from its center of origin. An idea-complex or a technique may be diffused from a center and be accepted by groups farther and farther away. Without contact by each accepting group with the originators, the idea-complex will lose some of its features as it is passed along.

An extremely good example of attenuated diffusion of a technique is offered by the reindeer culture of the Eurasian tundra. Reindeer are found in their natural state in the tundra and originally roamed wild over the area, spending the summer period in the north and wintering in the forest edge to the south. This pattern of movement holds even among those reindeer that have been domesticated for generations, and the reindeer peoples must follow the migrations dictated by the reindeer's instinctive response to climate and season. As a result, Eurasian tundra peoples tend to summer in the northern reaches of the tundra and withdraw during the long cold period to the edge of the forest.

According to one theory, the domestication of reindeer was started by the horse-owning tribes to the south, particularly in the vicinity of Lake Baykal. Although this theory is possible and has not been disproved, it is more logical to assume that the domestication of reindeer originated in northeastern Europe, where the tundra people called Lapps were long in touch with cattle-owning sedentary peoples. The Nomadic Lapps have the most complex reindeer culture, with all the patterns of use that characterize the use of cattle. Reindeer are milked by the Lapps, they are used for pulling sleds, they are herded into corrals, and sometimes they are treated almost as members of the family. In the areas to the east of the Lapps, reindeer are used chiefly for transport and are only occasionally milked. Still farther eastward, in the Chukchi area, reindeer are only semidomesticated and are kept in loose herds only for convenience in obtaining meat and hides. Finally, in the restricted Eskimo area of Eurasia opposite Alaska, the reindeer has no formal contact with man and is merely an object for hunting.

The use of the reindeer well illustrates the general "law" that the more complex a trait is in an area, the closer is this area to the point of origin. It may be inferred that the reindeer was domesticated in northeastern Europe, the locale of the most complex set of traits associated with the use of the reindeer by man.

Independent Development of Ideas

Some ideas have been thought of independently, in separate places and at different times, and ideas which are apparently related may be unique. Such seems to be the case with syllabic writing forms and the alphabet. Groups as far apart in time and space as the early Egyptians, 7th-century Koreans, 9th-century Japanese, and 13th-century Mayans have independently invented syllabaries. Syllabaries are ways of writing a language in which one symbol represents an entire syllable rather than its constituent sounds.

So far as we know, true alphabetic writing has been invented not more than twice in human history. All alphabets presently in use derive at some remove from the Phoenician, devised between 1200 and 1000 B.C. The Ugaritic alphabet, invented near Latakia in Syria, preceded the Phoenician alphabet by over 300 years. The two are totally unrelated, and the Ugaritic died out before it had opportunity to spread. More important than the fact that one alphabet died out is the fact that it was invented in an area (the eastern Mediterranean) where experimentation with syllabaries, and various combinations of these with single-sound marks, had long been common. The invention of the alphabetic idea was "in the air," so to speak.

The Greeks borrowed their alphabet from the Phoenicians (Fig. 26.6). They called the first two letters *alpha* and *beta,* which have no meaning in Greek but mean "ox" and "house" in Semitic languages such as Phoenician. Our own form of the alphabet is a Roman version of Greek usage which was

Fig. 26.6. Cast of the alphabetic Moabite Stone, 850 B.C. Divisions of words are shown by dots.

adopted while Greece was still under Phoenician influence. Its use in legal, religious, and monument-carving connections has preserved fairly closely until modern times the ancient Phoenician forms. Arabic and Hebrew alphabets derive from the Phoenician also but are more rounded in form, being copied from the cursive business modifications introduced by the Aramaeans during the 7th century B.C.

From the eastern shore of the Mediterranean, alphabetic writing spread first toward southern Asia and later to central Asia.

The pre-Christian diffusion was mainly to India and adjacent areas, and much of it was accomplished over water routes. The Brahmi alphabet used to write Sanskrit spread, with local modifications, throughout southeastern Asia and into Indonesia and the Philippines. Even today on Palawan Island in the Philippines, love letters are written by primitive peoples in a Sanskrit-influenced alphabet. Under the stimulus of knowledge of the Pali and Mongolian versions of alphabetic writing, the Koreans in 1392 devised an alphabet which has remained in use to this day.

Mostly post-Christian in time, the second diffusion of the alphabet reached the peoples of central Asia by way of land routes. Aramaean forms influenced Uigur Turk writing, which in turn molded the forms of the Mongol alphabet. In 1599, because of the fiat of a ruling prince, the Manchus adopted a version of the Mongolian alphabet. Thus, some 200 years after the Koreans had adopted an alphabet based upon a southern Asian model, the neighboring Manchus adopted a central Asian form. The spread of the alphabet throughout the Old World was thus essentially completed.

Ideas continue to spread in modern times. Most of the ideas go from the highly industrial urbanized areas to the lesser-developed and predominantly rural subsistence-agricultural areas. The whole problem of speeding economic development in lesser-developed areas, which is one of the cardinal points of United States foreign policy, lies in the successful diffusion of ideas which are familiar to us but as yet untried and untested by those we want to help. The U.S.S.R. also has a program of promoting the economic development of lesser-developed areas; though their purposes are different from those of the United States, they meet with the same problems of adapting a high level of technology to areas where a low technological level has long existed.

In the modern period, with the advent of steamships, railroads, and automobiles, the exchange of people with different ideas has gone on apace. The rate of interchange of ideas has become rapid and has been aided by the newer media of communication such as newspapers, radio, and television. By making books widely available, the growth of literacy, which is an outgrowth of the invention of printing, has aided in the spread of ideas; and we now find two large continental powers, the United States and the U.S.S.R., engaged by their own admission in a "war of ideas," trying to gain the support of the "uncommitted peoples of the world."

The cultural exchange programs between the United States and the U.S.S.R. are an attempt by each nation, openly admitted by both nations, to influence the people of the other nation in its favor. It is thought in the United States that if Russia permits its people to come here, they can somehow be shown that the American way of life is peaceful. Russians believe that if Americans go to Russia, they will see the growth that the Russian nation has made under "socialism," will admire the Russian industrial prowess and military skills, and will thereby be influenced to some degree in a policy of friendliness toward Russian ambitions in the world.

The past is prologue.
Inscription on the portico of the
United States Archives Building

CHAPTER 27

Techniques in Human Geography

The human geographer has a large kitbag of techniques that enable him to investigate the ways in which man has changed the landscape into which he is born. No one geographer uses all of the techniques to be described here, but all these methods of discovery have at one time or another been used by geographers.

It will be apparent that no device for discovering new facts or new relationships is outside the domain of use if it contributes new or significant results. This fact is well illustrated in an article by Carl O. Sauer on the antiquity of man in the Americas. In his study Sauer used information from such diverse fields as blood-type analysis, glacial climatology, archaeology, linguistic geography, cultural anthropology, and the study of racial distributions to shed light upon his reconstruction of man's migrations and early activities in this hemisphere (Fig. 3.2). In addition, he made a major contribution to the theory (discussed in Chapter 13 of this book) that the Indian habit of hunting by firing dry grass promoted the expansion of grasslands. Sauer's paper should serve as an inspirational guide to the young geographer and as a reminder that there is no orthodoxy of method when a search for truth is in progress.

Most frequently, research in human geography starts from concern with a more narrow problem than the history of man in two hemispheres. The desire to resolve a specific quandary motivates much geographic study. For example, one geographer posed the question of whether the gradual drying-up of North Africa (Fig. 27.1) in the past millennium, noted by numerous authorities, was due to climatic changes or to human acts. After detailing the arguments for each side of the question, he examined historical records for evidence. His study led him to conclude that the apparent desiccation in North Africa is mainly a "cultural drying-up," the result of overgrazing by goats and overcutting of forests for fuel. This conclusion is not only of interest to the human and historical geographer; it is also of crucial importance to the administrators of the newly independent nations there.

It should be apparent from the foregoing chapters and these examples that it is not possible to separate human geography, when defined as "how man has changed the earth," from an intimate concern with the time dimension. Change implies time. Because man is mobile and wanders about his environment, study of how he has modified the earth at particular times is necessary for an understanding of later conditions.

Techniques used by geographers in their research range from the simple to the complex. Frequent use of maps showing varying distributions of different items or traits is what distinguishes geographers as a group. Comparison of a distribution on maps of identical areas at different times may give

393

Fig. 27.1. Mosaic depicting animals common in Morocco in late Roman times. Many of these animals have now disappeared from the area.

valuable clues to further lines of inquiry. Similarly, two simultaneous distributions on maps of the same area may provide clues as to derivative relationships. For example, if a map of villages in the Naga area between India and Burma shows that settlement is on ridges, inquiry as to the reasons for this configuration would follow.

If a study of distribution of truck gardens were to show that they are only on river-bottom land that is close to a city, and if no commercial vegetable gardens were found on low-lying land far from the city or on higher land close to the city, we would be justified in concluding that there are two conditions necessary to the occurrence of such gardens. Field investigation might add

the information that the gardens are operated by one or two minority ethnic groups.

In studies that cover a remote or inaccessible period of time, geographers become concerned with techniques of dating the basic information which they put on maps. Once gathered and mapped, information may be subjected to more complex techniques of analysis than visual comparison of maps.

Techniques of Dating

A geographer does not always go about confirming a date for a localized event by himself. He frequently relies upon results collected by other scholars for different purposes. In the past two decades it has become possible to date rather accurately the life period of organic material by analysis of the fourteenth isotope of carbon, since this isotope has a known half-life, or decay rate. Ancient boats in peat bogs in Japan and Scandinavia have been thus dated, as have Polynesian campfires and thousands of other human artifacts. The journal *Science* contains references to new datings and has bibliographies of dating compilations.

Other methods of dating involve pollen analysis (generally of pollen from bogs), analysis of the width of tree rings, and the study of varves (dark and light annual deposits) from glacial lake beds. Bogs and glacial lake beds are valuable to the geographer because they are both old and undisturbed and thus offer complete records for long periods. Lichen-growth dating is a new field whose results may soon become of use to the human geographer. However, more commonly the geographic researcher relies for dating purposes upon written and pictorial records (cave drawings, baked-clay maps, parchment cadastral maps, and so forth).

Sources of Exact Information. One does not often regard literature and poetry as raw material for geographical use. However, there are certain cases in which such material is not only useful but the only source of information available. For instance, the *Georgics* of Horace gives information about the condition of agriculture during the decline of the Roman Empire. Frontier guards' poems in the Japanese poetry collection called the *Manyōshū* are an invaluable record of reactions to the northeastward movement of the frontier. Similar valuable material on the expansion of political control in early Russia is available in the recently translated *Song of Igor's Campaign*.

Travel diaries yield information which is useful in reconstructing past landscapes and the ways of life that were changing them. Of particular use are the diaries kept by Arab travelers after the initial rapid spread of

Islam and those kept by Chinese Buddhists traveling to and from India. *Ennin's Travels in T'ang China* is a mine of information on 9th-century China as seen by a Japanese pilgrim. Within the United States many early diaries of travel and settlement are in the possession of state and county historical societies and in the attics of descendants of pioneers; geographers hope that these records will yield information that will make clearer the process of frontier settlement in particular and of human geography in general. The geography student can make no better beginning than to read *The Travels of William Bartram,* which describes the diarist's travels through the Carolinas, Georgia, and Florida in the 1770's.

Dating of events through use of diary information can be supplemented in most countries by information in governmental files on post offices. Settlement studies have been made by geographers on the basis of this information in many parts of the United States, including Georgia (Fig. 27.2). In

Fig. 27.2. Isochronic map of the settlement of Georgia. (Courtesy of Wilbur Zelinsky and the *Georgia Historical Quarterly*.)

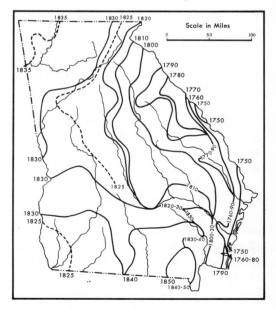

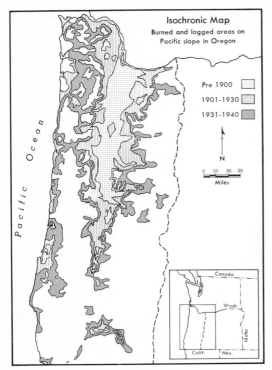

Isochronic Map
Burned and logged areas on
Pacific slope in Oregon

Pre 1900
1901-1930
1931-1940

N

0   10   20   30
       Miles

Pacific Ocean

Canada

Wash.

Idaho

Calif.   Nev.

Fig. 27.3. Isochronic map of burned and logged areas in western Oregon. (Courtesy of Kenneth A. Erickson and the Association of Pacific Coast Geographers.)

time-oriented studies the data often are summarized on isochronic maps. Such a map was used in a paper on the post-1890 spread of logging in western Oregon (Fig. 27.3). These maps also enable a person to visualize a process such as migration or the spread of new settlement.

Supplementary information on specific changes is available in old local newspapers. Again, the files of local historical societies are an almost untapped mine of useful leads for historical geographers. That such societies are no longer called "historical and geographical societies" is evidence of an unfortunate decline in interest among geographers. Many groups who have migrated have kept good records of what, to them, are crucial events. For instance, the migration of the Mormons to the Middle West, and later

to Utah and adjacent areas, is well documented.

Government records of various sorts constitute good sources of information; where, as in China, such records have actually been compiled *as* regional or local descriptions, everything is at hand for analysis. The Library of Congress contains thousands of *hsien* (county, or local) records from which the process of change in the Chinese landscape can be studied. The climatic information alone in these records would throw great light upon the weather regimens that confronted the Chinese farmer and merchant in the past. It goes without saying that extremes such as floods, famines, droughts, and food riots find a prominent place in such local records.

Records maintained by commercial groups, such as companies and corporations, are useful to the human geographer. Dozens of studies have appeared, for instance, based upon the records of the Hudson's Bay Company and of the East India companies, Dutch and British.

Sources of Deducible Information. Though it is often not possible in an investigation to assign absolutely a specific date to an occurrence, many techniques are available for assigning either a relative date or an estimate of a date within a certain range. The assignment of a relative date may mean that we know that one innovation came before another but cannot tell definitely when either appeared in a landscape. One example of relative dating concerns relict peoples in southern Asia. We know that as invaders settled in the Indian subcontinent, they gradually pushed the original inhabitants onto the less desirable lands, generally upwards into the hills. Since succeeding groups of invaders repeated this process, there is now in the remote hill and mountain areas a sort of stratification of peoples from bottom to top, representing respectively newer to older groups. We do not know definitely when each group arrived in the area, but we can deduce that a tribe living at a certain height on the mountains came there later than another tribe living nearer the summits.

A somewhat reverse situation exists in the Burma-Thailand area, where groups have for centuries arrived from the plateaus and highlands of southern China. Each arriving group has gradually pushed its predecessor group a bit lower down towards the plains and has at a later date itself been displaced by newly arriving tribes. Thus we can deduce, unless contrary evidence is forthcoming, that the higher a tribe lives in this area, the newer it is in the area.

Sometimes it is possible to deduce how long two groups of people have been separated from each other by studying the degree to which their once-common language has diverged. It is a fairly widely accepted hypothesis that a language will through the course of a thousand years retain 81 per cent of its original list of words for common objects and actions. For a variety of reasons, speakers will have begun to use new words for the remaining 19 per cent. By studying the amount of vocabulary still used in common by two groups, it is possible to date within five or six decades the crucial separation of the two groups. Such studies are known as lexico-statistical dating, or glottochronology. Linguistic anthropologists have studied the major languages and dialects of the world by these methods, and their results can be used as deduced dating by the human geographer in his effort to restore the history of migration and settlement.

Evidence of migrations may be useful in restoring the record of settlement. The Maori migration from the Society Islands area to New Zealand was the subject of traditional chants designed to keep the memory of the migration alive. As time passed, the exploits of each generation were added to the chants, and the dates of the original migration were deducible within a certain degree of error before carbon 14 analysis and language dating confirmed the estimate. The migration routes that Sauer postulated for the spread of the Amerind population (Fig. 3.2) are not proved beyond a doubt, but they remain the strongest possible hypothesis.

When records are lacking in an area or are difficult to come by, it is often possible to deduce a part of the history of settlement by a study of house types. If the house types are classifiable by ethnic groups, a map may be made of the settlement according to ethnic preference for certain house styles. This is the case if house types remain relatively constant through the time period under consideration but differ by culture groups. If there is a relatively uniform house-type preference by all groups (as there tends to be in suburban United States) but a tendency to vary through time, it is possible to date the settlement by house type. We are all familiar with urban areas that are classifiable by bungalows in the 1920's style, or by post-1945 ranch-style houses.

The house-type example is a sort of modern-day archaeological sequence. Archaeologists have been constantly concerned with dating, and their studies have run from early relative dating techniques to more modern and exact estimate dating techniques. The student interested in these techniques would be well advised to become acquainted with the journals *Antiquity* and *American Antiquity*.

Sometimes a sequence study can be done by using the relict structures in the landscape. These are structures that are no longer used but are still in existence. Some relict structures in the Willamette Valley of Oregon are the hop-drying sheds of the 1920's and early 1930's, which are now unused because of the intense competition from other producing areas. Etruscan tombs, Roman lighthouses, hilltop castles in Japan, and abandoned Eskimo camps are other instances of relict structures.

Some peoples give names to their house lots, relating them to the places from which they have come, such as the house lots of their ancestors. Where this is true (as it is in parts of the Far East), settlement can be traced by a study of house-lot names. Forrest

Pitts[1] once worked in Okinawa, where it is quite easy to trace connections between houses in different villages. No precise dating exists, but ranking of the sort "this house branched from that one" is possible.

The distribution of dialects can aid in a reconstruction of settlement and migrations. Ways of speech in coastal colonial America moved inland, in general, along the latitudes of their origin. Though there was some mixing of the dialects beyond the Appalachians, it is still possible for dialect geographers to trace the most likely origin or origins of a Middle-Western way of speaking, including pronunciation and choice of words. For instance, a *frying pan* is called a *skillet* by some and a *spider* by others.

The study of place names frequently gives good clues concerning the settlement of an area; where place names of different types occur, it may be possible to study the sequence of occupation of the area through the names of places. In Japan many place names contain the word for "hemp," thus indicating not only the dependence of the early Japanese on this fiber but also the areas where it was dominantly grown.

The dispersion and agglomeration of settlement sometimes gives clues to the geographical history of an area. Periods of unrest may result in the building of dwellings close together for defense, while periods of peace may permit more dispersed settlement in a rural area.

Archaeologists have found that primitive drawings in caves and on rocks can give them valuable hints about the cultural level of the people who drew them. Similarly, geographers can use the drawings to make inferences about the way the people used the landscape they inhabited. In the past few years the examination of cave drawings has shown a great deal about the people who inhabited the Sahara during the wetter periods of postglacial history.

The holy books of the great religions may contain raw material for the reconstruction of past landscapes. Denis Baly has shown what can be done with the material in the Bible. Similar valuable studies could no doubt be made of the Koran, the Zend-Avesta, and the body of Greek myths.

In aerial photographs it is possible to find patterns of previous occupance of an area, even when the patterns are not visible from the ground. Dating may be possible only in a relative way, but the information is valuable nonetheless. Many old Roman roads and field patterns in Britain have been found through examination of aerial photographs. Similar results may be expected from examination of air photographs of the areas of pre-Columbian civilization in the Americas. Occasionally, mysteries are created rather than solved by aerial photographs. An instance is a photograph published in the June, 1954, issue of *Antiquity*. Captured from German files after World War II, it shows a sunken coastline with a series of building and field patterns. Many areas of the world have sunken coastlines, and it is not known in which area the photograph was taken. Enterprising students may consult the library file of *Antiquity* for other such photographs, if they wish to work on this sort of problem.

In an area which has undergone recent rapid change, it is often possible to write a geographical history of that change by comparing air photographs taken at different periods. This is particularly possible in city fringe areas. Similar comparisons can be made through a longer series of ground photographs.

Techniques of Analysis

Once the human geographer has dated his distributions, he maps them. The map may be an isochronic map showing spread through time. Or there may be a series of maps for different time periods, upon which may be placed related information that is pertinent to the analysis. The geographer uses maps to help answer the perennial questions, "Where?" and "Why there?"

[1] F. R. Pitts, W. P. Lebra, and W. P. Suttles, *Post-War Okinawa,* Washington, D.C., Pacific Science Board, National Research Council, 1955.

Analysis of Settlement from Maps. In college classes, students are often given a map and asked to describe the human occupance, the man-made forms, within the map's area. So that the users of this book will be able to do this in an efficient and complete manner, a check list with examples is given here.[2]

Description of the settlement forms themselves precedes comment upon the relations of the forms to the local inhabitants. Pattern elements may be described in both verbal and mathematical categories.

Verbal descriptive categories	Examples
Arrangement of continuities	Fences, windbreaks, railroads, linear utilities, drainage interruptions, canals, roads.
Arrangement of discontinuities	Relative positions of building symbols, places where road types change, relative placement of churches and cemeteries.
Shape of discrete forms	Political-boundary shapes, cultivated areas.
Relative sizes of discrete forms	Buildings, fields, groves of trees.
Compass orientation of continuities	Road orientations.
Nonvisible items	Place names; nonpolitical boundaries, such as reserves; ownership lines; political and administrative enclaves.

Mathematical descriptive categories	
Number	Number of symbols, churches, barns, other buildings.
Density	Farmhouse density, other rural-building density, road-net density.
Propinquity	Clustering and dispersion of buildings.[3]

	Examples
Absolute size	Nonpolitical exclaves, groves; enclaves, such as cleared land in forest.
Isolates	Single occurring items, such as watercourse-spanning devices; mines—open-pit, strip, shaft; wells, factory stacks, water towers, windmills, quarries and gravel pits, beacons, relay towers, radomes, lighthouses, radio and television towers. Longitude and latitude coordinates may be used to place these.

The settlement forms may have both functional and time relationships with the people living in the map area, the local populace.

Functional Relationships	Examples
Ecological	Forms which are used by and operated for the local populace, for example, long horizontal wells, and water towers.
Exotic	Forms which are within the cultural environment of, and which may be used by, the local inhabitants, but which were built or set up by, and are operated mainly for, nonlocal groups. An example is a railroad in a hillbilly area.
Disjunct	Forms which have no relation to the local inhabitants, by way of origin or use, and which are not in their cultural environment. Examples are oil wells in the Sahara, airbases in Morocco, and radomes in Eskimoland.

[2] This list was developed and used by F. R. Pitts in his classes at the University of Oregon.
[3] James A. Barnes and Arthur H. Robinson, "A New Method for the Representation of Dispersed Rural Population," *Geographical Review,* Vol. 30, No. 1 (January 1940), p. 135.

Time relationships	Examples
Antecedent forms	Forms which came before the local inhabitants settled the area. Examples are some of the railroads in the Great Plains of the United States and the Pampas of Argentina.
Superimposed forms	Forms, generally exotic, which came after the local settlement, and which were imposed upon an existing landscape.
Subsequent forms	Forms which are a newer version of an older form, for example, a new superhighway in an area with other highways.
Inherited forms	Forms which are inherited from ancestors, or from other cultural groups, and which are still in use full strength.
Relict forms	Forms which are still in the landscape, but which are either not in use or little used. An example is most portions of Inca roads.

An unused colonial post road in the Carolinas might be described as an *ecological relict* form. A limited-access superhighway across the Navajo Reservation in Arizona would be described as a *superimposed disjunct* form, while the same highway near Phoenix would be considered to be an *ecological subsequent* form.

Maps showing distributions by dots are the sort most universally understood by laymen and probably are the type most frequently used by geographers. The population maps of Chapter 5 are examples. A variant of dot maps showing massed or agglomerated distributions, as in cities, makes use of visually-appearing volumes. Spheres and cubes are used, for instance, where dots for small values cannot be used owing to great

concentration of population. Figure 27.4, showing the distribution of Baptists in the United States, is of this type.

A somewhat more sophisticated map technique is the *isopleth,* which shows the areal distribution of ratios. Two isopleth maps of an area at different time periods can often be very effective in telling a story. Good examples of this are maps of population density in northwestern Ohio (Fig. 27.5) before and after the draining of the Black Swamp. Both the value and limitations of visual comparisons of isopleth maps have been discussed by Harold McCarty.

Choropleth maps are useful when exact distributions are not known but data are available for small political units. In such maps the data are presented as if they uniformly covered the area of the political subdivision.

Various approaches to analysis of geographic distributions are possible. The ecological and comparative approaches are older and more traditional, while the statistical and simulation approaches are products of the last two decades and are still in the process of development.

Ecological Approach. In the main, the approach to explanations of distributions through basic interactions, or ecology, is verbal. Maps, however, are often used in the intermediate stages of study. A study of man's adaptations to various climates (Chapter 8) is one illustration of the ecological approach. The land-tenure portion of this book (Chapter 15) is another. Land use and conservation (Chapter 21) rely heavily on ecology and theories concerning it.

The underlying rationale for the small-area studies that have been so popular in American colleges is ecological and derives from the French school of regional geography. It is assumed in these studies that if a reasonably small area is selected and the various interrelations of factors within the area are examined in detail, a meaningful pattern of interdependencies will emerge. Such has been the case in the more successful of these studies. Often, however, the

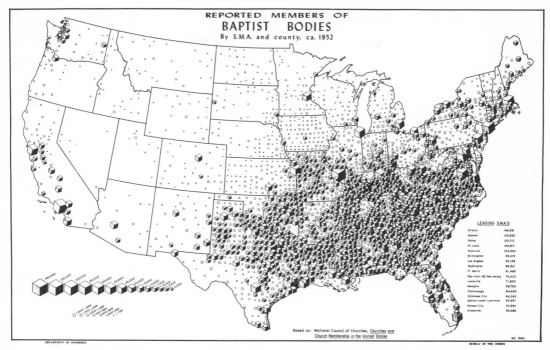

Fig. 27.4. Distribution of Baptists in the United States, using cubes to indicate high concentrations. (Reprinted by permission of the Association of American Geographers.)

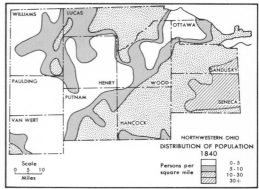

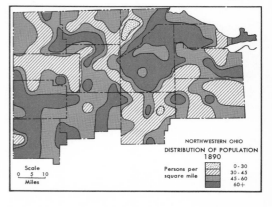

great mass of detail available has prevented adequate analysis within the investigator's time limit. The recent advent of high-speed data processing should provide a "shot in the arm" to small regional studies.

Comparative Approach. A variant of the ecological approach, using two or more areas, is the comparative approach. Here, rather than study all the pertinent interrelations between factors in two areas, the human geographer selects two areas that are alike in main physical factors. Then he studies, say, the effect on the land—the alike physical factors—of two different human factors. The human factors might be two national groups, as in the Hodgson study described below, or might be the differing effects of history on an area inhabited by a

Fig. 27.5. Isopleth map of population density in northwestern Ohio in 1840 and in 1890. (Reprinted by permission of the Association of American Geographers.)

homogeneous group, as in the Japan study cited below.

Robert Hodgson studied two patterns of land occupance in the Lake Champlain lowland, the French to the north and the British-American to the south. The factors equated were the elements of the natural environment, and the variable element was the cultural heritages of the farmers and townfolk of the lowland. Needless to say, such a study is the reverse of studies made by early environmental determinists, who considered the effects of varied environments upon people of a single culture. Hodgson summarized his study as follows:

While the French-Canadians and the New Englanders have always utilized the land in the same general way, they have differed greatly in detail. In the actual settlement of the land, the French settled on the river bank, the New Englanders on the local heights. The French settled densely and continuously while the New Englanders settled sparsely and thinly. The French were interested in general farming with an emphasis on sustenance production. The New Englanders, after the development of transportation, were commercial producers. Interested as they were in commerce, the New Englanders selected the mill site as the location of their village while the French-Canadians grouped about the church. These tendencies have continued even into the modern landscape.[4]

A more recent study using the comparative approach was done by Forrest Pitts in regard to land fertility and rural prosperity in Japan.[5] An effort was made to get at the reasons for the high level of productivity in the Inland Sea area and the relatively moderate annual yields elsewhere. To be explained also was the paradox of this high yield in spite of adverse factors which included summer drought, small landholdings,

and a high rate of tenancy. To do this, three villages in the Inland Sea area were matched with three villages in areas less productive. All were matched in size, population, soil quality, relative distance from large cities, lack of sea frontage or light industry, and climatic similarity. The assumption was made that, in areas having these elements in common, the causes of differences in prosperity could be laid to the history of the areas in terms of feudal administration policies and the present condition of the villages in the technological sense.

Results of the inquiry were several. The three villages located on well-irrigated alluvial fans had greater prosperity than those located on less well-drained areas. Villages in which the feudal authorities had actively encouraged the growing of commercial crops on a large scale were the most prosperous today. Multiple sources of irrigation in the prosperous areas permitted a high degree of control over cropping practices. And a large variety of home industries in the prosperous areas permitted the farmers to maintain their standard of living in spite of smaller landholdings. The conclusion of the study was that prosperity in rural Japan is a function of diversified agriculture, a highly developed irrigation system, and multiple sources of income as expressed in off-the-farm employment and a wide variety of home industries. All these tend to overcome the lack of security to which the less developed areas are subject.

A comparative study of Nova Scotia has yielded many new insights into the comparative approach. Further uses of this approach may be enriched by statistical methods now being developed.

Statistical Approach. The variety of possibilities in using statistical techniques in human geography can be only briefly noted in this section. Statistical methods are most useful when used to explore problems that have traditionally concerned geographers, particularly when the data may be put in quantitative form and when such quantification answers significant questions. Since

[4] Robert D. Hodgson, *The Champlain-Richelieu Lowland: A Study in Historical Geography.* Doctoral dissertation, University of Michigan, 1951.
[5] Forrest R. Pitts, *Comparative Land Fertility and Land Potential in the Inland Sea and Peripheral Areas of Japan.* Doctoral dissertation, University of Michigan, 1955.

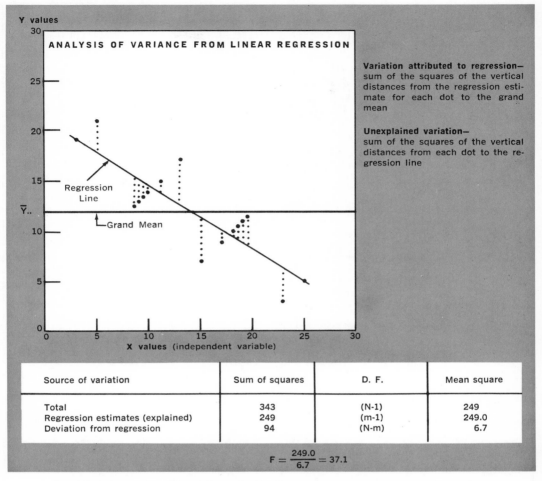

Fig. 27.6. A graphic illustration of calculations in the analysis of variance from linear regression.

these methods are tools of analysis, it follows that there is no distinct field called statistical geography.

With the coming into common use of high-speed computers, it has become possible to analyze for geographic purposes masses of numerical data, the processing of which was formerly too time-consuming for the individual investigator. For example, some 10,000 correlations between numbers of stores of 150 different types in a large number of American cities and towns were recently calculated by a UNIVAC computer in less than 30 minutes. Comparable speed is possible in calculating interrelations among other data.

The most common statistical formulation of geographic relationships has been through multiple regression, by which the relative influences of different factors under consideration can be sorted out and evaluated. The portions of information not explained by the regression equation—the residuals or "unexplained variation" (Fig. 27.6)—may be mapped by isopleths. Residuals are differences between values actually observed for a particular place and those estimated from a general-trend line. Values above the trend line are termed positive; values below the trend line are called negative residuals. The pattern obtained after placing residual values

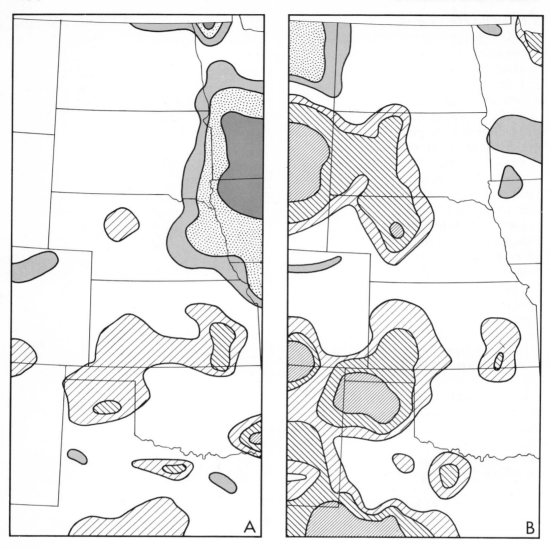

KEY FOR BOTH MAPS

MAP A: Persons per
        square mile

| Over -6 | -4 to -6 | -2 to -4 | -2 to +2 | +2 to +4 | +4 to +6 | Over +6 |

MAP B: Percent of
        actual density

| Over -200 | -100 to -200 | -50 to -100 | -50 to +50 | +50 to +100 | +100 to +200 | Over +200 |

Fig. 27.7. Maps showing the differences between (1) the actual rural farm population density and (2) the densities that would exist if there were perfect multiple
correlation among the variations of density and average annual precipitation and
distance from an urban center of 10,000 or more population. Map A expresses the
differences in density terms and Map B in percentages of actual densities. (Reprinted by permission of the Association of American Geographers.)

on a map may be clear enough to suggest to the trained geographer a factor that has been left out of consideration. A recent study of the Great Plains attempted to explain the rural density of population in terms of its relation to average annual rainfall and distance of the farmers from cities. The residuals of this study are plotted in Figure 27.7. Positive values of residuals cluster around the Corn Belt and along the Platte River. Negative values of residuals are found in former dust-bowl centers and in areas of rough topography. By looking at the maps, a geographer with field experience in the Great Plains could suggest other pertinent factors which would decrease the proportion of unexplained variation.

Regional geography is being aided by the application of statistical methods to geographic problems. The chi-square statistic, which measures the degree to which an actual distribution "fits" an expected or a theoretical distribution, has been used for delineation of regional boundaries. Discriminatory analysis may be used for assigning new areas to already delimited regions. A method of obtaining multifactor uniform regions has been developed. This technique permits the grouping of smaller regions into larger regions under the condition that each of the larger regions is as uniform as possible. That is, we start with exact values for a given number of indices, work by grouping alike regions together, and when a final pair of regions is grouped into a single whole, end with complete generalization. Somewhere between the two extremes of many small regions and one aggregate is the correct number of uniform regions the geographer is interested in.

Tests for covariance may be used to discover subregions within a region already delimited by some stated criterion. If two areas have the same rate of change in values in a certain direction, they are said to covary, even though the values may not be similar or overlap. Fig. 27.8 illustrates how covariance is calculated.

Other statistical studies have included the use of formal set theory in the field of agricultural geography in order to find the place where a specific land use will yield maximum profit. And in settlement geography there are possible applications of nearest-neighbor statistics in the identification of map patterns. Nearest-neighbor measures explain the statement, "All elements of group A are closer to each other than they are to any element of group B."

The nascent geographer need not shy away from a familiarity with statistical methods, for most of these techniques require only a short exposure, a term or so, to simple matrix algebra. Some types of problems remain in geography, however, that are too complex to be solved with explicit formulas. Such problems may be amenable to investigation by simulation.

Simulation Approach. In recent years a new approach has been devised for studying the spread of acceptance of new ideas, techniques, or items of material culture. The spread is imitated in a lifelike manner by using random numbers according to a simple list of directions on how and where to place the numbers in any given area. The placing of the numbers represents acceptance of the innovation.

The original work in developing the method was done by Torsten Hägerstrand of Sweden. He studied the acceptance of government farm subsidies, the spread of tuberculosis control in cattle, the spread of a layman's church organization, and the ownership of cars in Sweden. In general, it is necessary in each case that the geographer know the distribution of the first few acceptances of the innovation. This first distribution is very important to the later form of the distribution and cannot itself be simulated. All simulation must be based on a real-world distribution of first acceptances.

The results of simulation of diffusion are put on an isopleth map and compared with actual distributions. If they coincide fairly well, the simulation has been a success. If the

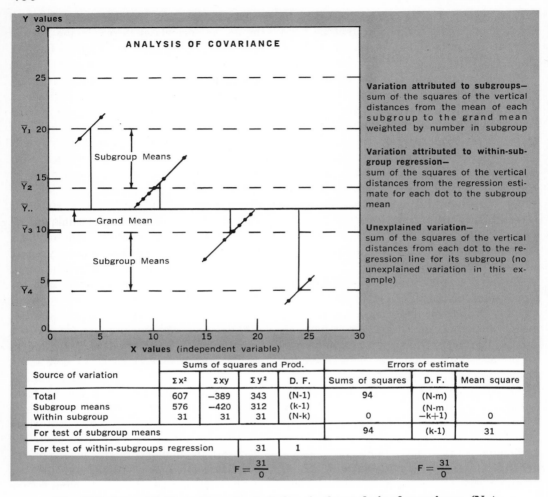

Fig. 27.8. A graphic illustration of calculations in the analysis of covariance. (Note that the values graphed are the same here as in Fig. 27.6.)

coincidence is not obvious, the method of choosing random numbers is altered in some way and the numbers reassigned until patterns coincide at an acceptable level. Figure 27.9 represents the actual distribution of farm subsidies in a Swedish area over a period of years. Isopleth lines are drawn where 20 per cent and 40 per cent of the farms entitled to the subsidy have accepted it by the year 1932. Figure 27.10 represents a simulation of acceptance of the subsidy in the same area after six generations. Each generation consists of one opportunity for each accepter to convince another person to accept the inno-

vation. The 20 per cent and 40 per cent isopleths of the simulation closely resemble those of the real situation.

Diffusion of ideas and techniques is most successful where many people in a small area accept an innovation and talk about it. The innovation is "in the air." Diffusion is least successful where scattered efforts are made and the individual innovator is miles from another accepter's moral support.

In the simulation technique lies a powerful new tool for human geographers concerned with the spread of ideas. Studies now under way involve the simulation of the

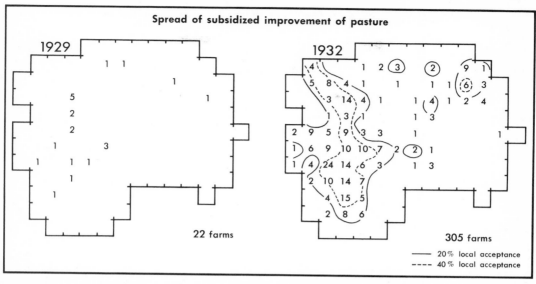

Spread of subsidized improvement of pasture

1929 — 22 farms

1932 — 305 farms

— 20% local acceptance
---- 40% local acceptance

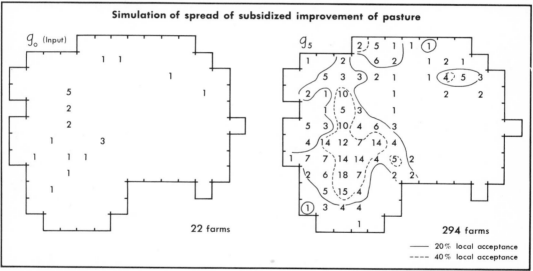

Simulation of spread of subsidized improvement of pasture

g_0 (Input) — 22 farms

g_5 — 294 farms

— 20% local acceptance
---- 40% local acceptance

Fig. 27.9 and 27.10. (Reprinted from Torsten Hagerstrand's "On Monte Carlo Simulation of Diffusion," from *Quantitative Geography*, William L. Garrison, ed., with permission of the publisher, Atherton Press, A Division of Prentice-Hall, Inc.)

spread of voluntary sterilization in India, the spread of hand tractors in Japan, and the spread of political institutions in East Africa. In the United States the spread of fluoridation of city water supplies is being studied by simulation methods.

It is also theoretically possible to start with an isopleth map of an uneven distribu-

tion at a given time, or stage of development, and, by subtracting random numbers rather than adding them to an area, produce a map that represents the distribution in a former time period. If current tests of this technique prove it to be feasible, another valuable new tool for human and historical geographers will become available.

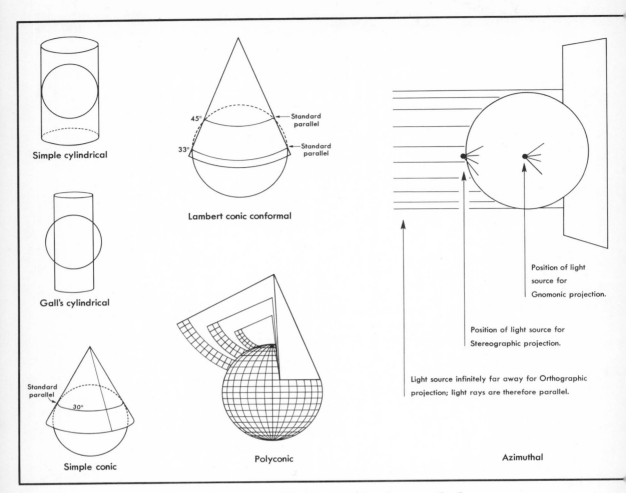

Fig. A.1. Diagrams showing principles of map projections.

APPENDIX A

Maps and Projections

Most people are familiar with the use of maps to show in convenient form the relation of areas or places to each other. Few are in practice familiar, however, with selection of scales for maps, or with the wide range of choices of map grids useful for varying purposes.

Scales and Selectivity

Geographers use the word *scale* to relate the sizes of the areas shown on their maps to the actual sizes of the areas. Thus, in practice, a map scale is always a fraction of the true size in nature. If we wish to show a distance of six miles on the earth by a map distance of six inches, the scale of the map is such that one map inch represents a mile, or 5280 feet, or 63,360 inches, upon the earth. We say that the *scale* of the map is 1/63,360 or 1:63,360. The standard United States Geological Survey (USGS) quadrangle map has a scale of 1:62,500. This is very close to being an "inch-to-a-mile" map.

A fair amount of detail may be shown on such a map. However, if we wish to show more area on a sheet of the same size, we must use a more compressed, or smaller, scale. We can think of *small-scale maps* as showing small amounts of detail, while *large-scale maps* show large amounts of detail for any given area. Geographers and other users of maps choose the scale which will most readily present the amount of detail they desire to show. For example, if a cartographer wanted to represent the rail system of the United States on a map the size of this page, he might choose a scale of 1:25,000,000. If he wanted to depict the details of the rail net within Chicago on a map the size of this page, he would likely choose to use a scale of 1:250,000.

Projections

A map is flat, and the earth is a sphere, though not perfectly so. The problem of portraying the details of the round earth upon a flat sheet of paper has occupied map makers for many centuries. Map makers naturally want to preserve the *true shape* and *true area relations* that are possible only on a globe. In the transfer of a spherical grid to the flat sheet, however, one property must be sacrificed to a degree if the other is emphasized.

Some of the map grids in common use may be described *as if* they were *projections* of the earth's *grid* from a *light source,* upon a sheet of paper *tangent* in some way to the globe. Most useful map grids are *constructed* from specific formulas. The tangent-type projections are three in number. The *cylindrical projections* are tangent along a great circle, most commonly the Equator or a meridian. *Conic projections* are tangent along one or two small circles, most commonly the lines of latitude. *Plane* or *azimuthal projections* are tangent at only one point upon the globe's surface (Fig. A.1).

Cylindrical projections include two Mercator projections, a Miller Cylindrical, a

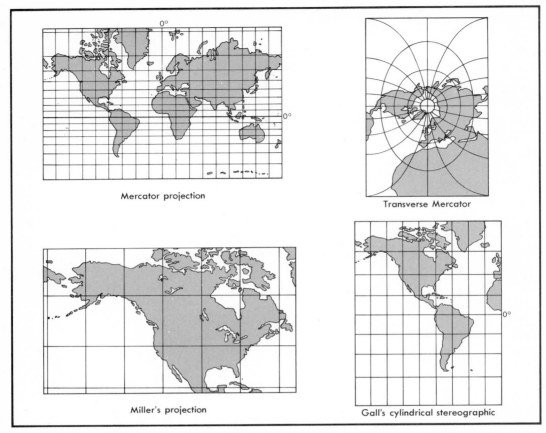

Fig. A.2. Cylindrical projections. (Transverse Mercator projection reprinted with permission from A. H. Robinson, *Elements of Cartography*, 1953, John Wiley and Sons, Inc.)

Gall's Stereographic, and others (Fig. A.2). The Mercator tangent to the Equator is used for ocean navigation, owing to the fact that parallels and meridians are shown as perpendicular to each other, which permits compass directions to be plotted on the sheet easily. The Transverse Mercator, which is tangent to a meridian rather than to the Equator, is now used for small-area topographic maps by both the USGS and the Japanese Geographical Survey Institute.

Conic projections include the Simple Conic, Lambert Conic Conformal, and the regular and Transverse Polyconics (Fig. A.3). The first two projections are useful for showing countries with a wide east-west

spread, and the third type is useful for countries with a long north-south dimension. The Polyconic was also used for the seven zones of USGS sheets until the adoption of the Transverse Mercator grid. The Transverse Polyconic may have any great circle as the "backbone" or central axis of successive conic maps, and it has been used effectively to show both the North Pacific Ocean (Fig. A.3) and the continent of Asia (see the National Geographic Society's *Map of Asia*).

Plane or azimuthal projections include the Azimuthal Equidistant, Lambert Equal-Area, Orthographic, Stereographic, and Gnomonic types, all of which may be centered at one of the poles (Fig. A.4), at a point

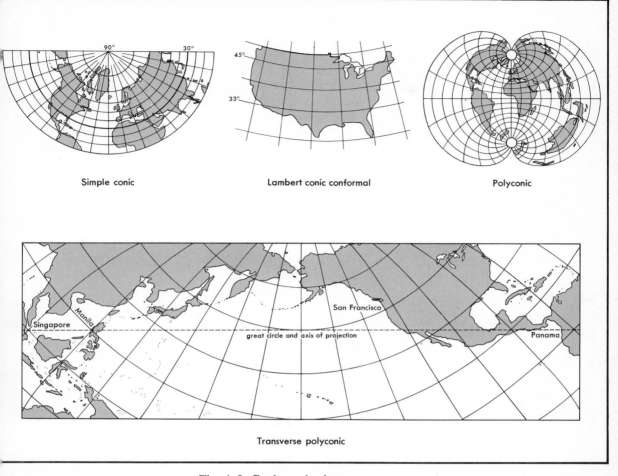

Simple conic

Lambert conic conformal

Polyconic

Transverse polyconic

Fig. A.3. Conic projections.

Fig. A.4. Various azimuthal projections centered at the North Pole.

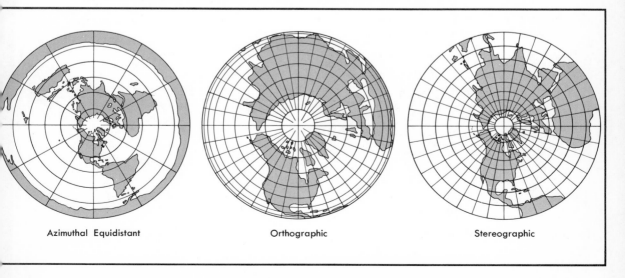

Azimuthal Equidistant

Orthographic

Stereographic

along the Equator (Fig. A.5), or at some intermediate point (Fig. A.6), in which instance it is called the Oblique case. The Gnonomic is the only map upon which all straight lines are great circles.

Constructed grids include the Bonne, the Sinusoidal, the Mollweide Equal-Area, Denoyer's Semi-Elliptical, the Aitoff Equal-Area (Fig. A.7), and the Bipolar Oblique Conic Conformal (constructed by Miller and Breimeister for the American Geographical Society's *Map of the Americas*). Inasmuch as some of these are ellipses, they can be "interrupted" at various places so that somewhat greater accuracy of shape or area may

be preserved. Most interrupt through water areas so that land areas may be better presented. These include the Boggs Eumorphic, Goode's Equal-Area, the Interrupted Sinusoidal, Goode's Homolosine Equal-Area, and Cahill's Projection (Fig. A.8). However, two fascinating maps of the oceans were published in the July, 1942, issue of the *Geographical Review*. Here the unity of the oceans was maintained by interrupting the continents (Fig. A.9).

The student can learn to use most projections properly without memorizing lists of "properties" if he keeps firmly in mind the properties of the earth's grid upon a globe.

Fig. A.5. Lambert Equal-Area projection centered on the Equator at 80 ° west.

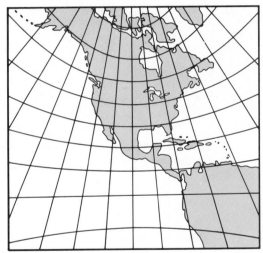

Fig. A.6. Oblique case of the Gnomonic projection.

Fig. A.7. Aitoff Equal-Area projection.

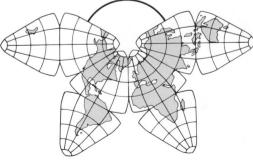

Fig. A.8. Cahill's projection.

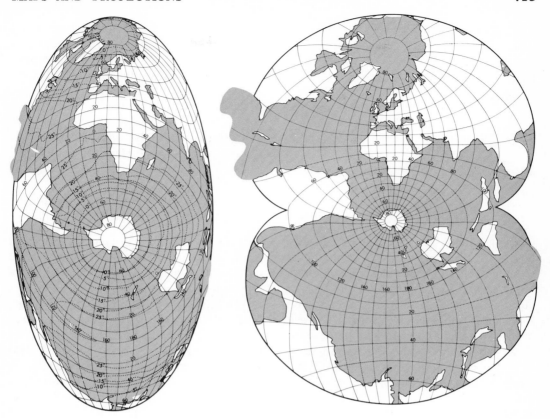

Fig. A.9. Maps showing the continuity of the world oceans. (Adapted from the *Geographical Review*, American Geographical Society, New York.)

APPENDIX B

The Use of Aerial Photographs
in Human Geography

The efforts of man to survey his surroundings has reached new levels with the advent of human flight. By means of the balloon, the airplane, and the space vehicle, man is enabled to view the earth from almost any elevation and with suitable perspective—today he can see the whole surface of the earth. This enables him to study human geography, as well as other subjects, in great detail. Such features as houses, roads, streams, canals, and land use can be studied with suitable aerial photographs and from these contour maps can be drawn, highways planned, crop acreages measured, timber stands estimated, and even a livestock census taken.

Most of the land surface of the earth has been photographed from the air, some of it many times, over a period of the last 30 years or more. Although the character of the photography varies widely, the most common aerial photography consists of overlapping vertical pictures, taken in straight-line flights. This means that every part of the land surface is shown on two or more photographs. Such photographs, when placed in the proper position and viewed with some type of stereoscope, provide three dimensional images. Even a single photograph provides a detailed "map" of most of the essential features of the land. Most vertical photographs are taken from planes flying at altitudes of from 5000 to 40,000 feet. With a given camera lens, one with a 12-inch focal length for example, the altitude of the plane controls the scale of the photograph. If great detail is wanted, the plane flies low, if wide coverage is wanted at less expense, the plane flies high.

The principle of viewing overlapping, vertical aerial photographs in order to see three dimensions, is similar to that employed by the old parlor stereoscope, in which two ground photographs taken of the same scene from different viewpoints were placed in slots and viewed through twin lenses, in order to focus one eye on one picture and one eye on the other picture. A small stereoscope, consisting of two lenses mounted on suitable legs so that it can be moved over the various parts of the aerial photographs, is commonly used.

In the preliminary inspection of a portion of two overlapping aerial photographs, as shown in Figure B.1, it will be observed, without the aid of a stereoscope, that although the pictures are generally similar they do have some noticeable differences. For example, in the upper margin of the pictures are two irregular, roughly parallel roads. It will be observed that these roads appear farther apart in the picture at the left than in the one at the right; and yet the scale of the pictures is the same. The small circles on the photographs indicate the centers—approximately the points directly below the camera. It will be observed that they are at some distance apart on the two photographs.

414

Fig. B.1. Portions of paired aerial photographs near Brookings, Oregon. Each rectangle is approximately 1.3 miles by 0.6 of a mile. The top of the pictures is to the north. The circles represent the centers of the original photographs.

These photographs are of an area located on a narrow coastal terrace in southern Oregon. Aside from the northeastern portion, the area represents relatively level land. When viewed with a stereoscope, many details of the landscape are visible on the photographs. The hilly, wooded portion has re-

cently been logged-over in part, and a great many irregular logging roads show up. On the terrace one of the conspicuous features is the main highway, U.S. Highway 101, which runs diagonally across the pictures. Other roads of various widths are also shown. It is possible to recognize and define the character of buildings, some in clusters of farm-steads. The field pattern is clearly visible and it is possible, in many cases, to determine the character of the crops. However, at the time these photographs were taken—late July —most of the crops had been harvested and the land had been cultivated in preparation for winter fallowing. With the aid of a stereoscope it can be seen that the dark bands, in the southern part of the picture, are belts of woodlands along gullies or shallow canyons that cut across the coastal plain. Other details of the relief also can be seen.

Not only are the features of the land recognizable on aerial photographs, but the features are susceptible to being mapped from the photographs. It is apparent that one photograph alone is not an accurate map because of distortion, but a pair affords the basis for making a highly accurate map of any of the features shown. For example, the photographs shown in Figure B.1 were taken as the first step in planning a new highway. The photographs enabled the planners to map the various significant features, such as the slope and character of the terrain, the types of vegetation encountered, the properties which had to be acquired for the new right-of-way, and the drainage problems to be solved.

Such aerial photographs are also of use to engineers, foresters, geologists, geographers, census takers, assessors, and various other persons. Altogether, many thousands of people are engaged today in the taking and interpretation of aerial photographs; and the great accumulation of these photographs in various government and private agencies constitutes a major resource for the study of human geography.

APPENDIX C

Climates

As suggested in Chapter 8, it is desirable to classify climatic data into categories or climatic types. Climate is the average condition and usual seasonal march of the weather, and it has long been the custom to refer to a kind of climate in terms of some place (the Sahara Climate, the Sudan Climate, etc.) rather than recite long lists of meteorological records. This makes it easier to compare the climate of similar regions and to correlate climate with natural vegetation, soils, and drainage features. At least one geographer has endeavored to correlate climate with human energy.

Of the numerous climatic systems devised, that of Wladimir Köppen is perhaps the best known and the most flexible. It can be presented in bare outline, or it can be elaborated even beyond the author's original conception.

The main reasons why people desire to classify climates are perhaps two. Classification brings a rather simple order out of the mass of records of rainfall, temperature, wind, etc. Secondly, it is evident that the great vegetation associations in nature are relatively few and cover broad areas. Since natural vegetation is in great part a response to climate, scholars reasoned that climatic classifications could be devised that would "fit" the zones of natural vegetation.

An American climatologist, C. Warren Thornthwaite, reasoned that if climate was classified to fit vegetation zones, a more *rational* system was needed that would give a "plant's eye view of climate" based upon the soil moisture available to the plant. Thornthwaite's 1948 system describes a climate by means of *four* categories. The four elements of this system are annual potential evapotranspiration, water surplus, water deficiency, and a moisture index. Because of the system's complexity, it is not presented in detail here. The reader is referred to the closely reasoned original.[1] Areas whose climates are classified by this system are generally presented in four separate maps to reduce the complexity of reading one map containing all the combinations.[2]

Most systems of classifying climate rely upon data for amounts of rainfall and degrees of temperature. Some systems have been devised using additional measures, but these remain of theoretical interest since, for vast areas of the earth, only rainfall and temperature data exist. In its broad outline the Köppen system is not unlike that of the early Greeks. Five broad zones are listed, four of which are based primarily on temperature:

A climates, humid and winterless.
B climates, dry (too dry for trees).
C climates, with mild winter and warm summer.
D climates, with severe winter and warm summer.
E climates, cold (too cold for trees).

Although there was not necessarily any indication of cause and effect relationships,

[1] C. W. Thornthwaite, "An Approach Toward a Rational Classification of Climate," *Geographical Review*, Vol. 38, No. 1 (January, 1948), pp. 55-94.

[2] For example: Jen-Hu Chang, "The Climate of China According to the New Thornthwaite Classification," *Annals,* American Association of Geographers, Vol. 45, No. 4 (December 1955), pp. 393-403.

417

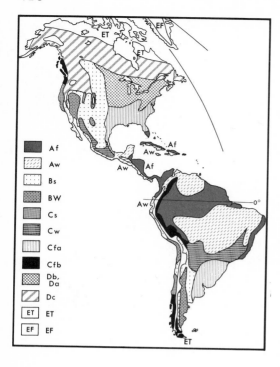

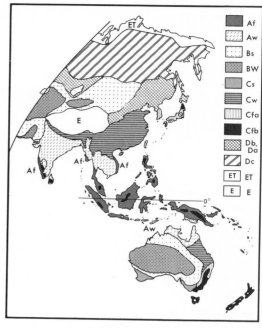

Fig. C.1, C.2, C.3. Generalized maps of the Köppen climates. (From *Syllabus for the Introductory Course in Economic Geography* by Richard Hartshorne and S. N. Dicken.)

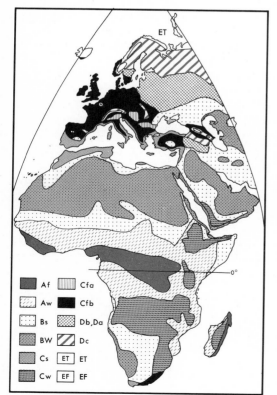

correlations of climate and human activity in particular climates were suggested in this text. Most of the world's people live in the *A, C,* and *D* climates. Most of the continental land masses of the earth are in the middle and high latitudes of the Northern Hemisphere; in the Southern Hemisphere, particularly in the higher latitudes, the continents are narrow or entirely missing. The distribution of climates is affected by relation to land and sea and by terrain. All the climates occur in both hemispheres except the severe-winter *D* climates, which depend on large masses of land in higher-middle latitudes. Because of the distribution of land masses, the climates are not symmetrically developed in both hemispheres (Figs. C.1, C.2, C.3).

The quantitative definitions of the major types are as follows:

A average temperature of the *coolest* month is above 64.4° F. (18° C.).

B arid climate (boundaries of *B* climates can be determined from the accompanying chart); *BS* denotes *steppe* areas, *BW* the true *desert* areas.

C average temperature of the *warmest* month is over 50° F. (10° C.); average temperature of the *coldest* month is between 64.4° F. (18° C.) and 32° F. (0° C.).

D average temperature of the *warmest* month is over 50° F. (10° C.); average temperature of the *coldest* month is less than 32° F. (0° C.).

E average temperature of the *warmest* month is below 50° F. (10° C.); if the warmest month averages between 32° F. (0° C.) and 50° F. (10° C.), it is a *tundra* climate, *ET;* if the average temperature of all months is below 32° F. (0° C.), it is a *frost* climate, *EF.*

Subsidiary symbols describing *rainfall* regimens are indicated by small letters, as follows:

f *in A climates,* at least 2.4 inches (6 centimeters) of rainfall in the driest month.
in C and D climates, at least 1.2 inches (3 centimeters) of rainfall in the driest month of summer.

s *in A climates,* dry season is at the high-sun periods; this climate is found on the coast south of Madras, India.
in B, C, and D climates, summer is dry, with the driest month of summer getting less than a third the amount of rain falling in the wettest month of winter.

m *in A climates only,* a monsoon regime (see nomograph).

w *in A climates,* a low-sun period dry season; one month must have less than 2.4 inches (6 centimeters) of rain; boundary between *Aw* and *Am* climates may be readily determined by reference to the chart.
in B, C, and D climates, rain falling in the wettest month of summer must be 10 or more times that falling in the driest month of winter.

n *in B and C climates,* frequent fog (*Nebel* in German).

Subsidiary symbols describing *temperature* regimens are indicated by small letters also, as follows:

a *in C and D climates only,* average temperature of the warmest month is over 71.6° F. (22° C.).

b *in C and D climates only,* average temperature of the warmest month is under 71.6° F. (22° C.).

c *in C and D climates only,* less than four months with temperatures over 50° F. (10° C.).

g *in A and C climates only,* a Ganges type of temperature regimen, where the hottest month comes before the high-sun solstice, and before the month with the most rainfall.

d *in D climates only,* average temperature of the coldest month is below −36.4° F. (−38° C.).

i *in those parts of A, B, and C climates* where the temperature range between the coldest and warmest month is less than 9 Fahrenheit degrees, or 5 Centigrade degrees; isothermal.

h *in B climates only,* average *annual* temperature is over 64.4° F. (18° C.).

k *in B climates only,* average *annual* temperature is under 64.4° F. (18° C.).

k' *in B climates only,* temperature of the warmest month is under 64.4° F. (18° C.).

Köppen Climate Chart

This nomograph (Fig. C.4) is presented here in place of the formulas that are generally used to determine classification of the dry climates for which rainfall and temperature data are available. Rainfall and temperature data are given in Table C.1. The reader of this book may wish to classify several of the stations by the Köppen criteria so that he will understand the maps of Köppen climates (Figs. C.1, C.2, and C.3).

In the paragraphs below descriptions are given of the various climates in outline form. With the definitions thus provided, the student can identify the climates from the climatic data for selected stations.[3]

[3] R. Hartshorne & S. N. Dicken, *Syllabus for the Introductory Course in Economic Geography* (Edwards Brothers, Ann Arbor, Michigan, 1939), pp. 81 ff.

AVERAGE
ANNUAL
TEMPERATURE
(in degrees Fahrenheit)   **AVERAGE ANNUAL PRECIPITATION** (in inches)

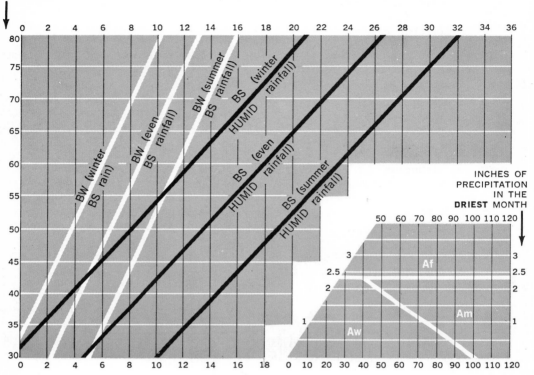

Fig. C.4. Nomograph for visual determination of Köppen A, B, and C climates.
To use the nomograph, find the month of lowest temperature. If it is above 64.4°
Fahrenheit, use the A climates graph at the lower right. Otherwise, enter the main
graph with annual temperature and precipitation averages. If the wettest month of
summer has more than *ten* times the precipitation of the driest month of winter,
use the right-hand lines. If the wettest month of winter has more than *three* times
the precipitation of the driest month of summer, use the left-hand lines. If neither
of these criteria applies, consider the precipitation "even."

I. TROPICAL CLIMATES (*A*)

Always hot—coolest month over 64° F.

A. TROPICAL RAINFOREST CLIMATE.
(Shown on map as Af.)

Type Area: Amazonia

1. Always hot. Growing season unbroken; 12 months long.
2. Always moist. No prolonged dry season. (If the total rainfall is great, 80 to 100 inches, a short rainless period is scarcely significant.)
3. Little seasonal variation in temperature; annual range less than 19° F.
4. Maximum rain at the time of vertical sun, minimum with low sun. Many stations near the equator show two maxima and two minima.
5. Cloudiness, humidity, and sensible temperature high.

6. Luxuriant, stratified, rainforest vegetation. Lianas, Epiphytes, etc.
7. Soils: Red lateritic tropical soils; some laterites.
8. Location: Belt near the equator 0–10 degrees wide; windward margins of highlands in the trade wind belt; highlands exposed to monsoon winds. In the latter there is a marked dry season, but because the total rainfall is so great, rainforest conditions exist to a large extent.

NOTE: To distinguish Tropical Rainforest (Af) from Winter Dry Tropical (Aw):

If the total annual rainfall is 40   60   80   100 inches, the driest month must have over 2.4   1.6   0.8   0.0 inches.

B. WINTER DRY TROPICAL CLIMATE. (Aw) Savanna.

Type Area: The Sudan

1. Always hot. Growing season (temperature aspects) unbroken; 12 months long.
2. Distinct dry season at time of lowest sun, maximum rain at time of highest sun. Rainy season may be divided by a short dry season.
3. Rainforest conditions in the wet season; desert conditions in dry season.
4. A transition from forest to steppe; dry season forests or grassy vegetation with drought-resistant trees, isolated in groves or near streams.
5. Soils: Red lateritic tropical soils; perhaps some chernozems in drier portions.
6. Location: On poleward margin of Tropical Rainforest; the lee side of highlands in the trade wind belt.

II. THE DRY CLIMATES (B)

Areas of deficient moisture

(The exact measurement of "moisture deficiency" is based not only on amount of rainfall but also on evaporation as determined by seasonal temperatures and rainfall. The formulas are too complicated to be given here; refer to Fig. C.4.)

A. DESERT CLIMATE. (BW) Arid.

Type area: Sahara

1. Extreme drought; moisture supply insufficient for grass.
2. Temperature conditions similar to those of adjacent humid regions; growing season anywhere from 1 to 12 months.
3. Subdivisions: hot desert and cold desert, separated by 32° F. isotherm for coldest month.
4. Plants adapted to extreme aridity: Cactus, agave, creosote bush, saltbush. Few vegetationless areas except the moving sand dunes.
5. Soils: Gray and brown desert soils.
6. Location: West coasts in lee of trade winds, latitude 20°–30°; remote interiors of continents, latitude 35°–45°.

B. STEPPE CLIMATE. (BS) Semiarid.

Type area: The Great Plains

1. Rainfall sufficient for closed grass formation but not for trees.
2. Effect of rainfall depends on the temperature and seasonable distribution of rain (this is true of all climates) so that a given amount of rain is more effective if accompanied by low temperatures.
3. Rainy season and temperature conditions (but not the amount of rain) similar to adjacent humid regions; growing season anywhere from 1 to 12 months. Two subdivisions: Hot Steppe and Cold Steppe, separated by isotherm of 32° F. for the coldest month.
4. Vegetation: Grass; tall grass in the more humid areas, short grass elsewhere.
5. Soils: Dark brown soils and chernozems.
6. Location: Transition zones between the arid and the humid areas, especially in the continental interiors.

III. TEMPERATE MESOTHERMAL CLIMATES (*C*)

Coldest month 32°–64° F.

(These climates are distinguished by having a *mild* cool season [winter] without permanent frost. In the first three the winters are generally very short, the warm season much longer and except in highlands as hot as in the tropical climates.)

A. WINTER DRY TEMPERATE CLIMATE. (Cw)

Type areas: Abyssinia, Ganges, Gran Chaco

1. Dry, mild winter; rainy, hot summer. (Rainiest month must have at least ten times the rain of the driest month.)
2. Growing season between 7 and 11 months.
3. Park Landscape: Scattered trees with grass.
4. Soils: Red and yellow subtropical loams.
5. Location: Adjacent to Winter Dry Tropical (Aw) in higher latitudes or in elevated areas.

B. SUMMER DRY TEMPERATE CLIMATE. (Mediterranean) (Cs)

Type area: Lands bordering Mediterranean Sea

1. Dry summer, rainy mild winter. (Rainiest month has at least three times the rain of driest month.) Regions near the sea usually have cool summer; inland the summers are hot.
2. Growing season between 7 and 11 months.
3. Grassy vegetation with forest in favorable location; *maquis, scrub,* or *chaparral* developed locally.
4. Soils: Red and yellow subtropical loams; *terra rosa.*
5. Location: West coasts of continents, latitude 30°–40°.

C. HOT SUMMER RAINY TEMPERATE. (Carolina) (Cfa)

Type area: Carolinas

1. Rain all the year (some snow in poleward portion), hot summers— warmest month over 72° F.
2. Growing season between 7 and 11 months.
3. Slight maximum of rainfall in summer or spring, but no dry season.
4. Broad-leaved deciduous forests; a few prairies; "pine barrens" on certain sandy soils.
5. Soils: Red and yellow subtropical loams; some humid prairie soils.
6. Location: East coasts, latitude 30°–40°.

D. COOL SUMMER RAINY TEMPERATE. (Puget Sound) (Cfb)

Type areas: Puget Sound, British Isles

1. Rain all the year with winter maximum in most localities.
2. Mild summer; warmest month under 72° F. Growing season generally between 4 and 6 months.
3. Range of temperature less than any types outside of tropical areas; especially low along coasts.
4. Deciduous and coniferous forests.
5. Soils: Gray and brown forest soils; podzols in poleward portions.
6. Location: West coasts, latitude 38°–62°.

NOTE: In terms of growing season, vegetation, and soils (and also agriculture), this type (Cfb) is much more like the following type (Db) than like the other C climates.

IV. HUMID MICROTHERMAL CLIMATES (*D*)

Warmest month over 50° F.
Coldest month under 32° F.

(These are the humid continental climates, characterized by a shorter warm season, which may include truly tropical hot spells, and a longer cold season including a continuous frozen season which may have truly polar cold spells. At all seasons the weather is influenced by cyclonic storms and is more fluctuating and uncertain than in any other type.)

Based on rainfall distribution and summer temperatures the following types can be recognized: Dfa, Dfb, Dfc, Dwa, Dwb, Dwc, but these are combined for the purposes of this book into the two following:

A. WARM SUMMER MICROTHERMAL CLIMATE. (Db—includes Dfa, Dfb, Dwa, Dwb.)

Type area: Great Lakes Region

1. Evenly distributed precipitation; snow in winter remains on the frozen ground for at least a few weeks up to 4 or 5 months.
2. Cyclonic storms frequent in winter, sudden changes in the weather, blizzards.
3. At least four months above 50° F. Growing season, 3 to 6 months, is therefore long enough for cultivation of at least hardier grains.
4. Hardwood and mixed forests with local prairies; coniferous forests in poleward portions.
5. Soils: Gray and brown forest soils; humid prairie soils; chernozems on drier margins; podzols on poleward margins.
6. Location: In the northern hemisphere only; interiors and east coasts of continents; higher middle latitudes.

B. SHORT SUMMER MICROTHERMAL CLIMATE. (Taiga) (Dc—includes Dfc, Dwc.)

Type area: Hudson Bay

1. Differs from Db in shorter growing season, longer frozen season, and generally less precipitation. Less than four months above 50°

F.; frost-free season much shorter; growing season 1 to 3 months.
2. Frozen period usually more than half the year; includes areas with lowest winter temperatures observed on earth's surface.
3. Coniferous forest, thin on northern margin. Many bogs.
4. Soils: Podzols.
5. Continental location 50°–70° north, also higher elevations 40°–60° north latitude.

V. COLD CLIMATES (*E*)

Warmest month below 50° F.

A. TUNDRA CLIMATE. (ET)

Type areas: Coast of Greenland, Northern Canada

1. Warmest month 32°–50° F. Too cold for tree growth. Precipitation mostly in summer.
2. Soil continually frozen; a few inches or more at surface thaws in summer.
3. Growing season: From a few days to a month, but never sure as frosts may occur at any time.
4. Vegetation: Mosses and lichens; some grasses and flowering plants.
5. Soils: Tundra.
6. Location: Lowlands in poleward regions; high plateaus and mountains just below snowline.

B. GLACIAL CLIMATE. (EF)

Type areas: Interior of Greenland, Antarctica

1. Warmest month below 32° F. Too low to melt accumulated snow and ice. No growing season whatever.
2. Almost lifeless; some algae and bacteria.
3. No soil; ground permanently covered with ice and snow; bare rock where blown clear.
4. Location: Only in high altitudes; chiefly in polar regions, but in highest mountains in any latitude, even on equator.

TABLE C.1

Climatic Data for Selected Stations[4]

Climatic stations are arranged in alphabetic order by continents. Geographic coordinates are given in degrees and minutes of arc. Altitude is in feet; temperature is in degrees Fahrenheit; and precipitation is in inches. The figures in the *Year* column refer to *average* temperature and *total* precipitation.

NORTH AMERICA

Station	Location ° '	Alt.	Jan.	Feb.	Mar.	Apr.	May	June	July	Aug.	Sept.	Oct.	Nov.	Dec.	Year
Abitibi	48 43 N	850	0	1	15	32	46	56	64	61	52	40	25	8	33
	79 22 W		1.8	1.4	2.1	1.2	2.6	2.4	2.6	2.6	2.6	2.9	2.1	2.0	26.4
Acapulco	16 50 N	10	78	78	79	80	83	83	83	83	81	81	80	79	81
	99 56 W		0.6	0.0	0.0	0.0	1.7	1.7	6.0	6.3	14.7	5.9	1.9	0.7	39.5
Anchorage	61 13 N	132	12	20	24	35	45	54	57	55	48	36	23	14	35
	149 50 W		0.8	0.7	0.6	0.4	0.5	0.6	1.6	2.6	2.5	2.1	1.1	0.8	14.3
Banff	51 25 N	4521	13	16	23	37	45	52	57	54	47	39	24	19	36
	115 30 W		1.4	0.8	1.3	1.2	2.4	3.0	2.5	2.4	1.7	1.2	1.8	1.1	20.7
Bermuda	32 18 N	150	63	63	63	66	70	76	80	81	79	74	69	65	71
	64 46 W		4.4	4.6	4.8	4.0	4.4	4.3	4.6	5.4	5.2	5.9	4.9	4.8	57.4
Boston	42 20 N	124	27	28	35	45	57	67	71	69	63	52	41	32	49
	71 09 W		3.4	3.1	3.7	3.7	2.9	3.2	3.3	3.3	3.5	2.8	2.9	3.4	38.9
Chicago	41 30 N	610	25	27	37	48	59	69	75	73	66	54	39	28	50
	87 24 W		1.8	1.6	2.7	2.6	3.4	3.4	3.1	3.3	3.5	2.4	2.1	1.8	31.8
Columbus	39 56 N	918	29	30	40	51	62	71	75	73	67	55	42	32	52
	82 56 W		2.9	2.1	3.4	2.7	3.1	3.3	3.5	3.2	2.6	2.4	2.2	2.6	34.1
Craig Harbor	76 12 N	12	−23	−23	−15	−4	17	33	41	38	29	12	5	−17	7
	79 35 W		0.4	0.2	0.5	0.5	0.5	0.8	0.9	1.8	0.5	1.4	0.8	0.2	8.5
Denver	39 32 N	5292	30	32	39	47	56	66	72	71	62	50	39	33	50
	105 00 W		0.3	0.6	1.3	2.1	2.0	1.3	1.6	1.5	1.2	1.0	0.6	0.7	14.0
El Paso	31 47 N	3762	45	49	56	63	72	80	81	79	74	63	52	45	63
	106 30 W		0.4	0.4	0.3	0.3	0.3	0.7	1.6	1.6	1.3	0.7	0.5	0.5	8.6
Fort Chipewyan	58 46 N	714	−13	−7	5	27	42	53	59	56	44	32	14	−2	26
	111 14 W		0.7	0.5	0.7	0.7	0.8	1.4	2.3	1.6	1.2	0.9	0.9	0.8	12.6
Havana	23 08 N	79	72	72	74	77	79	82	82	82	81	79	76	72	77
	82 22 W		2.9	1.8	1.9	2.2	4.8	6.4	4.8	5.4	5.8	6.6	3.1	2.4	48
Honolulu	21 19 N	38	71	71	71	73	75	77	78	78	78	77	74	72	75
	157 52 W		3.8	4.2	3.8	2.2	1.8	1.1	1.3	1.4	1.5	1.9	4.2	4.2	31.6
Juneau	58 18 N	72	27	30	34	41	48	54	57	55	50	43	36	31	42
	134 24 W		7.2	5.6	5.4	5.5	5.2	4.0	5.0	7.3	10.2	11.2	9.1	7.6	83.2
Los Angeles	34 03 N	361	54	56	57	60	62	65	70	71	69	65	61	55	62
	118 15 W		3.2	3.3	2.6	1.0	0.4	0.1	0.0	0.0	0.2	0.5	1.1	2.4	14.8
Mazatlan	23 12 N	13	68	68	70	72	76	81	83	83	83	80	75	70	76
	106 25 W		0.7	0.5	0.2	0.1	0.1	1.3	6.1	8.3	7.5	2.3	0.8	0.7	28.6
Merida	20 58 N	72	72	74	78	80	83	82	81	81	81	78	76	73	78
	89 37 W		0.9	0.7	1.1	0.9	2.8	6.8	4.4	5.8	5.5	3.2	1.8	1.3	35.2
Miami	25 28 N	8	66	68	72	74	79	81	82	82	81	77	73	69	76
	80 07 W		2.4	2.0	2.4	3.4	7.1	7.4	5.3	6.4	8.9	9.0	3.3	1.7	59.2
Montgomery	32 30 N	240	48	51	58	65	73	80	82	81	76	66	56	49	66
	86 20 W		5.1	5.5	6.4	4.3	3.8	4.2	4.7	4.2	2.9	2.4	3.1	4.5	51.1
Montreal	45 30 N	187	13	14	26	41	55	65	70	67	59	47	33	20	42
	73 35 W		3.8	3.2	3.5	2.5	3.0	3.5	3.7	3.5	3.5	3.3	3.5	3.7	40.6
New Orleans	30 00 N	9	54	57	63	70	76	82	84	83	80	73	63	57	70
	90 30 W		4.5	4.1	5.0	5.5	5.2	5.0	6.8	6.1	5.3	3.0	3.9	5.9	60.3
New York	40 25 N	10	33	33	41	50	61	70	75	73	67	57	46	36	54
	74 00 W		3.3	3.4	3.6	3.4	3.1	3.6	4.2	4.2	3.7	3.5	2.5	3.3	41.6
Omaha	41 16 N	1105	22	25	37	51	62	72	77	75	66	54	39	27	50
	95 56 W		0.8	0.9	1.2	2.0	3.0	4.0	3.1	3.2	3.4	1.9	1.3	0.9	25.5
Phoenix	33 16 N	1114	51	56	61	68	77	85	90	89	84	72	60	53	72
	112 02 W		0.8	0.9	0.7	0.4	0.1	0.1	1.0	0.9	0.7	0.4	0.7	0.9	7.6
St. Johns	47 34 N	125	23	22	28	35	43	51	59	59	54	45	37	29	40
	52 42 W		5.4	5.1	4.5	4.2	3.6	3.6	3.7	3.6	3.8	5.4	6.1	4.9	53.8
Salt Lake City	40 27 N	4220	29	34	42	51	60	69	78	76	66	55	41	33	54
	111 31 W		1.3	1.6	2.0	1.8	1.9	0.7	0.6	0.9	1.0	1.4	1.3	1.3	15.8

[4] From *Weather and Climate*, C. E. Koeppe and G. C. De Long. Copyright, 1958. McGraw-Hill Book Company, Inc. Used by permission.

Station	Location ° '	Alt.	Jan.	Feb.	Mar.	Apr.	May	June	July	Aug.	Sept.	Oct.	Nov.	Dec.	Year
San Francisco	37 27 N	8	49	51	53	54	56	57	57	58	60	59	56	51	55
	122 16 W		4.4	4.0	3.0	1.1	0.6	0.2	0.0	0.0	0.4	1.0	2.1	3.6	20.2
San Juan	18 29 N	82	75	74	75	76	78	79	80	80	80	79	78	76	78
	66 07 W		4.1	2.8	3.0	4.4	5.1	5.3	5.7	5.9	6.1	5.5	7.0	5.7	60.5
Seattle	47 27 N	376	40	42	45	50	55	60	64	64	59	52	46	42	52
	122 15 W		4.9	3.5	2.8	2.0	1.7	1.4	0.6	0.7	1.6	2.7	4.8	5.2	31.8
Spokane	47 55 N	1943	27	31	40	48	56	62	70	68	59	48	38	31	48
	117 28 W		1.8	1.4	1.2	1.0	1.2	1.1	0.5	0.6	0.8	1.1	2.0	2.0	14.6
Springfield	37 17 N	1324	34	35	45	56	64	73	77	76	70	58	46	36	56
	93 22 W		2.4	1.8	3.3	3.8	4.8	5.1	3.5	4.2	3.4	3.2	2.6	2.0	40.2
Veracruz	19 10 N	49	71	73	75	79	81	82	82	82	80	76	75	71	77
	96 10 W		0.4	0.6	0.6	0.1	4.3	12.5	14.8	8.9	11.6	9.0	3.2	2.0	68.0
Washington	38 54 N	112	34	35	43	54	64	72	77	74	68	57	46	36	55
	77 03 W		3.2	3.0	3.5	3.3	3.6	3.9	4.4	4.0	3.1	3.0	2.5	3.0	40.5

SOUTH AMERICA

Station	Location ° '	Alt.	Jan.	Feb.	Mar.	Apr.	May	June	July	Aug.	Sept.	Oct.	Nov.	Dec.	Year
Asuncion	25 21 S	312	80	80	78	72	67	63	64	66	70	73	76	80	72
	57 35 W		5.7	5.2	4.8	5.5	4.7	2.8	2.3	1.6	3.3	5.6	5.8	6.1	53.4
Barra do Corda	5 35 S	266	78	77	77	77	77	76	76	78	80	80	80	79	78
	45 28 W		6.7	8.7	8.0	6.1	2.3	1.0	0.7	0.7	1.0	2.5	3.9	5.7	47.3
Bogota	4 34 N	8678	56	58	59	59	59	58	57	57	57	58	58	58	58
	74 05 W		2.3	2.4	4.1	5.7	4.5	2.4	2.0	2.2	2.4	6.4	4.6	2.6	41.6
Caracas	10 30 N	3050	69	69	69	73	74	73	72	73	73	71	71	69	71
	66 55 W		0.9	0.3	0.6	1.2	2.8	4.0	4.8	3.8	4.2	4.4	3.3	1.6	31.9
Ciudad Bolivar	8 08 N	125	79	80	81	82	82	80	80	81	82	82	81	79	81
	63 33 W		0.6	0.4	0.3	1.2	5.1	5.5	7.1	6.7	4.7	3.1	3.8	1.6	40.1
Cuyaba	15 36 S	541	80	80	80	79	77	74	75	77	81	81	81	80	79
	56 06 W		9.5	8.3	8.3	4.0	2.0	0.3	0.2	1.1	2.0	4.5	5.9	8.1	53.6
Evangelists Island	52 25 S	174	47	47	46	45	41	40	37	39	40	42	43	45	43
	75 12 W		12.8	8.9	12.3	11.6	8.8	8.5	8.9	8.6	7.7	9.0	10.3	9.6	117.0
Jujuy	24 11 S	4166	71	69	66	62	57	52	52	55	62	65	69	70	63
	65 22 W		6.5	5.5	5.4	1.3	0.5	0.2	0.2	0.1	0.4	1.5	2.6	5.2	29.4
Lima	12 02 S	518	73	74	74	70	66	63	61	61	61	63	66	70	67
	77 02 W		0.0	0.0	0.0	0.0	0.1	0.2	0.4	0.4	0.4	0.2	0.1	0.0	1.8
Maracaibo	10 38 N	26	81	82	83	84	84	85	85	85	84	82	82	82	83
	71 37 W		0.1	0.0	0.3	0.5	2.5	2.5	2.2	2.4	3.0	4.8	3.3	0.6	22.2
Quixeramobim	5 16 S	679	83	82	81	81	80	80	80	80	82	83	83	83	86
	39 15 W		3.1	3.5	5.7	4.8	3.7	1.5	0.8	0.4	0.1	0.0	0.2	1.1	24.1
San Juan	18 30 S	2140	78	76	71	62	54	47	48	50	59	65	71	76	63
	66 12 W		0.7	0.3	0.3	0.1	0.1	0.0	0.0	0.0	0.1	0.3	0.2	0.4	2.5
Santiago	33 25 S	1703	68	67	63	57	52	48	47	48	55	56	61	65	56
	70 45 W		0.0	0.1	0.2	0.6	2.3	3.2	3.4	2.4	1.2	0.6	0.2	0.2	14.4
Ushuaia	54 50 S	8	50	49	47	41	37	33	34	35	39	43	44	49	47
	68 20 W		1.7	2.1	1.7	1.9	1.5	1.6	1.2	0.9	1.2	1.5	1.9	1.8	19.0

EUROPE

Station	Location ° '	Alt.	Jan.	Feb.	Mar.	Apr.	May	June	July	Aug.	Sept.	Oct.	Nov.	Dec.	Year
Aberdeen	57 10 N	79	39	39	40	43	48	53	56	56	53	48	42	39	46
	2 06 W		2.2	2.1	2.2	2.1	2.3	1.9	2.9	2.8	2.6	3.1	3.1	3.1	30.4
Amsterdam	52 23 N	5	38	38	42	47	56	59	63	63	59	51	42	40	50
	4 55 E		2.0	1.5	1.9	1.6	1.9	2.0	2.9	3.2	2.5	3.4	2.3	2.7	27.9
Barcelona	41 23 N	131	46	48	51	56	62	68	74	73	69	61	54	48	59
	2 08 E		1.4	1.3	1.7	2.0	1.5	1.3	1.1	1.4	3.0	1.8	1.7	21.2
Bergen	60 24 N	144	34	34	36	42	49	55	58	57	52	45	39	36	45
	5 19 E		8.8	7.1	6.1	4.4	4.7	4.2	5.6	7.7	9.3	9.2	8.7	8.7	84.6
Bordeaux	44 50 N	154	41	44	48	54	60	65	70	70	66	57	48	42	55
	0 34 E		2.5	2.0	2.3	2.5	2.8	2.8	1.9	2.0	2.6	3.6	3.2	2.7	30.9
Bucharest	44 29 N	302	27	33	42	52	62	69	73	72	64	54	41	34	52
	26 08 E		1.3	1.1	1.7	1.7	2.5	3.5	2.7	2.0	1.6	1.7	1.9	1.6	23.3
Copenhagen	55 40 N	16	32	32	34	42	51	59	62	61	55	47	40	34	46
	12 34 E		1.3	1.3	1.5	1.3	1.5	1.8	2.3	2.6	1.8	2.1	1.7	1.8	20.7
Corinth	37 54 N	16	50	50	53	59	66	75	81	80	74	68	59	52	64
	22 53 E		2.6	2.1	1.5	1.2	0.9	0.5	0.2	0.2	0.9	1.9	2.2	2.9	17.1
Gibraltar	36 06 N	90	55	56	57	60	65	69	73	75	72	66	60	56	64
	5 21 W		4.6	4.5	4.7	2.7	1.6	0.5	0.0	0.1	1.3	3.3	6.4	5.4	35.1
Graz	47 04 N	1211	29	32	40	48	58	62	67	65	59	50	41	31	49
	15 26 E		1.0	1.1	1.6	2.7	3.3	4.9	4.8	4.6	3.7	3.4	2.1	1.5	34.8

Station	Location ° '	Alt.	Jan.	Feb.	Mar.	Apr.	May	June	July	Aug.	Sept.	Oct.	Nov.	Dec.	Year
Helsinki	60 10 N	39	21	20	25	34	46	57	62	60	51	42	32	25	40
	24 57 E		1.8	1.5	1.4	1.4	1.7	1.8	2.2	2.9	2.5	2.6	2.5	2.0	24.3
Istanbul	40 58 N	59	43	40	47	53	62	70	74	75	68	63	54	47	58
	28 50 E		3.3	2.8	2.2	1.6	1.2	1.3	1.0	1.4	3.7	2.1	2.6	4.6	27.8
Lisbon	38 43 N	312	51	52	55	58	62	67	71	72	69	62	57	51	60
	9 09 W		3.0	3.1	3.0	2.4	2.4	0.7	0.2	0.2	1.3	2.9	3.9	3.4	26.5
London	51 28 N	18	41	41	43	47	55	60	63	62	58	51	44	41	51
	0 19 W		1.9	1.6	1.6	1.6	1.8	2.0	2.2	2.2	2.0	2.6	2.3	2.3	23.9
Milan	45 28 N	482	32	38	46	55	63	70	75	73	66	56	44	36	54
	9 10 E		2.4	2.3	2.7	3.4	4.1	3.3	2.8	3.2	3.5	4.7	4.3	3.0	39.8
Moscow	55 45 N	480	12	15	23	38	53	62	66	63	52	40	28	17	39
	37 35 E		1.1	0.9	1.2	1.5	1.9	2.0	2.8	2.9	2.2	1.4	1.6	1.5	21.0
Munich	48 11 N	1670	28	31	37	46	54	60	63	62	56	46	36	30	46
	11 33 E		1.7	1.4	1.9	2.7	3.7	4.6	4.7	4.2	3.2	2.2	1.9	1.9	34.2
Naples	40 52 N	489	47	49	52	57	64	71	76	76	71	63	55	49	61
	14 15 E		4.2	3.7	3.4	3.4	2.4	1.7	0.5	1.1	3.2	5.4	5.6	5.3	39.9
Oslo	59 55 N	82	25	26	29	40	51	60	63	60	52	42	33	26	42
	10 43 E		1.3	1.1	1.2	1.3	1.5	1.9	2.7	3.2	2.4	2.4	1.7	1.6	22.1
Paris	48 48 N	164	38	39	44	50	56	62	66	65	60	52	43	40	51
	2 30 E		1.5	1.2	1.6	1.7	2.1	2.3	2.2	2.2	2.0	2.3	1.8	1.7	22.6
Prague	50 06 N	1217	30	32	39	48	57	63	67	65	59	49	39	32	48
	14 17 E		0.9	0.8	1.1	1.5	2.4	2.8	2.6	2.2	1.7	1.2	1.2	0.9	19.1
Reykjavik	64 09 N	52	32	33	35	39	45	49	52	51	46	39	35	33	41
	21 57 W		3.9	3.3	2.7	2.4	1.9	1.9	1.9	2.0	3.5	3.4	3.7	3.5	34.1
Sarajevo	43 52 N	2091	31	32	42	49	56	62	66	65	59	50	42	34	49
	18 26 E		2.4	2.3	2.9	2.9	3.4	3.9	2.5	2.4	3.1	3.7	3.2	2.9	35.5
Tromsö	69 35 N	20	26	24	27	32	39	47	52	51	44	36	30	27	36
	19 00 E		4.3	4.4	3.1	2.3	1.9	2.2	2.2	2.8	4.8	4.6	4.4	3.8	40.8
Valencia	51 50 N	30	44	44	45	48	52	57	59	59	57	52	48	45	51
	10 20 W		5.5	5.2	4.5	3.7	3.2	3.2	3.8	4.8	4.1	5.6	5.5	6.6	55.6

ASIA

Station	Location ° '	Alt.	Jan.	Feb.	Mar.	Apr.	May	June	July	Aug.	Sept.	Oct.	Nov.	Dec.	Year
Akmolinsk	51 12 N	1148	0	3	12	33	56	66	70	65	53	36	19	8	35
	71 23 E		0.6	0.5	0.5	0.6	1.0	1.8	1.4	1.5	1.0	1.0	0.7	0.6	11.2
Alexandrovsk	50 54 N	52	0	4	15	32	42	52	60	62	54	40	23	8	33
	142 10 E		1.7	0.9	1.5	1.4	1.4	1.5	2.5	3.1	3.6	2.7	2.0	2.2	24.5
Baghdad	33 15 N	220	47	53	60	70	81	90	94	94	87	76	61	50	72
	44 25 E		1.1	1.1	1.2	0.8	0.2	0.0	0.0	0.0	0.1	0.8		1.2	6.6
Bangalore	12 59 N	3021	68	72	77	80	78	74	72	72	72	72	70	68	73
	77 28 E		0.2	0.3	0.6	1.2	4.5	3.0	4.1	5.8	7.4	6.2	2.4	0.4	36.0
Bangkok	13 44 N	7	77	80	84	85	85	84	83	83	82	81	79	77	82
	100 30 E		0.3	0.8	1.4	2.3	7.8	6.3	6.3	6.9	12.0	8.1	2.6	0.2	55.0
Bombay	19 00 N	37	74	75	78	82	85	82	80	79	79	81	79	76	79
	72 48 E		0.1	0.0	0.1	0.0	0.7	20.6	27.3	16.0	11.8	2.4	0.4	0.0	79.4
Cape Chelyuskin	77 43 N	20	−14	−13	−19	−5	15	30	35	33	27	13	−7	−15	7
	104 17 E		0.2	0.1	0.0	0.1	0.1	0.5	1.0	0.9	0.3	0.3	0.2	0.1	3.8
Cherrapunji	25 15 N	4309	53	55	61	64	66	68	69	69	66	61	55		63
	91 44 E		0.5	2.7	9.4	28.2	46.3	95.9	98.5	79.8	38.0	21.3	3.2	0.3	424.1
Darjeeling	27 04 N	7376	40	42	50	56	58	60	62	61	59	55	48	42	53
	88 25 E		0.6	1.1	1.8	3.8	8.7	24.9	32.3	26.1	18.4	4.5		0.2	122.7
Haifa	32 49 N	33	54	58	60	66	71	76	80	82	80	75	65	58	69
	35 00 E		6.1	3.5	2.1	1.0	0.3	0.0	0.0	0.0	0.1	0.8	3.6	6.4	23.9
Hong Kong	22 18 N	109	60	59	63	70	77	81	82	82	81	76	69	63	72
	114 10 E		1.3	1.6	2.9	5.4	11.5	15.5	15.0	14.2	10.1	4.6	1.7	1.1	84.9
Igarka	67 32 N	40	−17	−14	−4	13	24	45	60	53	43	23	−1	−22	13
	86 50 E		1.0	0.6	0.7	0.8	0.9	1.7	2.1	2.0	2.0	1.8	1.5	0.6	15.7
Kaifeng	34 54 N	377	30	37	47	58	70	79	83	79	70	60	47	36	58
	114 25 E		1.5	0.4	0.6	2.4	2.1	2.2	6.0	5.7	2.7	0.7	0.8	0.4	25.5
Kashgar	39 24 N	4255	19	32	46	61	70	75	80	78	69	57	39	26	54
	76 07 E		0.2	0.0	0.2	0.3	0.3	0.3	0.3	0.1	0.1	0.2	0.1	0.1	2.2
Madras	13 05 N	22	75	77	80	84	89	88	86	84	84	81	78	76	82
	80 15 E		1.1	0.3	0.3	0.6	1.8	2.0	3.8	4.5	4.9	11.2	13.6	5.4	49.6
Miyako	39 38 N	98	31	32	37	47	54	61	68	72	65	55	45	36	50
	141 59 E		2.7	2.6	3.5	3.8	4.7	5.0	5.3	7.0	8.5	6.7	3.2	2.5	55.5
Peshawar	33 59 N	1113	50	53	63	74	84	91	90	88	82	71	59	51	71
	71 43 E		1.5	1.2	2.0	1.7	0.7	0.3	1.2	2.1	0.8	0.2	0.4	0.6	12.8
Quetta	30 15 N	5500	40	41	51	60	67	74	78	75	67	56	47	42	58
	67 05 E		2.1	2.1	1.8	1.1	0.3	0.2	0.5	0.6	0.1	0.1	0.3	0.8	10.0

Station	Location ° '	Alt.	Jan.	Feb.	Mar.	Apr.	May	June	July	Aug.	Sept.	Oct.	Nov.	Dec.	Year
Saigon	10 47 N	36	79	81	84	86	84	82	81	82	81	81	81	79	82
	106 40 E		0.6	0.1	0.5	1.7	8.5	13.0	12.2	10.6	13.2	10.5	4.5	2.2	77.6
Seistan	31 03 N	2001	46	51	60	71	80	88	91	88	80	69	57	48	69
	61 30 E		0.3	0.4	0.5	0.1	0.0	0.0	0.0	0.0	0.0	0.1	0.1	0.4	1.9
Singapore	1 18 N	10	78	79	80	81	82	81	81	81	80	80	79	79	80
	103 55 E		8.5	6.1	6.5	6.9	7.2	6.7	6.8	8.5	7.1	8.2	10.0	10.4	92.9
Taipei	25 02 N	30	60	59	63	69	75	80	83	82	79	73	68	62	71
	121 31 E		3.4	5.3	6.7	6.4	8.9	11.1	8.3	11.8	10.2	5.3	2.7	3.0	82.7
Tehran	35 50 N	3800	34	42	48	61	71	80	85	83	77	66	51	42	62
	51 35 E		1.6	1.0	1.9	1.4	0.5	0.1	0.2	0.0	0.1	0.3	1.0	1.3	9.3
Tortkul	41 28 N	341	23	30	42	58	72	80	84	79	68	52	38	29	55
	61 05 E		0.4	0.3	0.7	0.6	0.3	0.1	0.0	0.0	0.0	0.1	0.2	0.3	3.0
Ulan-Bator	47 55 N	4347	−11	−3	12	33	46	58	63	60	47	31	8	−6	28
	106 50 E		0.1	0.0	0.1	0.2	0.3	1.0	2.9	1.9	0.8	0.2	0.2	0.1	7.8

AFRICA AND VICINITY

Station	Location ° '	Alt.	Jan.	Feb.	Mar.	Apr.	May	June	July	Aug.	Sept.	Oct.	Nov.	Dec.	Year
Alexandria	31 12 N	105	58	59	63	67	72	76	79	81	79	76	69	62	70
	29 53 E		2.0	0.9	0.4	0.1	0.0	0.0	0.0	0.0	0.0	0.2	1.3	2.3	7.2
Algiers	36 24 N	72	53	55	58	61	66	71	77	78	75	69	62	56	65
	3 30 E		4.2	3.5	3.5	2.3	1.3	0.6	0.1	0.3	1.1	3.1	4.6	5.4	30.0
Bahrdar	11 36 N	6037	65	64	71	70	68	68	65	65	65	65	65	62	66
	37 25 E		0.0	0.0	0.4	1.1	3.1	4.6	16.6	11.3	9.7	3.9	1.0	0.1	52.2
Beira	19 50 S	23	82	82	80	78	74	70	69	70	74	77	79	80	76
	34 51 E		11.6	8.2	10.0	4.1	2.3	1.4	1.0	1.0	0.8	1.5	5.2	10.1	57.2
Bloemfontein	29 07 S	4583	74	71	68	61	53	46	46	51	58	65	68	72	61
	26 12 E		3.6	3.1	3.5	1.8	1.0	0.4	0.3	0.4	0.8	1.5	2.1	2.3	21.2
Capetown	33 56 S	40	70	71	68	64	59	56	55	56	58	61	65	68	62
	18 20 E		0.7	0.6	0.9	1.9	3.7	4.4	3.6	3.3	2.3	1.6	1.1	0.8	24.8
Casablanca	33 37 N	164	53	54	57	59	64	68	72	73	71	67	60	56	63
	7 35 W		2.0	2.0	2.4	1.2	0.8	0.2	0.0	0.0	0.1	1.2	2.8	2.6	15.3
Dakar	14 40 N	98	71	72	72	73	76	81	83	82	83	83	79	74	77
	17 26 W		0.0	0.1	0.0	0.0	0.1	0.7	3.4	9.7	5.0	1.4	0.1	0.2	21.0
Douala	4 04 N	43	80	80	79	80	80	78	76	76	77	77	79	79	78
	19 41 E		1.7	3.6	8.4	8.6	11.6	21.4	29.7	27.2	20.5	16.7	6.3	2.5	158.2
Durban	29 52 S	50	76	76	75	72	68	64	63	65	67	69	72	74	70
	31 03 E		4.6	5.3	6.0	3.6	2.6	1.8	1.7	1.8	2.7	5.1	4.7	5.2	45.1
Elizabethville	11 40 S	4055	72	72	72	69	66	61	61	65	71	75	74	72	69
	27 34 E		9.8	9.8	8.5	1.8	0.2	0.0	0.0	0.0	0.1	1.3	4.8	11.2	47.5
Fort Lapperrine	23 01 N	3280	55	58	65	74	79	84	84	83	80	73	65	58	71
	5 10 E		0.2	0.1	0.1	0.2	0.6	0.2	0.1	0.4	0.1	0.1	0.0	0.2	2.3
Kumasi	6 41 N	840	78	81	81	81	81	78	76	76	77	79	80	79	79
	1 37 W		0.6	2.3	5.6	5.7	7.0	9.1	4.8	2.9	7.2	8.0	3.9	1.2	58.2
Mbabane	26 19 S	3816	69	66	66	62	59	54	54	57	61	65	66	67	62
	31 09 E		9.9	7.6	7.9	2.6	1.3	0.5	0.9	1.1	2.2	5.0	6.8	8.4	54.2
Mongu	15 17 S	3488	77	77	76	75	71	67	66	71	79	82	79	77	75
	23 05 E		8.7	8.5	6.0	1.1	0.2	0.0	0.0	0.0	0.1	1.4	4.1	7.7	37.8
Nairobi	1 16 S	5490	66	67	68	67	65	63	61	62	64	67	66	65	65
	36 50 E		1.6	2.0	5.1	7.7	5.5	1.7	0.6	1.1	1.0	2.4	4.2	2.5	35.4
Nova Lisboa	12 46 S	5627	68	67	68	67	65	63	65	66	70	71	68	68	67
	15 44 E		8.7	8.9	8.4	6.1	1.1	0.0	0.0	0.1	0.5	5.1	8.9	9.5	57.6
Porto Amelia	13 06 S	197	81	81	80	79	77	75	74	74	76	78	80	82	78
	40 32 E		6.3	7.5	7.7	5.4	0.7	1.3	0.4	0.1	0.1	0.6	0.8	4.3	34.9
Pretoria	25 45 S	4350	73	72	69	64	58	53	52	57	64	70	70	72	64
	28 12 E		5.4	4.2	3.6	1.2	0.6	0.1	0.3	0.5	0.6	2.5	4.7	4.4	28.1
Stanleyville	0 30 N	1400	78	78	78	78	79	77	76	76	76	77	77	77	77
	25 11 E		2.2	3.5	6.0	6.4	5.9	4.5	4.8	5.5	7.7	8.0	7.7	4.0	66.2
Timbuktu	16 45 N	886	71	74	82	89	94	94	91	88	90	88	80	71	85
	2 55 W		0.0	0.0	0.0	0.1	0.2	0.8	2.7	2.6	1.3	1.1	0.0	0.0	8.8

OCEANIA

Station	Location ° '	Alt.	Jan.	Feb.	Mar.	Apr.	May	June	July	Aug.	Sept.	Oct.	Nov.	Dec.	Year
Adelaide	34 56 S	140	74	74	70	64	58	53	52	54	57	62	67	71	63
	138 36 E		0.8	0.6	1.1	1.8	2.8	3.0	2.6	2.4	1.8	1.8	1.0	0.8	20.6
Auckland	36 52 S	260	67	67	66	61	57	54	52	52	54	57	60	64	59
	174 46 E		2.6	3.0	3.1	3.3	4.4	4.8	5.0	4.2	3.6	3.6	3.3	2.9	43.8
Bourke	30 10 S	456	84	83	78	68	58	54	51	56	63	70	76	82	68
	146 00 E		2.0	1.9	1.6	1.4	1.1	1.0	0.9	0.9	1.0	1.1	1.3	1.1	15.2
Broome	17 57 S	63	86	85	84	83	76	71	70	73	77	81	85	86	80
	122 15 E		6.2	6.1	3.8	1.4	0.6	0.1	0.2	0.2	0.1	0.1	0.1	3.7	22.6

Station	Location ° ′	Alt.	Jan.	Feb.	Mar.	Apr.	May	June	July	Aug.	Sept.	Oct.	Nov.	Dec.	Year
Daru	9 04 S	26	82	81	81	81	80	79	77	77	79	80	81	82	80
	143 12 E		11.9	11.4	12.7	13.1	9.6	3.9	4.0	2.0	1.6	2.0	4.1	7.6	83.9
Dunedin	45 47 S	236	58	58	55	52	47	44	42	44	48	51	53	56	51
	170 44 E		3.3	2.8	3.0	2.8	3.3	3.2	3.0	3.1	2.8	3.1	3.3	3.5	37.2
Guam	13 24 N	67	81	81	81	82	82	82	81	81	81	81	82	81	81
	144 38 E		3.5	3.1	3.0	2.3	4.5	6.2	15.7	15.3	13.5	12.7	8.2	4.9	92.9
Jakarta	6 11 S	23	79	79	80	80	81	80	79	80	80	81	80	79	80
	126 50 E		12.0	12.6	8.4	5.5	4.3	3.6	2.6	1.7	2.7	4.7	5.7	7.8	71.9
Kajoemas	7 56 S	3051	68	68	69	69	69	69	68	69	71	72	71	69	69
	114 09 E		18.8	17.6	18.1	8.6	5.8	2.5	1.6	0.6	0.5	1.9	8.0	15.6	99.6
Manggar	2 52 S	16	79	80	80	81	81	81	82	82	82	81	80	80	81
	108 16 E		12.1	8.2	10.4	9.1	10.0	7.9	6.7	5.1	4.1	6.3	9.8	13.9	103.6
Manokwari	0 53 S	98	80	80	80	80	80	80	80	80	80	81	81	81	81
	133 58 E		12.1	9.3	13.1	11.1	7.8	7.4	5.5	5.6	5.0	4.8	6.5	10.3	98.5
Melbourne	37 39 S	115	67	67	64	59	54	50	49	51	54	58	61	65	58
	144 58 E		1.9	1.8	2.2	2.3	2.2	2.1	1.9	1.8	2.4	2.7	2.2	2.3	25.8
Nauru	0 30 S	26	82	82	82	83	83	82	82	83	83	83	83	82	83
	167 00 E		8.6	11.1	6.5	5.5	5.7	5.0	6.7	6.1	6.5	5.3	6.8	10.5	84.3
Pago Pago	14 19 S	10	83	82	83	81	81	80	80	80	80	80	82	82	81
	170 41 E		24.5	20.5	19.2	16.5	15.4	12.3	10.0	8.2	13.1	14.9	19.2	19.8	193.6
Rabaul	4 13 S	52	82	82	82	82	82	82	81	80	82	82	82	82	81
	152 15 E		14.8	10.4	10.2	10.0	5.2	3.3	5.4	4.7	3.5	5.1	7.1	10.1	89.8
Sydney	33 51 S	138	72	71	69	65	59	55	53	55	59	63	67	70	63
	151 13 E		3.6	4.4	4.9	5.4	5.1	4.8	5.0	3.0	2.9	2.9	2.8	2.8	47.6

APPENDIX D

Soils

Soil Formation

Soil is the name we apply to the mantle of earth which consists of decomposed rocks and which has generally been altered through time by the physical action of seasonal temperature differences and rainfall amounts and by the biological action of earthworms and various funguses.

In areas of rather uniform altitude where the climate has been much the same for a long time (say 5000 years), the original differences in parent material (primary rock or silt type) gradually come to be muted and somewhat masked by the smoothing action of the constant climatic conditions and by the addition of decaying material from the natural vegetation—plants that in themselves are a reflection of the dominant climate. Such widespread soils are called *zonal* soils, partly because they tend to lie within certain climatic zones and partly because they appear as zones on a map. In the U.S.S.R. these zones generally trend east-west, while in North America they run north-south.

Less widespread are the transitional types between the zonal soils. These blend the characteristics of two or more zonal soils and are called *intrazonal* or "between-zones" soils. Nonzonal or *azonal* soils are found where climatic conditions, living organisms, and natural vegetations have not had an opportunity to alter the parent material significantly. Such azonal soils are to be found in the lower parts of river valleys, in sandy or rocky deserts, or upon hills and mountains (Fig. D.1).

Soil Description

A soil may be described in a number of ways—by its color, profile (depth of topsoil and subsoil), acidity, texture, and parent material. Thus the 1938 *Yearbook of Agriculture* describes two related soils in southeastern Colorado:

Baca and Prowers soils are most extensive and there are a number of somewhat similar soils associated with them. These soils are mostly silt loams and silty clay loams, though there are also some sandy soils. The latter are especially subject to wind erosion. Baca soils are brown granular friable soils with brown crumbly clay subsoils underlain by grayish-brown chalky layers of accumulated carbonate of lime. Prowers soils have somewhat lighter colored gray or grayish-brown surface soils over subsoils of yellowish-brown, somewhat granular and friable calcareous clay or clay loam, with a chalky gray clay at 1 or 2 feet beneath the surface.[1]

It also describes the soils found in a plateau area of northeastern Maine:

Caribou soils cover about half the area. Under forest, Caribou loam has a layer of duff 2 to 4 inches thick underlain in turn by a gray floury loam 1 to 2 inches thick, and a dark-brown or rusty-brown firmer layer 3 to 6 inches thick, grading into a yellow-brown, firm but friable loam and at 15 inches into a pale-yellow material of the same texture and structure. At about 24 inches lies the substratum of firm, greenish-gray, little modified till, underlain by

[1] United States Department of Agriculture, "Soils and Men," *Yearbook of Agriculture* (Washington, 1938), p. 1089.

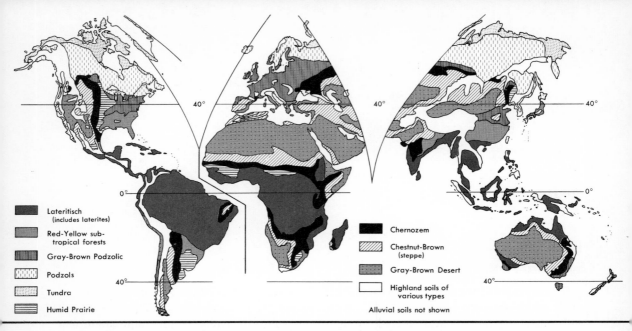

D.1. Major soil areas of the world, showing zonal soils. (From *Syllabus for the Introductory Course in Economic Geography* **by Richard Hartshorne and S. N. Dicken.)**

bedrock at 3 to 6 feet below the surface. The soil is acid but the underlying parent material is alkaline. Drainage is good.[2]

The rather intimate relation between soils and the vegetation zones in which they lie is shown in the two diagrams below.

Schematic Representation of Distribution of Climatic Types, Vegetative Formations, and Major Zonal Soil Groups on a Hypothetical Level Continent in the Northern Hemisphere

DISTRIBUTION OF CLIMATIC TYPES AND VEGETATIVE FORMATIONS

Dry cold   Wet cold

Perpetual Snow and Ice				
Tundra				
Taiga				
Arid	Semiarid	Subhumid	Humid	Wet
Desert Grasses and Shrubs	Steppe	Grassland	Forests	Rainforest

Dry hot   Wet hot

[2] *Ibid.*, p. 1022.

DISTRIBUTION OF MAJOR ZONAL SOIL GROUPS ON A CLIMATIC BASE

Dry cold   Wet cold

Perpetual Snow and Ice			
Tundra Soils			
Podzols			
Sierozems and Desert soils	Chestnut and Brown soils	Prairie soils and Chernozems	Podzols
			Gray-Brown Podzolic soils
			Red and Yellow Podzolic soils
			Lateritic soils

Dry hot   Wet hot

The Great Soil Groups. Soil science in the late 1950's and early 1960's has been in a state of change owing to new discoveries and to re-evaluation of older data. The classifications given in the table below may become partially outmoded, but they will remain for some time into the future a reliable and helpful guide for the understanding of geographic texts in economic and human geography.

TABLE D.1

Soil Classification in the Higher Categories[3]

Order	Suborder	Great Soil Groups
Zonal soils	1. Soils of the cold zone	Tundra soils
	2. Light-colored soils of arid regions	Desert soils Red Desert soils Sierozem Brown soils Reddish-Brown soils
	3. Dark-colored soils of semiarid, subhumid and humid grasslands	Chestnut soils Reddish Chestnut soils Chernozem soils Prairie soils Reddish Prairie soils
	4. Soils of the forest-grassland transition	Degraded Chernozem Noncalcic Brown or Shantung Brown soils

[3] James Thorp and Guy D. Smith, "Higher Categories of Soil Classification: Order, Suborder, and Great Soil Groups," *Soil Science,* Vol. 67, No. 2 (February, 1949), p. 118.

	5. Light-colored podzolized soils of the timbered regions	Podzol soils Gray Wooded, or Gray Podzolic soils* Brown Podzolic soils Gray-Brown Podzolic soils Red-Yellow Podzolic soils*
	6. Lateritic soils of forested warm-temperate and tropical regions	Reddish-Brown Lateritic soils* Yellowish-Brown Lateritic soils Laterite soils*
Intrazonal soils	1. Halomorphic (saline and alkali) soils of imperfectly drained arid regions and littoral deposits	Solonchak, or Saline soils Solonetz soils Soloth soils
	2. Hydromorphic soils of marshes, swamps, seep areas, and flats	Humic-Glei soils* (includes Wiesenboden) Alpine Meadow soils Bog soils Half-Bog soils Low-Humic Glei* soils Planosols Ground-Water Podzol soils Ground-Water Laterite soils
	3. Calcimorphic soils	Brown Forest soils (Braunerde) Rendzina soils
Azonal soils		Lithosols Regosols (includes Dry Sands) Alluvial soils

TUNDRA SOILS have dark brown peaty layers over grayish horizons mottled with rust. The substrata are of permafrost (ever-frozen materials), and the natural drainage is poor.[4]

DESERT SOILS are light gray or light brownish-gray, low in organic matter, and are closely underlain by calcareous material.

RED DESERT SOILS are light reddish-brown on the surface, with brownish-red or red heavier subsoil closely underlain by calcareous material.

SIEROZEMS are pale grayish soils grading into calcareous material at a depth of one foot or less.

* New or recently modified great soil groups.

[4] Soil descriptions are from Thorp and Smith, *supra*, and from pp. 993-1001 of *Yearbook of Agriculture*, 1938.

BROWN SOILS have a brown top layer grading into a whitish calcareous horizon one to three feet from the surface.

REDDISH-BROWN SOILS have a reddish-brown top layer grading into red or dull-red heavier subsoil and then into a whitish calcareous horizon, either cemented or soft.

CHESTNUT SOILS have a dark brown friable and platy soil over brown prismatic soil with lime accumulation at a depth of 1½ to 4½ feet.

REDDISH CHESTNUT SOILS have a dark reddish-brown cast in the surface soil, with heavier and reddish-brown or red sandy clay below; lime accumulation is at a depth of two feet or more.

CHERNOZEM SOILS have black or very dark grayish-brown friable soil to a depth ranging up to three or four feet grading through lighter color to whitish lime accumulation.

PRAIRIE SOILS have very dark brown or grayish-brown soil grading through brown to lighter-colored parent material at a depth of two to five feet.

REDDISH PRAIRIE SOILS are dark brown or reddish-brown in the upper layers grading through reddish-brown heavier subsoil to parent material, and are moderately acid.

DEGRADED CHERNOZEM SOILS have a very nearly black top layer, a somewhat bleached grayish layer under this, the subsoil rather heavy, and with vestiges of lime accumulation in deep layers.

NONCALCIC BROWN SOILS have a brown or light brown friable upper soil over pale reddish-brown or dull red subsoil.

PODZOLS have a few inches of leaf mat and acid humus, a very thin dark gray upper layer, a whitish-gray layer a few inches thick, a dark or coffee-brown upper subsoil, and a yellowish-brown lower subsoil; they are strongly acidic.

GRAY WOODED SOILS have a moderately thin duff layer over a thin organic-mineral horizon, over a light-colored bleached horizon, with subsoil layers being first a brown more clayey, blocky, or nuciform horizon, grading below into lighter-colored and more friable horizons.

BROWN PODZOLIC SOILS have leaf mat and acid humus over thin dark gray upper layer, and thin gray brown or yellowish-brown layer over brown subsoil which is only slightly heavier than the surface soil, and the whole seldom over two feet thick.

GRAY-BROWN PODZOLIC SOILS have a thin leaf litter over mild humus over dark-colored surface soil two to four inches thick over grayish-brown leached horizon over brown heavy subsoil; they are less acidic than podzols.

RED-YELLOW PODZOLIC SOILS are well-developed, well-drained acid soils having thin organic and organic-mineral horizons over a light-colored bleached horizon, over a red, yellowish-red, or yellow and more clayey subsoil; whose parent materials are all more or less siliceous.

REDDISH-BROWN LATERITIC SOILS have reddish-brown or dark reddish-brown friable granular clayey layers over deep-red friable and granular clay; the deep substrata are reticulately mottled in places.

YELLOWISH-BROWN LATERITIC SOILS have brown friable clays and clay loams over yellowish-brown heavy but friable clays, and are acid to neutral in reaction.

The LATERITE SOILS are under review as to terminology, but have been usually defined as having red-brown surface layers, with red deep subsoil, and red or reticulated parent material, very deeply weathered; and with free oxides of iron and aluminum.

SOLONCHAK SOILS have a gray thin salty crust on the surface, fine granular mulch just below, and grayish friable salty soil farther down; salts may be concentrated above or below.

SOLONETZ SOILS have very thin to a few inches of friable surface soil over a whitish leached horizon underlain by a dark brown heavy horizon.

SOLOTH SOILS have a thin grayish-brown horizon of friable soil over a whitish leached horizon underlain by a dark brown heavy horizon.

HUMIC-GLEI SOILS are a group of poorly to very poorly drained hydromorphic soils with dark-colored organic-mineral horizons of moderate thickness underlain by mineral glei horizons; they occur naturally under either swamp-forest or herbaceous marsh vegetation mostly in humid or subhimid climates of greatly varying thermal efficiency.

ALPINE MEADOW SOILS have a dark brown soil grading, at a depth of one or two feet, into grayish and rust soil, streaked and mottled.

BOG SOILS are brown, dark brown, or black peat or muck over brown peaty material.

HALF-BOG SOILS have dark brown or black peaty material over grayish and rust-mottled mineral soil.

LOW-HUMIC GLEI SOILS are imperfectly to poorly drained soils with very thin surface horizons, moderately high in organic material, over mottled gray and brown glei-like mineral horizons with a low degree of textural differentiation.

PLANOSOLS are intrazonal, having one or more horizons abruptly separated from and sharply contrasting to an adjacent horizon because of cementation, compaction, or high clay content, and are usually but not always found with a fluctuating water table.

GROUND-WATER PODZOL SOILS have an organic mat over very thin acid humus, over a whitish-gray leached layer up to two or three feet thick, over brown or very dark brown cemented hardpan or ortstein; the substrata are deep and grayish.

GROUND-WATER LATERITE SOILS have a gray or gray-brown surface layer over a leached yellowish-gray layer, over thick reticulately mottled cemented hardpan at a depth of one foot or more; hardpan up to several feet thick; concretions throughout.

BROWN FOREST SOILS have a very dark brown friable surface layer grading through lighter-colored soil to the parent material; little illuviation; high degree of absorbed calcium.

RENDZINA SOILS have a dark grayish-brown to black granular layer underlain by gray or yellowish, usually soft, calcareous material; generally developed on limestone.

LITHOSOLS are an azonal group of soils having an incomplete solum and no clearly expressed soil morphology, and consisting of a freshly and imperfectly weathered mass of hard rock or hard rock fragments; largely confined to steeply sloping land.

REGOSOLS are dry and loose sands, and some soils developed on unconsolidated materials such as loess.

ALLUVIAL SOILS are stratified silts with little profile development, but usually with some organic material accumulated.

Population and Area

The population and total-area figures and most of the arable-area figures are from latest estimates as reported in *The Worldmark Encyclopedia of the Nations,* New York, Harper, 1960. Some arable-area figures are from the *U.N. Statistical Yearbook,* 1951. Listed below are 148 countries and dependencies. Not listed are 45 small countries and island groups: Aden Colony, Aden Protectorate, Andorra, Antarctica, Azores, Bahamas, Bahrein, Bhutan, Bonin Islands, (Panama) Canal Zone, Canary Islands, Cape Verde Islands, Channel Islands, Cook Islands, Faeroe Islands, Falkland Islands, Gilbert and Ellice Islands, Greenland, Guadeloupe, Hong Kong, Ifni, Jammu and Kashmir, Kuwait, Liechtenstein, Macao, Maldive Islands, Martinique, Midway, Monaco, Nauru, New Hebrides, Sikkim, Pitcairn, former Portuguese India, Portuguese Timor, Qatar, Reunion, St. Helena, St. Pierre, San Marino, São Tomé and Principe, Seychelles, Trucial Oman, Vatican City, Virgin Islands. For some items no data (n. d.) are available.

Country or Dependency	Population	Area in Square Miles	Arable Area in Square Miles	Gross Density per Square Mile	Nutri- tional Density Per Square Mile
Afghanistan	13,000,000	256,000	32,000	51	407
Albania	1,507,000	11,097	1,450	136	1,040
Algeria	10,265,000	80,920	25,000	127	410
Angola	4,392,000	481,350	n. d.	9	———
Argentina	20,256,000	1,072,700	117,000	19	175
Australia	10,166,000	2,974,581	50,000	3	203
Austria	6,933,905	32,369	6,800	214	1,018
Basutoland	658,000	11,716	1,740	56	378
Bechuanaland	337,000	275,000	772	1	437
Belgium	9,078,635	11,779	2,590	770	3,500
Bolivia	3,349,000	424,162	2,121	8	1,580
Brazil	68,000,000	3,286,170	164,308	21	414
British Honduras	88,000	8,866	772	10	114
British Somaliland	650,000	68,000	773	10	842
Brunei	80,277	2,220	2,220	36	36

Country or Dependency	Population	Area in Square Miles	Arable Area in Square Miles	Gross Density per Square Mile	Nutritional Density Per Square Mile
Bulgaria	7,629,254	42,818	18,800	178	406
Burma	20,255,000	261,789	31,300	78	654
Cambodia	4,845,000	66,590	3,120	73	1,550
Cameroun	3,187,000	166,800	4,480	19	710
Canada	17,732,000	3,851,809	272,000	5	65
Central African Republic	1,177,000	241,700	n. d.	5	——
Ceylon	9,388,000	25,332	5,670	370	1,655
Chad	2,600,000	495,368	n. d.	5	——
Chile	7,298,000	286,296	22,800	25	320
China	660,000,000	3,800,000	437,000	174	1,510
Colombia	13,824,000	455,335	8,180	30	1,690
Congo	13,658,185	905,380	193,000	15	71
Congo Republic	795,000	134,750	n. d.	6	——
Costa Rica	1,100,000	19,647	1,680	56	656
Cuba	6,466,000	44,218	35,370	146	183
Cyprus	549,000	3,572	1,690	154	325
Czechoslovakia	13,522,000	49,366	28,600	274	473
Dahomey	1,725,000	43,630	n. d.	40	——
Denmark	4,500,700	16,530	12,600	272	357
Dominican Republic	2,894,000	19,332	9,200	150	315
Ecuador	4,169,204	105,000	11,600	40	359
El Salvador	2,520,367	8,259	5,120	305	492
Ethiopia	16,000,000	456,265	43,400	35	369
Fiji	374,284	7,040	548	53	682
Finland	4,433,700	130,120	10,900	34	407
France	45,355,000	212,681	150,000	213	303
French Guiana	27,863	35,135	13	1	2,140
French Polynesia	79,000	1,544	n. d.	51	——
French Somaliland	69,000	8,494	8	8	9,000
Gabon	420,709	102,317	n. d.	4	——
Gambia	289,000	4,000	852	72	340
Germany (East)	17,410,670	41,635	19,100	418	911
Germany (West)	52,958,700	95,913	55,200	553	960
Ghana	6,690,730	91,843	4,600	73	1,455
Greece	8,216,000	51,182	13,630	161	603
Guatemala	3,500,000	42,042	11,600	83	302

Country or Dependency	Population	Area in Square Miles	Arable Area in Square Miles	Gross Density per Square Mile	Nutritional Density Per Square Mile
Guinea	2,800,000	95,000	n. d.	39	——
Haiti	3,464,000	10,700	1,775	123	1,950
Honduras	1,888,000	43,277	9,700	44	195
Hungary	9,929,000	35,919	20,800	278	481
Iceland	170,156	39,758	397	4	430
India	420,000,000	1,266,210	478,000	332	880
Indonesia	89,600,000	575,450	65,700	156	1,364
Iran	19,723,000	628,000	62,800	31	310
Iraq	6,590,000	17,555	10,220	376	645
Ireland	2,864,000	26,599	18,400	108	156
Israel	2,054,434	7,992	1,550	252	1,300
Italy	48,594,000	116,256	37,200	418	1,305
Ivory Coast	3,100,000	127,500	n. d.	24	——
Japan	94,500,000	142,726	23,100	641	4,100
Jordan	1,527,000	36,715	2,070	42	738
Kenya	6,351,000	224,960	6,180	28	1,030
Korea (North)	8,000,000	37,811	9,650	212	830
Korea (South)	22,926,000	37,415	8,750	612	2,590
Laos	1,690,000	88,780	2,400	19	700
Lebanon	1,650,000	4,015	922	41	1,790
Liberia	1,500,000	43,000	7,000	35	214
Libya	1,091,830	685,000	4,700	2	232
Luxembourg	322,000	999	555	322	580
Malagasy Republic (Madagascar)	5,191,085	227,900	19,300	23	269
Malaya	6,278,763	50,690	8,600	125	731
Mauritania	624,000	470,000	n. d.	1	——
Mauritius	613,888	720	320	852	1,930
Mexico	32,348,000	760,373	61,800	43	523
Micronesia (Trust Territory)	70,594	687	n. d.	103	——
Morocco	10,330,000	171,305	20,300	60	508
Mozambique	6,234,000	302,250	3,023	21	2,060
Muscat and Oman	550,000	82,000	3,750	7	147
Nepal	8,431,537	54,372	5,630	155	1,497
Netherlands	11,416,700	12,528	4,176	880	2,640
Netherlands Antilles	194,000	390	19	497	10,000
Netherlands New Guinea (Trust Territory)	700,000	159,375	n. d.	4	——

Country or Dependency	Population	Area in Square Miles	Arable Area in Square Miles	Gross Density per Square Mile	Nutritional Density Per Square Mile
New Caledonia	60,000	8,500	309	7	194
New Guinea (Australian Trust Territory)	1,341,000	93,000	n. d.	14	——
New Zealand	2,343,000	103,736	3,770	23	622
Nicaragua	1,378,000	57,143	7,429	24	185
Niger	2,555,000	458,875	8,100	6	316
Nigeria	33,043,000	339,169	25,000	97	1,320
Northern Rhodesia	2,300,100	288,130	n. d.	8	——
Norway	3,565,000	124,710	4,020	29	888
Nyasaland	2,770,000	11,600	n. d.	239	——
Outer Mongolia	1,000,000	591,000	318	2	3,140
Pakistan	87,000,000	364,737	212,200	239	407
Panama	1,029,000	28,745	4,430	35	226
Papua	452,000	90,600	9,400	5	48
Paraguay	1,718,000	157,047	6,280	11	273
Peru	10,524,000	514,059	6,960	20	1,530
Philippines	24,718,000	115,600	22,000	214	1,123
Poland	29,500,000	120,359	80,240	245	368
Portugal	9,023,000	35,598	13,500	266	700
Puerto Rico	2,342,428	3,435	1,545	685	1,515
Rio Muni and Fernando Po	215,000	10,828	n. d.	20	——
Romania	18,058,604	91,700	37,400	191	483
Ruanda and Burundi	4,700,000	20,916	5,480	214	858
Ryukyu Islands	849,000	840	n. d.	1,010	——
Samoa (East and West)	124,820	1,205	34	103	3,700
Sarawak	675,000	47,500	1,087	14	620
Saudi Arabia	6,000,000	600,000	30,000	10	200
Senegal	2,550,000	78,000	n. d.	33	——
Sierra Leone	2,260,000	27,925	15,400	81	146
Solomon Islands	114,000	11,500	n. d.	10	——
Somalia	1,330,000	178,000	31,200	8	43
Soudan (Mali)	4,300,000	464,752	n. d.	9	——
Southern Rhodesia	2,900,000	150,333	46,300	19	63
Southwest Africa	539,000	317,725	n. d.	2	——
Spain	29,362,388	194,945	38,600	150	761
Sudan	11,390,000	967,500	2,770	12	4,100
Surinam	240,000	55,143	150	4	1,600

Country or Dependency	Population	Area in Square Miles	Arable Area in Square Miles	Gross Density per Square Mile	Nutritional Density Per Square Mile
Swaziland	260,000	6,704	938	39	277
Sweden	7,475,000	173,615	13,900	43	538
Switzerland	5,246,000	15,941	1,054	330	4,960
Taiwan (Formosa)	10,038,000	13,808	3,570	725	2,800
Tanganyika	8,788,466	363,000	11,600	24	756
Thailand	21,881,000	198,270	32,000	111	684
Togo	1,161,314	21,850	2,508	53	462
Tonga	59,627	270	144	220	414
Tunisia	3,830,000	48,194	14,600	79	262
Turkey	26,880,000	299,992	100,000	90	269
Uganda	5,770,000	93,981	10,800	61	534
U.S.S.R.	208,826,000	8,600,000	3,980,000	24	54
Union of South Africa	14,673,000	472,359	70,800	31	207
United Arab Republic	29,420,000	458,432	31,400	64	936
United Kingdom	51,609,500	94,214	27,280	548	1,890
United States	179,500,000	3,675,632	710,000	49	253
Upper Volta	3,531,571	105,811	7,380	33	478
Uruguay	3,000,000	72,172	5,770	42	520
Venezuela	6,607,000	352,150	7,750	19	853
Vietnam (North)	13,300,000	55,910	7,460	238	1,783
Vietnam (South)	12,800,000	65,000	11,600	197	1,103
West Indies	3,128,000	16,155	n. d.	194	——
Yemen	4,500,000	75,000	3,750	60	1,200
Yugoslavia	18,498,000	98,766	56,300	188	304
Zanzibar	304,000	1,020	312	298	980

References

General

BRUNHES, JEAN. *Human Geography* (Abridged Edition). Rand McNally and Company, New York, 1952.

DICKEN, SAMUEL N. *Economic Geography* (2d Edition). D. C. Heath and Company, Boston, 1955.

ESPENSHADE, EDWARD B., JR., ed. *Goode's World Atlas* (Eleventh Edition). Rand McNally and Company, Chicago, 1960.

KISH, GEORGE. *Economic Atlas of the Soviet Union*. University of Michigan Press, Ann Arbor, Michigan, 1960.

LEWIS, SIR CLINTON G., and CAMPBELL, J. D., eds. *American Oxford Atlas*. Oxford University Press, New York, 1951.

Oxford Economic Atlas of the World. Prepared by The Economist Intelligence Unit and The Cartographic Department of the Clarendon Press, 2d Edition, Oxford University Press, New York, 1959.

ROSTLUND, ERHARD. *Outline of Cultural Geography*. California Book Company, Ltd., Berkeley, California, 1955.

RUSSELL, R. J., KNIFFEN, F. B., and PRUITT, E. L. *Culture Worlds*. The Macmillan Company, New York, 1961.

THOMAS, W. L., JR., ed. *Man's Role in Changing the Face of the Earth*. University of Chicago Press, Chicago, 1956.

VISINTIN, L. *Grande Atlante Geografico* (5th Edition). Istituto Geografico de Agostini, Novara, Italy, 1959.

WILLIAMS, JOSEPH E., ed. *Prentice-Hall World Atlas*. Prentice-Hall, Inc., Englewood Cliffs, New Jersey, 1963.

Part I. Some Basic Facts

ACKERMAN, EDWARD A. "Geographic Training, Wartime Research, and Immediate Professional Objectives," *Annals of the Association of American Geographers* 35:121-143, 1945.

BAKER, J. N. L. *A History of Geographical Discovery and Exploration*. Houghton Mifflin Company, London, 1931.

COON, CARLETON S. *The Story of Man*. Alfred A. Knopf, New York, 1955.

DICKINSON, R. E., and HOWARTH, O. J. R. *The Making of Geography*. Oxford University Press, London, 1933.

HARTSHORNE, RICHARD. *The Nature of Geography*. Annals of the Association of American Geographers, Lancaster, Pennsylvania, 1939.

———, *Perspective on the Nature of Geography*. Published for The Association of American Geographers by Rand McNally and Company, Chicago, 1959.

JAMES, PRESTON E., and JONES, CLARENCE F., eds. *American Geography, Inventory and Prospect*. Published for the Association of American Geographers by Syracuse University Press, Syracuse, New York, 1954.

JONES, S. B. "The Enjoyment of Geography," *Geographical Review* 42:543-550, 1952.

MARSH, GEORGE P. *Man and Nature*. Charles Scribner and Company, New York, 1864.

PLATT, R. S. "Environmentalism Versus Geography," *American Journal of Sociology* 53:351-358, 1948.

POLO, MARCO. *The Travels of Marco Polo, The Venetian*. Everyman's Library, E. P. Dutton and Company, New York, 1927.

RAISZ, ERWIN. *General Cartography* (2d Edition). McGraw-Hill Book Company, Inc., New York, 1948.

SAPPER, KARL. "Economic Geography" in *Encyclopaedia of Social Sciences*, Edwin R. A. Seligman, ed., 6:626-628, The Macmillan Company, New York, 1931.

SAUER, CARL O. "The Morphology of Landscape," *University of California Publications in Geography*, 2:19-54, University of California Press, Berkeley, 1925.

———, "Cultural Geography" in *Encyclopaedia of Social Sciences*, Edwin R. A. Seligman, ed., 6:621-624, The Macmillan Company, New York, 1931.

———, "Foreword to Historical Geography," *Annals of the Association of American Geographers*, 31:1-24, 1941.

————, *Agricultural Origins and Dispersals.* American Geographical Society, Series 2, New York, 1952.

SEMPLE, ELLEN CHURCHILL. *Influences of Geographic Environment on the Basis of Ratzel's System of Anthropo-Geography.* Henry Holt and Company, New York, 1911.

————, *The Geography of the Mediterranean Region. Its Relation to Ancient History.* Henry Holt and Company, New York, 1931.

VALLAUX, CAMILLE. "Human Geography" in *Encyclopaedia of Social Sciences,* Edwin R. A. Seligman, ed., 6:624-626, The Macmillan Company, New York, 1931.

VIDAL DE LA BLACHE, PAUL. *Principles of Human Geography.* Henry Holt and Company, New York, 1950.

WHITTLESEY, DERWENT. "Sequent Occupance," *Annals of the Association of American Geographers,* 19:162-165, 1929.

Part II. The People

BAKER, O. E. "Population, Food Supply, and American Agriculture," *Geographical Review* 18:353-373, 1928.

BOWMAN, ISAIAH. *The Pioneer Fringe.* American Geographical Society, Special Publication No. 13, New York, 1931.

BROWN, HARRISON. *The Challenge of Man's Future.* The Viking Press, New York, 1954.

CASTRO, JOSUÉ DE. *The Geography of Hunger.* Little, Brown and Company, Boston, 1952.

CHILDE, V. G., *Prehistoric Migrations in Europe.* Harvard University Press, Cambridge, Massachusetts, 1950.

EAST, W. G., and MOODIE, A. E., eds. *The Changing World.* World Book Company, New York, 1956.

FRANKLIN, BENJAMIN. "Observations Concerning the Increase of Mankind, Peopling of Countries, etc." in *The Writings of Benjamin Franklin,* Albert Henry Smyth, ed., Vol. III, pp. 63-73, The Macmillan Company, New York, 1907.

JEFFERSON, MARK. "Looking Back at Malthus," *Geographical Review* 15:177-189, 1925.

————, "Distribution of the World's City Folks: A Study in Comparative Civilization," *Geographical Review* 21:446-465, 1931.

KLIMM, L. E. "Empty Areas in the Old Northeast: With Examples from New Jersey,"

Annals of the Association of American Geographers 43:178-179, 1953.

MALTHUS, THOMAS R. *An Essay on Population.* Vol. I, Everyman's Library, E. P. Dutton and Company, New York, 1927.

REDFIELD, ROBERT. *The Primitive World and Its Transformations.* Cornell University Press, Ithaca, New York, 1953.

SAUER, CARL O. "A Geographical Sketch of Early Man in America," *Geographical Review* 34:529-573, 1944.

SIMPSON, GEORGE G. *The Meaning of Evolution.* Mentor Books, New York, 1951.

STONE, K. H. *Alaskan Group Settlement: The Matanuska Valley Colony.* United States Department of the Interior, Bureau of Land Management, Washington, 1950.

THOMPSON, WARREN S. "The Spiral of Population" in *Man's Role in Changing the Face of the Earth,* W. L. Thomas, Jr., ed., pp. 970-986, University of Chicago Press, Chicago, 1956.

THORNTHWAITE, C. W. "Internal Migration in the United States," *Study of Population Redistribution,* Bulletin 1, University of Pennsylvania, Philadelphia, 1934.

TREWARTHA, G. T. "A Case for Population Geography," *Annals of the Association of American Geographers* 43:71-97, 1953.

United Nations Annual, *Demographic Yearbook,* New York.

———— Annual, *Statistical Yearbook,* New York.

VOGT, WILLIAM. *People.* William Sloane Associates, New York, 1960.

WOYTINSKY, W. S., and WOYTINSKY, E. S. *World Population and Production.* The Twentieth Century Fund, New York, 1953.

Part III. The Place

ACKERMAN, E. A. *Water Resources in the United States.* Resources for the Future, Series No. 6, Washington, 1958.

BATES, HENRY WALTER. *The Naturalist on the River Amazons.* Everyman's Library, E. P. Dutton and Company, New York, 1914.

BLUMENSTOCK, DAVID. *The Ocean of Air.* Rutgers University Press, New Brunswick, New Jersey, 1959.

BROOKS, C. E. P. *Climate Through the Ages: A Study of Climatic Factors and Their Varia-*

tions. McGraw-Hill Book Company, New York, 1949.

CHURCH, J. E. "Snow Surveying—Its Principles and Possibilities," *Geographical Review* 23:529-563, 1933.

COON, CARLETON S. "Climate and Race" in *Climatic Change*, Harlow Shapley, ed., pp. 13-34, Harvard University Press, Cambridge, Massachusetts, 1953.

GEIGER, R. *The Climate Near the Ground*. Harvard University Press, Cambridge, Massachusetts, 1950.

HAMSUN, KNUT. *Growth of the Soil*. Alfred A. Knopf, Inc., New York, 1921.

HUTTON, GRAHAM. *Midwest at Noon*. University of Chicago Press, Chicago, 1946.

JAMES, PRESTON E. *A Geography of Man*. Ginn and Company, Boston, 1959.

KOEPPE, CLARENCE E., and DE LONG, GEORGE C. *Weather and Climate*. McGraw-Hill Book Company, New York, 1958.

KUENEN, PHILIP H. *Realms of Water*. Cleaver-Hume, London, 1955.

LANDSBERG, H. E., and JACOBS, W. C. "Applied Climatology," in *American Meteorological Society, Compendium of Meteorology*, 976-992, American Meteorological Society, Boston, 1951.

LINSLEY, R. K. "Report on the Hydrologic Problems of the Arid and Semi-Arid Areas of the United States and Canada," *Reviews of Research on Arid-Zone Hydrology*, pp. 128-152, UNESCO, Paris, 1953.

MARSH, GEORGE P. *The Earth as Modified by Human Action*. Charles Scribner's Sons, New York, 1885.

MEIGS, PEVERIL. "Water Problems in the United States," *Geographical Review* 42:346-366, 1952.

SHAPLEY, HARLOW, ed. *Climatic Change*. Harvard University Press, Cambridge, Massachusetts, 1953.

THORNTHWAITE, C. W. "The Climates of North America According to a New Classification," *Geographical Review* 21:633-655, 1931.

———, "The Climates of the Earth," *Geographical Review* 23:433-440, 1933.

———, *Atlas of Climatic Types in the United States*, 1900-1939. United States Department of Agriculture, Miscellaneous Publications 421, Washington, 1941.

———, "An Approach Toward a Rational Classification of Climate," *Geographical Review* 38:55-94, 1948.

THORNTHWAITE, C. W., and MATHER, J. R. *The Water Balance*. Drexel Institute of Technology, Publications in Climatology, Volume 8, No. 1, Laboratory of Climatology, Centerton, New Jersey, 1955.

United States Department of Agriculture. "Soils and Men," *Yearbook of Agriculture*, Washington, 1938.

———, "Climate and Man," *Yearbook of Agriculture*, Washington, 1941.

———, "Water," *Yearbook of Agriculture*, Washington, 1955.

———, "Soil," *Yearbook of Agriculture*, Washington, 1957.

WHITE, GILBERT, ed. *The Future of Arid Lands*. American Association for the Advancement of Science, Washington, 1956.

Part IV. Man's Use of the Earth and the Mark He Makes on it

AMES, OAKES. *Economic Annuals and Human Culture*. Botanical Museum of Harvard University, Harvard University, Cambridge, Massachusetts, 1939.

ANDERSON, EDGAR. *Plants, Man, and Life*. Little, Brown and Company, Boston, 1952.

———, "Man as a Maker of New Plants and New Plant Communities" in *Man's Role in Changing the Face of the Earth*, W. L. Thomas, Jr., ed., pp. 763-777, University of Chicago Press, Chicago, 1956.

ASHTON, T. S. *The Industrial Revolution 1760-1830*. Oxford University Press, New York, 1958.

AYRES, EUGENE. "The Age of Fossil Fuels" in *Man's Role in Changing the Face of the Earth*, W. L. Thomas, Jr., ed., pp. 367-381, University of Chicago Press, Chicago, 1956.

BALZAK, S. S., VASYUTIN, V. F., and FEIGIN, Ya G. *Economic Geography of the U.S.S.R.* Macmillan Company, New York, 1952.

BASEDOW, HERBERT. *The Australian Aboriginal*. F. W. Preece and Sons, Adelaide, 1929.

BENNETT, H. H. *Soil Conservation*. McGraw-Hill Book Company, New York, 1939.

BROWN, RALPH H. *Historical Geography of the United States*. Harcourt, Brace and Company, New York, 1948.

CAIN, S. A. *Foundations of Plant Geography.* Harper and Brothers, New York, 1944.

CHILDE, V. G. *The Dawn of European Civilization.* 5th Edition. Routledge and Kegan Paul, London, 1950.

COON, CARLETON S. *Caravan: The Story of the Middle East.* Revised Edition. Henry Holt and Company, New York, 1958.

CRIST, RAYMOND E. "Land Tenure Problems in Venezuela," *American Journal of Economics and Sociology* 1:143-154, 1942.

CURTIS, JOHN T. "The Modification of Mid-latitude Grasslands and Forests by Man" in *Man's Role in Changing the Face of the Earth,* W. L. Thomas, Jr., ed., pp. 721-736, University of Chicago Press, Chicago, 1956.

DICKINSON, ROBERT E. *City Region and Regionalism: A Geographical Contribution to Human Ecology.* Kegan Paul, Trench, Trubner and Company, London, 1947.

DRURY, JOHN. *Historic Midwest Houses.* University of Minnesota Press, Minneapolis, 1947.

FIRTH, RAYMOND. *Malay Fishermen: Their Peasant Economy.* Kegan Paul, Trench, Trubner and Company, London, 1946.

FITZGERALD, WALTER. *Africa, A Social, Economic, and Political Geography of Its Major Regions.* 4th Edition. E. P. Dutton and Company, London, 1943.

FORBES, R. J. *Notes on the History of Ancient Roads and Their Construction.* Amsterdam, 1934.

———, *Man the Maker: A History of Technology and Engineering.* Henry Schuman, New York, 1950.

———, *Metallurgy in Antiquity.* E. J. Brill, Leiden, 1950.

FRANKLIN, T. B. *A History of Agriculture.* G. Bell, Ltd., London, 1948.

GREGORY, J. W. *The Story of the Road.* A. Maclehose and Company, London, 1931.

GUTKIND, E. A. *The Expanding Environment: The End of Cities, the Rise of Communities.* Freedom Press, London, 1953.

———, "Our World from the Air: Conflict and Adaption" in *Man's Role in Changing the Face of the Earth,* W. L. Thomas, Jr., ed., pp. 1-44, University of Chicago Press, Chicago, 1956.

HARRIS, C. D. "A Functional Classification of Cities in the United States," *Geographical Review* 33:86-90, 1943.

HARRIS, C. D., and ULLMAN, E. L. "The Nature of Cities," *Annals of the American Academy of Political and Social Science* 242:7-17, 1945.

HARTSHORNE, RICHARD. "Location Factors in the Iron and Steel Industry," *Economic Geography* 4:241-252, 1928.

HARTSHORNE, R., and DICKEN, S. N. "A Classification of the Agricultural Regions of Europe and North America on a Uniform Statistical Basis," *Annals of the Association of American Geographers* 25:99-120, 1935.

JEFFERSON, MARK. "The Civilizing Rails," *Economic Geography* 4:217-231, 1928.

JOHNSON, JAMES H. "Studies of Irish Rural Settlement," *Geographical Review* 48:554-566, 1958.

JONES, S. B. "The Economic Geography of Atomic Energy, A Review Article," *Economic Geography* 27:268-274, 1951.

KNIFFEN, F. B. "Louisiana House Types," *Annals of the Association of American Geographers* 26:179-193, 1936.

KOLLMORGEN, WALTER M., and JENKS, GEORGE F. "Suitcase Farming in Sully County, South Dakota," *Annals of the Association of American Geographers* 48:27-40, 1958.

———, "Sidewalk Farming in Toole County, Montana, and Traill County, North Dakota," *Annals of the Association of American Geographers* 48:209-231, 1958.

KROEBER, A. L. *Cultural and Natural Areas of Native North America.* University of California Publications in American Archaeology and Ethnology, Volume 38, University of California Press, Berkeley, 1939.

KÜCHLER, A. W. "A Physiognomic Classification of Vegetation," *Annals of the Association of American Geographers* 39:201-210, 1949.

MALIN, JAMES C. "The Grassland of North America: Its Occupance and the Challenge of Continuous Reappraisals," in *Man's Role in Changing the Face of the Earth,* W. L. Thomas, Jr., ed., pp. 350-366, University of Chicago Press, Chicago, 1956.

MAYER, H. M. "Moving People and Goods in Tomorrow's Cities," *Annals of the American Academy of Political and Social Science* 242:116-128, 1945.

MCLAUGHLIN, DONALD H. "Man's Selective Attack on Ores and Minerals" in *Man's Role in Changing the Face of the Earth,* W. L. Thomas, Jr., ed., pp. 851-861, University of Chicago Press, Chicago, 1956.

MORGAN, F. W. "Pre-War Hinterlands of the German Baltic Ports," *Geography,* Volume 34, 1949.

MUMFORD, LEWIS. *The Culture of Cities.* Harcourt, Brace and Company, New York, 1938.

MURPHY, RAYMOND E. "Landownership on a Micronesian Atoll," *Geographical Review* 38:598-614, 1948.

ORDWAY, SAMUEL H., JR. "Possible Limits of Raw-Material Consumption" in *Man's Role in Changing the Face of the Earth,* W. L. Thomas, Jr., ed., pp. 987-1009, University of Chicago Press, Chicago, 1956.

PEARCY, G. E., and ALEXANDER, L. M. "Pattern of Commercial Air Service Availability in the Western Hemisphere," *Economic Geography* 27:316-320, 1951.

———, "Pattern of Air Service Availability in the Eastern Hemisphere," *Economic Geography* 29:74-78, 1953.

PRUNTY, MERLE JR. "The Renaissance of the Southern Plantation," *Geographical Review* 45:459-491, 1955.

SAUER, CARL O. "Destructive Exploitation in Modern Colonial Expansion," *Proceedings of the International Geographical Congress,* Volume 2, Section IIIC:494-499, Amsterdam, 1938.

———, "Early Relations of Man to Plants," *Geographical Review* 37:1-25, 1947.

SCHEBESTA, PAUL. *Among the Forest Dwarfs of Malaya.* Hutchinson and Company, Ltd., London, 1929.

SEARS, PAUL B. *Deserts on the March.* University of Oklahoma Press, Norman, Oklahoma, 1947.

SHANTZ, H. L., and ZON, R. "Natural Vegetation," in United States Department of Agriculture, *Atlas of American Agriculture,* Washington, 1924.

SINGER, CHARLES, HOLMYARD, E. J., HALL, A. R., and WILLIAMS, TREVOR I., eds. *A History of Technology,* 5 volumes, Oxford University Press, New York, 1954-1958.

STAMP, L. D. "Fertility, Productivity, and Classification of Land in Britain." *Geographical Journal,* 96:389-412, 1940.

STRAHLER, ARTHUR N. "The Nature of Induced Erosion and Aggradation" in *Man's Role in Changing the Face of the Earth,* W.

L. Thomas, Jr., ed., pp. 621-638, University of Chicago Press, Chicago, 1956.

THOMAN, RICHARD S. *The Geography of Economic Activity.* McGraw-Hill Book Company, New York, 1962.

THOMAS, ELIZABETH M. *The Harmless People.* Alfred A. Knopf, New York, 1959.

ULLMAN, E. L. "The Railroad Pattern of the United States," *Geographical Review* 39:242-256, 1949.

———, "The Role of Transportation and the Bases for Interaction" in *Man's Role in Changing the Face of the Earth,* W. L. Thomas, Jr., ed., pp. 862-880, University of Chicago Press, Chicago, 1956.

United States Department of Agriculture. "Grass," *Yearbook of Agriculture,* Washington, 1948.

———, "Trees," *Yearbook of Agriculture,* Washington, 1949.

VAN ROYEN, WILLIAM, and BOWLES, OLIVER. *The Agricultural Resources of the World,* Vol. I. Prentice-Hall, Inc., New York, 1952.

———, *The Mineral Resources of the World,* Vol. II. Prentice-Hall, Inc., New York, 1954.

VAVILOV, N. I. *The Origin, Variation, Immunity, and Breeding of Cultivated Plants.* Translated from the Russian by K. Starr Chester. Chronica Botanica, Volume 13, Chronica Botanica Company, Waltham, Massachusetts, 1951.

VOGT, WILLIAM. *The Road to Survival.* William Sloane Associates, New York, 1948.

Water Resources Policy Commission. *Report to the President,* (3 volumes). Washington, 1950.

WHITAKER, J. R. *The Life and Death of the Land.* George Peabody College for Teachers, Peabody Press, Nashville, Tennessee, 1946.

WHITAKER, J. R., and ACKERMAN, E. A. *American Resources, Their Management and Conservation.* Harcourt, Brace and Company, New York, 1951.

WHITTLESEY, DERWENT S. "Major Agricultural Regions of the Earth," *Annals of the Association of American Geographers* 26:199-240, 1936.

WISSMANN, HERMANN VON. "On the Role of Nature and Man in Changing the Face of the Dry Belt of Asia" in *Man's Role in Changing the Face of the Earth,* W. L. Thomas, Jr., ed., pp. 278-303, University of Chicago Press, Chicago, 1956.

WOYTINSKY, W. S., and WOYTINSKY, E. S. *World Commerce and Governments*. The Twentieth Century Fund, New York, 1955.

ZIMMERMAN, E. W. *World Resources and Industries*, 2d Edition. Harper and Brothers, New York, 1951.

Part V. Toward One World

ACKERMAN, EDWARD A. *Japan's Natural Resources and Their Relation to Japan's Economic Future*. University of Chicago Press, Chicago, 1953.

ALEXANDER, JOHN W. "International Trade: Selected Types of World Regions," *Economic Geography* 36:95-115, 1960.

BOGGS, S. WHITTEMORE. *International Boundaries: A Study of Boundary Functions and Problems*. Columbia University Press, New York, 1940.

———, "National Claims in Adjacent Seas," *Geographical Review* 41:185-209, 1951.

CAHNMAN, WERNER J. "Frontiers between East and West in Europe," *Geographical Review* 39:605-624, 1949.

CARSON, RACHEL. *The Sea Around Us*. Oxford University Press, New York, 1951.

———, *The Edge of the Sea*. Houghton Mifflin Company, Boston, 1955.

COKER, R. E. *This Great and Wide Sea*. University of North Carolina Press, Chapel Hill, 1947.

DEUTSCH, KARL W. "The Growth of Nations: Some Recurrent Patterns of Political and Social Integrations," *World Politics* 5:168-195, 1953.

GARRISON, WILLIAM L., and MARBLE, DUANE F. "The Spatial Structure of Agricultural Activities," *Annals of the Association of American Geographers* 47:137-144, 1957.

GOTTMANN, JEAN. "The Political Partitioning of Our World: An Attempt at Analysis," *World Politics* 4:512-519, 1952.

GRAHAM, MICHAEL. "Harvests of the Seas" in *Man's Role in Changing the Face of the Earth*, W. L. Thomas, Jr., ed., pp. 487-503, University of Chicago Press, Chicago, 1956.

HALL, H. DUNCAN. "Zones of the International Frontier," *Geographical Review* 38:615-625, 1948.

HIGHET, GILBERT. *The Migration of Ideas*. Oxford University Press, New York, 1954.

HODGEN, MARGARET T. *Change and History: A Study of the Dated Distributions of Technological Innovations in England*. (Viking Fund Publications in Anthropology, No. 18), Wenner-Gren Foundation for Anthropological Research, Inc., New York, 1952.

JONES, STEPHEN B. *Boundary Making: A Handbook for Statesmen, Treaty Editors, and Boundary Commissioners*. Carnegie Endowment for International Peace, Washington, 1945.

———, "A Unified Field Theory of Political Geography," *Annals of the Association of American Geographers* 44:111-123, 1954.

MACKINDER, SIR HALFORD. "The Round World and the Winning of the Peace," *Foreign Affairs* 21:595-605, 1943.

MASON, PHILIP. *An Essay on Racial Tension*. Royal Institute of International Affairs, 345 East 46th Street, New York, 1954.

MOODIE, A. E. *Geography Behind Politics*. Hutchinson's University Library, London, 1949.

MOUNTJOY, ALAN B. "The Suez Canal at Mid-Century," *Economic Geography* 34:155-167, 1958.

MURPHEY, RHOADS. "The Decline of North Africa Since the Roman Occupation: Climatic or Human?" *Annals of the Association of American Geographers* 41:116-132, 1951.

POUNDS, NORMAN J. G. "The Origin of the Idea of Natural Frontiers in France," *Annals of the Association of American Geographers* 41:146-157, 1951.

SARGENT, A. J. *Seaways of the Empire* (2d Edition). London, 1930.

———, *Seaports and Hinterlands*. London, 1938.

SEALY, KENNETH R. *The Geography of Air Transport*. Hutchinson's University Library, London, 1957.

STANISLAWSKI, DAN. "Origin and Spread of the Grid-Pattern Town," *Geographical Review* 36:105-120, 1946.

THOMAN, RICHARD S. "Foreign Trade Zones in the United States," *Geographical Review* 42:613-645, 1952.

VAN DOREN, MARK, ed. *The Travels of William Bartram*. Barnes and Noble, Inc., New York, 1940.

Index

A horizon soil, 147, 149
aborigines, Australian, 170, 171
Abyssinia, 422
Ackerman, Edward A., 68, 441, 442, 445, 446
adaptation to climate, 94, 105
adobe, 95
adobe house, 204
aerial photograph, 13, 26, 398, 414, 415
Afghanistan, 376, 435
Afghans, 304
Africa, 62, 74, 358
Africa, route around, 21
Age, Ice, 29
age composition of groups, 73
Age of Discovery, 35
agricultural geographers, 26
agricultural technology, 79
agriculturalists, seed, 187
agriculture, 40
agriculture
  diversified, 402
  intensity of, 67
  Mediterranean, 309
  plow, 190
agriculture typology, 212
air, 74, 75
air pressure, 106
air temperatures, 74
air-conditioning, 94
airplane, 290, 297
airway, 297, 298, 299
Aitoff equal-area projection, 412
Alabama, 138
Alaska, 303, 359
Albania, 435
Alexander, John W., 446
Alexander, L. M., 445
Algeria, 435
alkali, 158

All-American Canal, 113, 352
Allen's Rule, 92
alloys, iron, 239
alluvial soils, 434
alluvium, 153
alphabet, 391
alpine meadow soils, 433
Alps, 139
aluminum, 239, 241, 242, 249
Amazonia, 420
American Homestead Laws, 214
American Indians, 165, 168, 169
Ames, Oakes, 443
Amsterdam, 273
Amu River, 140
analysis
  comparative approach to, 401
  discriminatory, 405
  ecological approach to, 400
  simulation approach to, 405
  statistical approach to, 402
  techniques of, 398
analysis of covariance, 406
analysis of settlement, 399
analysis of variance, 403
Anatolia, 383
Anderson, Edgar, 176, 182, 443
Andes, 139
Angola, 359, 435
animal
  browsing, 121, 190
  distribution of domestic, 186
  domestic, 188
  draft, 186, 187, 188
  grazing, 190
  herd, 186

meat, 186
origins of domestic, 181, 186
pack, 188
riding, 186
sea, 121
wild, 186
annual precipitation, 404
antarctic, 368
Antarctic circle, 105
Antarctica, 367, 423
anthracite coal, 245
anti-Malthusians, 70, 71
apple, 178
aqueduct, 253
aqueducts, 141, 348
aquifer, 133
Arab geography, 19
Arabia, 304
arable land, 79
Arabs, 304
Aral Sea, 67
Archimedan screw, 255
Arcos de la Frontera (Spain), 117
Arctic Circle, 105
Arctic Ocean, 368
area, 435
area, culture, 380
area of continents, 53
Argentina, 61, 113, 305, 314, 435
Aristotle, 15
art, religious, 384
artesian well, 133
artichoke, Jerusalem, 179
asbestos, 241
Ashton, T. S., 258, 443
Asia, 67, 74
asphalt, 241, 293, 347
ass, 187, 310
Athens, 345, 383
Atlantic Ocean, 323
atomic power, 253

attenuated diffusion of ideas, 390
Aude, River, 6
auger, 252
Australia, 74, 139, 194, 247, 305, 313, 314, 361, 376, 435
Austria, 435
automatic-control device, 264
automation, 263, 264
automobile, 259, 260, 261, 262, 384
avocado, 179
ayllu, 221
Ayres, Eugene, 443
azimuthal equidistant projection, 410
azimuthal projection, 409, 410, 411
azonal soils, 429, 432
Aztecs, 35, 40

B horizon soil, 147, 149
Baffinland, 23
Baghdad Pact, 373, 376
Baker, J. N. L., 441
Baker, O. E., 442
Baly, Denis, 398
Balzak, S. S., 443
bamboo, 95
banana, 109, 178, 315
banana plantation, 316
Banff, 99
Baptists, 401
barley, 178, 181, 182, 310, 312, 385
Bartram, William, 395, 446
Baruch, Bernard, 301
Basedow, Herbert, 443
basketry, 252
Basutoland, 435
batata, 185
Bates, Henry Walter, 108, 442
beans, 179
beaver, 194
Bechuanaland, 110, 435
bedrock, 147, 149
beet, 185
beets, sugar, 312
Belem (Brazil), 107, 108
Belgium, 376, 377, 435

Bell, Patrick, 259
Benares, 116
Benguela Current, 324
Bennett, H. H., 443
Benz, Karl, 261
Berbers, 304
Bergmann's Rule, 92
beriberi, 183
Berkeley (California), 128
Berlin Conference of 1884, 358
Bessemer converter, 258
Bhave, Vinoba, 235
Bhoodan Movement, 235
bipolar oblique conic conformal projection, 412
birch, 194, 306
Birmingham, 244
birth rate, 49, 51, 73
bison, 192, 193
Bjarni, 17
Black Belt (Ala.), 154
black earth soils, 157
Black Sea, 66, 67
bloc
    economic, 341
    Soviet, 342, 343
blocs
    neutrality, 377
    treaty, 375
Blue Grass Region (Ky.), 155
Blumenstock, David, 442
boards, marketing, 333
bocage, 207
bog soils, 433
Boggs eumorphic projection, 412
Boggs, S. Whittemore, 446
Bolivia, 435
Bombay, 354
Bonne projection, 412
borrowing, diffusion by, 175
boundary, international, 44
boundary limits, maritime, 369
boundary problems, 362
Bowles, Oliver, 445
Bowman, Isaiah, 41, 442
Brazil, 305, 314, 435
Brazil nuts, 306
Brazilian plateau, 139

bread wheat, 182
bread-in-bulk city, 344
breadfruit, 178
breeding, selective, 177
Briare Canal, 348
bridges, 348
bridges, land, 32
British Caribbean Federation, 361
British Commonwealth, 341
British Guiana, 361
British Honduras, 361, 435
British Isles, 422
British Somaliland, 435
Broek, Jan O. M., 112
bronze tools, 381
Brooks, C. E. P., 323, 442
brown forest soils, 434
brown podzolic soils, 433
brown soils, 432
Brown, Harrison, 85, 442
Brown, Ralph H., 443
Brunei, 435
Brunhes, Jean, 25, 26, 100, 124, 199, 441
brush, 192
brushlands, 103
Brussels Canal, 348
Buckle, Henry, 24
Buffalo grass, 193
buffer nations, 376
building minerals, 241
building stone, 241, 242
Bulgaria, 436
Burkesville (Ky.), 82
Burma, 436
burnt-over land, 195
bush fallowing, 211
Bushmen, 40, 172
butter, 313

C horizon soil, 148, 149
cacao, 178, 179, 315
cactus, prickly-pear, 194
Cahill's projection, 412
Cahnman, Werner J., 446
Cain, Stanley A., 444
Calcutta, 354
Calgary (Canada), 112
California, 59, 60, 113, 310, 330

calorie intake, 76
calories, original, 78, 79
Cambaluc, 20
Cambodia, 436
camel
 bactrian, 187
 dromedary, 187
camera, 264
Cameroun, 436
camote, 185
campagne, 207
Campbell, J. D., 441
Canada, 139, 247, 306, 314, 335, 341, 361, 436
Canal de Miribel, 350
Canal du Centre, 351
Canal du Midi, 6, 348
canalization of rivers, 350
canals
 irrigation, 352
 river-fed, 347
 summit-level, 348
Canary Islands, 18
Canton, 354
Capek, Karel, 146
Capetown (U. of S. A.), 273
Carcassonne, 6, 7, 8
Carolinas, 422
Carpathians, 139
Carpini
 John de Piano, 19, 20
Carson, Rachel, 321, 446
Cartier, 22
cases, 113
cash crops, 231, 315
cash renting, 232
cash tenancy, 228, 231
Caspian Sea, 329
cassava, 109, 179, 182, 185
cassowary, 170
Castro, Josue de, 442
cattle, 186, 187, 192, 305
cattle
 beef, 188
 dairy, 188
 wild, 186
caucasoid, 38, 39
cave dwellings, 201
cedar, 306
celestial properties, 24
cement, 239, 241
centers, trade, 344

Central African Republic, 436
central business district, 266, 272
Central Mexico, 60
central place theory, 270
Central Plateau of Mexico, 60
Ceylon, 436
Chaco, 116
chad, 436
Chandernagore, 364
changing climate, 122
chaparral, 102, 103
chariot, war, 251
Charleston (S.C.), 115
chart, Koppen climate, 419
cheese, 313
chemical minerals, 241
chemical weathering, 152
chemicals, 241
chernozem, 157
chernozem soil, 144
cherry, 178, 306
chi-square statistic, 405
Chicago, 118, 267, 274
Chichimecs, 35
chicle, 306
Childe, V. G., 442, 444
Chile, 61, 62, 241, 310, 436
Chile, population map of, 62
China, 67, 70, 139, 239, 304, 365, 381, 436
China, migration from, 43
Chinook, 168
Chita (U.S.S.R.), 118
chlorination of water, 142
choropleth map, 400
Christ, Raymond E., 444
chromium, 248
Chukchi, 40, 303
Chungchow, 20
Chuquicamata, 241
Church, J. E., 443
Ciboney, 35
circulation, 288
circulation, water, 127
circulation of ideas, 379
cities
 primate, 269
 size of, 268
citron, 178, 310

citrus fruits, 178, 310
city, 266, 271, 272
city planning, 274
climate, 11, 26, 90, 105, 106, 279, 323, 417
climate
 A, 107, 417
 adaptation to, 94
 adaptations to, 105
 Af, 107
 Am, 110
 Aw, 107, 109
 B, 417
 Bs, 111
 Bw, 111, 113
 C, 417
 Cf, 114
 changing, 122
 cool summer rainy temperate, 422
 Cs, 114, 116
 Cw, 114, 116
 D, 417
 desert, 421
 Df, 118
 Ds, 118
 Dw, 118
 E, 417
 Ef, 120
 Et, 120
 frost, 120, 121
 glacial, 423
 hot summer rainy temperate, 422
 humid mesothermal, 114, 422
 Koppen, 106, 418
 man's effect on, 121
 Mediterranean, 114, 121
 monsoon, 110
 nomograph for, 420
 short summer microthermal, 423
 steppe, 421
 summer dry temperate, 422
 temperate mesothermal, 114, 422
 tropical rainforest, 420
 tundra, 120, 423
 warm summer microthermal, 423

climate (*Cont.*)
  winter dry temperate, 421, 422
climatic data, 424
climatic types, 430
clothing, 74, 93, 94
cloud seeding, 122
coal, 80, 81, 83, 84, 239, 244, 245, 246, 248, 263
Cocks, Richard, 387
coffee, 178, 315, 316
coffee belt, 116
cogged wheel, 251
coke, 256
Coker, R. E., 446
coking coal, 239, 249
cold deserts, 111
cold steppes, 111
collective farm, 210
collectives, 219
colloids, 147
Colombia, 436
colonialism, 358
colonies, 357, 358
Colorado, 97
Colorado Plateau, 97, 98
Colorado River, 97, 113, 137
Columbia River, 168
Columbo Plan, 341
Columbus, Christopher, 22, 322
combine, 258
Common Market, 341, 342, 343
communal tenure, 211, 217
communes, 219
communication, 26, 288
Communism, primitive, 220
comparative approach to analysis, 401
compass, magnetic, 21
complex, culture, 380
concepts, strategic, 373
condominiums, 362
Congo, 247, 436
Congo Republic, 436
Congo River, 140, 169
conic projection, 17, 409, 410, 411
conservation, 301, 307
Constantinople, 347
constructed map grid, 412

construction minerals, 241
consumption, food, 78
consumption of energy, 83
continental shelf, 327
continents
  area of, 53
  population of, 53
conversion of sea water, 134
converter, Bessemer, 258
Cook, James, 23
Coon, Carleton S., 38, 92, 226, 229, 236, 441, 443, 444
copper, 238, 239, 241, 242, 381
corn
  hybrid, 188
  kafir, 183
  spread of hybrid, 388
corn-belt farming, 314
Cornwall Canal, 352
corporate ownership, 233
corporate ownership of land, 235
corroboree, 171
Cort, Henry, 256
Cosmas Indicopleustes, 16, 17
Costa Rica, 436
cotton, 385
cotton, spread of commercial, 388
cotton belt, 154, 316
Council of Mutual Economic Assistance, 343
country, 355
covariance, 405
covariance, analysis of, 406
cowpeas, 178
coyote, 193
crank, 253
crescent
  inner, 373
  outer, 373
crop
  cash, 231
  fiber, 179
crop yields, 147
cropping
  multiple, 310
  strip, 315
  two-story, 310

crops
  cash, 315
  root, 185
Crusades, 18
Ctesibius, 252
Cuba, 436
cultivated plants, 177
cultivated plants, dispersion of, 180
cultivation, 177, 185
cultivation
  patch, 190
  shifting, 190
cultural changes related to migrations, 47
cultural differences, 175
cultural diffusion, 47
cultural elements, 104
cultural landscape, 26
culture
  hoe, 307
  neolithic, 250
  paleolithic, 250
  plow, 308, 309
culture area, 380
culture complex, 380
culture pearl, 328
culture trait, 380
current, ocean, 324
currents of migration, 42
Curtis, John T., 444
cut-over land, 195
cutting, selective, 190
cycle
  hydrologic, 126, 128, 146
  water, 124, 127
cylindrical projection, 409, 410
Cyprus, 436
Czechoslovakia, 436

Dahomey, 436
Daimler, Gottlieb, 261
dairying, 313
Damao, 364
dams, 101, 140, 143
Darwin, Charles, 24
data, climatic, 424
dating
  carbon fourteen, 395
  lexico-statistical, 397
  lichen-growth, 395

pollen analysis, 395
  relative, 396
  techniques of, 394
  tree ring, 395
  varves, 395
Davis, John, 23
Davis, Kingsley, 358
De Long, George C., 424, 443
deadening, 195, 196
death rate, 50, 51, 73
decreases in population, 49
deer, 186
definition of urban population, 58
degraded chernozem soils, 433
dendritic population pattern, 59
Denmark, 436
Denoyer's semi-elliptical projection, 412
density
  gross, 435, 436, 437, 438, 439
  nutritional, 53, 56, 435, 436, 437, 438, 439
  population, 52, 53, 59, 61
desert, 102, 107, 111, 113, 114
desert soils, 158, 432
Deutsch, Karl, 356, 446
dialects, 398
diamonds, 248
Diaz, Bartholomeu, 22
Dicken, Samuel Newton, 282, 283, 284, 418, 419, 441, 444
Dickinson, Robert E., 441, 444
diet, 77, 78
diffusion by borrowing, 175
diffusion by migration, 175
diffusion of ideas, 379
diffusion of plants, 185
digging stick, 380
discovery of oceans, 21
discriminatory analysis, 405
diseases, tropical, 108
dispersal of fields, 215
dispersion of cultivated plants, 180

disposal, waste, 128
disputes over fishing areas, 372
distillation of water, 134
distribution of domestic animals, 186
distribution of population, 48, 52
district, residential, 272
Diu, 364
division of labor, 215
Dnepr River, 140, 347
Dodge, Richard Elwood, 331
domestic animals, distribution of, 186
domestic animals, origins of, 186
domesticated animals, origins of, 181
domestication of plants, 176, 188
domestication of reindeer, 390
Dominican Republic, 436
Don River, 67
Don-Volga Canal, 349
Donbas, 67, 244
donkey, 187
dot map, 400
drainage, 26
Drake well, 82
drill
  hand, 250
  wheat, 260
drought, 31, 111, 192
drought, periodic, 101
drought hazard, 157
drugs, 241
Drury, John, 444
dry lands, 111
dry pampa, 112
Dublin, 115
Dufex, George J., 367
Dunlop, John B., 261
Durian, 35
dysentery, 108

earth house, 203
earthquake hazards, 205
earthquakes, 325
East Europe, 139
East, W. G., 442

ecological approach to analysis, 400
ecological rules, 91
economic bloc, 341
economic geography, 270
Ecuador, 436
Egypt, 101, 113, 139, 304, 361, 371, 375, 377
Eider Canal, 354
einkorn wheat, 182
Eisenhower Doctrine, 375
Ejido, 221
El Salvador, 436
Elbe River, 347
electric lighting, 82
electric power, 82
electricity, 137, 138
electricity, generation of, 129
emmer wheat, 182
Emu, 170
enclaves, 363, 365
energy, 79
energy
  consumption of, 83
  hydroelectric, 82, 100, 138, 140, 246
  nuclear, 82, 83, 84
  solar, 82, 83, 84
  world's supply of, 80
energy produced, 84
engine
  internal-combustion, 245, 253, 259, 260, 262
  Lenoir gas, 261
  steam, 82, 253, 256
England, 335
English Channel, 354
entrepot, 344
environment, 11, 24, 89
Eratosthenes, 15
Eric the Red, 17
Ericson, Leif, 18
Erie, Lake, 138
Erie Canal, 349, 352
erosion, 302
erosion, soil, 316
eskimo, 23, 35, 36, 37, 40, 121, 165, 166, 167, 168, 303
Espenshade, Edward B. Jr., 441
Ethiopia, 436

eucalyptus, 170
Eugene (Ore.), 3, 4, 8
Euphrates River, 101
Euphrates Valley, 113
Europe, 64, 74, 139, 239
European Coal and Steel Community, 341
European Free Trade Association, 342
evaporation, 111, 128
evidence of migration, 32
exploration, 21, 37, 242
exports, 337, 338, 340

factory, farm, 235
fall line, 344
fallout, radioactive, 372
fallowing, bush, 211
family, size of, 73
farm factory, 235
farm surplus problem, 79
farming, 258
farming, 309, 311, 314
federation, political, 361
fee-simple tenure, 222
Feigin, Ya. G., 443
ferries, 344
ferroalloys, 239
fertility rate, 49
fertilizer, 153, 241
fertilizer, mineral, 241
feudalism, 232
fiber crop, 179
fibers, synthetic, 306
fields, dispersal of, 215
fig, 178
Fiji, 436
filtration plants, 143
Finland, 306, 375, 436
fir, 306
fire, 31, 79, 190, 191
fire, man's use of, 30
Firth, Raymond, 444
fish, 325, 327, 328, 340
fish pemmican, 169
fishing, 163, 303
fishing areas, disputes over, 372
fishing nets, 250
Fitzgerald, Walter, 444
fixed rent, 231, 232
flax, 179

Fleck, Sir Alexander, 259
flood control, 140, 143
flood stage, 130
floods, 140
food, 31, 74, 75
Food and Agricultural Organization, 341
food consumption, 78
forage, 312
Forbes, R. J., 256, 444
forced migrations, 44, 70
fords, 344
forecast of world population, 74
forecasts, population, 71
forest production, 306
forests, 102, 103, 190, 192, 194, 195, 233, 306
form, settlement, 399, 400
formal set theory, 405
formations, vegetative, 430
Formosa, 68
Fox, Luke, 23
fragmentation, 224
frame house, 202, 203
France, 312, 336, 436
France, South, 139
Franklin, Benjamin, 442
Franklin, T. B., 444
Franz Canal, 350
Free Trade Zone, 341
freehold, subsistence, 224
freehold tenure, 211, 222, 224, 225
freighter, ocean, 290
French Guiana, 436
French Indochina, 375
French Polynesia, 436
French School of Regional Geography, 400
French Somaliland, 436
French Union, 341
Friedrich Wilhelm Canal, 348
Frobisher, Martin, 23
Front Range, 97, 98, 99, 100
frozen soils, 152
fruits, citrus, 178, 310
fuel, 194, 195
fuels
    fossil, 75, 81, 82
    mineral, 246

future population, 70

Gabon, 436
Gall's stereographic projection, 410
Gama, Vasco da, 22
Gambia, 436
Ganges, 422
Garonne River, 6
Garrison, William L., 407, 446
Gas
    coal, 81
    natural, 80, 81, 83, 84, 239, 263
gas lighting, 81
gas turbine, 262
gasoline, 245
gathering, 163, 303
gear, 253
Geiger counter, 242
Geiger, R., 443
generation of electricity, 129
geographers
    agricultural, 26
    rural settlement, 26
    urban, 26
geography, 14
geography
    Arab, 19
    economic, 270
    Greek, 14
    Moslem, 18
    philosophy of, 24
    settlement, 405
geography in dark ages, 16
geography of infectious diseases, 26
geology, 24
geomorphology, 24
Georges Banks, 326
Georgia, 395
germanium, 248
Germany, 311, 312
Germany (East), 436
Germany (West), 336, 436
Ghana, 361, 436
glacial periods, 29
glacial stages, 30
glaciation
    Gunz, 30
    Mindel, 30

Riss, 30
Wurm, 30
Gloger's Rule, 91
glottochronology, 397
gnomonic projection, 410, 412
Goa, 359, 364
goat, 188, 305, 310
Gobi, 112, 304
Godlund, Sven, 384
gold, 238, 242
Goode's equal-area projection, 412
Goode's homolosine equal-area projection, 412
Goodyear, Charles, 261
Gosling, L. A. Peter, 231
Gottmann, Jean, 446
Graham, Michael, 446
grain, 181
grain sorghums, 183
grain transport river, 349
grains, small, 312
grama grass, 192, 193
Gran Chaco, 422
Grand Banks, 326
Grand Canal, 349
Grand Canyon, 98
grape, 178, 310, 312
grass, 182, 192, 193
grassland, semiarid, 102
grasslands, 103, 190, 192, 193, 194
grasslands, settlement of, 259
gravel, 239, 241, 242
gray wooded soils, 433
gray-brown podzolic soils, 433
grazing, 193, 304, 305, 306
grazing animal, 190
Great American Desert, 192
Great Australian Desert, 170
Great Bear Lake, 247
Great Britain, 342, 375
Great Lakes, 138, 351, 352, 423
Great Plains, 111, 192, 421
Greater East Asian Co-Prosperity Sphere, 375
Greece, 375, 436
Greeks, 105, 321
Greenbelt (Maryland), 275

Greenland, 303, 359, 423
Gregory, J. W., 444
grey forest soils, 156
grid, map, 409
grid pattern, 383
gross density, 435, 436, 437, 438, 439
ground water, 126, 127, 131, 132, 133, 142, 143
ground-water laterite soils, 434
ground-water podzol soils, 434
ground-water runoff, 130
growth of nations, 355
growth of political communities, 355
growth of population, 41, 48
growth rate, population, 72
Guatemala, 436
Guinea, 361, 437
Gulf of Maricaibo, 330
Gulf of Mexico, 330
Gulf of St. Lawrence, 22
Gulf Stream, 323, 326
gum, 306
Gunz glaciation, 30
Gutkind, E. A., 444
Gutkind, Erwin A., 89
Gwadar, 364
gypsum, 241

Hagerstrand, Torsten, 405, 407
Haiti, 437
half-bog soils, 434
Hall, A. R., 381, 445
Hall, H. Duncan, 362, 446
hamlet, 208, 266
Hamsun, Knut, 144, 443
hand drill, 250
Hanno, 190
Hanno the Carthagenian, 322
Hanseatic League, 346
hard water, 142
hardwoods, 195
Harlow (England), 275
harpoon, 250
Harris, C. D., 444
Harrison, H. S., 250
Harts, Portolano, 18
Hartshorne, Richard, 282, 418, 419, 441, 444

Hausa, 356, 361
Haushofer, Karl, 373
Hawaii, 359
hay, 312
head-of-navigation city, 344
Hearne, Thomas, 387
heartland, 373, 374
heating, space, 84
Henry the Navigator, Prince, 21
herding, nomadic, 304
Hero, 252
Herodotus, 14, 15
Highet, Gilbert, 446
hill lands, 96
Himalayas, 140
hinterland, 269, 270
Hobson, William, 347
Hodgen, Margaret T., 446
Hodgson, Robert D., 401, 402
hoe, 40
hoe culture, 153, 307
Holmes, Oliver Wendell, Jr., 379
Holmyard, E. J., 381, 445
home industries, 402
Homestead Laws, American, 214
homesteading, 227
Honduras, 437
honey, 312
Hong Kong, 354
Hoover Dam, 137
hops, 312
horizontal well, 132
horse, 187, 253
hot deserts, 111
hot steppes, 111
house, 199
house
adobe, 204
earth, 203
frame, 202, 203
log, 200, 201
portable, 205
prefabricated, 205
sod, 204
stone, 203
tent, 200
trailer, 200
wooden, 201

house trailers, 205
house type, 200
houseboats, 205
houses, orientation of, 94
housing, 26
housing, materials used in, 95
Howarth, O. J. R., 441
Hudson Bay, 23, 423
human geography, 9, 10, 24, 25, 26, 37, 40
human geography
    methods of, 13
    techniques in, 393
    tools of, 13
human occupation, restrictions to, 90
human power, 80
human properties, 24
human settlements, 108
Humboldt Current, 324
humic-glei soils, 433
humid mesothermal lands, 115, 121
humid microthermal lands, 118
humid prairie, 192
humidity, 74, 107
humus, 147, 152
Hungary, 314, 437
hunting, 163, 303
hurricanes, 325
Hutton, Graham, 119, 443
hybrid corn, 188
hybridization, 177
hydroelectric energy, 82, 100, 138, 140, 246
hydroelectric plants, 131
hydroelectric projects, 143
hydroelectricity, 247
hydrologic cycle, 126, 128, 146

Ibn, Haukal, 19
IBO, 356, 361
Ice Age, 29, 30
Iceland, 340, 437
Ichang, 20
ideas
    attenuated diffusion of, 390
    circulation of, 379
    diffusion of, 379
    independent development of, 391
    rejection of, 389
Idrisi, 19
igloo, 37
immigration, 51
immigration quotas, 47
Imperial Valley, 113
imports, 338, 339, 340
Incas, 35, 40
independent invention, 175
India, 17, 67, 70, 110, 111, 139, 247, 358, 361, 377, 381, 437
India, migration from, 43
Indian groups (Amerind), 40
Indian Reservations, 364
Indian Union, 361
Indians, 193
Indians, American, 165, 168, 169
Indicopleustes, Cosmas, 16, 17
Indonesia, 437
Indus Plain, 101
Indus River, 19
Indus Valley, 113
industrial minerals, 241
Industrial Revolution, 256, 257
industrial waste, 128
industries, home, 402
inertia-guidance devices, 264
infectious diseases, geography of, 26
information, sources of, 395, 396
inland sea, 402
inland waterways, 349, 350
inner crescent, 373
innovation, 405, 406
insecticides, 153
institutional ownership, 233
intensity of agriculture, 67
intercontinental migration, 43
intercultivation, 310
interglacial periods, 29
interglacial stages, 30
internal combustion engine, 80, 82
internal migrations, 45, 46
internal-combustion engine 245, 253, 259, 260, 262
international boundary, 44
international migration, 44
interrupted sinusoidal projection, 412
Intracoastal Waterway, 349
intrazonal soils, 429, 432
Iran, 67, 375, 437
Iraq, 113, 361, 375, 376, 437
Ireland, 437
iron, 238, 263
iron, pig, 239
Iron Age, 381
iron alloys, 239
iron ore, 239, 242, 244, 249
iron ships, 260
iron smelting, 381
irrigation, 66, 100, 101, 112, 124, 127, 128, 129, 132, 134, 135, 136, 139, 143, 177, 183, 310, 314, 316, 402
irrigation canals, 352
island, world, 373
isochronic map, 395, 396, 398
isohyets, 106
isopleth map, 400, 401
isotherms, 106, 107
Israel, 45, 342, 437
Italy, 64, 65, 66, 139, 314, 381, 437
Ivory Coast, 437

Jacobs, W. C., 443
Jamaica, 361
James, Preston E., 441, 443
Japan, 67, 68, 335, 375, 402, 437
Japan Current, 326
Java, 68
Jefferson, Mark, 266, 269, 442, 444
Jefferson, Thomas, 251, 302
Jen-Hu Chang, 417
Jenks, George F., 444
Jerusalem, 16
Jerusalem artichoke, 179

Jews, 304
Jews, migration of, 44, 45
Johnson, James H., 444
Jones, Clarence F., 441
Jones, Stephen B., 441, 444, 446
Jordan, 437

Kafir corn, 183
Kamchatka Current, 326
kangaroo, 170
Kano, 63
Karachi, 354
Karakorum, 19
Karikul, 364
keel, 21
Kenya, 361, 437
kerosene, 81, 82
Kirgiz, 304
kidney beans, 179
Kiel Canal, 354
Kiev, 66
Kirghiz, 40
Kish, George, 441
klimata, 105
Klimm, Lester E., 442
Jerry start
Kniffen, Fred B., 441, 444
Kobe, 345, 354
Koeppe, Clarence E., 424, 443
Kolkhoz, 210
Kollmorgen, Walter M., 444
Koppen climate, 418
Koppen climate chart, 419
Koppen climates, 106
Koppen, Wladimir, 106, 417
Korea, 375
Korea (North), 437
Korea (South), 437
Krivoi Rog, 67
Kroeber, A. L., 444
Kuchler, A. W., 444
Kuenen, Philip H., 443
Kurds, 304

labor, division of, 215
labor supply, 278
Labrador, 303, 359
Labrador Current, 326
Lachine Rapids, 352
Lake Erie, 138, 352

Lake Maracaibo, 329
Lake Ontario, 138, 352
Lambert conic conformal projection, 410
Lambert equal-area projection, 410
Lambton, Ann, 221, 231
Land
    arable, 79
    burnt-over, 195
    corporate ownership of, 235
    cut-over, 195
    mulk, 226
    national ownership of, 233
    ownership of, 210
    reclamation of, 254, 256
    subsidence of, 143
land bridge, 34
land bridges, 32
land reform, 219, 228, 230, 232
land use, 301
land use in Old World, 39
landform, 11, 94
Landsberg, H. E., 443
Landscape, 26
Languedoc, 256
Laos, 437
Lapps, 40, 121, 303
large agglomeration of population, 57
large-scale map, 409
laterite soils, 433
lateritic soils, yellowish-brown, 433
latex, 261
lathe, 251, 252
latifundias, 221
Latin America, 74
Lauenburg, 347
Law of Manu, 214
Lawrence, Gulf of St., 22
Le Blanc, Maurice, 262
leaching, 152, 154, 157
lead, 238, 239, 241
Lebanon, 375, 437
Leif Ericson, 18
lemon, 310
Lenoir gas engine, 261
Lenoir, Etienne, 260
lentils, 178

Lesser Antilles, 361
levees, 140, 141
lever, 252
Lewis, Sir Clinton G., 441
lexico-statistical dating, 397
Liberia, 356, 437
Libya, 437
lichen-growth dating, 395
Liebig, Justus von, 147
life zone, 89, 94
light metals, 241
lighting, 81, 82
lima beans, 179
lime, 241
limestone, 155, 241, 293
limitation of population, 56
Lincoln, Abraham, 355
line, power, 300
linguistic tensions, 366
Linsley, R. K., 443
lithosols, 434
livestock, 312
livestock farming, 311
lock, 347, 348
log house, 200, 201
logging, 307
logging, strip, 196
loom, 250, 252
Los Angeles, 60
Louisiana Purchase, 233
Low Countries, 311
low-humic glei soils, 434
lowlands, 65
Lubeck, 347
lumbering, 194
Luxembourg, 376, 377, 437

macaroni wheat, 182
machine tools, 257
machinery
    power, 239
    threshing, 258
machines, 250
Mackinder, Sir Halford, 373, 446
madras, 354
Magellan, 22, 322
Maginot Line, 378
magnesium, 239, 241
magnetic compass, 21
magnetic tape, 264
magnetometer, 242

mahogany, 306
maize, 103, 179, 181, 182, 183, 184, 312
major soil areas of world, 430
Malagasy Republic (Madagascar), 437
Malay Peninsula, 172
Malaya, 437
Malin, James C., 444
malt beverages, 312
Malthus, Thomas R., 70, 71, 72, 442
Malthusian thesis, 70
Man's effect on climate, 121
Man's use of fire, 30
Manchuria, 68
Mandalay (Burma), 109
mandates, 358, 362
manganese, 239, 242, 248
mangels, 312
manioc, 109, 179, 387
manufacturing, 277, 278, 281
manufacturing region, 282, 283, 284, 285, 286
Maori, 214
map, 13, 23, 53, 393, 409
map
   choropleth, 400
   dot, 400
   isochronic, 395, 396, 398
   isopleth, 400, 401
   large-scale, 409
   Roman, 321
   small-scale, 409
map grid, 409
map grid, constructed, 412
map projection, 23, 408
map scale, 409
map-making, 23
maple, 306
maple, sugar, 194
maquis, 103
Maracaibo, Gulf of, 330
Maracaibo, Lake, 329
Marble, Duane F., 446
Marco Polo, 19, 20
Mariinsk Canal, 350
Maritime Boundary Limits, 369
Mark Twain National Forest, 196
market, 279

marketing boards, 333
Marsh, George P., 190, 441, 443
Marshal Plan, 341
Mason, Philip, 366, 446
mass production, 262
materials, raw, 278, 340
materials used in housing, 95
Mather, J. R., 128, 443
maui well, 133
Maull, Otto, 357
Mauritania, 437
Mauritius, 111, 437
Mayas, 35, 40
Mayer, Harold M., 351, 444
McAdam, John L., 346, 347
McCarty, Harold, 400
McCormick, Cyrus H., 258
McLaughlin, Donald H., 444
meat, 312
meat animal, 186
Mecca, 266
mechanical weathering, 152
Medenine (Tunisia), 201
Mediterranean, 321, 322
Mediterranean lands, 116
Mediterranean peoples, 39
Mediterranean Sea, 422
Meek, C. K., 210, 223
Meigs, Peveril, 443
Meikle, Andrew, 258
melanin pigmentation, 91
Mendoza Oasis, 113
merchantilism, 357
Mercator projection, 23, 409
Mesolithic period, 250
Mesopotamia, 101
mesothermal lands, 114
metal technology, 381
metallic minerals, 242
metals, light, 241
methods of human geography, 13
Mexico, 113, 165, 305, 437
Mexico
   Central, 60
   Central Plateau of, 60
   Gulf of, 330
Michigan, 306
Micronesia (Trust Territory), 437
migration, 42, 304, 396

migration
   currents of, 42
   diffusion by, 175
   evidence of, 32
   intercontinental, 43
   international, 44
   reasons for, 31
   routes of, 32
migration from China, 43
migration from Europe to America, 41
migration from India, 43
migration in modern times, 41
migration of Jews, 44, 45
migrations, 29, 31
migrations
   cultural changes related to, 47
   forced, 44, 70
   internal, 45, 46
   prehistoric, 33, 34
   restrictions on, 46
migrations in historic times, 34, 35
Milan, 347
Milan Canal, 348
milk, 186, 187, 188, 313
Milk River, 139
mill, water, 253
Miller cylindrical projection, 409
millet, 178, 181, 183, 385
mind sphere, 29
Mindel glaciation, 30
mine, strip, 244
mineral content of soil, 147
mineral exploration, 242
mineral fertilizer, 241
mineral fuels, 246
mineral resources, 26
minerals, 11, 75, 238, 337
minerals
   building, 241
   chemical, 241
   construction, 241
   industrial, 241
   metallic, 242
   strategic, 248, 249
mining, 307
Minnesota, 306
Miri, 226

Missouri Basin Project, 138
Missouri River, 138, 139
Missouri Valley, 138
Moabite Stone, 391
Mohenjo-Daro, 383
moisture, 106
Mollweide equal-area projection, 412
molybdenum, 248
Mongolia, 304
Mongolians, 304
mongoloid, 38, 39
Monnet, Jean, 343
Monroe Doctrine, 374, 375
monsoon, 111
Moodie, A. E., 442, 446
Morgan, F. W., 345, 445
Morgan, Lewis H., 220
Morman settlements, 143
Morocco, 19, 437
Mort, Thomas, 260
Moscow, 356
Moslem geography, 18
Moslem world, 19
motion, rotary, 250
motor car, 293, 294
motor truck, 290, 293, 294
mouldboard plow, 251
mountain men, 99
Mountjoy, Alan B., 446
Movement, Bhoodan, 235
Mozambique, 359, 437
mulk land, 226
multifactor uniform regions, 405
multiple cropping, 310
multiple hypothesis, 104
Mumford, Lewis, 445
Murphey, Rhoads, 446
Murphy, Raymond E., 445
Muscat and Oman, 437
Muscle Shoals, 138
Muskingum River (O.), 130

Nagoya, 68
Nahalal (Israel), 209
Nairobi, 361
Naples, 65, 116
Narr, Karl J., 163
nation, 355
national forest, 233

national growth, uniformities of, 356, 357, 358
national ownership of land, 233
national park, 233
national pike, 346
nations
  buffer, 376
  growth of, 355
  new, 359
natural elements, 104
natural environment, 24
natural gas, 80, 81, 83, 84, 239, 263
natural increase, 51, 72
natural landscape, 26
natural reservoirs, 138
natural vegetation, 11, 26, 102, 103, 192
nearest-neighbor statistics, 405
necessitism, 25
negative residuals, 403
Negroes, 39, 44
negroid, 38, 39
neo-Malthusians, 71
Neolithic culture, 250
Nepal, 437
Netherlands, 437
Netherlands Antilles, 437
Netherlands New Guinea (Trust Territory), 437
nets, fishing, 250
neutrality blocs, 377
New Caledonia, 438
New England, 60
New Guinea (Australian Trust Territory), 438
new nations, 359
New Orleans, 58
New York Barge Canal, 349
New York State Barge Canal, 352
New Zealand, 74, 305, 311, 313, 438
Newfoundland, 359
Niagara Falls, 101, 137, 138
Niagara River, 137, 138
Nicaragua, 438
nickel, 238, 239
Niger, 438
Niger River, 63

Nigeria, 63, 356, 361, 438
Nile River, 101, 370
Nile Waters Agreement of 1929, 371
nitrate, 138, 241
nitrogen, 138
nomadic herding, 304
nomograph, 419
nomograph for climate, 420
noncalcic brown soils, 433
Nootka, 168
Nordics, 39
Normandy, 256
North America, 59, 74
North Atlantic Treaty Organization, 373, 375, 376
Northern Rhodesia, 361, 438
Northwest Passage, 22, 23
Norway, 137, 306, 438
Notestein, 74
nuclear energy, 82, 83, 84
nuclear power, 247
nutritional density, 53, 56, 435, 436, 437, 438, 439
Nyasaland, 361, 438

oak, 306
oasis, 304
oats, 178, 181, 182, 312
oblique case of gnomonic projection, 412
ocean, 321
ocean current, 324
ocean freighter, 290
ocean transport routes, 352
oceans, discovery of, 21
offshore oil deposits, 233
Ohio, 401
oil, 80
oil
  olive, 310
  palm, 306
  whale, 81, 82
oil deposits, offshore, 233
oil tanks, 82
oil wells, 82
oilseed, 179
olive, 178
olive oil, 310
olive tree, 310
Olympic mountains, 130

Ontario, Lake, 138
open hearth process, Siemen's, 258
open-field system, 220
opossum, 170
orange, 310
ore, 242
ore, iron, 239, 242, 244, 249
Organization of American States, 374
orientation of houses, 94
original calories, 78, 79
origins, plant, 179
origins of domestic animals, 186
origins of domesticated animals, 181
origins of seed plants, 181
Orleans Canal, 348
orthographic projection, 410
Osaka, 68, 345
Ostyak, 303
Ottar, 322
Otto, Nikolaus A., 260, 261
outer crescent, 373
Outer Mongolia, 111, 359, 438
overland route, 100
overpopulation, 31, 71
ownership
  corporate, 233
  institutional, 233
  state, 233
ownership of land, 210
ownership of land, corporate, 235
ownership of land, national, 233
ownership of water, 142

Pacific Northwest, 313
pack animal, 188
paddle wheel, 253
Pakistan, 67, 113, 356, 358, 438
Paleolithic Culture, 250
Palestine, 44, 45, 375
palm oil, 306
pampa, dry, 112
Panama, 438
Panama Canal, 353, 354

paper making, 382
Papua, 438
Paraguay, 377, 438
parent material, 152
Paris, 267
park, national, 233
Pataliputra, 383
patch cultivation, 190
Patna, 383
peach, 178
peanut, 179
Pearcy, G. E., 445
pearl, culture, 328
peas, 178
peat, 80
Pedler, F. J., 333
Peking, 20
Penang, 35
Pendletion, Robert L., 153
penstocks, 138
peoples, primitive, 173
pepper, 179
period of exploration, 21
periodic drought, 101
periods
  glacial, 29
  interglacial, 29
permafrost, 158
Peru, 61, 438
petroleum, 80, 81, 82, 84, 239, 245, 246, 263, 330
Petty, William, 71, 72
Philadelphia and Lancaster Turnpike, 346
Philippines, 376, 438
philosophy of geography, 24
Phoenicians, 321, 322
phosphate, 241
photo-satellite, 264
photographs, aerial, 26, 398, 414, 415
physiography, 24
Picardy, 256
pig iron, 239
pigmentation, 92
pigmentation, melanin, 91
pine, 306
pineapple, 179
pipelines, 82, 143, 263, 290, 300, 354
Piraeus, 345, 383
Pittsburgh, 244, 273

plains, 95, 96
plane projection, 409, 410
planning, city, 274
planosols, 434
plant associations, 103
plant origins, 178, 179
plant selection, 185
plantation, banana, 316
plantations, 154, 235, 315
plants
  cultivated, 177
  diffusion of, 185
  dispersion of cultivated, 180
  domestication of, 176, 188
  origins of seed, 181
  stories of, 108
plateaus, 97
platinum, 242
Plato, 15
Platt, Robert S., 441
Platte River, 139
Platypus, 170
Pleistocene, 29
Pliocene, 29
plow, 40, 147, 183, 192, 251, 381
plow
  mouldboard, 251
  steel, 260
plow agriculture, 190
plow culture, 308, 309
Po Plain, 64, 65, 66, 314
Po River, 65
podzol, 156
podzolic soil, red-yellow, 144
podzolic soils, gray-brown, 433
podzols, 433
point four, 341
Poitou, 256
Poland, 311, 312, 438
polar lands, 120
polder, 254, 313
political communities, growth of, 355
political federation, 361
political geography, 26
pollen analysis dating, 395
pollution, water, 100
pollution of water, 143
Polyani, Michael, 250

Pondichery, 364
Pontine Marshes, 255
poplar, 306
population, 26, 67, 435
population
  decreases in, 49
  definition of urban, 58
  distribution of, 48, 52, 65
  forecast of world, 74
  future, 70
  growth of, 41, 48, 70
  large agglomeration of, 57
  limitation of, 56
  urban, 57
  world, 79
population density, 52, 53, 54, 55, 59, 61, 65, 404
population distribution of Europe, 64
population forecasts, 71
population growth rate, 72
population map of Chile, 62
population of continents, 53
population pattern, dendritic, 59
population patterns, 59, 60
population pyramid, 73
port-outport, 345
portable house, 205
Portland (Ore.), 332
Portolano Charts, 18
Portugal, 19, 247, 438
Portuguese Guinea, 359
Portuguese India, 359
Portuguese Macao, 364
Portuguese Timor, 359
positive residuals, 403
possibilism, 25
potash, 241
potato, 182
potato,
  sweet, 179, 185, 386
  white, 178, 185, 312, 386
potatoes, 312
potter's wheel, 251
pottery, 251
Pounds, Norman J. G., 446
power, 253, 279
power
  atomic, 253
  electric, 82
  human, 80

nuclear, 247
steam, 83, 257
water, 75, 80, 82, 84, 101, 137, 139, 140
power line, 300
power machinery, 239
prairie, 103
prairie, humid, 192
prairie soils, 433
precipitation, 106, 111, 128, 130
precipitation, annual, 404
predators, 193
prefabricated house, 205
prehistoric migrations, 33, 34
Pretoria, 8
prickly-pear cactus, 194
primate cities, 269
prime movers, 256
primitive communism, 220
primitive peoples, 173
primitive peoples in modern times, 35
Prince Henry the Navigator, 21
Pritchett, H. S., 72, 73
problems, river-water, 370
produced, energy, 84
production, 26
production, forest, 306
projection, 409
projection
  Aitoff equal-area, 412
  azimuthal, 409, 410, 411
  bipolar oblique conic conformal, 412
  Boggs eumorphic, 412
  Bonne, 412
  Cahill's, 412
  conic, 17, 409, 410, 411
  cylindrical, 409, 410
  Denoyer's semi-elliptical, 412
  Gall's stereographic, 410
  gnomonic, 410, 412
  Goode's equal-area, 412
  interrupted sinusoidal, 412
  Lambert conic conformal, 410
  map, 23, 408
  Mercator, 23, 409
  Miller cylindrical, 409

Mollweide equal-area, 412
oblique case of gnomonic, 412
orthographic, 410
plane, 409, 410
regular polyconic, 410
simple conic, 410
stereographic, 410
transverse Mercator, 410
projects, hydroelectric, 143
properties
  celestial, 24
  human, 24
  terrestrial, 24
prospecting, 242
Provence, 256
Pruitt, Evelyn L., 441
Prunty, Merle, Jr., 445
Ptolemy, 17, 18
Ptolemy, Claudius, 16
public domain, 233
Peurto Rico, 280, 438
Puget Sound, 168, 422
pulley, 252
pump, 252
Pyrenees, 139
Pytheas, 322

qanat, 132
quack grass, 182
quartz, 248
quinine, 306
quotas, immigration, 47

rabbit, 193, 194
races, 38
racial groups, 37
racial tensions, 366
racial types, 91
radar, 264
radar warning systems, 377, 378
radiation, solar, 106
radio, 264
radioactive fallout, 372
railhead town, 344
railroads, 262, 290, 347, 375, 384
railway, 294, 295, 296
rain making, 122
rainfall, 107
rainfall regimens, 419

rainforest, 108
rainforest, tropical, 107
Raisz, Erwin, 441
ranch, 305
Rangoon, 354
Rann of Cutch, 329
Ratzel, Friedrich, 25, 144
raw materials, 278, 340
reaper, 258, 259, 260
reclamation of land, 254, 256
recreation, 138
red desert soils, 432
red-yellow podzolic soil, 144, 433
reddish chestnut soils, 432
reddish prairie soils, 433
reddish-brown lateritic soils, 433
reddish-brown soils, 432
redevelopment, urban, 274
Redfield, Robert, 442
refrigeration, 259, 260
regimens
    rainfall, 419
    temperature, 419
region, manufacturing, 282, 283, 284, 285, 286
regional geography, 24
regional geography, French school of, 400
regions, multifactor uniform, 405
regosols, 434
regular polyconic projection, 410
reindeer, 121
reindeer, domestication of, 390
rejection of ideas, 389
relative dating, 396
religious art, 384
rendzina soils, 434
rent, fixed, 231, 232
renting, cash, 232
reproduction
    seed, 177
    vegetative, 177
reservoirs, 127, 133, 140, 143
reservoirs, natural, 138
residential district, 272

residuals, 403
residuals
    negative, 403
    positive, 403
resources, mineral, 26
restrictions on migrations, 46
restrictions to human occupation, 90
Rhone River, 6
rhumb line, 18
rice, 109, 110, 153, 178, 181, 385, 386
rice farming, 309
riding animal, 186
rimland, 373, 374
Rio Grande, 370
Rio Muni and Fernando Po, 438
riparian rights, 142
Riss glaciation, 30
River Aude, 6
river-delta town, 344
river-fed canals, 347
river-water problems, 370
rivers, 347
rivers, canalization of, 350
road, 288
road materials, 293
roads, 291, 292, 346
Robinson, Arthur H., 410
Rocky Mountains, 98, 99
rodent, 193
Roger II, 19
Roman map, 321
Roman walls, 377
Romania, 314, 438
Romans, 321
Rome, 381
root crops, 185
Rostlund, Erhard, 441
rotary motion, 250
route around Africa, 21
routes
    ocean transport, 352
    sea, 353
    trade, 344, 346
    world air, 299
routes of migration, 32
Ruanda and Burundi, 438
rubber, 261, 262, 315
rubber, wild, 306

Ruhr, 244
run-off, 128
runoff, ground-water, 130
rural settlement geographers, 26
Russell, Richard J., 363, 441
Russia, 66, 139, 304, 356
rye, 178, 181, 182, 312
Ryukyu Islands, 438

Sable Banks, 226
Sahara, 421
Saigon, 354
salmon fishermen, 168
salt, 242
Sambhar Salt Lake, 329
Samoa (East and West), 438
Samoyed, 40, 303
Samoyede people, 22
sampans, 71
San Francisco, 60
San Joaquin Valley, 114
sand, 239, 241, 242
Santa Fe Trail, 100
Sapper, Karl, 441
Sarawak, 438
Sardinia, 65
Sargent, A. J., 446
Saudi Arabia, 375, 438
Sauer, Carl O., 3, 26, 178, 179, 181, 186, 393, 441, 442, 445
Sault Ste. Marie Canal, 351
savanna, 103
savanna, tropical, 107, 109, 110
savanna lands, temperate, 116
savannas, 153
scale, 409
scale, map, 409
Schebesta, Paul, 35, 172, 445
screw, 252
sea animals, 121
sea routes, 353
sea transport, 353
sea water, 134, 329
sea water, conversion of, 134
Seabrook (N.J.), 128
seafood, 325
Sealy, Kenneth R., 446
Sears, Paul B., 445

seas, 321
SEATO, 376
sedentary agriculturists, 165
seed agriculturalists, 187
seed agriculture, spread of, 385
seed plants, origins of, 181
seed reproduction, 177
seed selection, 184
seepage, 128
seismograph, 264
selection, plant, 185
selective breeding, 177
selective cutting, 190
selenium salts, 152
Semang, 35, 36, 172, 173
semi arid grassland, 102
Semple, Ellen Churchill, 25, 442
Senegal, 438
sensing device, 263
Seri, 35
settlement, 206, 207
settlement, analysis of, 399
settlement form, 399, 400
settlement geography, 405
settlement of grasslands, 259
settlements, 108, 143, 199
sewage, 128
sewage disposal, 100
Seychelles, 111
shale, 241
Shanghai, 354
Shantz, Homer L., 445
Shapley, Harlow, 443
share tenants, 230, 231
sharecropping, 228, 229, 231, 232
sharecropping tenure, 211
shatter belts, 363
sheep, 188, 305
shellfish, 328
shelter, 94
shifting cultivation, 190
shifting field agriculture, 153
ships, iron, 260
short summer microthermal climate, 423
Siberia, 303
Sicily, 65
sickle, 251, 252

Siemen's open hearth process, 258
sierozem soil, 144
sierozems, 432
Sierra Leone, 438
silver, 238, 242
simple conic projection, 410
Simpson, George G., 442
simulation approach to analysis, 405
Singapore, 76, 354, 364
Singapore River, 71
Singer, Charles, 381, 445
Sinju, 20
Siwash, 168
size of cities, 268
size of family, 73
skimming well, 133
small grains, 312
small-grain farming, 311
small-scale map, 409
Smith, Guy D., 431
Smith, J. Russel, 277
Smoky Hill River (Kans.), 141
Snake River, 131
snow, 139
snuff, 387
social geography, 26
sod, 190, 192
sod house, 204
soft water, 142
softwoods, 306
soil, 11, 26, 144, 159
soil
    A horizon, 147, 149
    B horizon, 147, 149
    C horizon, 148, 149
    chernozem, 144
    mineral content of, 147
    red-yellow podzolic, 144
    sierozem, 144
    tundra, 158
soil acidity, 429
soil areas of world, major, 430
soil bacteria, 147
soil color, 147
soil complex, 146
soil description, 429
soil erosion, 150, 316

soil fertility, 149, 151, 152, 154
soil formation, 429
soil groups, zonal, 431
soil parent material, 429
soil profile, 144, 148, 149, 429
soil profiles, 152
soil science, 146
soil texture, 146, 147, 429
soil types, 152
soils, 429
soils
    alluvial, 434
    alpine meadow, 433
    azonal, 429, 432
    black earth, 157
    bog, 433
    brown, 432, 433, 434
    chernozem, 432
    chestnut, 432, 157
    cold, 151
    degraded chernozem, 433
    desert, 158, 432
    frozen, 152
    gray wooded, 433
    gray-brown podzolic, 433
    grey forest, 156
    ground-water laterite, 434
    half-bog, 434
    humic-glei, 433
    intrazonal, 429, 432
    laterite, 433
    low-humic glei, 434
    noncalcic brown, 433
    prairie, 433
    red desert, 432
    red-yellow podzolic, 433
    reddish chestnut, 432, 433
    reddish-brown, 432, 433
    rendzina, 434
    solonchak, 433
    solonetz, 433
    tropical, 153
    tundra, 432
    warm, 151
    yellowish-brown lateritic, 443
    zonal, 429, 430, 431
solar batteries, 83
solar energy, 82, 83, 84

solar radiation, 106
solar stove, 263
Solomon Islands, 438
solonchak soils, 433
solonetz soils, 433
Somalia, 438
sorghums, 178, 181, 386
sorghums, grain, 183
Sorre, Maximilian, 11
Soudan (Mali), 438
sources of information, 395, 396
South Africa, 172, 305, 310
South Africa, Union of, 361
South America, 61, 139
South France, 139
Southern Rhodesia, 361, 438
Southwest Africa, 359, 438
Soviet Bloc, 342, 343
sovkhozi, 218
soybean, 178, 386
space heating, 84
Spain, 311, 438
spear, 250
speech, 31
spheres of influence, 374
sphericity of earth, 16, 17, 321
spices, 315
spinach, 385
spoked wheel, 251
spread of commercial cotton, 388
spread of hybrid corn, 388
spread of seed agriculture, 385
spruce, 306
Spykman, N. J., 373, 374
squash, 179
St. John River, 129
St. Lambert Lock, 101
St. Lawrence, Gulf of, 22
St. Lawrence-Great Lakes Seaway, 100, 101, 349, 351, 352, 353
St. Lawrence River, 352
St. Pierre Banks, 326
stages
    glacial, 30
    interglacial, 30
Stamp, L. D., 445

standard of living, 70
Stanislawski, Dan, 446
state farms, 218
state ownership, 233
statistic, chi-square, 405
statistical approach to analysis, 402
statistics, 26
statistics, nearest-neighbor, 405
steam engine, 80, 82, 253, 256
steam power, 83, 257
steam turbine, 262
steel, 239
steel plow, 260
steppe, 103
steppe climate, 421
steppe lands, 111
steppes, 112
steppes
    cold, 111
    hot, 111
stereographic projection, 410
stereoscope, 414
stick, digging, 380
stockade, 202
stone, 239
stone, building, 241, 242
stone house, 203
Stone, Kirk H., 442
stories of plants, 108
storm cellars, 94
Strabo, 15
Strahler, Arthur N., 445
strategic concepts, 373
strategic minerals, 248, 249
strategy, 372
stream flow, 129
stream height, 129
stream velocity, 129, 130
street pattern, 273
strip cropping, 151, 315
strip logging, 196
strip mine, 244
subsidence of land, 143
subsistence freehold, 224
subsoil, 147, 148, 149
suburbs, 209
Sudan, 375, 421, 438
Sudbury, 247

Suez Canal, 353, 354
sugar beets, 312
sugar cane, 178, 315, 385
sugar cane fields, 115
sugar maple, 194
sulfur, 241
sulfuric acid, 241
summer dry temperate climate, 422
summit-level canals, 348
sunflower, 179
sunlight, 178
sunshine, 83
supply of energy, world's, 80
Surinam, 438
survey, 23
Swaziland, 439
Sweden, 306, 439
sweet potato, 179, 185, 386
Switzerland, 139, 377, 439
synthetic fibers, 306
Syr River, 140
Syracuse (N.Y.), 123
Syria, 361

Tabernacle of Moses, 16
tacking, 21
Taiga, 423
Taiwan (Formosa), 439
Tanganyika, 361, 439
Tannu Tuva, 359
tape, magnetic, 264
tapioca, 109, 185
taro, 178, 385
tarpan, 187
Tashkent, 67
Tasman, Abel, 23
Tax, Sol, 165, 364
taxes, 279
Taylor Grazing Act, 233
tea, 178, 181
teak, 306
techniques in human geography, 393
techniques of analysis, 398
techniques of dating, 394
technology
    agricultural, 79
    metal, 381
Teilhard de Chardin, Pierre, 29

telephone, 264
television, 264
temperate mesothermal climate, 422
temperate savanna climate, 114
temperate savanna lands, 116
temperature, 106, 107, 111
temperature regimens, 419
tenancy, cash, 228, 231
tenant, 210
tenant tenure, 211, 228
tenants, share, 230, 231
Tennessee River, 138
Tennessee Valley Authority, 138
Tennessee Valley Project, 138
tensions
    linguistic, 366
    racial, 366
tent house, 200
tenure
    communal, 211, 217
    fee-simple, 222
    freehold, 211, 222, 224, 225
    sharecropping, 211
    tenant, 211, 228
    tribal, 211, 214, 216
tepees, 95
terraces, 146
terrestrial properties, 24
territories, 358
territories, trust, 362
Texas, 305
textiles, 250, 338, 339, 341
texture, soil, 147
Thailand, 375, 377, 439
thicket, 103
Thoman, Richard S., 269, 445, 446
Thomas, Elizabeth Marshall, 172, 445
Thomas, William L., Jr., 441
Thompson, Warren S., 52, 73, 442
Thornthwaite, C. W., 128, 417, 442, 443
Thorp, James, 431
three-field, 220
threshing machinery, 258

Tibet, 359
tides, 82, 325
Tigris River, 101
Timor, 364
tin, 238, 239, 241, 248
Titusville, (Pa.), 82
tobacco, 155, 179, 387
Toda-Mexicana Canal, 352
Togo, 439
Tokyo, 68
tomato, 179
Tonga, 439
tools, 34, 238, 250
tools
    bronze, 381
    machine, 257
tools of human geography, 13
topsoil, 147, 148, 151
tornado, 94
Torres, Luis Vaez de, 23
Touggourt (Algeria), 114
town, 208, 266
town
    railhead, 344
    river-delta, 344
    valley-mouth, 344
trace elements, 151
trade, 333
trade, world, 331, 332, 334, 335
trade centers, 344
trade routes, 344, 346
trailer house, 200, 205
trait, culture, 380
Trans-Siberian Railway, 66
transhumance, 304
transistor, 264
transpiration, 128
transport, 84
transport, sea, 353
transportation, 279, 288, 289, 290
transverse Mercator projection, 410
transverse polyconic projection, 410
Trave River, 347
treaty blocs, 375
tree, olive, 310
tree farm, 306

tree farming, 195, 196
tree ring dating, 395
Trewartha, G. T., 442
tribal tenure, 211, 214, 216
Trinidad, 361
Tropic of Cancer, 105
Tropic of Capricorn, 105
tropical diseases, 108
tropical forest, 306
tropical lands, 107
tropical rainforest, 107
tropical rainforest climate, 420
tropical savanna, 107, 109, 110
tropical soils, 153
truck, motor, 290, 293, 294
true area relations, 409
true shape relations, 409
trust territories, 362
tsunami, 325
Tula Frontier Line, 378
tundra, 121
tundra climate, 120, 423
tundra soil, 158
tundra soils, 432
tungsten, 239
Tungus, 303
Tunisia, 439
turbine
    gas, 262
    steam, 262
    water, 262
Turkestan, 19, 66
Turkey, 304, 342, 439
Turks, 304
turnpikes, 346, 347
two-story cropping, 310
type, house, 200

U.S. Reclamation Service, 143
U.S.S.R., 66, 67, 74, 156, 239, 244, 247, 306, 311, 312, 343, 349, 365, 374, 378, 439
Uganda, 361, 439
Ukraine, 66, 67
Ulan Bator, 111
Ullman, E. L., 344, 444, 445
underpopulation, 61
unexplained variation, 403

uniformities of national growth, 356, 357, 358
Union of South Africa, 361, 439
United Arab Republic, 361, 439
United Kingdom, 336, 439
United Nations, 341
United States, 54, 192, 197, 239, 305, 306, 314, 316, 335, 341, 350, 361, 364, 374, 376, 378, 401, 439
United States Geological Survey, 409
Upper Volta, 439
Ural Mountains, 66
uranium, 83, 242, 246, 247, 248
urban geographers, 26
urban population, 57
urban population, definition of, 58
urban redevelopment, 274
Uruguay, 377, 439
use, land, 301
use-occupancy, 214
Uzbek S.S.R., 67

Vallaux, Camille, 442
valley-mouth town, 344
Van Doren, Mark, 446
Van Royen, William, 445
Van Valkenbury, Samuel, 357
vanadium, 239, 248
Vancouver Island, 168
Varenius, Bernard, 23, 24
variance, analysis of, 403
variation, unexplained, 403
varves dating, 395
Vasyutin, V. F., 443
Vavilov, N. I., 445
vegetation, 107
vegetation, natural, 11, 26, 102, 103, 192
vegetation types, 102
vegetative formations, 430
vegetative reproduction, 177
vehicle, wheeled, 251
veld, 112
Venezuela, 305, 330, 439
Vidal de la Blache, Paul, 14, 25, 442

Vietnam (North), 439
Vietnam (South), 439
Vikhvine Canal, 350
village, 208, 266
Vinacke, Harold M., 375
Visitin, L., 441
Vogt, William, 442, 445
Volga River, 140
von Thunen, Johann Heinrich, 270
von Wissmann, Hermann, 445

walls, Roman, 377
walnut, 306
waqf, 236
war chariot, 251
warm soils, 151
warm summer microthermal climate, 423
warning systems, radar, 377, 378
Warriner, Doreen, 232
Warsaw Pact, 375, 376
waste, industrial, 128
waste disposal, 128
water, 11, 74, 75, 100, 101, 124
water
    chlorination of, 142
    distillation of, 134
    ground, 126, 127, 131, 132, 133, 142, 143
    hard, 142
    ownership of, 142
    pollution of, 143
    sea, 134
    soft, 142
water balance, 128
water budget, 128
water circulation, 127
water cycle, 124, 127
water mill, 253
water pollution, 100
water power, 75, 80, 82, 84, 101, 137, 139, 140
water requirements, 75
water supply, 141
water table, 128
water turbine, 262
water wheel, 253
waterways, inland, 349, 350
Watt, James, 256

weapons, 238
weather, 105, 106
weathering
    chemical, 152
    mechanical, 152
weaving, 251, 252, 380
wedge, 252
well
    artesian, 133
    horizontal, 132
    maui, 133
    skimming, 133
Welland Canal, 352
wells, 127, 131
West Germany, 336
West Indies, 439
whale oil, 81, 82
whaling, 326
wheat, 178, 181, 182, 310, 312, 315, 385
wheat
    bread, 182
    einkorn, 182
    emmer, 182
    macaroni, 182
wheat drill, 260
wheat-belt farming, 314
wheel
    cogged, 251
    paddle, 253
    potter's, 251
    spoked, 251
    water, 253
wheeled vehicle, 251
Whelpton, 73
Whitaker, J. R., 445
white death rate, 51
white potato, 178, 185, 386
white potatoes, 312
White, Gilbert, 443
Whitney, Eli, 262
Whittlesey, Derwent S., 442, 445
Wiens, Harold J., 365
wild animal, 186
wild cattle, 186
wild rubber, 306
Willamette Valley, 168
Willats, E. C., 215
William of Rubruck, 19, 20
Williams, Joseph E., 441

Williams, Trevor I., 445
Williamsburg Canals, 352
winch, 252
wind, 106
windmill, 80, 253, 254, 256
wine, 310
winter dry temperate climate, 422
winter dry tropical climate, 421
wood, 75, 80, 81, 82
wood lots, 195
wooden house, 201
wool, 188
world air routes, 299
world island, 373
world population, 79
world population, forecast of, 74
world ridge, 98

world's supply of energy, 80
world trade, 331, 332, 334, 335
Woytinsky, E. S., 42, 74, 288, 442, 446
Woytinsky, W. S., 42, 288, 442, 446
Wurm glaciation, 30

Yaghan, 35
Yakuts, 303
yam, 178, 185
yellow fever, 108
yellowish-brown lateritic soils, 433
Yellowstone River, 139
Yemen, 439
yield per acre, 79
Yokohama, 354
Yoruba, 214, 356, 361

Yucatan, 40
Yugoslavia, 376, 377, 439
Yukagir, 303

Zaborski, Bogdan, 363
Zambezi River, 140
Zanzibar, 439
zebra, 187
zebu, 188
Zelinsky, Wilbur, 395
Zimmerman, E. W., 446
zinc, 238, 239, 241
Zon, R., 445
zonal soil groups, 431
zonal soils, 429, 430, 431
zone of accumulation, 157
zoning, 276
Zuider Zee, 255
Zulu, 91
Zulu village, 8, 9

Photo Credits

Page	Credit
6	French Government Tourist Office
9	United Nations
10	Los Angeles Chamber of Commerce
12	Panagra
36	Sawders from Cushing
37	National Film Board
55	U.S. Army, Corps of Engineers
56	Left: Commodity Stabilization Service
	Right: U.S. Air Corps
58	Standard Oil Company (N.J.)
71	Singapore Information Services
76	G. H. Metcalf from Black Star
83	National Coal Association
91	All photos from Philip Gendreau, N.Y.
	(b) Ray Garner from Gendreau
93	a: Richard Harrington from Black Star
	b: Ewing Galloway
	c & d: Philip Gendreau, N.Y.
95	a, b, & d: Philip Gendreau, N.Y.
	c: German Tourist Information Service
96	Commodity Stabilization Service
97	Commodity Stabilization Service
98	Kolb Bros. Studio, Grand Canyon
99	Canadian Pacific Railway
101	André Sima from The St. Lawrence Seaway Authority
102	a: Weyerhaeuser Company
	b & c: U.S. Forest Service
	d: W. M. Johnson, Soil Survey, Soil Conservation Service, U.S. Department of Agriculture
109	CIAA
110	Monkmeyer Press Photo Service
111	Three Lions
113	Bureau of Reclamation
115	Photo by Rotkin from Standard Oil Company (N.J.)
117	Bernard G. Silberstein
119	Arthur Rothstein, Library of Congress
120	Samuel N. Dicken
122	U.S. Air Force Photo
125	Top: Aluminum Power Company, Canada
	Bottom: U.S. Air Force Photo
129	Canadian Department of Mines
131	State of Idaho, Department of Highways
135	Soil Conservation Service
137	Bureau of Reclamation
141	Photo by Slack, U.S. Department of Agriculture
145	All photos by Roy W. Simonson, Soil Survey, Soil Conservation Service, U.S. Department of Agriculture
147	b: Bert S. Gittins Advertising, Inc.
	c & d: Allis Chalmers Manufacturing, Inc.
150	U.S.D.A. Photo
151	Soil Conservation Service
153	Roland Lange from Black Star
154	Soil Conservation Service
155	U.S.D.A. Photo
156	Photo by Guy D. Smith, Soil Survey, Soil Conservation Service, U.S. Department of Agriculture
157	Photo by Roy W. Simonson, Soil Survey, Soil Conservation Service, U.S. Department of Agriculture
158	Photo by Don Erb, Santa Fe Railway
166	Ewing Galloway
167	Ewing Galloway
168	Photo by U. B. Scheffer, U.S. Fish and Wildlife Service
169	Three Lions
171	Philip Gendreau, N.Y.
173	Sawders from Cushing
177	Philip Gendreau, N.Y.
183	F. R. Pitts
184	Courtesy of Agency for International Development
187	Both Photos by U.S. Signal Corps, National Archives
188	Ewing Galloway
191	U.S.D.A. Photo
193	U.S.D.A. photo by Ackerman
195	U.S. Forest Service
196	Both photos by U.S. Forest Service
200	a: Division of Parks, Illinois
	b: W. Bosshard from Black Star
	c: Hays from Monkmeyer Press Photo Service
	d: Herbert Lanks from Black Star
201	Screen Traveler, from Gendreau
203	Samuel N. Dicken
204	U.S.D.A. photo by Ackerman
208	Top: Three Lions
	Center: H. Michael McMahon
	Bottom: Ewing Galloway
209	Israel Office of Information
218	United Nations
234	Standard Oil Company (N.J.)
236	Republic of the Sudan
239	American Museum of Natural History, N.Y.
243	Samuel N. Dicken
244	Philip Gendreau, N.Y.
245	Philip Gendreau, N.Y.
252	The Metropolitan Museum of Art, Anonymous Gift, 1930
254	Radio Times Hulton Picture Library
255	Top: Camera Press from Pix
	Bottom: Netherlands Information Service

Page *Credit*
259   Top: Radio Times Hulton Picture
         Library
      Bottom: International Harvester
261   Top: Radio Times Hulton Picture
         Library
      Bottom: Science Museum, London
263   Left: International Rectifier Corporation
      Right: Through courtesy of Dr. M. L.
         Khanna, National Physical Labora-
         tory of India, New Delhi
267   Fairchild Aerial Surveys
268   Three Lions
273   a: Aerial photograph KLM Aerocarto
         n.v.—Netherlands
      b: Fairchild Aerial Surveys
275   Engravings: *Landscape*
      Upper photo: National Archives
      Lower photo: Harlow Development
         Corporation
285   Consulate General of Japan, N.Y.
286   Fotografias de Todo o Brasil, Rio de
         Janeiro
289   Malmed from Black Star

Page *Credit*
291   Three Lions
298   Cessna Aircraft Company
305   Santa Fe Railway Photo
307   Left: Photo by U.S. Forest Service
      Right: McCulloch Corporation
308   Bern Keating from Black Star
311   French Government Tourist Office
312   Karl Gullers from Rapho-Guillumette
313   Netherlands Information Service
315   Courtesy of Caterpillar Tractor Com-
         pany
316   Courtesy United Fruit Co.
326   Three Lions
327   National Film Board
328   George Pickow from Three Lions
329   Standard Oil Company (N.J.)
332   Ackroyd Photography, Inc.
383   Embassy of Pakistan
391   Courtesy of the Oriental Institute, Uni-
         versity of Chicago
394   NEA Photo
415   Oregon State Highway Department

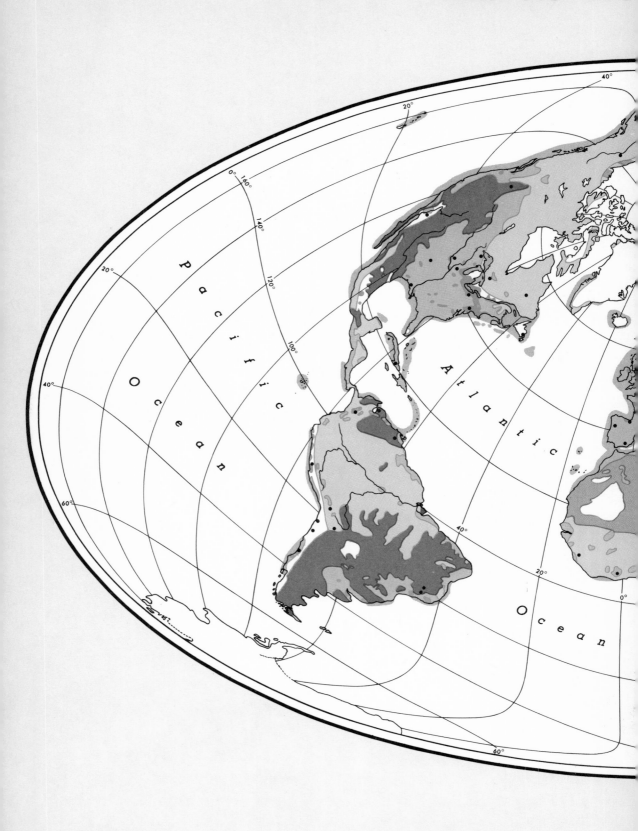